MATHEMATICAL MODELS
for
ENVIRONMENTAL PROBLEMS

MATHEMATICAL MODELS
for
ENVIRONMENTAL PROBLEMS

Proceedings of the International Conference held
at the University of Southampton, England,
September 8–12, 1975

Edited by: C. A. Brebbia
Department of Civil Engineering, University of Southampton

PENTECH PRESS
LONDON

First published, 1976 by PENTECH PRESS LIMITED
London: 8 John Street, WC1N 2HY

ISBN 0 7273 1301 0

D
624.0184
MAT

Reproduced Photolitho by
UNWIN BROTHERS LIMITED
The Gresham Press, Old Woking, Surrey
A member of the Staples Printing Group

CONTENTS

PART I. PAPERS

1. Regional Models

^{r}age

1.1 Strategic Models of Energy Usage 1
D. P. Bloomfield and D. J. Fisk, Building Research
Establishment, U.K.

1.2 The Interdependence between Environment and 13
Transportation Planning
R. Hamerslag, Dwars, Heedrik en Verhey, B.V. Holland

✓ 1.3 Mathematical Modelling for Regionalization of Resource 27
Recovery
J. Kühner and J. J. Harrington, Harvard University, U.S.A.

1.4 Human Activity, Pollution and Resources 43
J. W. Bryant, University of Sussex, U.K.

1.5 A Model Criterion for Site-Selection of Large Scale Technical 55
Facilities in the 'Upper Rhine Region'
G. Halbritter, Nuclear Research Center, Karlsruhe, Germany

1.6 Parameter Estimation of a Distributed System Related to the 71
Biomass Dynamics in Aquatic Ecosystems
F. Argentesi, G. Di Cola and L. Guerri, Ispra, Instituto
Italiano di Idiobiologia and University of Pavia, Italy

2. Hydraulic Systems

2.1 Design of Large Urban Sewer Systems with a Waterflow 79
Simulation Program
P. Kaufmann and C. de Rham, Balzari Blaser Schudel, Bern,
Switzerland

2.2 A Mathematical Model for the Analysis of Multi-Reservoir 87
Flood Control Systems
J. S. Windsor, University of Natal, South Africa

2.3 Optimization Methods for Planning Waste Water Manage- 99
ment Systems
H. Orth and W. Ahrens, University of Karlsruhe, Germany

✓ 2.4 Modelling of Aquifer Behaviour for Long Time Periods 115
using Interactive Analogue−Digital Computers
K. R. Rushton and J. E. Ash, University of Birmingham, U.K.

2.5 A Stochastic Model of Levee Failure 129
F. Szidarovszky, L. Duckstein and I. Bogárdi, Eötvös
University, Budapest, University of Arizona and Water
Resources Centre, Budapest

2.6 Finite Element Models for Circulation Studies 141
C. A. Brebbia and P. Partridge, University of Southampton, U.K.

3. Air Pollution

3.1 On the Calculation of Optimal Long-term Air Pollution   161
Abatement Strategies for Multiple-Source Areas
*S.-Å. Gustafson and K. O. Kortanek, Royal Institute of
Technology, Stockholm and Carnegie-Mellon University,
U.S.A.*

3.2 The Air Pollution Abatement MASC-AP Model   173
L. F. Escudero, IBM Science Centre, Madrid

3.3 The Application of Numerical Modelling to Air Pollution in   183
the Forth Valley
*A. W. C. Keddie, G. H. Roberts and F. P. Williams, Warren
Spring Laboratory, Stevenage, U.K.*

3.4 Shallow-Water Approximation for the Transport of Pollutants   201
in an Urban Basin
C. Y. Liu and W. R. Goodin, University of California, U.S.A.

3.5 Changes in Atmospheric Pollution Concentrations   221
*R. J. Bennett, W. J. Campbell and R. A. Maugham, University
College, London*

4. Water Pollution

4.1 Computer Modelling of Pollutant Transports in Lake Erie   237
*D. C. L. Lam, Canada Centre for Inland Waters, Burlington,
Ontario*

4.2 A Water Quality Optimization Model for Non Serial River   253
Systems
M. B. Bayer, University of Calgary, Canada

4.3 Simulation of Nonlinear Stochastic Equations with Applica-   269
tions in Modelling Water Pollution
*C. J. Harris, University of Manchester Institute of Science
and Technology, U.K.*

4.4 A Mathematical Model for Estimating Pollution Loadings in   283
Runoff from Urban Streets
*R. Sutherland and R. McCuen, Harza Engineering Co., Chicago
and University of Maryland, U.S.A.*

4.5 The Advection–Dispersion Equation for an Isotropic Medium   299
Solved by Fractional-Step Methods
G. K. Verboom, Delft Hydraulics Laboratory, Holland

4.6 Solution of the Advective-Diffusion Equation by the Method   313
of Moving Coordinate Systems with particular reference to
the Modelling of Estuarine Pollution
B. M. Mollowney, Water Research Centre, Stevenage, U.K.

4.7 Stochastic Modelling of Bi-Hourly River Dissolved Oxygen   329
Records Monitored at a Fixed Cross-Section
*Y. J. Litwin and E. F. Joeres, Hydrocomp, Palo Alto
California and University of Wisconsin – Madison, U.S.A.*

5. Thermal Problems

5.1 Modelling the Effects of Weather, Heating and Occupancy   353
on the Thermal Environment inside Houses
*P. Basnett, Electricity Council Research Centre, Capenhurst,
U.K.*

5.2 Mathematical Modelling of Thermal Pollution in Rivers   367
J. J. McGuirk and D. B. Spalding, Imperial College, London

5.3 Computation of Artificial Temperature Stresses due to   387
Discharges from Nuclear Power Plants
*T. Audunson, H. Rye and A. Thendrup, River and Harbour
Authority, Technical University of Norway*

6. Modelling Techniques

6.1 The Anatomy of the Modelling Process   401
R. H. McCuen, University of Maryland, U.S.A.

6.2 Random Search Optimization: Stopping Rules   413
P. Thoft-Christensen, Aalborg University Centre, Denmark

6.3 On the Accuracy of Solutions of the Navier Stokes Equations   423
for Unsteady Viscous Flow at High Reynolds Numbers
*T. Bratanow, H. Aksu, T. J. Spehert and G. A. Exner,
University of Wisconsin − Milwaukee, U.S.A.*

PART 2. DISCUSSION

1.   **Discussion: Regional Models**   439

2.   **Discussion: Hydraulic Systems**   447
Written Contribution. Topological Study of Finite Differential   482
Element Nets.

3.   **Discussion: Air Pollution**   471
Written Contribution. Computation of Atmospheric   482
Contamination Produced by a Source of Gaseous Emissions.
Written Contribution. Computation of SO_2 − Long Term   487
Concentration in the Venetian Area.

4.   **Discussion: Water Pollution**   499

5.   **Discussion: Thermal Problems**   519
Written Contribution. Experimental and Analytical Evaluation of   524
Thermal Alterations in the Mediterranean.

6.   **Discussion: Modelling Techniques**   529
List of Participants   531

PREFACE

Contrary to popular belief scientific research has always been related to social needs of necessity in the long run. The state of knowledge, the economic resources and the political climate are the basic determinants of scientific research. Within this framework, scientists pursue their goals. The difference between this and previous societies is the speed with which these social needs and goals change. For instance, the demand for cars regardless of resource depletion or pollution has been transformed in a very short time by a growing concern for such problems.

Nowadays, the individual scientist is torn between old, well-defined objectives and new, but still incoherent ones. The difficult process of shaping vague political or social aims into technological possibilities then begins. Scientists involved in this process frequently point out to society the potential dangers of scientific discoveries, but this is an unrewarding task and it is not perhaps surprising that, on the whole, they avoid such controversy.

It is, however, increasingly difficult for the scientist to ignore the social implications of his work, as indeed it is for the non-scientist to ignore his dependence on scientific skills to preserve the environment. The rapidity with which the environmental sciences have taken shape is proof that this was not so much a new departure as a change in orientation, which has excited scientists and stimulated them to break new ground. This stimulus has been especially productive in the fields of mathematical models which are now being adopted as a technique by disciplines traditionally as far apart as biology and engineering, and at the same time attaining a scale and degree of complexity hitherto unknown. Cross fertilization should be fruitful and it was with this idea in mind that the Conference was held.

As with the Conference, the book is multidisciplinary, but continuity is maintained by focussing attention on the common characteristics running through the whole modelling spectrum. The papers are divided into the following groups: Regional Models, Hydraulics Systems, Air Pollution, Water Pollution, Thermal Problems and Modelling Techniques. An edited version of the discussion held during the Conference is included in Part 2 of the book and will enhance the reader's understanding of the papers.

C. A. Brebbia
February 1976

STRATEGIC MODELS OF ENERGY USAGE

D P Bloomfield and D J Fisk

Building Research Establishment

INTRODUCTION

The sharp rise in the world price of crude oil has led to
considerable reappraisals of projected energy demand futures.
The uniqueness of this price change means that much of the
past econometric data has become an unsatisfactory base for
future extrapolation. This paper describes a model which
has been built to determine the main characteristics of
energy consumption by building services during a period in
which there may be considerable changes in the optimum choice
of fuel and level of thermal insulation. The model is intended to be used to simulate the qualitative pattern of energy
consumption and enable experience to be gained of the long-
run implications of certain energy use strategies. The general properties of energy consumption in a stock of buildings
and their importance in the national energy picture will
first be described, followed by a brief explanation of the
model's construction and characteristic behaviour.

ENERGY USE IN BUILDINGS

An analysis(1) of the use of energy in the UK economy estab-
lishes the major importance of energy use in buildings. Between 40% - 50% of the UK consumption of primary energy can
be attributed to building services, and the dominant part
of this fraction is used in the domestic sector.

Three time constants can be identified in the response of
the energy consumption of buildings to a change in the cost
of energy. The short-run response is that characterised by
the patterns of use of existing appliances and buildings.
This is equivalent to a rise in the price of the energy
required to heat the dwelling to a specified standard. Extensive studies have been made on this aspect, in the late 1950s,
and more data on newer dwellings is likely to be available

1

soon. In General the consumer trades off his standard of
periphery heating, such as in bedrooms and hallways, against
a rise in the effective price of energy.

The medium run response to a change in the cost of useful
energy is that characterised by the useful life of the existing appliances. This time constant is not only a function
of the appliance's physical construction but also of its economic performance. The perceived useful life may be shortened
by changes in the availability of fuel which leave an appliance dependent on scarce or very expensive fuel.

The longest time constant is that associated with the built
form and construction of the dwelling. Dwellings built today
will be expected to last to at least the year 2040. Past
experience indicates that they will last much longer. The
built form of the dwelling can have a substantial influence
on its energy consumption. Dwellings offering substantially
the same living accommodation can differ in their energy consumption by a factor of 2 to 3, merely from variation in built
form. The location of dwellings can make provision of alternative energy supplies, such as gas or district heating mains
prohibitively expensive except at the time of construction.
Groups of dwellings not connected to to such systems may then
become at later date an energy liability which cannot be economically surmounted. Again, one of the most convenient and
effective means of improving thermal insulation, cavity fill,
can only be applied to about a third of the existing housing
stock, because of the prevalence of pre-1930s solid brick
walls.

The existence of the two longer time constants introduce an
added complexity to the estimation of future energy use in
buildings. The system has two extended parameters; the age
distribution of appliances and the age distribution of dwellings which provide a 'memory' of decisions taken perhaps
more than 6 decades previously. Such extended parameter
modelling is not possible with conventional econometric techniques although the latter can handle short run fluctuations
quite well. Perhaps the most fundamental difficulty in constructing an econometric model incorporating both appliance
and dwelling age, is lack of data. Most surveys give data
in a two-dimensional form, appliance type against economic
class, for example. A re-analysis of the source data into
larger dimensions, invariably leads to very small sample cell
densities.

STRATEGIC MODELS

Although numerical prediction may become increasingly difficult because of the nature of the system, it is still possible
to draw qualitative conclusions on strategy by using modelling

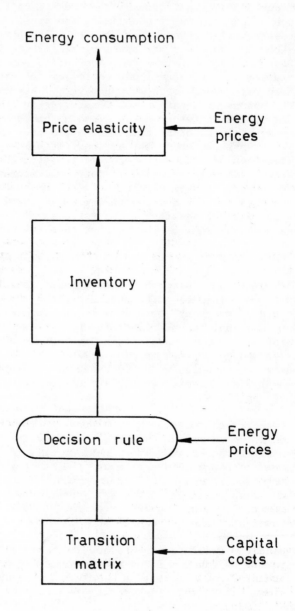

Figure 1 Structure of model

techniques. A model can be built which simulates the behaviour of energy consumption in the stock under varying energy prices and availabilities. The model's aggregated statistics, such as the number of households and appliance types, can be set equal to those in the UK economy, but its individual extended parameters are set arbitrarily by the model builder. The behaviour of this model under different energy management strategies is then unlikely to follow the behaviour of the UK energy economy closely. However, like the behaviour of the economy of a nation not dissimilar to the UK, the performance of different strategies in the model provide a base for broad judgment of different approaches and for identifying sensitive areas for action. It also enables the identification of behavioural characteristics of extended parameter models not included in more traditional dynamic energy models. The system simulation needs to be more flexible than in a predictive model as the strategic predictions have to be checked for sensitivity to 'structural' assumptions in the model as well as the initial boundary conditions.

CONSTRUCTION OF MODEL

The model to be described here consists of three main program components (Fig 1). The extended parameter behaviour derives from an 'Inventory' of all dwellings (classified by type and age) and appliances (classified by type and age). Even for relatively simple models this Inventory can demand a very large storage. For example, a simulation of space heating energy consumption with two types of insulation standard and four types of available appliance requires storage of about 5000 variables.

The energy consumption of the stock in the Inventory is defined in the short-run by a price elasticity function for each member of the stock. This function defines both the present level of energy consumption and the short-run change in consumption due to a change in external price. It also enables the inclusion of an increase in consumer expectation with time and gives an implied price for the disutility should a particular fuel become in short supply.

The medium and long-run changes in energy consumption are governed by the remaining two program components, the decision procedure and a transition matrix. The transition matrix gives a 'cost' for transferring from one appliance and building component to any other. The decision procedure compares this cost with the change in running cost for each dwelling and on the basis of this comparison undertakes any changes in the Inventory. Finally, dwellings at the end of their life are removed from the Inventory and new dwellings are entered with the optimum system as determined by the decision procedure and transition matrix.

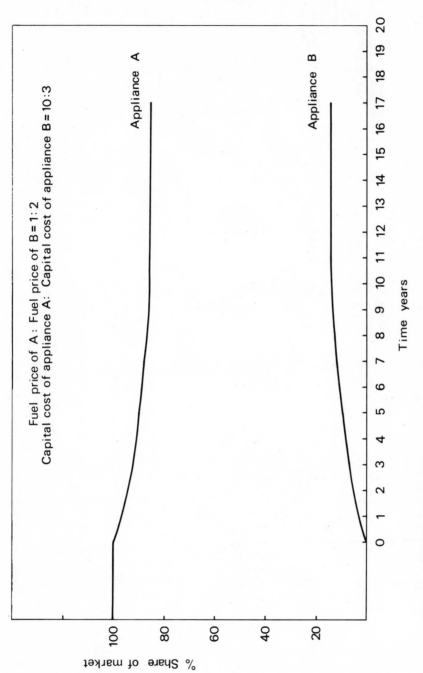

Fuel price of A : Fuel price of B = 1 : 2
Capital cost of appliance A : Capital cost of appliance B = 10 : 3

Appliance A

Appliance B

% Share of market

Time years

Figure 2 Effect of differing capital costs of appliances

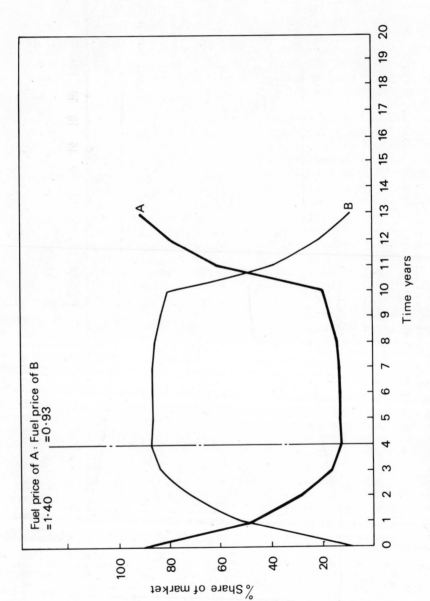

Figure 3   Effect of changes in the relative cost of fuels

One example of such a decision procedure, and the one used
in the illustrative runs to follow, is the comparison of the
discounted cash flows of the current system run to the end of
the dwelling's life with the discounted cash flow of an alternative system. Although by no means the optimum economic
procedure, it does display the essential features of most
decision rules. It is a function not only of the relative
running costs and capital costs of the two systems, but also
of the ages of the existing appliance and dwelling. In this
way both the medium and long run time constants appear in
the model's behaviour.

Implicit in the structure of the model is that each household
alters its energy consumption pattern independently of the
behaviour of any other. The only interaction is via the mechanism of the exogenously defined prices. Thus sectors of
the model economy can be separated out and run independently
to give a clearer picture of the changes taking place. Such
sectoring is common in normal dynamic modelling. The extended
parameter model differs, however, in that no single sector is
homogeneous. Figure 2 gives an example for a sector using
the decision rule above. After year '0' appliance type B is
introduced with a running cost higher than that of A although
with a lower capital cost. The market of A remains very large,
and it remains the optimum choice for new dwellings. Appliance
B, however, has made an impact on the market. These appliances are in dwellings with useful lives of the order of the
lifetimes of the appliances. Here low capital cost takes
priority in the decision rule. The extent of this 'hard core'
depends on the time horizon of the decision rule (in this
case the size of the discount rate) and on the number of dwellings within this time horizon. This final equilibrium situation could be approximated by dividing the sector into 'old'
and 'new' subsectors in a conventional dynamic model, but
the division between these two would fluctuate with time
depending on the history of construction in this sector over
the previous six to ten decades.

In addition to variations in the rate of past construction,
fluctuations in the relative cost of different fuels and different appliances can introduce inhomogeneities in the sector.
Figure 3 gives one such example. Appliance A has previously
been using a low cost fuel. At year '0' this fuel is tripled
in cost and market penetration begins by appliance B. The
stock thus continues with a disproportionately large number
of new B type appliances dating from year '0'. When the
price of the B type fuel is readjusted some while later, the
owners of these new B type appliances are 'locked in' with
that appliance type by the decision rule although type A
appliance is now the optimum choice for other dwellings.
Since these owners dominate the B type ownership inventory,
the A type makes little impression for a number of years.

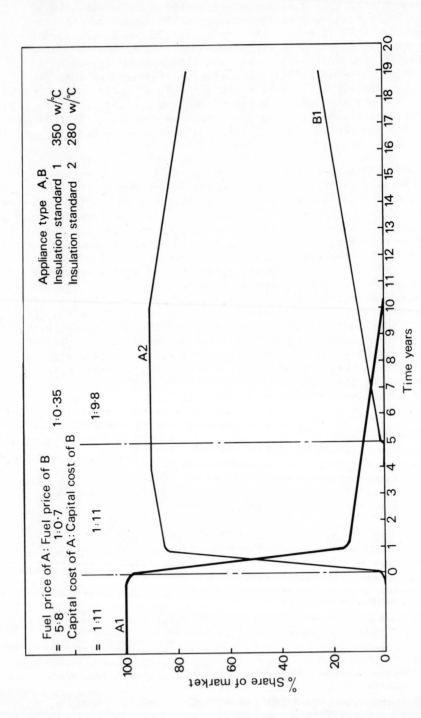

Figure 4 Interaction between insulation standards and appliance types

A particularly interesting example occurs in space heating
where there is a choice between both insulation standards and
appliances (Figure 4). A high increase in fuel costs at year
'0' encourages a general improvement in thermal insulation
level. A new appliance type is introduced at 5, with a high
capital cost but a low running cost. All those dwellings with
the new insulation standard find that the older appliance
with lower capital cost but higher running cost remains a
better buy, although for new stock the new appliance and the
older insulation standard optimise the decision rule. Thus
the sector has become inhomogeneous simply because of the
sequencing of the price rise and the introduction of the new
appliance type. If the new appliance had been available at
the time of the price rise, the stock would come to an equilibrium perhaps five times as fast.

The model as described contains one important omission. The
Inventory imposes an artificially high correlation between
events in the past and those in the present, because each
appliance and each dwelling is assumed to last exactly its
predetermined lifetime. Thus an event such as the price rise
in Figure 2 is 'frozen' in the housing stock for something
like 50 to 60 years. This is easily modified when the
Inventory is updated by simply advancing a given fraction
of appliances of each age to their terminal date. The fraction is given by the life expectancy distribution of the
appliance. In this way an event such as the price rise in
Figure 2 is very gradually 'smoothed away' in the Inventory
as the model progresses.

It is clear from what has been said, that it is important to
be able to recover the changing ownership distributions in
order to interpret the changing energy consumption of the
model. To achieve this, an image of the Inventory after each
complete scan by the decision procedure is kept in backing
store. This also enables the model to be run in a partially
interactive mode on a batch input without needless repetition
of earlier parts of the run. A separate report writing package can then be used to access the backing store and reanalyse
the successive images of the Inventory in any desired manner.

A picturesque example of the need for such analysis is given
in the case when the ages of two competing appliance types
differ. Instead of coming to a rapid equilibrium, the
decision rule used here sets up a saw tooth oscillation which
disappears only when all the original stock is replaced after
some 60 years (Figure 5). Clearly some 'reswitching' back
to the apparently less economic appliance is taking place.
Analysis of the Inventory shows that the decision rule permits this on the number of occasions when a switch to the
less economic appliance results in the last appliance only
just outliving the dwelling. When there is no correlation

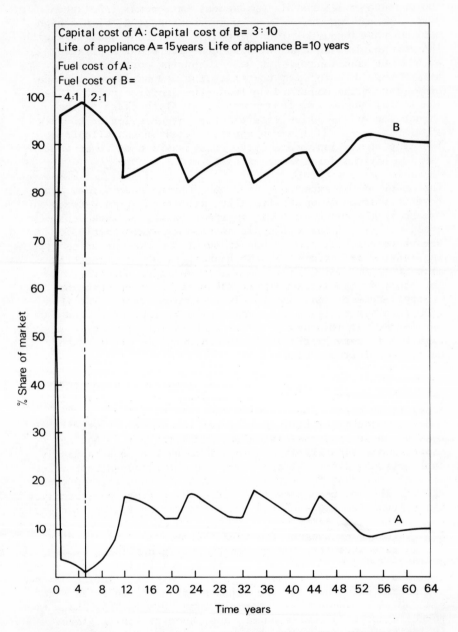

Figure 5 Effect of a relative price change when appliances have different lifetimes

between appliance and dwelling ages, this phenomenon is not made explicit in the output. However, when, as in this example, there is a high correlation because of some prior event, nearly all the dwellings have the same age of appliance. The 'reswitching' in old dwellings is then made clear by the sawtooth behaviour. This behaviour, of course, is derived from an anomaly in the decision rule and the absence of a randomised appliance lifetime. It serves to emphasise the need to be able to analyse the origin of any 'fine structure' observed in the model's response.

CONCLUSION

Energy consumption by buildings represents a substantial proportion of the primary energy consumption of the UK. Changes in energy use within buildings are a function in the medium and long-run of extended variables associated with the long time constants of built form and appliance life. This extended variable system is not amenable to full econometric analysis because of the quality of data available. Tests of the impact of various strategies may still be carried out, however, on an extended parameter model which simulates the time constants associated with a stock of buildings. An example of one such model has been given and some of its general characteristics described. It is intended to use the model in gaining experience of the long-run implications of decisions on the built form constraints of energy usage. It will also enable the construction of approximations of extended parameter behaviour to be made for inclusion in improved predictive models.

ACKNOWLEDGMENT

The work described forms part of the research programme of the Building Research Establishment of the Department of the Environment and this paper is produced by permission of the Director.

REFERENCE

1. BRE Working Party Report (1974). Energy Conservation: A Study of Consumption in Buildings and Possible Means of Saving Energy in Housing.

THE INTERDEPENDENCE BETWEEN ENVIRONMENT AND TRANSPORTATION
PLANNING
R. HAMERSLAG

Head of transportation modelling unit, Dwars, Heederik en
Verhey B.V., Amersfoort.

1. INTRODUCTION

In most traffic studies previously carried out the transport
flows were calculated with a given land-use allocation of the
working population and employment.
The number of trip ends, distribution, choice of means of
transport, choice of route and allocation to a network were
then calculated sequentially. The extent of the required infrastructure was determined on the basis of the transportation demand thus calculated.

A major objection to traffic studies conducted in this way is
that the impact of transportation planning on land-use and
socio-economic activities cannot be calculated. In the present
paper therefore the theoretical relation between transportation demand, land-use and infrastructure will be considered.
The theoretical treatment is based on the theory of individual
consumer behaviour and on the assumption that there must be
equilibrium between supply and demand of working population,
employment and infrastructure in each traffic zone.

2. THE MODEL

2.1. The demand function
From the theory of behavioural science has been derived
(e.g. Hamerslag, 1972), that the effort by mode in the year
(t)

Z_{ijvt} is a function of the perceived travel time by mode $Z_{ijv}(t)$, travel cost $C_{ijv}(t)$, income $y^{(t)}$

$$Z_{ijv}^{(t)} = Z(T_{ijv}^{(t)}, C_{ijv}^{(t)}, y^{(t)}) \qquad (1)$$

The perceived time and cost are functions of the actual time and cost and the travel times and costs in the past. The effort decreases as the actual income increases. A trip between i and j, trip purpose, is given by the equation:

$$P_{ij}^{(t)} = k_x \cdot l_i^{(t)} \cdot m_j^{(t)} \cdot Q_i^{(t)} \cdot X_j^{(t)} \Sigma_v F_{ijv}^{(t)} \qquad (2a)$$

for each i, j, v and purpose m (subscript m omitted) where:

$Q_i^{(t)}$ and $X_j^{(t)}$ are the polarities of, respectively, working at i and living at j (see 2.5.) in the year t.

$l_i^{(t)}$ and $m_j^{(t)}$ are the so-called balance factors. They have been added to the set of equations in order to enable the demand function to be adjusted to the supply function. These factors take account of the additional effort (positive or negative) that is needed in order to satisfy the constraints. k_x is a coefficient that should be determined in such a way that $\Sigma P_{ij}^{(t)}$ equals the total of exogene forecast employment. $F_{ijv}^{(t)}$ is the simultaneous distribution function for the mode of transport v.

$$F_{ijv} \overset{def}{===} F_v(Z_{ijv})$$

In the case of the dynamic model the traffic flows are calculated from the data of one or more preceding years. This gives the following equation:

$$P_{ij}^{(t+1)} = P_{ij}^{(t)} \Delta l_i \Delta m_j \cdot \Delta Q_i \Delta X_j \Delta F_{ij} \qquad (2b)$$

The symbol Δ denotes the ratio between the value of the quantity in question in the year (t+1) and its value in the year (t). For the sake of simplicity is assumed that the polarities between t and t+1 are equal to ΔG_i and ΔH_j (see 2.3.)

$$\Delta F_{ij} \overset{def}{===} \Sigma_v F_{ijv}^{(t+1)} / \Sigma_v F_{ijv}^{(t+1)}$$

2.2. The supply functions
The development of employment, is in part dependent on accessibility and in part independent of this factor. The following supply functions are used for the static version:

$$A_i^{(t)} = (1_i^{-g})^{(t)} \; G_i^{(t)} \quad \text{for each } i \qquad\qquad (4a)$$

(4a) gives for the dynamic version for employment

$$A_i^{(t+1)} = A_i^{(t)} \; \Delta1_i^{-g} \; \Delta G_i \quad \text{for each } i \qquad\qquad (4b)$$

The dynamic version of the supply function for the working population is:

$$B_j^{(t+1)} = B_j^{(t)} \; \Delta m^{-h} \; \Delta H_j \quad \text{for each } j \qquad\qquad (4c)$$

where:

G_i = the exogenic estimate of the employment
H_j = the exogenic estimate of the working population

g and h = coefficients

2.3. Equilibrium

In the following formulas s, r and u are defined as elasticities.

$$r \overset{\text{def}}{=} \frac{1}{1+g} \; ; \quad s \overset{\text{def}}{=} \frac{1}{1+h} \; ; \qquad\qquad (5a, 5b)$$

Supply and demand must be in equilibrium. The equilibrium can be calculated by elimination of the unknowns in:

$$\Delta1_i, \; \Delta m_j, \; A_i^{(t+1)}, \; \text{and } B_j^{(t+1)} \quad \text{in the}$$

supply and demand functions.

This gives the following equations

$$\Delta1_i = \left\{ \frac{A_i(t) \; \Delta G_i}{\sum_j \sum_v \Delta k_* \; \Delta m_j \; \Delta Q_i \; \Delta X_j \; \Delta F_{ij} \; P_{ij}(t)} \right\}^r \quad \text{for each } (6a)$$

$$\Delta m_j = \left\{ \frac{B_j^{(t)} \; \Delta H_j}{\sum_i \sum_v \Delta k_* \; \Delta1_i \; \Delta Q_i \; \Delta X_j \; \Delta F_{ff} \; P_{ij}(t)} \right\}^s \quad \text{for each } (6b)$$

In these equations the volume of transport $P_{ij}^{(t)}$ in the year (t), the existing working population and employment and $B_j^{(t)}$ in the year (t), the elasticities r and s, the changes in the exogenically estimated working population ΔH_j and employment ΔG_i and the changes in polarities ΔQ_i and ΔX_j are assumed to be known.

The unknowns Δl_i and Δm_j can be determined by an iterative
process in accordance with the Gauss-Seidel principle. The
convergence of this process does not result in any problems
as long as no extreme values of the elasticities are used.
The number of trips is obtained by substitution of Δl_i and
Δm_j into the equation (2b) from which the working population
and the employment are obtained.

2.4. The elasticities and transportation models

In various transportation models implicit assumptions are
made as to the elasticities of the constraints.
It can be seen from (5a) that if $r = 1$ then $g = 0$, so that
$A_i^{(t)} = G_i^{(t)}$ (4a). The endogenously calculated $(A_i^{(t)})$ and the
exogenously estimated employment $(G_i^{(t)})$ are equal.
In this case a fixed constraint is used.
It can also be proved that if $r = o$ no constraint is used.
The same can be proved for s. This gives rise to the conclusion that the model with elastic constraints generalizes
the transportation models with one and two constraints and
those without constraints.

If fixed constraints are used, it is implicitly assumed
that the land-use is given and is not influenced by the
transportation demand. These models can only be used if
the working population and employment in a future situation
can be estimated at the correct equilibrium.
Since this equilibrium is dependent on the transport volume
and the latter in turn is dependent on the quality of the
future transport system, it will in general not be possible
to satisfy this condition.
If a model without constraints is used, then it is assumed
that the allocation of population and employment will be
determined by the transportation demand calculations only.
This is not very reasonable.
If no zero or one values of the elasticities of the constraints are used, interdependence will be obtained between
allocation of population and employment, transportation demand and the transportation system.

The assumptions as to elasticities have considerable influence on the results of the calculation process with the static version of the model (except in the case of the model
with two fixed constraints).
The calculations with the dynamic model were likewise performed for various values of the elasticities of the constraints. The effect of these elasticities on the working
population and employment calculated with the dynamic model
is much less than in the case of the static model.

3. SENSITIVITY ANALYSIS

3.1. Introduction

In order to get an impression of the model properties a sensitivity analysis has been carried out. Therefore exogenous estimates are kept as simple as possible. The estimates of employment and working population are equal in all zones and are kept constant. Furthermore it is assumed that the polarities do not change between two forecasting years and that they are equal in all zones.
The distribution function is log normal.
The scope of the network is given in the figures.
For legend of the next fig. see fig. 3.1.
In the following paragraph some of the results of the sensitivity calculation with the dynamic version of the model are concerned.

3.2. Trip effort

The trip effort is a function of the trip time and the trip cost. During the experiments with the dynamic model this effort was varied from high to low values which showed that the spatial separation diminishes between equidistantly traffic zones.

The trip effort affects the allocation of working population and employment. The extent to which this occurs depends in part also on the values of the elasticities (r and s).
For the use of $r = -1$ and $s = 0.2$ the development of the population and employment is rather realistic (see Figs. 3.2 and 3.3). With high trip effort the trips are made over short distances. As a result, the working population and the employment in each traffic zone are equal. Because of the assumption adopted with regard to polarities, the population is uniformly distributed over all traffic zones.

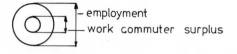
- employment
- work commuter surplus

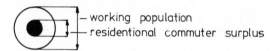
- working population
- residentional commuter surplus

Figure 3.1. Legend of figure 3.2, 3.3, 3.7, 3.8 and 6.1
W is the value of the effort of the links. The effort on the thick lines is o.25 times the effort on the thin lines.

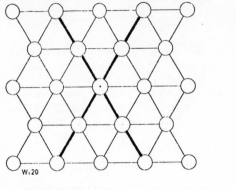

1 Exogenic estimates

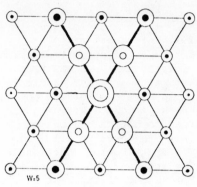

2 Urbanisation

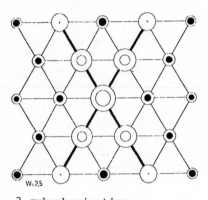

3 suburbanisation

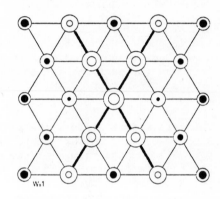

4 Explosion

Figure 3.2 The sensitivity for travel effort. Black circle is residential commuter surplus.

With a somewhat lower effort the population will concentrate in the traffic zones which are relatively favourably situated. Few trips are as yet made outside the population's own traffic zone, however.

A further lowering of the trip effort will lead to a further increase in concentration. A proportion of the population will go to live in the country (suburbanisation). The centrally situated regions get a surplus of work commuters and the eccentrically situated ones get a surplus of residential commuters.

If the trip effort becomes still lower, the working population and the employment will decrease further and more people will go to live in traffic zones situated farther outwards (exploding cities). The at first favourably situated traffic zones can be said to lose their advantage.

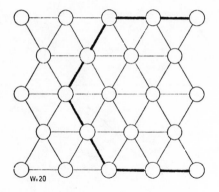

1 Exogenic estimates

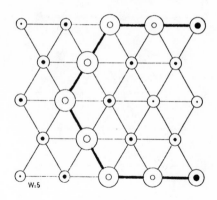

2 Urbanisation

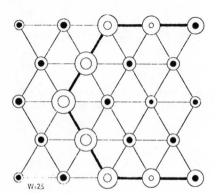

3 Suburbanisation

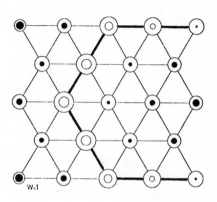

4 Explosion

Figure 3.3 The sensitivity for the travel effort. Black is
residential commuter surplus.

Another interesting result of these calculations is that the
population and the employment are found to concentrate around
links with low effort (heavy drawn lines).
The major cities will also have undergone an extra increase
in size as a result of the better quality of the city-directed
transport system (Fig. 3.2).
The provinces of North Holland and South Holland in the Netherlands comprise what once used to be a marshy region that was
much less accessible than the surrounding region. The towns
and cities which form the western conurbation known as "Rand-
stad Holland" arose around the edge of this marshland. The model causes these peripheral urban areas to grow (Fig. 3.2).
Although the results were obtained with a number of general
assumptions, a realistic description of regional development
in broad outline can be obtained.

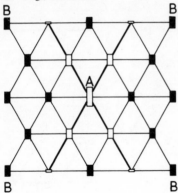

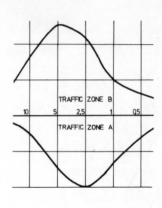

Figure 3.4 The extra effort
achieve equilibrium in the
traffic zones (black positive, white negative)

Figure 3.5. The extra effort
achieve equilibrium in
traffic zones A and B as
a function of the effort
of one link.

3.3. The extra effort needed to reach the equilibrium
The balancing factors have been added to the model in order
to obtain equilibrium.
The balancing factors are a function of this extra effort,
which is partly compensated by a higher salary, usually involving more highly qualified work.
The extra effort is shown in fig. 3.4. In the central traffic
zone the extra effort is much higher than in the surrounding
traffic zones, whereas the extra effort in "out of town" traffic zones is negative.

In fig. 3.5 the extra effort in both the central areas and in
the eccentrically located traffic zone is given as a function
of the mean effort link. The value of the extra effort increases with the decrease of the value of the effort of one link.
Lowering the effort results in a decrease of the extra effort
in these central zones. This means that the explosion of towns
in the model is accompanied by a relative decrease of well
paid, highly qualified work in such towns.
In this case too, the development observed in the model is in
accordance with reality.

3.4. Land-use and transportation planning
Fig. 3.6. represents a central city with three satellite towns.
The exogenic estimates are given in fig. 3.6.a.
The results of the calculations with low car availalities are
given in fig. 3.6b. The model calculates endogenously a city
centre, centres of the satellite towns and dwelling zones.
The importance of the centres of the satellite town increases
with the distance to the central city.

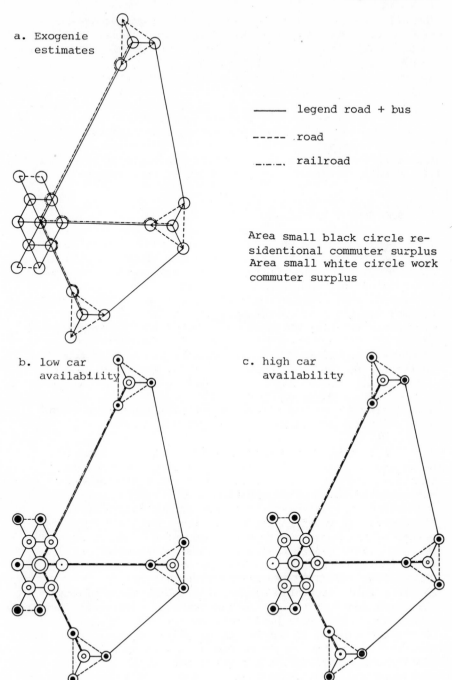

a. Exogenie
   estimates

——— legend road + bus

----- .road

_._._. railroad

Area small black circle residentional commuter surplus
Area small white circle work
commuter surplus

b. low car
   availability

c. high car
   availability

Figure 3.6 The sensitivity for transportation system and
         landuse planning.

The calculations have also been made for high car ownership
(fig. 3.6c). The centre of the major town decreases and so
do the centres of the satellite towns. New developments occur
in bordering zones of the central town.
Another result is the increase of the residentional commuter
surplus of the satellite towns.

The satellite town in fig. 3.6 has a triangular scope.
Calculation have also been made with a satellite town along
the railway line.
This results in a stimulation of the activities in the centre
of the major town and a larger amount of traffic into the
town.

4.   INSTRUMENT VARIABLES

Instrument variables in a model are explanatory variables
which may be assumed to be influenceable. This exercise of influence (e.g., by the public authorities) may be desirable in
order to obviate undesirable situations.
At present the model can be used to achieve certain objectives
in land-use planning or transportation planning by varying
exogenous variables for land-use and for the transportation
system.
If certain objectives can be formulated, it is also possible,
in theory, to find the optimal solution. The model provides
a possibility to develop decision-making models in this way.

5.   ESTIMATION OF THE COEFFICIENT AND DETERMINATION OF THE
     EXISTING SITUATION

In order to apply the method in more detailed studies it is
necessary to estimate the form of the supply and demand
functions and the elasticities and to ascertain the existing
situation by means of observations.
The form of the deterrence function can be determined in
three ways. If interest is focused more particularly on the
volume of transport and to a less extent on the utilisation
of land and if public transport plays only a minor part, it
will suffice merely to estimate the deterrence function
(Hamerslag, 1972/1973, Evans and Kirby, 1973).
If there is considerable use of alternative means of transport, the coefficients of the simultaneous deterrence function
(Hamerslag, 1974) will have to be determined.
On the other hand, if further information on implications as
to land use is required, a method will have to be used which
simultaneouly estimates the coefficients of the distribution
functions and the elasticities.

The calculation of a dynamic model is performed with an origin and destination table of the transport in the existing situation. Because of the high cost involved, the compilation of such a table is impracticable. It is therefore necessary to compile a basic matrix which is optimally established with the aid of the available relevant observations.
The author has explained how such a basic matrix was compiled (Hamerslag, 1972) using census data. Meanwhile a new method of determining the basic matrix, which makes use of still more relevant observations, is being developed.

6. COMPARATION WITH THE ALLOCATION MODELS OF THE LOWRY TYPE

An important group of models for the determination of allocation on population and employment are the Lowry type models (according to the interpretation of Wilson (1970) and Batty (1971). It is possible to calculate also the impacts of transportation planning on land-use with the models. There are the following differences between the models.

The model with elastic contraints is a transportation model. The land-use planning variables can be used explicitly in the model.
The split between service employment and basic employment is necessary in the Lowry model, because basic employment is the generator of this model.
The basic employment is difficult to forecast, however, because it depends on the size of the study area and on the forecasting year.
In the model with elastic constraints no differences between basic and service employment are needed.

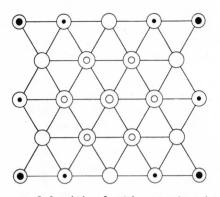 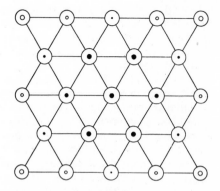

model with elastic constrants   lowry type model

Figure 6.1 Comparison of calculation results, black area is resicential commuter surplus.

In the Lowry type model the population development is located
around the basic employment if no hard constraints in zones
are used. Such constraints therefore influence the outcomes of
the calculations.
An advantage of the model with elastic constraints is that it
does not need these hard constraints.
The calculations with the Lowry type models have been compared
with the model with elastic constraints (fig. 6.1). The basic
employment is equal in all zones and is 70% of the total employment. No hard constraint in zones are used.
In the Lowry model development of the residential districts
takes place in the centre of the area. This calculation results are far less in accordance with reality.

7.   CONCLUDING OBSERVATIONS

In this paper the interdependence of transportation demand,
land-use and the transport system is studied. A model has
been developed, based on the theory of consumer behaviour.

A distinctive feature of this model is that elastic constraints
are applied instead of fixed constraints. By using specified
values of these elasticities a modal is obtained with one or
with two fixed constraints, or without constraints.
When these models are applied there will, in general, be no
consistency between populations, employment, the transportation demand and the transport system. The model with elastic
constraints obviates this objection.

In the static model the assumptions which are made regarding
the elasticity of the constraints, greatly influence the land-
use and the transportation demand.
In the dynamic model the transport flows are much less sensitive to the assumption made about the elasticities.
Besides, the assumption made as to the attractiveness of a
region is better in the dynamic than in the static model. The
dynamic traffic model is therefore preferable to the static
traffic model.
The value of the deterrence function used (log-normal), affects
the land-use and the transport volume. With a systematic decrease in the trip effort in time, the value of the deterrence
function increases in a particular relation, with the result
that the transport volume increases.
The initial situation adopted for the dynamic model is a situation of high trip effort, so that everybody lives and works
in his own traffic zone. As a result of increase in the trip
effort the development of favourably situated traffic zones
is simulated. A further increase in the trip effort results
in sururbanisation.
If the effort is reduced still more, the initially formed urban concentrations disappear.

The calculation has also been performed with a network in which certain parts have lower effort. The development outlined here is found to occur around the links in which this lower effort is present. It is also possible to simulate the development in a central city and satellite towns under influence of increasing car availibility.
In order to reach certain objections in transportation demand or in land-use, planning instrument variables can be used. The model is very sensitive to the trip effort. The trip effort is composed of trip times and trip costs. Trip time and trip costs can therefore be used as instrument variables.

The results of the calculations have been obtained with simplified assumptions as to explanatory variables. Greater refinement is attainable by estimation of the coefficients in the demand functions.
Furthermore, a method is being developed whereby the existing situation, which is used as the initial value in the dynamic process, is simulated with the aid of relevant traffic and transport observations.

ACKNOWLEDGEMENT

This study has been undertaken as part of the Zuid-Holland Traffic and Transportation Study, version 8 (Fortuyn and Sloet tot Everlo, 1974).

REFERENCES

Batty, (1971) An experimental model of urban dynamics; PTRC, Urban growth models, London.
Evans, S.P. and Kirby H.R. (1973) A three dimensional furness procedure for calibration gravity models. PTRC London.
Fortuyn, L.G.H. and Sloet tot Everlo, F. (1974) Provinciale vervoers- en verkeersstudie van Zuid-Holland. Verkeerstechniek, september, oktober.
Hamerslag, R. (1972) Prognose-model voor het personenvervoer in Nederland ANWB. Den Haag, pag. 23-27, pag. 74-76 en pag. 159-165.
Hamerslag, R. (1973) Automatische calibratie van distributie-functies. Een toepassing van "likelihood" schattingsmethode van Fisher. Verkeerstechniek nr. 11.
Hamerslag, R. (1974) Het schatten van coëfficiënten in het simultane verkeersmodel. Colloquium vervoerplanologisch speurwerk. Technische Hogeschool, Delft.
Kirby, H.R. (1972) Theoretical requirement for calibration of gravity models. Symposium Proceedings. Urban Traffic model research, PTRC London, page 97-110.
Lowry (1974) A model of metropolis Report RM-4035-RC. Rand Corporation Santa Monica (cit. Wilson).
Manheim, M.L. (1972) Practical Implications of some fundamental properties of travel demand models, HBR. 328.
Wilson, A.G. (1970) Generalising the Lowry model. Urban and regional planning. Pion Limited, London.

MATHEMATICAL MODELING FOR REGIONALIZATION OF RESOURCE RECOVERY

J. Kühner and J. J. Harrington

Harvard University, Cambridge, Massachusetts

INTRODUCTION

Increased attention has recently been given to planning
regional solid waste management (SWM) systems. Rapidly esca-
lating costs, more stringent environmental regulations and
expanding technological choices have enhanced the potential
usefulness of systematic generation and evaluation of alternative plans. Mathematical programming approaches to the
planning and management of conventional solid waste (SW)
systems is increasingly common. But there exist only very few
attempts to use programming techniques for the analysis of
resource recovery systems (for example, Haddix and Wees, 1975).
Resource Recovery (RR) has become a very popular means, in the
public's view, to master the SWM problem, but has not been
implemented on a large technological scale. Therefore, good
planning of such systems is very important. Thus the primary
focus of this paper is on the incorporation of RR into the
modeling analysis.

For our purposes RR includes principally energy and
secondary materials. Figure 1 is a schematic presentation of
the contractual, material and monetary considerations address-
ed in the model. The exogenous inputs are presently outside
the scope of the model. In general supply and demand sectors
are given in terms of temporal and spatial characteristics, as
well as SW composition, energy quality and secondary materials
attributes. Transport and processing options included in the
model are those judged to be economically, technically and
institutionally viable.

The application of Paretian Environmental Analysis (PEA),
as developed by Dorfman and Jacoby (1972), is an important
departure from conventional regional analysis. PEA attempts
to identify the preferences of each of the interest groups
involved in the decision making process. No single decision
maker is presupposed. Incorporating the objective of each
interest group marks a significant departure from ordinary

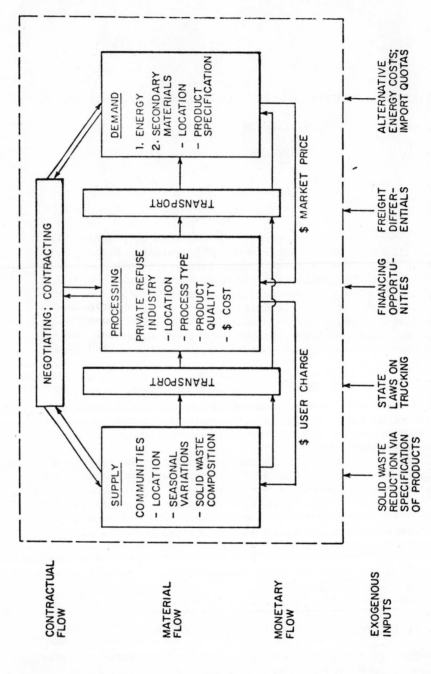

Figure 1 Free-body cut of interactions in resource recovery

cost benefit analysis. There the costs or benefits are evaluated from the viewpoint of a national or regional goal, while
here relevant costs and benefits are those perceived by each
interest group. Thus the consequences of regional plans for
each interest group can be evaluated and the trade-offs among
the groups be illuminated. This is an especially important
consideration since communities regard issues of location
(source vs. sink community) with great interest. Expressing
the distributions of costs and benefits and the transfers
among participants facilitates the analysis of the potential
for implementing regional plans in a decentralized decision
making environment, prevailing in New England.

Another major feature of this analysis is the use of
mathematical programming algorithms and codes to generate not
simply the globally optimal solution, but a number of nearly
optimal solutions. In our experience (Kühner and Harrington,
1973) several of these are markedly different, as perceived by
individual interest groups. While they have closely equal
values in terms of regional net benefits, for example, fiscal,
socio-economic and institutional characteristics are not uni-
versally dominated by the globally optimal solutions. Many
undesirable alternatives are eliminated by identifying and delimiting the Pareto frontier. Plans are Pareto admissible
when "there does not exist any feasible alternative that is
preferred by some interest party and that is not detrimental
to the interest of any other party" (Dorfman and Jacoby, 1972).

Finally, this type of modeling offers to industry a means
of assessing technology and alternative development strategies.
Legislators may be guided by quantifying the likely outcomes of
alternative subsidy schemes. Responsible executive agencies,
at the state level, may use the analysis to assist in formulating requests for proposals (RFP) for regional resource
recovery systems.

ASSUMPTIONS FOR MODEL FORMULATION

The following types of interest groups are involved in implementing regional RR: 1)communities that will supply the SW; 2)
private refuse industry will own and operate the resource recovery plant (even though the land might be owned by the
state); 3)industries and utilities are potential markets for
the energy output from RR operations; and 4)secondary materials
industries are potential customers for the products recovered,
in addition to the energy (see Table 1).

Focusing on the situation in New England we have not, at
this stage, included states in the set of interest groups even
though these states, their planning agencies, and federal
agencies are interested in the actual implementation of resource recovery. Their political power within the total decentralized decision-making process is relatively small and
limited to contracting with the private refuse industry. For
example, in Massachusetts, the state bureau of solid waste

Table 1

Interest Groups in the Resource Recovery (RR)-Analysis and Their Objectives and Constraints In a Decentralized Decision-Making Environment

Interest Group	Objective	Supply	Processing	Demand
community and other industrial and commercial waste generator	min. impact on tax rate* or min. disposal costs	-land availability for landfilling (alternative disposal) -budget and debt limits -financing method -location of process -length of contract and other specifications (e.g. min. delivery per time period)		
private refuse industry	max. profits		-supply of SW (minimum influx) -demand for recovered materials (distance of markets) -potential oversaturation of market for certain products -financing method -area of influence (system entry points) -location in urban area (environmental impact)	
market for energy	min. costs for alt. fuel sources			-substitutability -quality specification -technologically optimal fuel mix -contractual details
market for secondary materials	max. profits			-quality specification -market situation -influence on demand

*The objective function for communities is approximately valid for comparisons using the same disposal mode, but scarcely valid for comparisons using several disposal modes.

disposal has an option on property in an industrially zoned
area of Haverhill. This property will be used as site for the
RR plant, which will serve the Greater Lawrence Area. The
state bureau sent out an RFP to private industries, interested
and qualified, to build, own and run a resource recovery
plant; and will select one of the industries and its proposed
process. Thus, the state has a certain power with regard to
the selection of the RR plant to be built on its land; but it
does not have sufficient political power to impose regionalization on communities, even to secure the SW necessary for the
chosen RR plant. The communities could make their own con-
tracts with the private refuse industry concerning the construction of RR plants. Clearly each state is involved in
enforcing all standards for solid waste processing and disposal. In general, interest groups, such as communities, are
frequently too highly aggregated units. Of course, aggrega-
tion facilitates the mathematical analysis, but may make the
results questionable (Kühner, 1974).

Some interest groups may overlap physically, e.g., the
resource recovery plant might be located within a community
that may have specific interests in resource recovery. Issues
involving zoning, taxation and traffic are often important,
but only partly captured by the analysis.

Interest groups and their objectives and constraints in a
decentralized decision-making environment are summarized in
Table 1. This arrangement of interest groups is a conceptual
freebody cut. It is entirely possible that markets for
secondary materials and subsequent manufacturers might be
located far from the potential site of the resource recovery
plant located for supply convenience.

Potential technologies for resource recovery operations
(Table 2) have characteristics that differ in terms of product
quality, marketability, location-allocation patterns of supply
and demand, etc. A special case arises when the site selection was based on the choice of the process, as well as the
location of the demand sector, for example, incineration for
steam development.

Table 2
Technologies for Resource Recovery

1. Separation of recoverable, noncombustible (ferrous, non-
   ferrous, glass) materials;
2. Incineration with steam recovery;
3. Incineration with electricity generation through utilization of the gases in turbines;
4. Combustion of shredded refuse as a supplementary fuel to
   coal;
5. Dry fuel as supplementary fuel (e.g. in suspension burning)
   ·or as main fuel;
6. Fuel from pulped wastes; and
7. Gaseous and liquid fuels from pyrolysis.

Most of the processes are available only with pilot-scale experience. As a result, estimates of technological efficiency and reliability and of capital and O-and-M costs are quite uncertain. Several cost estimates have already been reported (Abert, 1974; ADL, 1973; GE, 1973; Hartman, 1974). But these estimates are already outdated due to inflation and no longer appropriate assumptions. For example, the original capital cost estimates for the resource recovery plant in Bridgeport, Conn. (approximately 20×10^6) have been exceeded by more than 100% even before construction has commenced. All estimates do concur in their expectations of significant economies of scale.

The quality of the energy generated, as well as the quality of the other secondary materials, is also quite uncertain. The interest in energy balances, e.g., (transport, processing and manufacturing) has risen greatly because apparently favorable energy balances have been frequently used by public groups that favor RR as means of pressuring governments to support RR. There have been a few attempts to provide reasonable estimates (GE, 1973). Intensive review has revealed that the energy estimates between similar processes and even within the same process show significant variances. Thus, results influenced by the introduction of an energy constraint should be carefully considered before they are used to draw unusual conclusions. An energy balance is included in the analysis by considering energy uses, involved in all transportation steps and in processing of SW, and energy savings in the demand sector by fuel addition for energy generation (dry fuel, gas, oil) and energy reduction in processing secondary materials (see Figure 1).

A number of financing mechanisms is available to finance a RR plant. For example, the private refuse industry has to compare the advantages and disadvantages of higher interest rates and more independence (revenue bonds) to lower interest rates and more dependence on the municipal decision-making body (general obligation bonds). For example, the RR plants in Connecticut will be financed via the bonding power of the Connecticut Resource Recovery Authority.

During the planning and then the implementation phase, the refuse industry tries to assure sale of recovered materials of specified quality by executing letters of intent with the demand sector. Such agreements have been more frequently issued for the sale of fuel than for the sale of the other materials (Ganotis, 1974). The refuse industry seems to be most interested in signing such agreements with the energy sector because, due to today's price situation, approximately 70 percent of the total revenue from the sale of recovered materials is expected from the sale of recovered fuel (e.g., Bridgeport, Conn.). But the glass and aluminum industries have also shown interest in the recovered materials, and have even signed letters of intent (e.g., with the RR-plant of Hempstead, N.Y.). The key problem, as seen by those industries, is the quality of the recovered materials. Risk

aversion and uncertainty about the point of saturation of the
market for such materials are additional factors. No reliable
demand forecasts are available; but some research has been
initiated (Franklin Institute, 1975). Arguments between
groups in favor of separating paper out of the SW stream and
groups in favor of recovering energy from the total paper load
have frequently arisen due to today's high value of recovered
fuels. The EPA (1974) has recently published figures which
show the impact of paper separation on the Btu value of the
fuel. Newspaper, corrugated paper from commercial and industrial sources, and mixed office papers account for about 47%
of all paper. Approximately 40 to 60% is recoverable. Given
a recovery rate of roughly 27%, separating paper out of the SW
stream does not impact the energy value much: separating out
15%, results in a Btu reduction of 4%, 27% in 7%, and 35% in
9%, respectively.

MODEL STRUCTURE

Basic Features

Various driving forces have determined our modeling and solution approach: 1)The shift toward planning regional RR
systems makes the question of wise investment over the coming
decades essential; thus, a dynamic investment model is proposed. 2)The complex regional question that arises as to whose
wastes should be treated, where and when, and by what processes is incorporated into a mixed integer programming formulation: location (with imbedded multiprocessing choices), allocation, transportation, sequencing and capacity expansion
modes should be superimposed. 3)Economies of scale of invest-
ments in RR plants can be handled by concave (separable) programming or by mixed integer programming; the latter is used
to give discrete ranges of capacity which have equal O-and-M
costs; 4)Our extensive experience in combining large-scale
mixed integer programming and Paretian Environmental Analysis
(Kühner, 1974) has led us to a similar approach. We take
advantage of the fact that good solutions near the mathematical optimum have frequently markedly different configurations.
Heuristics are applied so that a significant subset of Pareto
admissible solutions is generated. 5)The SW supplied by the
communities is taken over by the RR industry at entry points
which are transfer stations or the plant itself. Hence the
communities' transport expenditures end at this point. 6)Two
ways exist to approach the question of user charges in the
formulation: a)The user charge is fixed as a coefficient,
added to the unit cost of the communities, and subtracted from
the unit O-and-M costs of the RR industry. The SW load from
a community to the entry point of the RR system or to an
alternative SWM option is a continuous variable. b)Assuming
that it is unrealistic that a community's SW load will be
split up, and attaching an integer variable to the SW load
which reflects the various transport options to the entry

points to be selected by the industry, the user charge ($/ton) can be handled as a continuous variable with the SW load as a constant coefficient. Constraints assuring that the user charge at the entry points is equal for all participating communities (Federal law) have to be introduced. We used the latter approach in order to increase the degree of freedom in the total system. 7)At this time we have not handled explicitly the decisions of the demand sector for secondary materials, rather we have exogenously specified demand and fixed prices for each material. On the energy sector side, we have also introduced a maximum demand for each recovered fuel type, which has to be understood as a technologically possible mix of natural and recovered fuels; we have also introduced the total demand of fuel of each potential customer of a RR plant which can be satisfied by recovered and alternative fuel sources. The objective function of the fuel user contains the costs for both the natural and the recovered fuel, so that the energy sector's decision as to an economically desirable, technologically feasible fuel mix is, in fact, explictly dealt with. Clearly, the demand sector for the other recovered materials could be treated in the same manner.

Model Formulation

In order to shorten and simplify the presentation due to lack of space the basic features of the model formulation are expressed verbally rather than algebraically. Table 3 shows the entries of categories of interest groups and of aspects to be dealt with in the decision making process. Some of them enter directly the objective function as variables (marked as x), others only exercise influence on the interest groups expressed in adjusted cost and technological coefficients (marked as √). For example, the transport of raw SW to the transfer station will be part of the communities' objective function; and transport from the transfer station (point of entry into the RR system) will be part of the RR industry's objective function. The O-and-M costs of the RR plant are directly included in the industry's objective function. But these costs exert an influence on the costs, incurred by the communities via the variable user charge in the objective function of the community, as well as on the costs to the demand sector via the prices charged for the recovered material. These prices are treated as coefficients rather than variables, because they are not solely determined by the interaction of the one RR plant and the demand sector, but rather by the whole market situation. A number of aspects can be dealt with only qualitatively in this framework, e.g., reliability of the processes and environmental soundness of operations. Thus they have been included in investment and operation costs.

A similar scheme could be devised for the constraint sets. But due to space limitations, we have concentrated on the presentation of the model's matrix (Table 4) excluding

Table 3

Aspects of Decision Making as Direct and Indirect Entries of Interest Groups' Decision Framework

Categories of Interest Groups / Decision Aspects	Com- munities	RR In- dustry	Energy Demand Sector	Secondary Materials Dealers
Plant Siting and Initial Investment (PL)	X*	X	√**	
Choice of Process and Initial Investment (CP)	√***	X	X	√
Ultimate Capacity of RR plant (UCRR)	√***	X	√	
Staging of RR plant (ERR)	√+	X	√+	√
SW handled in RR plant (OR)	√	X		
Location & Capacity of Transfer-station (LCTR)	X	X		
Transport (raw SW) TSW		X		
Transport (RR materials) TRR		X	√++	√++
Storing (RR materials) SR		X	√	√
Processing Residue (PR)		√		
Alternative SWM (ASWM)	X	√		
Alternative Fuel (AFUEL)			X	
User Charge (UCH)	X	X	√	√
Cash Flow RR Materials (CFRR)	√	X	X	X

X = Decision variable in the interest group's objective

√ = Decision influences economic and technological parameters

*   Only of interest to the host-community (tax-income)

**   Only of interest when steam generation is the processing choice

*** Public Participation in financing is possible

\+   Utilization rate of the capacity influences the ORM-costs, and hence the charge to the community and the price to the energy sector

\+\+   Transport costs have to be covered by the seller

Table 4

Matrix of Model Formulation

Constraints (rows) \ Decision Variables (columns)	PL	CP	TSW COM	TSW RR	OR	PR	SR	TRR	UCRR	ERR	LCTR	UCH	CFRR	ASWM	AFUEL	Combinations of subscripts (notation text)
Mass Balance (Comm)			X											X		i,t
Budget Restr. (Comm)			X									X		X		i,t
User Charge Equality												X				i-1,t
Cost-Revenue-User Ch. Balance			X		X	X	X	X				X	X			s,l,t
Maximum capacity of Transfer			X								X					sl,t
Mass balance (Transfer)			X	X												sl,t
Maximum capacity (RR plant)	X	X			X				X	X						s,k,l,t
Minimum capacity (RR plant ranges)		X			X				X	X						s,l,t
Techn. choice continuity (RR)	X	X														s
Capacity Expansion Mech.		X							X	X						s,k,t-1
% of SW to be recovered			X		X	X	X									s,t
Mass Balance (RR)			X		X	X	X	X								s,k,t
Maximum Demand (Energy S.)								X							X	d,t
Maximum Demand (recovered M.)								X								d*,t
Storage capacity (RR)							X									s
Energy balance			X		X	X		X						X	X	t
Environmental restriction						X										s

the objective functions (Table 3). By considering Tables 3
and 4 together, three types of constraint sets are noted: 1)
constraints concerned only with one category of interest
groups, e.g., mass balance and municipal budget for the
communities, or the mass balance at the RR plant; 2)constrain-
ts, coupling 2 or 3 interest group categories, such as the
mass balance at the transfer station or the takeover of recovered materials by the demand sector. 3)Coupling constraints
for all categories of interest groups, such as the cost-revenue-usercharge balance. Of course, coupling constraints do
not have to cover all interest groups of an interest group
category, but only subsets. The matrix is quite sparse, which
is a result of including a number of special constraints.
Some of the constraints, such as mass-balances and capacity
limitations, etc. are similar to the ones in our previous
large-scale modeling efforts on conventional SWM. But others,
such as cost-revenue-usercharge balances, energy balances,
demand specification, storage capacity of untreated and un-
sellable recovered materials are included for the first time
in the analysis.

How many variables and constraints have to be expected in
a real world example? Let i denote the number of communities,
s1 the potential transfer stations, s the potential locations
of RR plants, k the potential industrial bidders (i.e. potentially different processes), 1 the discrete capacity segments,
d the demand locations, and t the number of time periods. Let
i=18, s1=6, s=4, k=5, 1=4, d=10 (with 5 of them being energy
demand) and t=3. Then we can calculate from the last column
of Table 4 the number of constraints as 669. This size is
mainly influenced by the constraint "maximum capacity of
resource recovery plants" being set up for each of the sub-
scripts describing the plant characteristics; but one constraint has always to control the various combinations of
processing location, mode, capacity, and time of inception.
To determine the number of variables without spatial details
(leading to heuristic exclusion of combinations) is very
difficult. The number could be up to 1900 with as much as
300 integer variables. This size of MIP has been solved quite
efficiently by the authors (Kühner and Harrington, 1974).
Additional heuristics (see below) will further reduce the size
(variables and constraints) of the problem after initial runs.

MODEL SOLUTIONS AND RESULTS

The objective function is made up of the sum of the net-benefit functions $NB_j(X,Q)$ of each interest group j, where NB_j
$(X,Q)=B_j(Q)-C_j(X)+T_j(X,Q)$. $B_j(Q)$ accounts for the benefits
derived from the environmental quality $Q, C_j(X)$ for the costs
imposed for the control option X, and $T_j(X,Q)$ for the transfers received (or paid) in connection with the plan. After
the first interviews with public officials in our previous

work on conventional SWM (Kühner 1974), we concluded that it is impractical to explicitly include benefits $B_j(Q)$. This fact also prevails here so that the net benefit function consists merely of cost and transfer payments.

Dorfman and Jacoby (1972) suggested the introduction of probing weights (w_i) and maximization of the resulting auxilary problem for different sets of weights to explore the Pareto Frontier. But our solution technique does not rely on the global optimum of the total net-benefit function and systematic changes of weights. We rather have taken advantage of the fact that good solutions near the optimum for a few weight combinations can be utilized in the same way as global optima for a large number of weight combinations. We believe this heuristic is valuable. First, a composite regional net-benefit function, on a present value basis, is an imperfect surrogate of real-world objectives. Second, the computational costs of achieving global optimality may be undesirably high in an MIP. Third, it has been shown that good solutions near the mathematical optimum (within 5%, say) generate valuable alternative plans. Many undersirable alternatives are eliminated by identifying and delimiting the Pareto frontier. Clearly, we are aware that this ad hoc method permits the identification of plans undominated with respect to the set of generated solutions; but it does not make apparent the degree to which this set of undominated solutions is representative of the complete set of Pareto-admissible solutions.

The actual generation of alternative SWM policies proceeds through a chain of three models: matrix generator, commercially available mixed integer programming algorithm (IBM, 1973) and, finally, the interpreting program. The interpreting program generates the present-value matrix for each interest group and alternative plan. Then it interprets the impact of each alternative plan by displaying the various socio-economic, financial, land-use, transport, etc. allocations in tables, calculating the costs, allocating them to the corresponding parties according to defined schemes, and interpreting them in terms relevant to decision makers. Table 5 is an example of the presentation of a present value matrix (limited to the communities). Due to lack of space, we do not show here additional output from the interpreting program.

A few changes of weights and the generation of numerous results for each set of weights reveal a number of robust solutions. It also makes clear that many alternative solutions are inferior, so that a number of variables do not enter the basis at all and many constraints are never binding. Hence the model size can be significantly reduced by eliminating these inferior elements. Heuristics, tailored to the actual example will be helpful for further reduction (see, for example, Kühner and Harrington, 1974, for an extensive description of such heuristics).

CONCLUSIONS AND SUMMARY

Table 5

MATRIX OF MIP SOLUTIONS*

Town	Solution No. 0**	1	2	3	4	5	6	7	8	9
AT	8609253.	5014370.	5014370.	5055460.	5055460.	5014370.	5014370.	5047250.	5072993.	5047250.
BE	184462.	192441.	192441.	193037.	193037.	189207.	189207.	192441.	189261.	189261.
DI	1231853.	1144285.	1144285.	1158784.	1158784.	1142323.	1142323.	1144285.	1144511.	1142511.
LA	572668.	593505.	593505.	595061.	595061.	585060.	585060.	593505.	585199.	585199.
MN	2494740.	1332019.	1332019.	1325982.	1325982.	1332019.	1332019.	1332676.	1333136.	1332676.
MI	2817909.	2595823.	2595823.	2597327.	2597327.	2587662.	2587662.	2595823.	2587797.	2587797.
NA	4934553.	2491182.	2491182.	2486313.	2486313.	2491182.	2491182.	2490179.	2487650.	2490179.
NO	1554372.	1540153.	1540153.	1636387.	1636387.	1531054.	1531054.	1538549.	1527474.	1529600.
PV	1508027.	701879.	701879.	757105.	757105.	701879.	701879.	701554.	700736.	701554.
RA	1072222.	1041143.	1041143.	1119085.	1119085.	1098156.	1098156.	1041143.	1098447.	1098447.
PF	924435.	952196.	952196.	835569.	835569.	952196.	952196.	859146.	859146.	859146.
SE	3386082.	2001932.	2001932.	1949640.	1949640.	2001932.	2001932.	1842452.	1836327.	1842452.
SO	2956531.	1898241.	1898241.	1898241.	1898241.	1898241.	1898241.	1898241.	1898241.	1898241.
SW	1750911.	1301352.	1301352.	1301352.	1301352.	1301352.	1301352.	1301352.	1301352.	1301352.
TA	4078544.	4311738.	4311738.	4524450.	4524450.	4246939.	4246939.	4311738.	4246413.	4246413.
FR	29379920.	20258112.	20567888.	21050688.	21378272.	21050688.	21378272.	20081536.	21219120.	21219120.
FT	606838.	1390859.	945123.	1390859.	945123.	1390859.	945123.	627764.	627546.	627546.
WP	1326876.	2574806.	2574806.	1326876.	1326876.	1326876.	1326876.	2576254.	1326876.	1326876.
Tot.ACRES :	680.	1170.	1170.	1340.	1340.	1185.	1185.	1110.	1125.	1125.
Tot.COVER IMPORT*** :	0.	0.	0.	0.	0.	0.	0.	0.	0.	0.
Tot.TO EASTBRIDGEWATER+ :	0.	0.	0.	0.	0.	0.	0.	0.	0.	0.

*Entries are PV of Costs ($)

**Solution 0 is SRPEDD's plan evaluated in interpreting program.

***cubic yards/period

+tons/period

We have presented a new modeling approach to regional RR. Interest groups, involved in the decentralized planning and decision-making process, are explicitly recognized by incorporating their net-benefit functions and their views of technological relationships. PEA provides a tool to illuminate the
tradeoffs among interest groups so that "good" alternative
plans can be generated. Robust solutions become a valuable
basis for the discussions and negotiations for a final decision. Major problems of comprehensive RR planning are discussed in order to underline real-world difficulties and to
point out facets which must be recognized for a successful
analysis. Plans are generated through a chain of three
models; large-scale MIP plays the central role. Effective use
of the interpreting program reduces the number of MIP runs,
summarizing the impact of a plan on each interest group and
also updating results. Future developments include making the
program interactive, in order to reduce the massive amount of
output that planners and decision makers have to handle. Results from our most recent applications will be presented at
the conference.

After such a large modeling effort with all its data
preparation, interviewing, and computing manipulations, a
critical review is necessary. The model could be easily ex-
panded, for example, to include locational decisions on secondary materials manufacturing. The industrial park planned in
Wallingford, Conn. is an example of a locational decision,
largely influenced by RR decisions. Whether that addition
would improve the analysis or would drive it toward increasingly large and unwieldy computer exercises remains to be seen.
Sensitivity checks for various combinations of important parameters would be essential. Modeling tasks for RR are so relatively new that a consensus of what constitutes a good analysis (scale and content) has not yet been achieved. In the
absence of experience with large-scale RR technology even
anticipating future problems that would have to be explicitly
dealt with in the analysis is difficult. PEA, as applied here,
is of great value; but a decomposition approach could also be
imagined whereby the state's RR agency would represent the
master program (e.g., with a goal of maximizing RR), while
supply and demand sectors form the subprogram categories.
Problems of convergence would be anticipated in the nonlinear
analysis.

In summary, providing real-world details and incorporating them in the modeling analysis presented here offer the
potential for improved decision-making in a field in which
large-scale implementation has not yet been achieved.

ACKNOWLEDGMENT

The National Science Foundation has supported this work with
grant NSF-GI-35117 to Harvard University. Paul Abel has
assisted with research on energy balances and demand for RR.

References

Abert, J. G., et al. (1974) The Economics of Resource Recovery from Municipal Solid Waste. Science, Vol. 183, 1052-1058.

Arthur D. Little, Inc. (ADL) (1973) A Systems Evaluation of Alternative Statewide Resource Recovery Techniques for the Disposal of Municipal Solid Waste, Report to Massachusetts State Department of Public Works, Cambridge, Mass.

Dorfman, Robert and Jacoby, Henry D. (1972) An Illustrative Model of River Basin Pollution Control;in Models for Managing Regional Water Quality, ed. by Robert Dorfman, Henry D. Jacoby, and Harold A. Thomas, Jr., Cambridge, Massachusetts, Harvard University Press.

Franklin Institute (1975) Potential for Resource Recovery in the U.S.

General Electric (GE) (1973) A Proposed Plan for Solid Waste Management for Connecticut, prepared in cooperation with Conn. State Dept. of Environmental Protection.

Ganotis, C. G. and S. A. Schneider (1974) Joint Government-Electric Utility Planning of Refuse Fuel Systems: A Research Report, MTR-2894, Mitre Company, Bedford, Mass.

Haddix,G. and M. Wees (1975) Solid Waste Planning Models with Resource Recovery, paper presented at 47th National ORSA/TIMS Meeting, Chicago.

Hartman, A. C. (1974) The Economics of Resource Recovery and Source Reduction; meeting: The Economics of Resource Recovery and Source Reduction.

IBM (1973) Mathematical Program System Extended (MPSX), Mixed Integer Programming (MIP), Program Description, (2nd edition).

Kühner, J. (1974) Centralization and Decentralization for Regional Solid Waste Management: Toward Paretian Environmental Analysis, Ph.D. - Thesis, Harvard University.

Kühner, J., and Harrington, J. J. (1973) Mathematical Models for Developing Regional Solid Waste Management Policies. Presented at Optimization in Civil Engineering Conference, University of Liverpool, forthcoming in: Engineering Optimization, Vol. 1.

Kühner, J., and Harrington, J. J. (1974) Large-Scale Mixed Integer Programming for Investigating Multi-Party Public Investment Decisions: Application to a Regional Solid Waste Management Problem, 45th National ORSA/TIMS Meeting, Boston, Mass.

U.S. EPA (1974) Energy Conservation through Improved Solid Waste Management, SW-125.

HUMAN ACTIVITY, POLLUTION AND RESOURCES

J. W. Bryant

University of Sussex

GENERAL APPROACH

Accelerating technological change, in a world of shrinking natural resources and growing human demand, has given birth to such catchphrases as 'spaceship earth' and 'the global village'. Underlying these expressions is the growing aware- ness of the dependencies and relationships which tie into a cohesive whole the bewildering variety of terrestrial eco- systems. Over the past two decades a conceptual framework, the systems view, has developed, which reflects this concern with dynamic unities and which provides a means of coping with the complexity of the new perspective.

The systems approach to resolving the immensely complex problems facing modern man is essentially extrospective; that is, it consists in looking outwards from the problematic situation itself to the context within which it is embedded. In this way, the problem's fundamental causes are attacked so that it may be eliminated rather than being transferred else- where. A good example of the need for such an approach occurs in the study of SO_2 emissions from electricity power stations.

In Britain, the CEGB has adopted a high chimney dispersion policy which results in reduced ground concentrations of waste gases in this country. However, viewed in a wider context, these gases probably contribute in large measure to the acid rains in Scandinavia as well as to uncertain climatic effects. Such 'sub-optimal' solutions may not be recognised as such until a total systems stance is adopted.

The main argument levelled against the systems approach is that it can give rise to unmanageable complexity or alterna- tively to arbitrary bounding of the problem, and so in either case useful solution is precluded. These disadvantages have been countered in the work described in this paper by using

a method of systematic and selective exploration of a complete
terrestrial model. This makes it possible to expand, as
necessary, the detail in the areas of crucial importance while
retaining in a simpler form the structure of the total context.

GENERAL MODEL

The total systems context of pollution is provided by a
general model of man and his environment. This draws out the
salient aspects of the inter-relationships between the systems
involved.

Since the problems of environmental pollution represent the
impact of human activities on the natural world, a fundamental
distinction can be made between man-made and natural systems.
Pollution problems arise partly from man's lack of understanding of the relationships between these two major systems
and partly from his lack of concern for the long-term consequences of his activities as he strives to attain the short-
term goals of human society.

The goal-directed character of man's activities make it useful
to introduce a further distinction between the physical and
metaphysical aspects of the man-made world. While it is
through human activity systems that man moulds his physical
environment, his goals are generated, his decisions made and
his control maintained through the manipulation of conceptual
models by human abstract systems.

The three macrosystems identified viz., human activity, human
abstract and natural systems are richly interrelated as shown
in Figure 1.

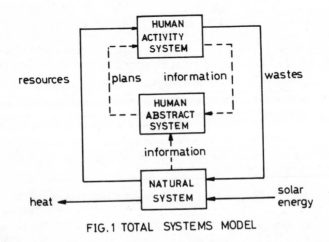

FIG.1 TOTAL SYSTEMS MODEL

Human activities draw on the resources of natural systems
which they use to implement the plans of human abstract
systems. These activities satisfy man's needs but they also
discharge their final wastes into the environment. The
constant inflow of solar energy enables the natural systems to
maintain themselves and in doing so to absorb the outputs of
human activities. As perceived by human abstract systems, the
natural world acts both as an inspiration and intellectual
challenge and as a stimulus for purposive change.

Each of the three components of the total system can be considered as transforming certain inputs, whether material, information or whatever, into certain outputs. The transformation function may be dynamic, but at any moment it
expresses the relationship between input and output flows.

Pollution is a natural system state that has been brought
about by human activity and that is perceived by the human
abstract system and regarded as undesirable. It is usually a
localised phenomenom and for it to occur, the natural system's
capability of absorbing the outputs of human society must be
inadequate. Additionally, for it to be recognised, there must
be a sufficient flow of information to the human abstract
system and an appropriate set of societal attitudes to the
observed natural events. The distinct contributions of the
three identified macrosystems to pollution can clearly be
seen.

Human Activity System

Human activities are concerned with the implementation of
human decisions in the physical world and are the material
source of pollution. Various stages can be recognised in the
transformation of those natural resources used by man,
between their removal from and their ultimate dissipation to
the environment:

1. Resource Extraction. Material is taken from natural
    systems
2. Production. Raw materials are made into artefacts
3. Service. Goods are handled, stored and transported
4. Consumption. Items are used and degraded
5. Waste Dispersion. Materials are discharged into natural
    systems

These stages can be recognised in any human activity sub-
system. For example, a steel works will extract oxygen from
the air for smelting; produce steel; handle manufacturing
wastes and finished goods; consume energy; and discharge slag
and waste gases into the surroundings. Such flows may involve
interactions with other activity sub-systems. Thus power is
obtained from the electricity generation sub-system and steel
sheets sold to car manufacturers. Such a set of flows can be

represented as in Figure 2, where the horizontal planes are the various transformation stages.

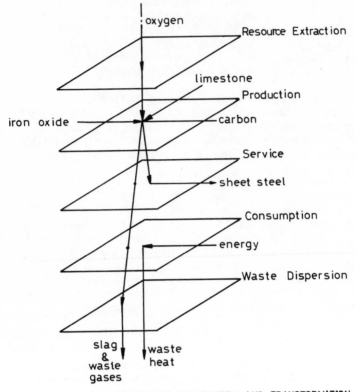

FIG 2 STEEL PRODUCTION SUB-SYSTEM AND TRANSFORMATION STAGES

In addition to the physical flows there are other inputs and outputs to human activity systems. Thus a sub-system as a whole will be influenced by the flow of plans from the corresponding human abstract system. Returning to the steelworks example, executive decisions will flow from the management abstract system and may modify the throughput of steel in the works or the power sources used. The manufacturing process will be monitored and information fed back to the controlling function to provide a basis for future decisions. Of course, informal monitors such as public environmental watchdogs may also be involved and information they receive about effluents may well result in public pressure and a subsequent change in management policy. This sort of interaction between sub-systems in different macrosystems is illustrated in Figure 3, and such a pattern is also found between a producer and its market or an organisation and the government.

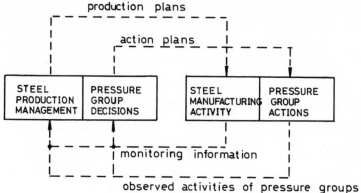

FIG.3 CONTROL LOOPS FOR STEEL PRODUCTION SUB-SYSTEM

Human Abstract System

Human abstract systems form the purpose generators which underly all man's activities and so are the basic cause of pollution. The currency of human abstract systems are information concepts and plans, and a number of steps can be identified in the flow through these systems:

1. Perception. Events are seen in the context of a model of reality
2. Assessment. The situation is examined and any problems defined
3. Solution. Alternatives are generated using the model of reality
4. Evaluation. Alternatives are examined for their contribution to goals
5. Implementation. A decision is taken and plans formulated

In contrast to the physical macrosystems, the flow through the human abstract system is stochastic rather than largely deterministic.

Naturally the decision making process in any sub-system is subject to the influence of other abstract sub-systems as well as by the direct perception of human activities and natural events. For instance, an individual may be influenced in his problem-solving activity by others in his family, social, business or other reference group as well as by such pressures as marketing or propaganda.

Natural System

Biological and geophysical resources combine to produce the amazing complexity of natural systems, the victims of pollution. Again, various stages can be distinguished in the passage of materials:

1. Energy Absorption. Solar energy and physical system outputs are received
2. Production. Photosynthesis, tissue growth and mineral formation occurs
3. Translation. Materials are moved
4. Consumption. Foods are consumed and geological erosion occurs
5. Energy Radiation. Heat is radiated and physical system outputs despatched

The correspondance of these stages to those in the human activity system is intentional, and serves to emphasise that man's activities are only a particular aspect of natural events.

Within the natural system, sub-systems may be defined in ecological terms, basing their delineation on the level of organisation exhibited. The many cross-links between sub-systems are largely responsible for the many, often unexpected side-effects of pollution.

Pollution
The general framework of the model will now be used to illustrate its application as a method of problem description. To provide a realistic but deliberately simplified example of a total systems analysis, the problem of oil spillage at sea has been chosen.

Annually thousands of millions of tons of oil are shipped to consuming countries and almost inevitably, human error or weather conditions lead to accidental spillages. If not dispersed, this oil may float ashore and cause both destruction of marine life and fouling of beaches. In such an event, many local authorities would naturally be concerned about the possible repercussions on the tourist trade and so might take action by detergent spraying.

The processes described are illustrated in Figure 4. In the human activity system can be seen the oil industry and its customers as well as the local authorities and holidaymakers. Corresponding human abstract systems are included while the natural systems depicted are the oil reserves and coastal ecosystem. Arrows indicate interaction flows of materials and information, but for clarity the links between abstract systems and their counterparts in the activity system have been represented by broad arrows in the diagram and only flows additional to these are otherwise included. The recycling between natural systems is similarly represented by a loop. It is emphasised that many other links might be found and this example has been deliberately shorn of complexity to facilitate understanding.

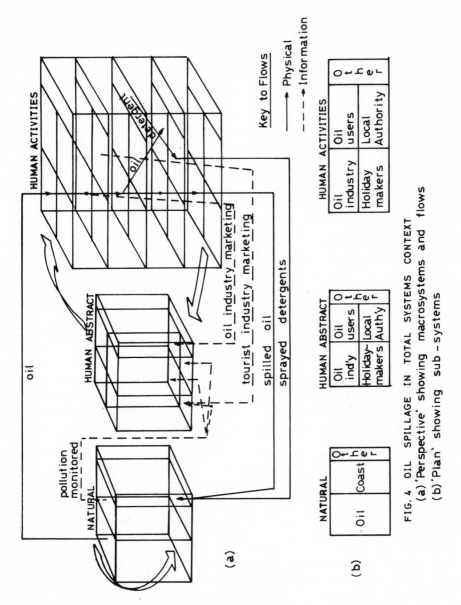

FIG. 4 OIL SPILLAGE IN TOTAL SYSTEMS CONTEXT
(a) 'Perspective' showing macrosystems and flows
(b) 'Plan' showing sub-systems

The model is also of considerable assistance in the
systematic generation of solutions to pollution problems.
As these problems arise from the human recognition of natural
system states resulting from human activities, each of the
three macrosystems offers solutions. For instance, the
pollution may be relieved by the reduction in scale or the
modification of the type of flows through the human activity
system; by the alteration of the flows of information to

human abstract systems or the change in human attitudes and
values; and by the engineering of the natural environment to
enable it to handle the polluting materials. The possibilities that are suggested, for example in the oil spillage
illustration, can be readily generated.

SOLUTION EVALUATION

There are three main elements in the evaluation of
alternative solutions to problems of environmental pollution.
Firstly, there must be a value scale of environmental quality
on which to assess environmental system states. Secondly,
there must be a method of predicting the environmental
consequences of alternative programmes of man-induced change.
Thirdly, there must be a way of synthesising these two
components to provide a basis for trade-off calculations and
decision-making. This paper is primarily concerned with the
second of these elements but the other two aspects will be
briefly discussed here.

It is felt that a ratio scale with an absolute environmental
zero is the most useful measure for environmental quality.
Such an absolute zero may be defined as the point at which
the environment has no potential to support life; in systems
terms a state of maximum entropy is attained. Quantitative
calibration can use either specially-designed monitoring
equipment or biological indicators.

The fabrication of a trade-off model is the most appropriate
way of exposing the inevitable conflicts of interest between
the many objectives and organisations involved in a pollution
situation. It is also possible with such a model to
juxtapose measurements on environmental, economic, social
and other scales. A single function optimising model might
conceal these complex considerations.

A descriptive model will now be discussed that offers a way
of assessing the environmental impact of human activities by
the provision of a physical balance sheet. When this is
coupled with current knowledge about natural systems as
revealed by ecological studies, it makes possible the
projection, in environmental terms, of the results of such
activities.

A human activity system may be represented as an assemblage
of interacting sub-systems linked by a network of flows. In
the simplest terms, a sub-system may be described by the
dynamic relationships between its input and output flow sets.
Then if a sub-system k, with N inputs f^{1k}, f^{2k}....f^{ik}....f^{Nk}
and M outputs f_{k1}, f_{k2}....f_{kj}....f_{kM} is considered at some
time t and if a time lapse of T occurs between input and out-

put, the sub-system may be represented by the transformation functions, F^i and F_j where,

$$f^{ik}(t) = F^i(f_{k1}(t+T), f_{k2}(t+T)..f_{kM}(t+T);t) \text{ all } i \qquad (1)$$

and $f_{kj}(t) = F_j(f^{1k}(t-T), f^{2k}(t-T)..f^{Nk}(t-T);t) \text{ all } j \qquad (2)$

It is assumed that F^i and F_j are defined at the time of input and output respectively. Additionally, there may be relationships between members of the input or output flow sets. If these are represented by the dependency functions G^i and G_j, they may be written,

$$f^{ik}(t) = G^i(f^{1k}(t), f^{2k}(t) \ldots f^{Nk}(t);t) \text{ all } i \qquad (3)$$

and $f_{kj}(t) = G_j(f_{k1}(t), f_{k2}(t) \ldots f_{kM}(t);t) \text{ all } j \qquad (4)$

The interacting flows may also be represented algebraically. If it is assumed that such interactions take place instantaneously and that any imbalance between the output generated at the originating sub-system and the input required at the destination sub-system is notionally 'held in stock' on the flowline, then the change in this 'inventory' s_1 for a flow, 1, linking sub-systems k' and k" can be written

$$\Delta s_1(t) = f_{k'1}(t) - f^{1k''}(t) \qquad (5)$$

Practical studies of environmental systems suggest assumptions that can be made about the form of the functions in Equations 1 to 4 and these will be mentioned later.

Once a system has been specified in terms of flow relationships, it is possible to calculate the flows occurring in the system as a whole, given information about an appropriate sub-set of flows. However, the complexity of such systems is an obstacle to their analysis in this way, and in the past has contributed to the tendency for planners to confine themselves within very narrow boundaries and thus to sub-optimise. For this reason a computer programming language FLOSI (FLOw SImulation) has been developed for system modelling.

The assumptions about the sub-system functions made in one of the simpler versions of FLOSI, which uses only static relationships, will now be described. Introducing the concepts of the scales of a sub-system T^k and T_k defined as,

$$T^k = \sum_{i=1}^{N} f^{ik} \quad \text{and} \quad T_k = \sum_{j=1}^{m} f_{kj} \qquad (6)$$

When many sub-systems are investigated, it is found that the input and output flows are proportional to the respective scales and in the special case of physical flows for which mass-energy is conserved ($T^k = T_k = T$), the Equations 1 to 4 become,

$$f^{ik}/r^{ik} = f_{kj}/r_{kj} = T \tag{7}$$

Where the r's are proportionately constants. Equation 7 forms the basis of the simulation and values of the constants r, must be supplied to the program for each sub-system and flow. These are simply the proportions of the process throughput contributed by the various flows, since, from Equations 6 and 7

$$\sum_{i=1}^{n} r^{ik} = \sum_{j=1}^{m} r_{kj} = 1 \tag{8}$$

Further relationships are used to constrain the values of all the input and output flows as such constraints are often found in practice as capacity limits on inputs or as emission limits on outputs. This is a special case of Equations 3 and 4 and if the constraint on input i is c^{ik}, and on output j is c_{kj}, can be represented by,

$$f^{ik} \leqslant c^{ik} \text{ all i } ; \quad f_{kj} \leqslant c_{kj} \text{ all j} \tag{9}$$

In the evaluation of a network of sub-systems, some flows will be known while others have to be calculated. In general, for any sub-system either none, some or all of the connecting flows are known. In the first case, evaluation is impossible, while in the last it need not be carried out. When some of the flows are known evaluation of the remaining flows is possible using Equation 7 if T can be found. The through-put, T, of a process, k, is essentially determined by the output flows which must be produced. Thus it is given by,

$$\underset{\substack{j \\ (\text{for } f_{kj} \neq 0)}}{\text{Max}} \frac{(f_{kj})}{(r_{kj})} \tag{10}$$

However, there are two exception conditions. Firstly, constraints may prevent the required throughput being achieved. This will be the case if Equation 10 is greater than,

$$\text{Min} \left[\underset{\text{all i}}{\text{Min}} \frac{(c^{ik})}{(r^{ik})} , \underset{\text{all j}}{\text{Min}} \frac{(c_{kj})}{(r_{kj})} \right] \tag{11}$$

In this case an evaluation cannot continue beyond this point.
The second possibility is that no output flows may be known
(all $f_{kj} = 0$). When this is so, the throughput is given by
the input flows as,

$$\underset{\underset{(\text{for } f^{ik} \neq 0)}{i}}{\text{Min}} \quad \left(\frac{f^{ik}}{r^{ik}}\right) \tag{12}$$

However constraints may operate, in which case T is the
smaller of the expressions 11 and 12. In this way the
throughput and hence all unknown connecting flows to a
process can be found.

The evaluation of linear systems is straightforward using
the methods that have been described but the incidence of
feedback loops is common in practical systems. The program
therefore includes facilities for the evaluation of two sorts
of recycling procedure. Here a recycled flow is taken to be
a flow into a sub-system which has been generated by another
sub-system dependent upon the first. The two sorts of recycling are differentiated on the basis of the use made of
the recycled flow in the process to which it is returned;
in one case it replaces, in the other it augments the
existing inputs. In the first procedure, if the recycled
flow is f^{rk} and if $p^{1k} \dots p^{n''k}$ are the amounts of flows
$f^{1k} \dots f^{n''k}$ which are replaced by one unit of recycled
flow, the amount of the recycled material used is,

$$\text{Min} \quad \left(f^{rk}, \quad \underset{\underset{(\text{for } i=1,n'')}{i}}{\text{Min}} \quad \left(\frac{f^{ik}}{p^{ik}}\right)\right) \tag{13}$$

and if this amount is written as f'^{rk}, the modified input
flows become,

$$f'^{ik} = f^{ik} - f'^{rk} p^{ik} \text{ for } i = 1 \dots n'' \tag{14}$$

With second procedure, if the recycled flow is f^{rk} and if
flows $f^{1k} \dots f^{n''k}$ are the inputs augmented by the recycled
material, the throughput of the process can be modified by
the multiplicative factor,

$$\left(1 + \frac{f^{rk}}{\sum_{i=1}^{n''} f^{ik}} \right) \tag{15}$$

However, it either may not be possible to increase the non-augmented inputs in line with the new throughput because of constraints, or output constraints may prevent any augmentation. In this case, the factor is the smaller of expression 13 and,

$$\text{Min} \left[\begin{array}{c} \text{Min} \\ i \\ (\text{for } i = n'' + 1, \, N) \end{array} \left(\frac{c_{ik}}{f_{ik}} \right), \begin{array}{c} \text{Min} \\ j \\ \text{all } j \end{array} \left(\frac{c_{kj}}{f_{kj}} \right) \right] \quad (16)$$

It is assumed that the recycled material replaces the flows $f^{1k} \ldots f^{n''k}$ in the proportions $r^{1k} \ldots r^{n''k}$ in which they occur before recycling. Obviously with augmentation recycling the feedback effects will cause flows to be recycled indefinitely. In the program the loop can be broken whenever the throughput factor approaches unity within less than some predetermined limits.

The basis of the FLOSI language has been described at some length to illustrate the flexibility of the underlying model. It is of interest to note that while FLOSI can be used to undertake analyses of quite complex human activity systems, especially in its more advanced versions, it can also be used for more straightforward tasks such as energy costing. The further development of descriptive models of the sort that have been described will probably make a significant contribution in the evaluation of alternative scenarios by decision-makers concerned with pollution and will grow in importance with the awareness of the economic, social and ecological penalties of an unrigorous approach to environmental problems.

ACKNOWLEDGEMENT

The author would like to thank the Science Research Council for supporting the research which this paper describes.

A MODEL CRITERION FOR SITE-SELECTION OF LARGER SCALE TECHNICAL FACILITIES IN THE "UPPER RHINE REGION".

G. Halbritter

Nuclear Research Center Karlsruhe, Germany

INTRODUCTION

In the densely populated areas of Central Europe projects supported by private and public investors call for site planning which incorporates the health protection of the population affected, as well as ecological criteria. An appropriate means is provided by quantitative analyses of the existing conditions, e.g. the outdoor pollutant concentrations, and predictions, respectively, about the consequences of planned projects. These analyses must relate to the actual sites for the projects with their specific environments such as the density of settlements, the sociological pattern of the population, and the specific ecological situation. A framework of orientation for the analyses is given by the problem chain emission - outdoor pollutant concentration-consequence-acceptability. There exists a wealth of methodological tools in order to evaluate the pollution levels which might be generated by the siting of industries, as well as for the mathematical optimization of such a siting. However, there is scarce information on suitable objective functions which ideally should deliver only one optimal solution. For the time being this ideal solution can only be approached step by step.

Into this investigation two requirements became incorporated:

(1) The siting has to guarantee a pollutant concentration which is inversely proportional to the population density.

(2) Costs (investment and operating) have to be minimized.

In general each of these requirements will lead to different sitings. But, dependent on certain constraints which will be mentioned further down the requirements (1) and (2) should become fulfilled by at least one optimal siting solution. At a glance the simultaneous handling of the two requirements will bring up the question how to compare apples and pears?

This question was overcome by the application of the vector valued optimization /ALLGAIER, KÖRTH, JÜTTLER/ which makes use of the constraints being the same for both requirements.
The vector-valued optimization method attempts to maximize the sum of the objective attainment values put forward by the two requirements. The scale of these values is confined by the optimal and the so-called "worst" solutions of the objective functions. The optimal solution is defined as the result of the individual scalar valued objective function. Evaluation of the objective function through linear programming that maximizes the total number of possible sites while observing the constraints will deliver the "worst" solution.
In this investigation serve as constraints:
(i) Minimum regional energy demand has to be satisfied.
(ii) Environmental standards have to be observed.
After the presentation of the models, a calculation of possible power plant sites in the "Upper Rhine Region" is made. The regarded pollutant is sulphur dioxide (SO_2).

MODEL ON SITE EVALUATION

The two objective functions have been given (requirements (1) and (2)) and are subject to the above mentioned constraints (i) and (ii). In the following, first the two objective functions called model 1 and model 2 are presented. Then the vector valued optimization is described and a specific model is evaluated. All models are specified for fossil fuel power plants.

Optimization of scalarvalued objective functions

Model 1

Minimization of the weighted pollutant concentrations $p_i \cdot x_i$ at all points i of the region subject to the environmental contraints b_i and minimum energy production constraints K_l within subregion l. The weighting p_i is done inversely proportional to the population density at point i. The total region is divided in L subregions, attributed to L conurbations. A minimum energy production must be guaranteed for each of these conurbations.
In matrix-notation the following problem results:

$$\min \underline{p}^T \cdot \underline{x} = \min p^T \cdot T \cdot \underline{x} \tag{1}$$

subject to the constraints

$$T \cdot \underline{x} \leq \underline{b}$$
$$T_1 \cdot \underline{x} \geq \underline{K}$$
$$\underline{x} \geq \underline{0}$$

$\underline{x}$ Vector of concentrations at the field points of the region

$\underline{b}$ Vector of environmental constraints at the field points

T   Transfer matrix (denotes contribution of pollutant from source at location j to receiver at location i).

T1 Matrix, denoting possible source points in the subregions (element = 1). Elements not appointed to source points of the subregion have the value zero.

$\underline{K}$ Vector of minimum energy production level energy in the sub-regions.

$\underline{x}$ Vector, describing the occupation of source points.

$\underline{p}$ Vector that takes care of weights attribtuted to population density.

The transfer matrix was calculated by means of a diffusion model. Both objective function and contraints being linear expressions, the optimization could be solved by the SIMPLEX-method /DANTZIG/.

Model 2

In this model the siting should achieve minimal investment- and operation costs. For the moment we only regard the following site-specific costs:

1.) Costs of transportation of secondary energy to the next centres of consumption (transmission lines, pipelines, pipes carrying hot water).
2.) Costs of cooling water.

As to power stations, the costs under item (1) can be divided into cost fractions for
- the electricity transport in transmission lines,
- the transport of the waste heat produced in power stations, each to the next center of consuption. As a first approach the electricity is assumed to be used up in the next conurbation. For distances larger than approximately 30 km economic trans-port of hot water carrying power plant waste heat is not yet feasible. For all costs (1) and (2) a distinction must be made between fixed costs (independent of the power installed) and variable costs (dependent on the power installed). A 20 years operating life can be anticipated for power stations. The annual costs can be broken down into
- costs of depreciation,
- costs of investment return,
- operating costs.
To be able to compare costs, they must be discounted to the date of beginning of operation. The cash value so obtained provides the basis of comparision.

To obtain the site specific costs for the site j, the cash value calculated per unit distance must be multiplied by the respective distances from the next center of consumption (cost fraction 1.) and from the next main canal (cost fraction 2.). The environmental constraints and the constraints imposed on the generation of energy are selected as in model 1. Then the following problem of minimization results:

$$\min \ (I1 \cdot \underline{e}^T \cdot D \cdot \underline{\delta} + I2 \cdot \underline{E}^T \cdot \underline{\delta} + IV1 \cdot \underline{e}^T \cdot D \cdot \underline{x} + IV2 \cdot \underline{E}^T \cdot \underline{x}) \qquad (2)$$

subject to the constraints

$$T \cdot \underline{x} \leq \underline{b}$$
$$T1 \cdot \underline{x} \geq \underline{K}$$
$$\underline{x} \geq \underline{0}$$

$\underline{e}$ Vector with components, all of them being equal to 1;

$\underline{\delta}$ Vector with components $\delta_j = \begin{matrix} 0 \ \text{if} \ x_j = 0 \\ 1 \ \text{if} \ x_j \ 0 \end{matrix}$

I1 Percentage of fixed costs for secondary energy transport systems per unit distance;

I2 Percentage of fixed costs for coolant transport systems per unit distance;

IV1 Percentage of variable costs for secondary energy transport systems per unit distance;

IV2 Percentage of variable costs for coolant transport systems per unit distance;

D_{kj} Matrix element expressing the distance between the place of energy generation j from the center of consumption k;

$E_{.j}$ Vector component expressing the distance of the place of energy production j from the next main canal.

The first and second term of the objective function - equation (2) - describe the fixed costs for secondary energy transport and coolant transport. The third and fourth term express the variable costs again for secondary energy and coolant transport. In the previous calculations only the third and fourth term have been considered, which means that only variable costs have been assumed. This simplification allowed to use familiar methods of linear programming.

Optimization of Vector Valued Objective Functions

The problem arises how to solve the conflicting objectives described in the different objective functions of model 1 and 2. The method of vector valued optimization presents a possibility of solution.

Vector valued optimization is understood to mean that a "joint optimum" is to be found for non-consistent different concepts of objectives. The approach developed by JÜTTLER and KÜRTH and refined by ALLGAIER is based on a solution of the conflicting objectives by the theory of games. The optimum compromise obtained is derived from a linear combination of all solutions corresponding to extreme points of the convex polyhedron X. X is the number of possible solutions to the problem. Among the extreme point solutions of X are both the optimum solutions for the individual objective functions and all such solutions which are non-optimum with respect to the objective functions. For K

objective functions which cannot be classified by their significance, the following optimization problem is encountered

$$\max c_k(\underline{x}) = \max \underline{c}_k^T \underline{x} \qquad k = 1, \ldots, K \qquad (3)$$

subject to the constraints

$$A \cdot \underline{x} \leq \underline{b}$$
$$\underline{x} \geq \underline{0}$$

This model is solved by serveral steps. First the maximum and
minimum values f^{ok} and f_{ok} of all objective functions $ck(x)$
are calculated. The convex polyhedron X is assumed to have N
corners which have to be determined in order to obtain the N
vectors of the extreme points of X

$$\underbrace{\underline{x}_1^* \ldots \ldots \underline{x}_K^*}_{\leq K} \quad \underbrace{\underline{x}_{K+1} \ldots \ldots \underline{x}_N}_{\geq N-K}$$

where

  $\underline{x}_k^*$ are the optimum solutions for $c_k(\underline{x})$ $k = 1, \ldots, K$

  $\underline{x}_n$ represents the extreme points of X $n = K+1, \ldots, N$

The matrix of the objective function values of the K objective
functions for the N possible solution vectors, the matrix of
the relative deviations of any solution vectors x_j from the
optimum solution, as well as the matrix H of the objective
attainments for any solution vectors x_j from the optimum solution are determined. The matrix H can be considered as the
pay-off matrix of a two-person-zero sum game. The optimum
strategy of the line player in H is assumed to be

$$\underline{p} = (p_1 \ldots \ldots p_K, \ p_{K+1} \ldots \ldots p_N)^T$$

The value of the game is assumed to be v.
The konvex linear combination of all extreme point solutions
with the scalars $p_1 \ldots p_j \ldots p_N$ yields the compromise occupation vector

$$\underline{x}^* = p_1 \underline{x}_1^* + \ldots p_K \underline{x}_K^* + p_{K+1} \underline{x}_{k+1} + \ldots + p_N \underline{x}_N \qquad (4)$$

This compromise occupation vector possesses the smallest
relative deviation of all K objective functions from the
individual optima compared with all other possible convex
linear combinations of the extreme point solutions. The deviation is 100 (1-v) percent at the maximum.
The determination of all corners of the convex polyhedron X is
very expensive in practice. Since the model approach for the
specific case of linear objective functions is equivalent to
a linear program with the objective of maximizing the lower
barrier of all objective attainments, the solution can be
formulated as follows:

$$\max \underline{e}_K^T \underline{x}^2 \tag{5}$$

subject to the constraints

$$-(C\underline{x}^1-\underline{f}_0)+(F^0-F_0)\underline{x}^2 \leq \underline{0}$$
$$A\underline{x}^1 \leq \underline{b}$$
$$\underline{x}^1 \geq \underline{0}$$
$$\underline{x}^2 \geq \underline{0}$$

where

$\underline{e}_K$ is the vector with K components, all of them being equal to 1;

$\underline{x}^1$ is the compromise vector of the dimension N obtained with the objective of maximizing the sum of the objective attainments of all K objective functions;

$\underline{x}^2$ is the vector of the dimension K of the objective attainment of all K objective functions;

$C(K,N)$ is the matrix of the coefficients of the K objective functions;

$\underline{f}_0$ is the vector of minimum solutions of the K objective functions;

F^0, F_0 are quadratic matrices (K dimension) whose diagonal elements comprise the maximum and minimum solutions, respectively, of the K objective functions.

Application of Vector Valued Optimization to Problems of Site Evaluation

The problem is to find the occupation number vector $\underline{x}$ for a given site pattern complying with the following objective concepts:

- minimum pollutant burden for the population,
- minimum costs

So, two alternative targets are obtained which are described in the Models 1 and 2. A solution is possible by the described model (5).

The problem traced in Models 1 and 2 are both minimum problems

Model 1: $\min \underline{p}^T \cdot T \cdot \underline{x} = c_1(\underline{x})$ (1)

Model 2: $\min \underline{e}^T \cdot D^+ \cdot \underline{x} = c_2(\underline{x})$ (2)

both subject to the earlier described constraints.

Corresponding to (5) the sum of objective attainments of $c_1(\underline{x})$ and $c_2(\underline{x})$ is to be maximized. This requirement is complied with by sign reversal of the objective function values $c_1(\underline{x})$ and $c_2(\underline{x})$. The problem remains of finding occupation number

vectors for "minimum" values of $-c_1(\bar{x}_1)$ and $-c_2(\bar{x}_2)$. A possible
ansatz is the maximum sum of the site occupation numbers,
observing at the same time the given contraints for Models 1)
and 2). The outcome of this calculation which considers neither
health protection nor cost requirements is used to calculate
the "minimum" values of the objective functions.

The matrix A of problem (5) includes the matrices T and T1 of
Models 1) and 2). The same holds for the limitation vector $\underline{b}$
of the problem (5). As a whole, the following problem is
obtained:

$$\max \ \underline{e}_K^T \cdot \underline{x}^2 \tag{6}$$

subject to the constraints

$$-\underline{p}^T \cdot T \cdot \underline{x}^1 + (-c_1(\underline{x}_1^*) + c_1(\underline{\bar{x}}_1)) \cdot x_1^2 \le c_1(\underline{\bar{x}}_1)$$

$$\underline{e}_K^T \cdot D^+ \cdot \underline{x}^1 + (-c_2(\underline{x}_2^*) + c_2(\underline{\bar{x}}_2)) \cdot x_2^2 \le c_2(\underline{\bar{x}}_2)$$

$$T \cdot \underline{x}^1 \le \underline{b}$$

$$T1 \cdot \underline{x}^1 \ge \underline{K}$$

$$\underline{x}^1 \ge \underline{0}$$

$$\underline{x}^2 \ge \underline{0}$$

CALCULATION OF THE TRANSFER MATRIX T

The transfer matrix T is established for the Nothern Upper
Rhine region, i.e. the Upper Rhine Valley from Mannheim to
Kehl. It is assumed that the energy is generated by means of
fossil fuels implying the emission of the sulphur dioxide
(SO_2). The pollutant concentrations caused by the emission
sources are considered in a field point grid extending 60 km
in the west-east and 120 km in the north-south directions. The
field point grid has a mesh size of 5 km - 12 base stations in
the west-east directions and 24 km in the north-south directions which means a total of 288 field points (FIG. 1). The
source point grid, containing the eligible, preestablished
sites, lies within the field point grid, limited to the rectangle built from points 40, 45, 244, 249. There are 108
source points. Care was taken that the main regions exposed
to pollutant concentration from sources located at the periphery of the source point grid do not lie outside the field
point grid. The elements T_{ij} of the transfer matrix T describe
the effect of a standard source at the point j of the source
point grid on the point i of the field point grid. This effect
is calculated by a diffusion model and stored in the matrix T
(288, 108). A standard power station unit of 100 MWe is taken
as a basis. The assumption that the burnt fuel oil (S) contains
2 wt.% of sulphur yields a sulphur dioxide (SO_2) emission of

about 0.9 t/h and a heat emission from the stack of about
3×10^3 kcal/sec. The stack height is taken to be 150 m. It
remains to be said that the assumed linear relation is very
badly fulfilled between the occupation number times the emission from the standard source and the pollutant concentration.
This error is reduced by the selected standard source of
average power.

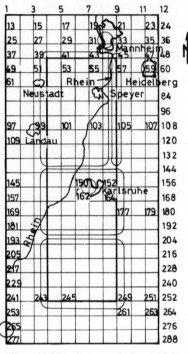

Fig. 1: Source point
grid and field point
grid in the region
"Northern Upper Rhine"
and appointment of sub-
fields of the source
point grid to the con-
urbations.

The diffusion model applied as well as some results of model
calculations will be briefly described.

Calculation of Local Distributions of Pollutant Concentrations

Using the ansatz (7) the diffusion of pollutants is calculated
for the Northern Upper Rhine Region /PASQUILL, SLADE/. This ansatz is used with respect to all large emitters located in the
region (point sources) and also with respect to the emissions
from domestic fuel and small consumption (area sources). The
pollutant concentrations obtained are added in a preestablished
field point grid. This calculation is made for 432 meteorological combinations. The 432 combinations are obtained from 12
wind directions, 6 wind velocities, and 6 stability classes of
the atmospheric stratification for one summer and one winter
season each /NESTER/. Dependent on the frequency of occurrence,
each meteorological combination contributes to the concentration at the field points. The resulting concentration distribution for each point of the field point grid can then be

evaluated with a view to the expected value (= long term emission) and with a view to a higher fractile value (for instance 95 % fractile = short term emission). The concentration $\chi(x,y,z)$ is calculated from:

$$\chi(x,y,z) = \frac{Q(x',y',H)\cdot(d1-d2)/d1}{\sqrt{\frac{\pi^3}{18}}\cdot\sigma_z(x-x')\cdot\bar{u}\cdot r} \cdot \left\{ \exp(-\frac{(z-H)^2}{2\sigma_z^2}) + \exp(\frac{(z-H)^2}{2\sigma_z^2}) \right\}$$

$$\cdot \exp\left(-\frac{r/\bar{u}}{\tau}\right) \qquad (7)$$

Q   source strength (µg/sec)

$\bar{u}$ wind volocity (m/sec)

H   "effective" emission height (m)

σ_z diffusion parameter for the vertical diffusion normal to the wind direction (m)

τ   mean stay time of the pollutant in the atmosphere (sec)

r   distance of the source point from the field point (m)

d1 distance between two sector center lines on the circle surrounding the source point with the radius r - (m)

d2 distance of the field point to sector centre line on the circle surrounding the source point with the radius r - (m)

The ansatz takes into account the removal of the pollutant by the wind, the turbulent diffusion in the vertical direction normal to the wind direction, the reflection of the pollutant on the soil, and a mean stay time of the pollutant in the atmosphere (deposition on the ground, chemical transformation, etc.). An interpolation is made of the value $\chi(x,y,z)$ within a 30^0-sector of the wind direction from the sector centre lines which include the field point (x,y,z). For greater distances the diffusion is mainly determined by the mixing height. Within this distance range equal distribution has been assumed of the pollutant between the earth surface and the mixing height. The actual emission height of the pollutant is taken to be the physical stack height plus an amount which depends on the emitted heat, the wind velocity and the predominant stability class, the so called "plume rise". The meteorological input data were taken from a weather statistic compiled over 3 years derived from measured values at the 200 m meteorological power of the Karlsruhe Nuclear Research Center /NESTER/. The values by PASQUILL were used for the diffusion parameter σ_z. The pollutant concentrations are calculated for the field point grid of Fig. 1. Fig. 2 shows concentrations taking into account all large emitters located in the Northern Upper Rhine region (62 sources). The lines traced are lines of equal concentration SO_2 expressed in µg/m^3 (isolines) for an annual average. Concentration structure with its maximum of 30 µg SO_2/m^3 north of Karlsruhe, which is marked by the south/west main wind direction can be noticed.

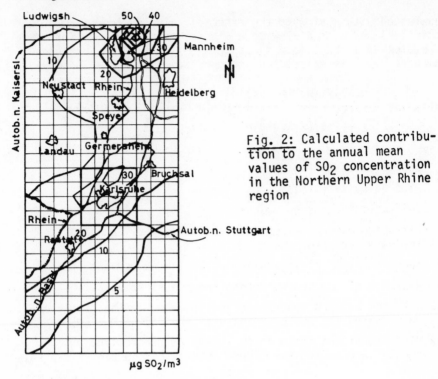

Fig. 2: Calculated contribution to the annual mean
values of SO_2 concentration
in the Northern Upper Rhine
region

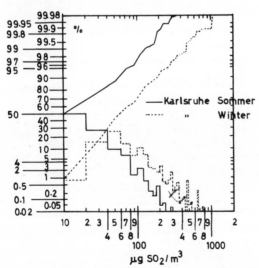

Fig. 3: Concentration frequency distribution of SO_2
at a field point within the
city of Karlsruhe for the
summer and winter seasons

Fig.2 shows calculated distributions of concentration frequencies for the summer and winter seasons at a field point within the city of Karlsruhe. The sources considered were the large emitters and emissions from domestic fuel and small consumption. Histograms (lower curves) have been plotted, i.e. frequency values summed up over 20 μg SO_2/m^3 areas each. These values allow to derive the fractile values (upper curves) indicating the probability that a given concentration is not exceeded. The change in distributions towards higher values from the summer to the winter seasons is very distinct. This exhibits the considerable influence of domestic fuel on SO_2-concentration in the city, although the SO_2-emissions due to domestic fuel total up to only 5 % of all SO_2-emissions in Karlsruhe.

The calculated concentrations in the Karlsruhe region which are due to the emissions by large emitters and domestic fuel yield an underestimation of 50 % at the maximum as compared to the measured ones. It must be taken into account that already the measured values of single years show variations of the order of 30 %. In /FAUDE/ a differentiated comparison was performed between the measured and the calculated values for five measuring stations located in the Karlsruhe area. The deviations indicated agree with values provided by other authors.

RESULTS OF CALCULATIONS ON SITE EVALUATION OF POWER PLANTS

The model region is again the Northern Upper Rhine region. The power plants under consideration generate energy from fossil fuels and are so emitters of sulphur dioxide (SO_2). The possible sites (108) are fixed by the source point grid (Fig. 1). The effects, i.e. the SO_2 concentrations, are considered at the field points of the field point grid (288). Within the field point grid and in the immediate neighborhood, respectively, four conurbations can be found:
1) Mannheim - field point 32,
2) Heidelberg - field point 59,
3) Karlsruhe - field point 151,
4) Kehl-Offenburg - field point 265.
The location of conurbations at individual field points is a considerable simplification which, however, can be considered adequate for the model calculation. Sub-areas of the source point grid are assigned to these conurbation (Fig. 1). They accommodate the sites for the facilities generating the percentage of total energy of the region corresponding to the conurbation. The percentages are:
- for Mannheim 40 %
- for Heidelberg 10 %
- for Karlsruhe 25 %
- for Kehl-Offenburg 25 %.
The required minimum power to be installed in the region was assumed to be 10 GWe. Besides these constraints environmental constraints are imposed, in this case standards of concentration

in particular. The concentration standards to be observed were
the values applicable in the Federal Republic of Germany. In
the calculations only the observation of the longterm standard
was taken into account which is 140 μg SO_2/m^3. Principally,
also the short-term standards which are very significant by
their effect can be incorporated into the constraints. When
fixing the concentration constraints the following influences
were taken into account:

1) Remote sources were taken into account globally by deduction
   of 20 μg SO_2/m^3 /FAUDE/.
2) The diffusion calculations yielded a winter mean value of
   80 μg SO_2/m^3 and an annual mean value of 45 μg SO_2/m^3 for
   concentrations caused by domestic fuel in the city of Karlsruhe. For field points located within the conurbations the
   annual mean value of concentrations due to domestic fuel
   was therefore deducted when fixing the constraints.
3) Areas neighboring the field point grid in the north and in
   the south are already much industrialized, obove all in the
   north. The influence by these areas was also taken into
   account by deduction of 20 and 10 μg SO_2/m^3, respectively,
   from the values applicable to the constraints for the grid
   boundary lines.

Complying with energy and environmental constraints, we now
calculate site occupation numbers for the following objective
functions:

1) Site distribution with the minimum impact dependent on the
   population density.
2) Site distribution with minimum costs for the plants.
3) Site distribution with the maximum power to be installed in
   the region.
4) Site distribution meeting as much as possible both requirement 1) and requirement 2) (maximization of objective
   attainments).

Fig. 4 shows the result of the calculation for the objective
function 1 - impact dependent on the population density. It is
characteristic of the result that the bottom right corners
within the sub-source point grid are preferred places. Very
large power station units are found there.

Fig. 5 shows the result of calculation for the objective function 2 - minimum costs for the plants. It is obvious for this
calculation that the sites come very close to the centres of
consumption. For the Karlsruhe conurbation a site within the
urban district is obtained. It can be assumed that this site
will be displaced when short-time concentration standards will
be taken into account. The result of this calculation must be
considered as preliminary, since exact information were not
available of the specific costs which had to be assessed on
very coarse assumptions.

Fig. 6 shows the distribution of occupation numbers for the
objective function 3 - maximum power to be installed in the
region. A total of about 26 GW is obtained for the installed
potential. Calculations leaving aside restrictive energy

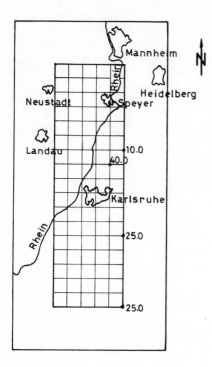

Fig. 4: Distribution in the source point grid of the occupation numbers for 100 MW power station units for minimum impact dependent on the population density (10 GW minimum capacity of energy generation)

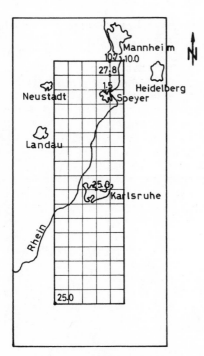

Fig. 5: Distribution in the source point grid of the occupation numbers for 100 MW power station units for minimum costs and 10 GW minimum capacity of energy generation

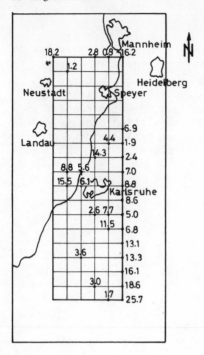

Fig. 6: Distribution in the source point grid of the occupation numbers for 100 MW power station units and maximum power to be installed

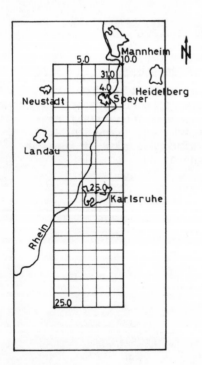

Fig. 7: Distribution in the source point grid of the occupation numbers for 100 MW power station units and maximization of the objective attainments

generation for the sub-regions yield the same site distributions. In this case, this results in a multitude of relatively
small power station units. The calculation demonstrates the
familiar maxim in regional planning that larger industrial
settlements implying air pollution should be erected always
east of the residential districts. However, at the same time
possibilities are shown how and where sites with capacities of
1 - 1.5 GW can be found with a full utilization of the "environmental impact potential."
Fig. 7 shows the result of the calculation for the objective
function 4 - maximization of the objective attainments. The
optimum value for the objective function 1 - minimum impact -
was reached by 99 % and the optimum value for the objective
function 2 - minimum costs - by 100 %.
These are very high values for objective attainment. It must
be remarked, that these results are very preliminary ones. But
they show, that the method of vector valued optimization is a
suitable tool for site-evaluation.

LIST OF REFERENCES

ALLGAIER R. (1974) Zur Lösung von Zielkonflikten.
Diss, TU Karlsruhe

DANTZIG G. (1963) Linear Programming and Extensions.
Princeton University Press, Princeton, N.J.

FAUDE D., BAYER A., HALBRITTER G. et. al. (1974) Energie
und Umwelt in Baden-Württemberg. KFK-1966 (UF). Karlsruhe.

JÜTTLER H. (1968) Ein Modell zur Berücksichtigung mehrerer
Zielfunktionen bei Aufgabenstellungen der mathematischen
Optimierung. In: Math. Modelle und Verfahren der Unterneh-
mensforschung. Köln, p. 11-31.

KÜRTH H. (1969) Zur Berücksichtigung mehrerer Zielfunktionen
bei der Optimierung von Produktionsplänen. In: Mathematik und
Wirtschaft, Band 6, Berlin, p. 184 - 201.

NESTER K. (1972) Statistische Auswertungen der Windmessungen
im Kernforschungszentrum Karlsruhe aus den Jahren 1968/69.
KFK-1606, Karlsruhe.

PASQUILL F. (1962) Atmospheric Diffusion. D. van Nostrand
Company Ltd.

SLADE D.H. (1968) Meteorology and Atomic Energy. U.S. Atomic
Energy Commission, Division of Technical Information.

PARAMETER ESTIMATION OF A DISTRIBUTED SYSTEM RELATED TO THE BIOMASS DYNAMICS IN AQUATIC ECOSYSTEMS

F. Argentesi *   L. Guerri[o]
G. Di Cola **

*   Dep. A. of Joint Research Center, Ispra, Italy.
** Collaborator of the Istituto Applicazioni del Calcolo.
    C.N.R. at the Istituto Italiano di Idrobiologia.
    Pallanza, Italy.
[o] Istituto di Matematica, Universita di Pavia, Italy.

ABSTRACT

A model, similar to one proposed by Riley, Stommel and Bumpus, concerning the biomass dynamics in aquatic ecosystem is considered. The dynamical processes are described by a set of P.D.E. with distributed parameters and with suitable initial and boundary conditions. The problem is to estimate in the best way the representative parameters such as the primary production, grazing and losses starting from a set of experimental observations relative to the state variables (i.e. phyto and zooplankton biomass).

The corresponding optimization problem is solved by means of numerical methods.

INTRODUCTION

Various models have been proposed for the study of the biomass dynamics and the energy flow of aquatic ecosystems. Most of them (see for instance Argentesi F., Di Cola G., Verheyden N. (1974); Parker R.A. (1973); Patten B.C. (1968)) are compartmental, lumped parameter models i.e. the space dependence is neglected and this may sometimes entail an excessive simplification of the ecosystem reality. A difficulty related to the evaluation of these models arises in the establishment of an adequate correlation between the responses of the model and the experimental observations.

As a rule these models have been used in a direct way that is the initial conditions and the values of the parameters have

been chosen in a more or less heuristic manner in order to fit
the experimental data.

We propose to formulate a model for the phyto- and zooplankton
dynamics of an aquatic ecosystem which in order to give a
realistic representation of the phenomena takes account of the
most significant space dimension and in which the representative parameters related to the most relevant processes considered are space and/or time dependent. The model is
relative to a system in which the production is light limited
(eutrophic system); this assumption allows a simplification
because it is possible to neglect the nutrient dynamics. The
model which is being considered is derived from that of Riley
G.A., Stommel H., and Bumpus D.F. (1949). The dynamical
processes are described by a set of partial differential equations with distributed parameters and with suitable initial
and boundary conditions. The space dimension considered is
the vertical direction.

Our purpose is to solve the inverse problem of the system
identification and, starting from a set of experimental data,
to evaluate in the best way the representative parameters such
as the net primary production, the grazing and the zooplankton
losses.

These parameters are difficult to measure with the exception of
the primary production for which a method of indirect measure
is available. Also the processes of eddy diffusion and sedimentation are taken into account. We assume the state variables directly observable and we propose to evaluate the
system parameters so that the ideal state differs as least as
possible from the observed state. This leads to an optimization problem in which a functional depending on the experimental observations, the state variables and the parameters
must be minimized taking into account the differential constraints of the model. This optimization problem is solved
numerically.

MATHEMATICAL MODEL

The biological processes considered in the model may be
summarized by the following graph:

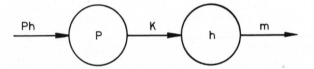

where p and h represent respectively the phytoplankton and the zooplankton biomasses, p_h is the unit rate of net primary production (primary production minus respiration), k is the unit grazing rate, m is the unit rate of zooplankton losses related to natural death, predation, respiration and incomplete phytoplankton assimilation. With regard to the physical processes we consider the eddy diffusion and the sedimentation of the phytoplankton along the vertical direction, while we assume that the zooplankton is not subject to these processes. The model is then described by the following system of P.D.E.

$$p_t = A \, p_{zz} - v \, p_z + p(p_h - k \, h)$$

$$h_t = h(k \, p - m) \tag{1}$$

$$0 \leqslant z \leqslant Z \qquad 0 \leqslant t \leqslant T$$

where t is the time, z the depth i.e. the vertical distance from the water surface;

h_t, p_t, p_z, p_{zz} are partial derivatives;

$A \, p_{zz}$ is the eddy diffusion term with A diffusion coefficient;

$- v \, p_z$ is the sedimentation term with v sedimentation velocity;

$p \, p_h$ is the net primary production;

$k \, p \, h$ is the grazing;

$m \, h$ is the overall zooplankton loss.

We make the assumption that the parameters k and m are dependent only on the time. Since we are considering an eutrophic system we assume that p_h is the product of two factors, one depending only on time and which is related to the time variations of the light intensity and the other depending only on space and which represents the vertical extinction linked with depth. We have then:

$$p_h = Q(z) \, q(t)$$

$$k = k(t)$$

$$m = m(t)$$

The parameters to be estimated are, on principle, A, v, Q, q, k, m but in order to reduce their number we assume that the coefficients A and v are known and constant.

The system of P.D.E. is subject to the initial conditions:

$$p(z,o) = p_o(z) \qquad h(z,o) = h_o(z) \tag{2}$$

and to the boundary conditions:

$$p_z = o \qquad \text{for } z = o$$

$$p_z = o \qquad \text{for } z = Z$$

(3)

The boundary condition at $z = o$ means that at the water surface there is no phytoplankton flow; the boundary condition
at $z = Z$ means that the phytoplankton concentration gradient
is zero and there is only sedimentation.

PARAMETER ESTIMATION

The parameters must be chosen so that the average squared
difference between the state variables supplied by (1) and the
experimental data $\tilde{p}$, $\tilde{h}$ be minimized. We have then the
following optimal control problem:

$$\text{minimize } J = \int_0^T \int_0^Z ((p - \tilde{p})^2 + (h - \tilde{h})^2) \, dz \, dt$$

where p, h are subject to the differential constraint (1)
with initial and boundary conditions (2) and (3). In order
to stabilize the solution of this problem it is better to add
to J a regularization term of the form:

$$\varepsilon \int_0^T \int_0^Z ((Q - Q^o)^2 + \ldots + (m - m^o)^2) \, dz \, dt$$

with a suitably small ε

The general form of this optimization problem is the following:
Let:

   $w = w(z,t)$ be a vector with r components called state
      vector.
   $u = u(z,t)$ be a vector with s components called control
      vector.
   $F = F(z, t, w, u)$ be a scalar function
   $f = f(z, t, w, w_z, w_{zz}, u)$ be a vector function with r
      components.

We want to minimize the functional:

$$J = \int_0^T \int_0^Z F(z,t,w,u) \, dz \, dt$$

with w subject to the differential constraint:

$$w_t = f(z, t, w, w_{zz}, u)$$

to the initial condition:

$$w(z, o) = w_o(z)$$

and to the boundary conditions:

$$B^{(o)} (w, w_z) = o \qquad \text{for} \quad z = o$$

$$B^{(1)} (w, w_z) = o \qquad \text{for} \quad z = Z$$

In our case $r = 2$, $s = 4$ the components of w are p, h; the components of u are Q, q, k, m. Moreover:

$$B^{(o)} = B^{(1)} = w_{1z} = p_z \; (w_1 \text{ first component of } w)$$

Keeping in mind the meaning of w, u it must be $w \geqslant o$, $u \geqslant o$ i.e. p, h, Q, q, k, m must be non negative.

In the following formulae u, δu, w, w_z ... δw, δw_z, ... are column vectors. We have:

$$\delta J = \int_0^T \int_0^Z (F_w \; \delta w + F_u \; \delta u) \; dz \; dt$$

$$\delta w_t = F_w \; \delta w + f_{w_z} \; \delta w_z + f_{w_{zz}} \; \delta w_{zz} + f_u \; \delta u$$

and:

$$\delta w = o \qquad \text{for} \quad t = o$$

$$B^{(o)}_w \; \delta w + B^{(o)}_{w_z} \; \delta w_z = o \qquad \text{for } z = o$$

$$B^{(1)}_w \; \delta w + B^{(1)}_{w_z} \; \delta w_z = o \qquad \text{for } z = Z$$

In our case:

$$\delta w_{1z} = \delta p_z = o \qquad \text{for } z = o \text{ and } z = Z$$

Since u, δu determine w, δw we can express δJ as function of δu. This result is achieved with the use of the adjoint system.

If η is a row vector with r components the adjoint system is defined by:

$$\eta_t = - \eta f_w + (\eta \, f_{w_z})_z - (\eta \, f_{w_{zz}})_{zz} - F_w.$$

with the end condition: $\eta(z, T) = o$ and, in our case, with the boundary conditions:

$$v \; \eta_1 + A \; \eta_{1z} = o \text{ for } z = o \text{ and } z = Z$$

where η_1 is the first component of η . We then obtain:

$$\delta J = \int_0^T \int_0^Z (\eta \; f_u + F_u) \; \delta u \; dz \; dt$$

The optimal values of the control parameters are usually obtained by means of iterative procedures.

In correspondence with the optimal solution it is

$$\eta \; f_u + F_u = 0$$

If u, w is an approximation then δu must be chosen such that $\delta J < 0$. Then u is modified and a successive better approximation u^1, w^1 is determined. To achieve this result various strategies can be followed. The simplest conceptually is that of the "steepest descent" where δu is chosen as:

$$\delta u = - (\eta \; f_u + F_u)^T$$

$((.)^T$ means transposed). A variant of this technique is the gradient method where $\delta u = - \alpha (\eta f_u + F_u)^T$ with $\alpha > 0$ and suitably chosen.

NUMERICAL TESTS

Since we did not yet have at our disposal reliable experimental data especially with regard to h we have carried out numerical tests considering a choice of parameters: $u = (Q, q, k, m)$ such that the corresponding state vector $w = (p, h)$ would exhibit the main features of the biological phenomena under study.

The vector u has been perturbed with perturbations of the order from 10% to 70% and the perturbed values chosen as initial approximation of u. We remark that the perturbations of u generate greater perturbations of w. The optimization problem has been solved by means of the gradient method. The results have been satisfactory with final differences between w and w of the order of 5 to 10%. In the near future, when experimental data relative to p, h will be available, we propose to apply the model to a real situation and to utilize also other optimization techniques.

CONCLUSIONS

We have formulated a distributed parameter model for the study
of the biomass dynamics of an aquatic ecosystem. The parameters of the system are the coefficients of primary production
grazing and overall zooplankton loss. With the exception of
the primary production, these parameters are difficult to
meausre. For this reason and under the assumption that the
model describes in a satisfactory way the biological phenomena
under study, the determination of the parameters by means
of the minimization of the average squared difference between
the state variables of the model and the experimental data
supplies useful information about the parameters and the
biological phenomena. Since the experimental data was not
yet completely available the numerical tests have been carried
out using as data theoretical values which exhibit the main
characteristics of the biological phenomena. The results have
been satisfactory.

The next developments of the research concern:

- the application of the model to a real situation when
  experimental data will be available.

- comparison with the results of different optimization
  techniques (quasi linearization method and penalization
  method).

- sensitivity analysis in order to evaluate the stability of
  the model and consequently the stability of the ecosystem.

REFERENCES

Argentesi,F., Di Cola,G., Verheyden N. (1974)
The Modelling of Bionears Dynamics in Aquatic Ecosystems.
The Mathematical Theory of the Dynamics of Biological
Populations. Edited by M.S. Bartlatt and R.W. Hiorus.
Academic Press: 269 - 288.

Patten, B.C. (1968) Mathematical Model of Plankton Production.
Int. Revue Hydrobiol, 53, 3:357 - 408.

Riley,G.A., Stommel, H., and Bumpus, D.F. (1949)
Quantitative Ecology of the Plankton of the Western North
Atlantic. Bull. Bingham Oceonogr. XII, 3:1 - 169.

DESIGN OF LARGE URBAN SEWER SYSTEMS WITH A WATER-FLOW SIMULATION PROGRAM

P. Kaufmann and C. de Rham

Balzari Blaser Schudel, Engineers and Planners
CH 3006 Bern Switzerland

INTRODUCTION

Needs of the Planning Engineer

One of the most current tasks of the engineer working on sewage systems is to plan networks so as to obtain a given sewage capacity with minimal construction costs.

This means that he has to exploit all the technical possibilities and local characteristics of the given network. Some of them are listed below:

- stormwater tanks
- storage sewers
- downward ramifications
- parallel sewers
- overflow sewers
- allowance to have some parts of the network running under pressure

All the classical methods of calculus (most by hand) cannot take account of these elements efficiently. Another way to tackle the problem is to start with the mathematical formulation (St. Venant an others) and to write computer programs. But the elements listed above are strongly non linear and so important, that they cannot be linearized or left out. This means that the equations have to be approximised by iteration, which leads to high computation time and costs.

New approach of the problem

The authors first listed 5 conditions which had to be satisfied to meet the need of the engineer, namely on efficient, cheap working tool:

1. The model had to have the possibility to include all normal and special elements of a sewage network.
2. The model had to work with any realistic rainstorm.
3. The model had to work for an overloaded network (all or part of the sewers under pressure) as well.
4. The computation costs had to be low.
5. The results had to be displayed clearly and be easily interpreted even by non-specialists.

The Solution: Simulation   The different conditions listed above did not let much freedom for the techniques to be used. It had to be continouus simulation. This type of model met the 5 conditions in the following way:
1. Each element of the system is a black box defined by its input/output characteristics. New ones can be programmed and added without any difficulties to the system.
2. The rain is given as input value to the element sewer in function of time and can therefore be chosen so as to be most realistic for the region concerned.
3. The problem of overloaded sewers was also solved by applying the black-box concept.
4. The program was cut into different parts and the use of Fortran IV with code-optimisation led to very low run-times.
5. The results are displayed in a compact way. As all the depths and levels in manholes are very important, they are given in absolute values as well as relative to the invert and ground levels.

THE SIMULATION CONCEPT

Basic Framework for the Model
The whole sewage network is cut into separate elements:
    sewers
    stormwater tanks
    overflow sewers
    storage sewers
    special elements

Each of these elements is defined by its input and output characteristics.

It is then possible to chain the elements together
so as to get an accurate model of the sewage network. The input and output values concern mainly the
following parameters:
Q   discharge (m3/s)
V   velocity   (m/s)
D   depth of flow above invert (m)

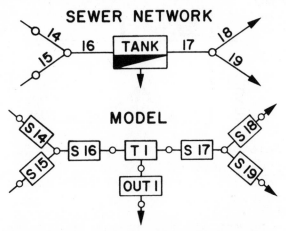

Figure 1   Network and corresponding model

Calculation of the runoff coefficient and delay
Before the simulation . one has to calculate the runoff coefficient and the runoff delay. The runoff
coefficient in due to the fact that only part of the
rain reaches the sewer, the other part being retained
on the surface or absobed by the ground. (Watkins
1962). For pratical use, the area can be caracte-
rised by two soil types: (Munz, 1966)
  A   natural, pervious surfaces (turf, forest, shrub-
      bery)
  B   impervious surfaces (asphalt, concrete, roof)
The runoff coefficient in the weighted mean of these
surfaces. The runoff delay is the time lag between
the beginning of the rainstorm and the beginning of
runoff. It depends on the soil type, slope, shape
of the area and geological conditions. (Ven Te Chow,
1964). Normally, runoff delays lie between 1 and 20
minutes.

These two runoff parameters determine the transformation of the rainfall hydrograph into the runoff
hydrograph.

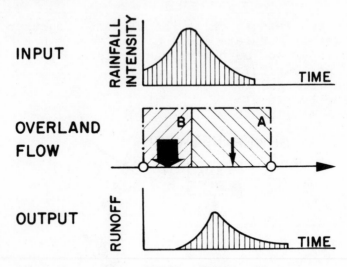

INPUT

OVERLAND
FLOW

OUTPUT

Figure 2   Raistorm and runoff hydrograph

The Fortran Program

The whole program consists of 3 main parts:
1. Input, tests of all datas
2. Simulation
3. Output with options for graphical display

The Input Program The input consists of all the
elements and their characteristics such as dimension, diameter, length, type of element, associated
area, and others. All these values are tested, eventually converted, summed and printed for the control. The wastwater discharge (due only to households and industry) is calculated and printed.

The Simulation The program was built up with special attention to the time-problem. The main input
to this program is the rainstorm, which is given
in function of time. During the simulation, all input and output values of the elements are updated
continouusly in function of time. In order to keep
the storage requirements as low as possible, all
results are written on disk-files as soon as they
are generated.

The Output Program This program has no other function than to rearrange all the datas of the simulation program for the output lists and the optional
graphic display. The lists show all maximum values
attained par element and the rain type for which
they were critical. The graphic display consists
of two parts. First, one can have values like discharges, velocities and depths printed in function
of time. Second the profile of any desired part of
the network can be plotted inclusive the maximum
levels attained for sanitary discharge and the discharge due to the rainstorm. Those two outputs can
be of interest for users who want to know more than
the maximum values at each node.

How to determine the Right Time Step
It is very important to choose the right value for
the time step. If it is too small, computation time
goes up and costs with it. On the other hand, too
big time steps make the calculation unprecise especially during strong variations of the rainstorm
intensity. The easiest way to find the right time-
step is to do it by trial and error.
Begin with a small one and increase it as long as
you do not get a significant change in the results.

EXPERIENCE WITH THE MODEL

Planning a New Network

The Input All the values that have to be given on
the data sheet are the followings:
    pipe number
    number of following element
    type of the pipe
    diameter (or height if not circular) m
    lenght   m
    invert elev., upper end   m
    invert elev., lower end   m
    ground elev., upper manhole   m
    ground elev., lower manhole   m
    area tributary of that pipe   ha
    runoff coefficient   %
    population density of the area   hab/ha
    constant discharges (industry)   l/s
    runoff delay   s
    roughness coefficient $m^{1/3}s^{-1}$

There are no more values in this list than needed for the computation by hand with the Rational Method.

The Output   A copy of the computer output ist shown in figure 3 and does not need explanation.

		15	17	22
NUMBER OF PIPE		15	17	22
UPPER ELEMENT 1		14	16	21
UPPER ELEMENT 2		0	0	0
UPPER ELEMENT 3		0	0	0
LOWER ELEMENT 1		16	24	24
LOWER ELEMENT 2		0	0	0
TYPE OF PIPE				
HEIGHT	CM	50	100	50
WIDTH	CM	50	60	50
LENGTH	M	61.20	66.60	116.10
SLOPE OF INVERT 0/00		15.69	10.06	11.46
AREA OF PIPE	M2	.196	.475	.196
ROUGHN COEFF M1/3/S		85	85	85
DISCHARGE FULL M3/S		.523	1.310	.447
VELOCITY FULL	M/S	2.67	2.76	2.28
GROUND UPPER	M ASL	60.13	59.21	59.37
GROUND LOWER	M ASL	59.72	58.94	58.94
INVERT UPPER	M ASL	56.60	54.71	55.47
INVERT LOWER	M ASL	55.64	54.04	54.14
DEPTH OF MANHOLE	M	3.53	4.50	3.90
TRIB AREA	HA	.680	.270	.540
TOT AREA	HA	1.700	5.800	2.080
RUNOFF COEFF	0/0	65	65	65
TRIB AREA RED	HA	.442	.175	.351
TOT AREA RED	HA	1.105	3.689	1.352
RUNOFF DELAY	MIN	4	5	8
POP DENSITY	HAB/HA	150	150	150
TRIB POP	HAB	102	40	81
TOT POP	HAB	255	956	312
INDUSTRY DISCH M3/S		0	0	0
SAN SEW DISCH	M3/S	.003	.012	.003
SAN SEW VELOC	M/S	.56	.63	.57
SAN SEW DEPTH	M	.02	.03	.02
SIGNIF RAINST	MIN	20	20	20
DISMAX/DISFULL	0/00	616	780	880
MAX WAT LEV	M ASL	56.86	55.36	55.82
TOP - WAT LEV	M	.24	.35	.16
GRND - WAT LEV	M	3.27	3.85	3.56
RAINST DURATION MIN		20	20	20
DISCH MAX	M3/S	.322	1.022	.393
VELOC MAX	M/S	2.77	2.87	2.46
DEPTH MAX UPEND	M	.26	.65	.34
DEPTH MAX LOEND	M	.51	1.02	.92

Fig. 3   Example of an output list.

How to correct an overloaded sewer system?
This example shows how the use of well placed storage sewers had the same effect than the change of a whole network of nearly 50 sewers.

The sewage network shown in figure 4 was heavily overloaded and offered different possibilities for corrections.

If the Rational Method (Method which is widely used
but does not take account of the intensity vs time
relationship of the rainstorm) was applied, nearly
all 50 sewers had to be changed to greater diameters.
We therefore tested different possibilities to introduce storage elements. The optimal solution was
to introduce two storage sewers of about 60 m lenght
and a diameter of 1.10 m (number 1300) and 1.50 m
(number 1384).

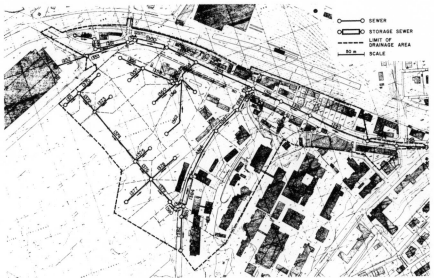

Figure 4: Corrections of an overloaded network by
introduction of two storage sewers.

Influence of the area shape on the sewer discharge
The program can of course be used to test the validity of assumptions made with the Rational Method.
The figure 5 shows the effect of different shapes
of the same area (6 ha) on the output hydrograph.
It is obvious that if one does not take account of
differences of that order in larger networks, one
cannot give any guarantee about the accurancy of
the optimality of the results either.

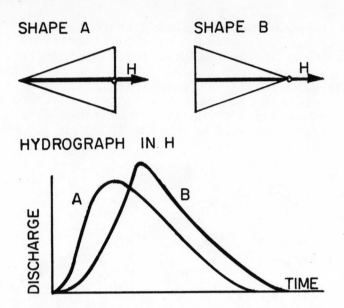

Figure 5   Effect of area shape on sewer discharge.

ABSTRACT

The authors built a simulation model to calculate
the hydrographes (discharges, depths, velocities and
volumes in function of time) at every node of large
sewage networks. The program (FORTRAN) includes
elements like stormwater tanks, outflow sewers,
storage sewers and downward ramifications. It has
been successfully applied for the optimal design of
networks, extensions and special cases.

REFERENCES

Munz, W. (1966) Die Wirkung verschiedener Gewässer-
schutzmassnahmen auf den Vorfluter, Schweiz. Zeit-
schrift für Hydrologie, Basel

Ven Te Chow (1964) Handbook of applied Hydrology,
MC Graw-Hill Book Compagny, New York

Watkins, L.H. (1962) The Design of Urban Sewer
Systems, Road Research Technical Paper No. 55, London

A MATHEMATICAL MODEL FOR THE ANALYSIS OF MULTI-RESERVOIR FLOOD CONTROL SYSTEMS

J.S. Windsor

University of Natal, Durban.

INTRODUCTION

The basic problem in the analysis of flood control systems is to determine the allocation and operation of flood storage which minimizes the total system costs. Two classes of decisions have to be considered. The first class consists of the long-run decisions which are used to determine the optimal, size, number, and location of flood control reservoirs in the river basin development. The second class are the short-run decisions which are used to define an optimal release policy under actual operating conditions. All of these decisions have to be made and their consequences evaluated in the face of streamflow variability.

The problem can be solved with relative ease in the case of single reservoir developments. When more than one reservoir is involved the problem becomes multi-dimensional and it is necessary to recognize component interaction in space and time. This necessitates the use of programming techniques which enable the entire system to be studied as an integrated system.

In this study a programming model is set-up which considers a proposed multi-reservoir system in conjunction with a number of flood damage centres. The method of solution involves a modified form of linear programming known as mixed integer programming. At the first level of optimization it is assumed that the non-linear cost functions for the reservoirs and damage centres are known, and flood variability at all significant points within the system is accounted for by using representative sets of recorded, or synthetically derived, flood hydrographs. Each potential flood combination is routed in turn through the proposed development and the model selects the long-run decision policy which minimizes total system costs, and at the same time provides a reasonably high degree of assurance against hydraulic failure.

At the second level a short-run optimization model is designed
to permit regulation of the entire system on a strictly foresight basis. This is accomplished by subdividing the flood
period into shorter operational periods and updating the
system release schedule as more information becomes available
regarding the changing run-off and climatic conditions. The
updated run-off hydrographs and currently available storage
levels are used as input data to the model which then selects
the optimal short-run release schedule. Repeating these steps
at suitable time intervals during the flood period ensures
that the operating plan is continually modified to match the
changing hydro - meteorogical and storage conditions.

DESCRIPTION OF SYSTEM

Figure 1 depicts the physical structure of the hypothetical
river basin development under investigation. The extension of
the procedure to handle other system topologies should be
immediately apparent and will not be considered herein. For
the purpose of analysis it is assumed that all the reservoirs
are provided with gated spillways for the optimal control of
flood water. Each reservoir is constrained by two design
variables, the spillway capacity C_i, and the flood storage
allocation V_i;   i=1,2,3, where i denotes the number of
potential reservoirs under investigation. These are treated
as decision variables along with the operating variables
denoted by $O_i^{t_n}$, the spillway release at reservoir i at the
start of time period t_n ($t_n = 1,2,\ldots, T_n$; where T_n denotes
the number of time periods in the composite set of flood
hydrographs produced at selected points within the drainage
basin by the nth storm, $n = 1,2,\ldots, N$)

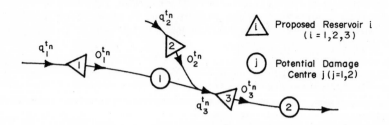

Figure 1.   System topology

To arrive at an optimal design it is necessary to know the
cost functions for each reservoir and damage centre. The
reservoir cost functions are assumed continuous and concave
over the range of interest, where the concavity of the curves

is brought about by economies of scale.   A value function of
this shape is shown in Figure 2, along with some piecewise
linear approximations.   The damage cost functions may take a
variety of forms depending on the nature of the problem.   Two
basic forms of damage cost functions which may arise in a
study of this nature are shown in Figure 3.

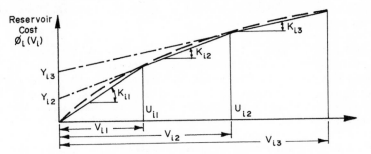

Figure 2.   Reservoir cost function, along with
piecewise linear approximations.

Although a number of important variables including flood
storage, flood duration, and velocity of flow may affect
flood severity (Homan, 1956) the basis of most damage estimates is the peak stage-damage cost function (Linsley and
Franzini, 1964).   This relates the flood damage incurred to
the flood stage in the reach under consideration.   Combining
this function with the stage-discharge curve for the reach,
flood damage can be identified in monetary terms as a function
of the peak flow.   The definition of this function is generally
the most difficult part of the problem.

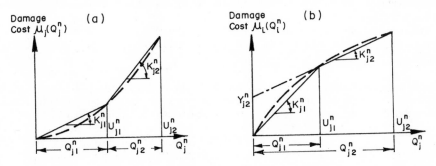

Figure 3.   Damage cost functions

Routing equations are incorporated in the analysis to describe
the space and time movement of flood water within the system.
The reservoir routing equations are based on a simple mass
balance relationship which states that inflow volume minus
outflow volume equals storage change during a given time

period. Routing in river channels is more complicated and
requires a relation which adequately represents wedge and prism
storage effects. One widely used assumption is that storage is
a function of the weighted inflow and outflow in the reach.
This forms the basis of the Muskingum routing equation (Linsley
and Franzini, 1964) which has been selected for this study. In
situations in which the control points are located a long
distance apart, provision should be made for run-off from the
intermediate drainage area.

As indicated in Figure 1 the inflows to reservoirs 1 and 2
consist of natural unregulated run-off hydrographs from
upstream catchments. For reservoir 3, on the other hand, the
inflow hydrographs consist partly of natural run-off from the
intermediate catchment and partly of the releases from the
upstream reservoirs. These are combined with each other after
allowing for differences in travel time of the translatory
waves, and the combined hydrographs are used to define the
total inflow to reservoir 3.

Long Run Analysis
In the long-run analysis the objective is to determine the
optimal size, number, and location of the flood control
reservoirs in the river basin development assuming that it is
designed to operate under a range of flood conditions up to
and including the probable maximum flood.

A problem exists, however, in the specification of flood
variability since the flood run-off is highly variable from
one year to the next and quite unpredictable, a long period of
flow record should be analyzed. A number of representative
flood events are then selected to comprise the sample set of
hydrologic events in space and time. These are used as input
data to the model, together with the synthetically derived
probable maximum flood for the individual sub-basins within the
system.

Each set of spatially distributed flood hydrographs is then
routed in turn through the potential system of flood control
reservoirs and interconnecting channels using a decision
policy that automatically minimizes the total system cost.
This corresponds to the sum of the annual fixed and operating
costs of the river basin development and the annual expected
cost of flood damage at all locations being protected. The
latter is obtained by multiplying the peak damage costs by
their probability of occurrence and then summing the weighted
damage costs for all damage centres within the system.

The model treats the reservoir storage and outlet capacities as
decision variables, along with the spillway releases, and is
structured to select the optimal mix for the system. An
implicit assumption is that all damage stages are reduced as

much as possible during each flood period by making best use of the available storage space.

Short Run Analysis

There are a number of methods of operating gated spillways during flood periods. The regulation plan proposed herein is based on the concept of reducing the peak discharges as much as possible at all locations being protected during each flood. Obviously, under actual operating conditions, where knowledge of the potential flood run-off increases with time, it is unlikely that a fixed operating schedule would be considered satisfactory. Instead, it would seem preferable to develop a flexible operating plan in which the system release schedule is continually being updated as more information becomes available regarding the changing climatic and run-off conditions. This is accomplished herein by the following two-step procedure. First, a set of flood hydrographs is generated at all significant points in the system by using suitable simulation techniques and updated hydro-meteorogical data. Second, the updated run-off hydrographs and the currently available flood storage levels are used as input data to a programming model to determine the short-run release schedule for the system. Repeating these steps at suitable intervals during the flood period ensures that the operating plan is continually being modified to match the changing hydro-meteorological and storage conditions. If a large flood develops, a revised estimate of the flood hydrograph is used, and new values of the flow releases are determined. Regulation of the entire system is therefore accomplished strictly on a foresight basis in a manner similar to what would occur under actual operating conditions.

FORMULATION OF THE MODEL

Because of the increasing complexity of water resources planning, design, and operational studies, there is an increasing need for a mathematical procedure that is capable of providing sound integration of the individual elements within the system. This necessitates the use of programming methods which enable the entire system to be studied at once, and in addition consider system operation as an integral part of the system design evaluation.

In this section a programming model is set up to consider the multiple reservoir system shown in Figure 1. The first step in the analysis is to divide the basin into routing reaches and then develop a set of mathematical expressions which describe the space and time movement of flood water within the basin. The basic expressions describing the characteristics of the three reservoir system under investigation are developed as follows.

Reservoir Mass Balance Equation   This equation is based on the
principle of continuity and states that during any time period
the inflow volume must equal the outflow volume plus or minus
any storage change. On the assumption that the flow varies
linearly during each discrete time period, Δt, the mass
balance equation may be stated as follows:

$$(O_i^{t_{n+1}} + O_i^{t_n}) \frac{\Delta t}{2} + (S_i^{t_{n+1}} - S_i^{t_n}) = (q_i^{t_{n+1}} + q_i^{t_n}) \frac{\Delta t}{2} \tag{1}$$

where Δt is the routing period, $q_i^{t_n}$ and $q_i^{t_{n+1}}$ are the inflows
to reservoir i at the start of time periods t_n and t_{n+1}, $O_i^{t_n}$
and $O_i^{t_{n+1}}$ are the corresponding outflows from reservoir i at
the start of time periods t_n and t_{n+1}, and $S_i^{t_n}$ and $S_i^{t_{n+1}}$ are
the reservoir storage volumes at the start of time intervals
t_n and t_{n+1} in a consistent set of units. The unregulated
flood run-offs to reservoirs 1 and 2 are treated as deterministic inputs to the model (sample sets of flood hydrographs
having been drawn from the records) and therefore appear as
elements in the right-hand side of the constraint set. The
inflow hydrographs to reservoir 3, on the other hand, are
composed partly of the controlled releases from reservoirs 1
and 2, modified to some extent by channel storage effects,
and partly of the uncontrolled run-off from the intermediate
drainage basin between the three dams. Only the deterministic
component of the total inflow, however, should appear in the
right-hand vector, the unknown flow components being transposed to the left-hand side of the constraint set.

Storage Constraint   Each reservoir is characterized by its
maximum flood storage volume. That is at any time t_n the
quantity of water stored in reservoir i must be equal to or
less than the maximum available storage volume, or

$$S_i^{t_n} \leqslant V_i \tag{2}$$

where V_i is the available flood storage capacity in reservoir
i. For potential reservoir developments, V_i would be regarded
as a decision variable and transposed to the left-hand side
of the constraint set. On the other hand, if the reservoir
has already been constructed to its maximum capacity, V_i
would be replaced by its known storage volume and appear as
an element in the right-hand vector.

Reservoir Release Constraint   Evaluation of the desired
operating rule must recognize that reservoir releases are
limited by the discharge capacities of the spillways. A
constraint is therefore required that states that the volume
of water discharged per unit time period should not exceed
the spillway discharge capacity, or

$$O_i^{t_n} \leqslant C_i \tag{3}$$

where C_i is the spillway discharge capacity of reservoir i and is regarded as a decision variable in a potential reservoir development. This constraint applies only to gated spillways where the flow is under control of an operator. In situations in which the flow is uncontrolled C_i would be expressed as a function of reservoir storage.

Channel Routing Equation   A simple travel time alorithm, based on the Muskingum equation is employed in this study to allow the times of each reservoir operation to be adjusted to the times of downstream reaches.   In situations where there is uncontrolled run-off from the intermediate drainage area, provision should also be made to augment the main stream flow at appropriate points in the channel reach.   The general form of the Muskingum equation for a river channel is

$$q_i^{t_n+1} = C_{io} 0_i^{t_n} + C_{i1} 0_i^{t_n+1} + C_{i2} q_i^{t_n} \qquad (4)$$

where $C_{io} + C_{i1} + C_{i2} = 1$, $0_i^{t_n}$ and $0_i^{t_n+1}$ denote the inflows to channel reach i at the start of time periods t_n and t_n+1, and $q_i^{t_n}$ and $q_i^{t_n+1}$ denote the corresponding outflows from channel reach i at the start of time intervals t_n and t_n+1.

Channel Flow Constraint at Damage Centres   This requires that the channel discharges at the damage centres at all times be equal to or less than the corresponding flood peak discharges at the damage centres, thus

$$q_{ij}^{t_n} \leqslant Q_j^n \qquad (5)$$

where $q_{ij}^{t_n}$ is the flood discharge in channel reach i at damage centre j at the start of time period t_n and may be estimated by the channel flow function if the distance between the reservoir and the damage centre is significant and Q_j^n is the optimal peak flood discharge at damage centre j for the set of flood hydrographs generated by the nth storm in the sample sequence of N storms.   The Q_j^n are related to the reservoir releases and are treated as decision variables in the model.

Nonnegativity Constraints   These state that the reservoir storages, inflows, outflows, and river flows cannot be negative, thus

$$S_i^{t_n}, q_i^{t_n}, 0_i^{t_n} \ q_{ij}^{t_n}, Q_j^n \geqslant 0 \qquad (6)$$

A feature of this constraint set is that every t_nth constraint appears in the same form for each discrete time period, the only change being in the right-hand elements when these are used to express the distribution of flows in space and time.

Long Run Objective Function   The decision variables in the

long-run analysis include the reservoir flood storage volumes
and outlet capacities and the flood peak discharges at the
various damage centres, the latter being related by the
channel routing equations to the reservoir flow releases.   The
objective is to select the level of these decision variables
that satisfies the system constraints and minimizes the
expected costs of the system.   Since damages occur on an
annual basis, it is necessary to convert all costs to
equivalent annual costs and then add these to obtain the total
annual costs for the system, thus

$$\text{Minimize} \left\{ Z = \sum_{i=1}^{3} \phi_i(V_i) + \sum_{i=1}^{3} \psi_i(C_i) + \sum_{j=1}^{2} \sum_{Q_j^n} P(Q_j^n) \mu_j(Q_j^n) \right\} \qquad (7)$$

where $\phi_i(V_i)$ is the annual cost of providing flood storage
capacity V_i at reservoir i, $\psi_i(C_i)$ is the annual cost of
providing a spillway discharge capacity C_i at reservoir i,
$\mu_j(Q_j^n)$ is the damage cost associated with the flood peak
discharge Q_j^n due to flood event n at damage centre j, and
$P(Q_j^n)$ is the probability of occurrence of peak flood event
Q_j^n generated by the nth storm.

Short Run Objective Function   The short run objective is to
synchronize the reservoir release schedules so as to
minimize the total damage cost at all locations being
protected, given the updated run-off hydrographs at all
significant points in the system, thus

$$\text{Minimize} \left\{ Z^n = \sum_{j=1}^{2} \mu_j(Q_j^n) \right\} \qquad (8)$$

where $\mu_j(Q_j^n)$ denotes the flood damage cost as a function of
peak discharge Q_j^n.

The long-run and short-run optimization problems therefore
involve the minimization of two non-linear objective functions
subject to a large number of constraints.   The next step in
the analysis is to replace the non-linear functions by
piecewise linear approximations.   This transforms the problems
into a mixed integer programming problem that can be solved
by standard solution procedures.

METHOD OF ANALYSIS

A powerful method for solving programming problems having
separable non-linear terms in the objective function involves
the conversion of the problem into a linear or mixed integer
programming problem by approximating each non-linear term by
a number of piecewise linear terms (Wagner, 1969).   The form
of the cost functions is important.   If the curves are convex
in shape, the cost minimization problem may be solved without

much difficulty. Concave cost curves, on the other hand, tend
to create difficulties unless they are incorporated into the
model with some special constraints. The method of solution
will now be illustrated by considering two basic forms of the
cost function, shown in Figure 3(a,b). It is assumed herein
that each function represents the peak discharge–damage cost
function for a different damage centre.

<u>Convex Cost Functions</u> The convex cost curve $\mu_j(Q_j^n)$ is first
approximated by piecewise linear approximations as shown in
Figure 3(a). This is accomplished by carefully selecting a
number of breakpoints, or points at which the slope of the
piecewise linear function changes. Define M as the number
of segments in the piecewise linear function approximating
$\mu_j(Q_j^n)$ and let

$$U_{1j}^n, \; U_{2j}^n, \; \ldots, \; U_{Mj}^n \tag{9}$$

be the ascending values of Q_j^n at which the slopes of the
piecewise linear segments change value. Next, subdivide
the peak discharge at damage centre Q_j^n into a set of
auxiliary variables such that

$$Q_j^n \; = \; \sum_m Q_{mj}^n \tag{10}$$

where $m = 1, 2, \ldots, M$ and each Q_{mj}^n is bounded as follows:

$$Q_{mj}^n \; \leqslant \; U_{mj}^n - U_{m-1j}^n \tag{11}$$

The non-linear cost function $\mu_j(Q_j^n)$ can now be defined in
terms of its piecewise linear approximations:

$$\mu_j(Q_j^n) \; = \; \sum_m K_{mj}^n \, Q_{mj}^n \tag{12}$$

where K_{mj}^n is the partial derivative of the objective function
with respect to Q_{mj}^n and is defined as

$$K_{mj}^n = \Delta Z^n \big/ \Delta Q_{mj}^n \tag{13}$$

The convex cost terms in Expressions (7) and (8) are now
replaced by their piecewise linear approximations as defined
in Equation (12). No additional constraints are required to
force the model to map out the piecewise linear approximations
of $\mu_j(Q_j^n)$ in their correct sequential order. This is so
because the convexity of $\mu_j(Q_j^n)$ causes the slope coefficients
of the piecewise linear segments to be monotone increasing,
and thus Q_{m-1j}^n is automatically used to its full extent
before Q_{jm}^n enters the solution.

Concave Cost Functions   Alternative forms of cost function
are shown in Figures 2 and 3 b. These are characterized by
decreasing average and marginal costs and as a result are not
as easily handled as the previous non-linear function. If
the same approach is used herein it will be found that the
optimal solution will select the low cost units before the
high cost units. This, of course, is impracticable.

The method selected herein for dealing with the problem of
concave cost curves is to treat the piecewise linear costs in
a multiple choice environment using the technique of integer
programming. By this means the individual segments are
treated as separate activities, and the model is forced to
select each activity in its correct sequential order by the
introduction of special constraints.

To see how this is accomplished, assume that the damage cost-
discharge curve $\mu_j(Q_j^n)$ is composed of linear segments, as
shown in Figure 3(b). Next replace the variable Q_j^n by a set
of auxiliary variables, thus

$$Q_i^n = Q_{mj}^n \tag{14}$$

where m = 1, 2, ..., M and Q_{mj}^n is bounded as follows:

$$0 \leqslant Q_{mj}^n < U_{mj}^n \alpha_{mj}^n \tag{15}$$

Again the U_{mj}^n are the ascending values of Q_{mj}^n at which the
piecewise linear segments of $\mu_j(Q_j^n)$ change slope, and α_{mj}^n
is defined as

$$\alpha_{mj}^n = 0 \text{ or } 1 \tag{16}$$

The structure of the problem requires that no more than one
linear segment of each piecewise linear cost curve should
appear in the solution. This constraint requires that

$$\sum_{m=1}^{M} \alpha_{mj}^n \leqslant 1 \tag{17}$$

The non-linear damage function can now be replaced by its
linear approximations, thus

$$\mu_j(Q_j^n) = \sum_{m=1}^{M} K_{mj}^n Q_{mj}^n + \sum_{m=1}^{M} Y_{mj}^n \alpha_{mj}^n \tag{18}$$

where Y_{mj}^n is a setup cost and K_{mj}^n equals the slope of the
piecewise linear segments of the damage cost function,
defined as

$$K_{mj}^{n} = \frac{\mu_j (U_{mj}^{n}) - Y_{mj}^{n}}{U_{mj}^{n}} \qquad (19)$$

The foregoing discussion for convex and concave functions in a single variable generalises at once to an objective function consisting of separable convex and concave functions. The next step then would involve the replacement of the non-linear functions in the long-run and short-run objective functions using relationships similar to those expressed in Equations (12 and (18), and then present the full technology of the model in matrix form. This transforms the model into a mixed integer programming problem that can be solved by standard solution procedures.

For any given sequence of flood events the model will scan all possible assignment combinations and select the particular pattern from the entire system which yields minimum overall cost. At the first level of optimization the model selects the optimal combination of design variables and at the second level of optimization it specifies the optimal reservoir release schedules given the appropriate set of input data.

The degree of difficulty in solving large dynamic, or multi-time period systems is a function of the number of rows in the matrix and the density of the matrix. Fortunately, with the staircase type structure of multi-time period models as the matrices become larger, they also become sparser. All efficient computer codes take advantage of this sparsity of matrices, and this is one reason why large problems may be solved by electronic computers.

SUMMARY AND CONCLUSIONS

A methodology is presented for the optimal design and operation of a multi-reservoir flood control system which employs mixed integer programming as the optimization tool. This approach recognizes component interaction in space and time and therefore offers a potentially powerful method for the analysis of integrated flood control systems involving a large number of interdependent decision variables.

In most practical situations difficulties arise in the determination of the model parameters such as system costs. Unless these are correctly specified it is difficult to state if an optimal, or near optimal, solution has been found. Post-optimality analysis should therefore be considered an integral part of the program to permit examination of the sensitivity of the minimum cost solution to a variety of criteria and input data.

A full scale multi-time period model undoubtedly involves a
large number of constraints. Arranging a programming matrix
of this size by manual means would be a time consuming task.
In such a case it may be necessary to employ a matrix
generator which would satisfy the needs of the system to be
developed.

REFERENCES

Homan, G.A., (1956) Analysis of factors affecting flood
damage, Proj. 1-2541, Stamford Res. Inst., Menlo Park, Calif.

Linsley, R.K., and J.B. Franzini, (1964) Water Resources
Engineering, 63-65, McGraw-Hill, New York.

Wagner, H.M., (1969) Principles of Operations Research,
553-554, Prentice-Hall, Englewood Cliffs, N.J.

OPTIMIZATION METHODS FOR PLANNING WASTE WATER MANAGEMENT SYSTEMS

H. Orth, W. Ahrens

Research Associates at the Institute of Siedlungs-
wasserwirtschaft, University of Karlsruhe

1. INTRODUCTION

Concerning the planning of regional waste water
management systems there is a trend from the traditional comparison of alternatives to the formulation
and solution of mathematical problems. Extended algorithms for optimization and high speed computer
open the possibility to handle large and realistic
problems. A combination of different techniques
allows to find better solutions of these problems
than it is possible by the traditional work. This
paper gives an overview of mathematical solutions
of the so called regionalization problem and selected algorithms and demonstrates the applicability
of the proposed methods at two examples.

The tendency towards a regionalization in water supply and solid waste disposal, two related areas, as
well as in waste water disposal may be explained by
the following:

a) a decrease in the unit costs of construction and
   operation of centralized plants,

b) an increase of costs in the transportation system
   as a consequence of the longer distances to be
   covered,

c) definite advantages and quantative benefits from
   planning, constructing and operating larger plants,

d) pressure from administrations to form regional
   management systems and

e) a stricter control and more stringent supervision of larger plants and thus a more reliable operation.

An optimization problem is called a regionalization problem, if -based on a set of technical data and cost functions- a waste water collection and treatment system with minimal costs is to be determined within a certain region, respectively planning area.

2. MODELS FOR THE REGIONALIZATION PROBLEM

A basic model which describes the regionalization problem is given by a concave objective function and a set of linear constraints as follows:

$$\Phi(x_i, x_{ij}) = \sum_{i \in V} \alpha_i x_i^{\beta_i} + \sum_{(i,j) \in W} \alpha_{ij} x_{ij}^{\beta_{ij}} \rightarrow MIN \dots\dots\dots 1$$

$$x_i + \sum_{(i,j) \in W} x_{ij} - \sum_{(j,i) \in W} x_{ji} = q_i \quad {\scriptstyle i \in E} \dots\dots\dots 2$$

$$x_i, x_{ij} \geq 0 \dots\dots\dots 3$$

$$\alpha_i, \alpha_{ij} \geq 0 \dots\dots\dots 4$$

$$\beta_i, \beta_{ij} \in [0,1] \dots\dots\dots 5$$

$$i = 1(1)m , \ j = 1(1)m$$

The objective function (1) which is to minimize subject to the convex set (2) and (3) takes into account construction, operating, maintenance and capital costs expressed in numbers α_i for treatment and α_{ij} for transportation (4) and economies of scale expressed in numbers β_i resp. β_{ij} (5). Equations (2) are node conditions by applying KIRCHHOFF's law. The basic formulation is called a one-period-model by a given fixed time horizon, and therefore it is appropriate to minimize the costs per annum.

In order to understand the proposed solution algorithms two main properties of the approach are to be brought to mind: The linear constraints describe a convex polyhedral set, the objective function is concave. A mathematical analysis shows that the solutions of the problem (1)-(5) are the basic feasible solutions of (2) which are local optima. Because there are no capacity constraints the basic feasible solutions obtain a 'tree' structure according to graph theory . This tree property is called the single assignment property, a property which is well-known in transportation theory and it is easy to show that the above problem is of the type of a tranship-ment problem. The single assignment property allows a transformation into a binary optimization problem by discreting the continuous variables x_i, x_{ij} over known finite sets of values S_i, S_{ij}, dependent on the structure of the networks and the inflows.

From

$$x_i \in S_i = (Q_{i_1}, Q_{i_2}, \ldots, Q_{i_{k_i}}), i \in V$$

$$x_{ij} \in S_{ij} = (Q_{ij_1}, Q_{ij_2}, \ldots, Q_{ij_{k_{ij}}}), (i,j) \in W \quad \ldots\ldots 6$$

and

$$x_i = \sum_{l=1}^{k_i} Q_{i_l} \cdot x_{i_l}^b$$

$$x_{ij} = \sum_{l=1}^{k_{ij}} Q_{ij_l} \cdot x_{ij_l}^b \quad \ldots\ldots 7$$

the following binary model is resulting:

$$\Phi(x_{i_l}^b, x_{ij_l}^b) = \sum_{i \in V} \sum_{l=1}^{k_i} c_{i_l} \cdot x_{i_l}^b + \sum_{(i,j) \in W} \sum_{l=1}^{k_{ij}} c_{ij_l} \cdot x_{ij_l}^b \rightarrow MIN \ldots\ldots 8$$

$$\sum_{\substack{l=1 \\ i \in V}}^{k_i} Q_{i_l} \cdot x_{i_l}^b + \sum_{(i,j) \in W} \sum_{l=1}^{k_{ij}} Q_{ij_l} \cdot x_{ij_l}^b - \sum_{(j,i) \in W} \sum_{l=1}^{k_{ji}} Q_{ji_l} \cdot x_{ji_l}^b = q_i \quad \ldots\ldots 9$$
$$i \in E$$

$$x_{i_l}^b, x_{ij_l}^b \in (0,1) \quad \ldots\ldots 10$$

$$i = 1(1)m, \ j = 1(1)m$$

with

$$c_{i_l} = \Phi_i(Q_{i_l}), c_{ij_l} = \Phi_{ij}(Q_{ij_l}) \quad \ldots\ldots 11$$

and

$$\Phi_i = \alpha_i x_i^{\beta_i}, \Phi_{ij} = \alpha_{ij} x_{ij}^{\beta_{ij}} \quad \ldots\ldots 12$$

This problem is linear in its objective function. Both, the continuous and the binary model, are roughly to solve with respect to computer storage requirements resp. computation time.

Approximations are possible and commendable. Firstly, an approximation of the concave cost function by one or more segments of fixed charge cost functions and secondly a discretisation only over a selected set of the possible values in order to reduce the number of binary variables. An effective combination of different solution techniques are discussed in chapter 4.2.

A fixed charge cost function is defined by:

$$f(x) = \begin{cases} ax + b & , x > 0 \\ 0 & , x = 0 \end{cases} \quad \dots\dots\dots 13$$

An approximation of the binary model is given by sets S_i, S_{ij} with

$$S'_i \subseteq S_i$$
$$\quad \dots\dots\dots 14$$
$$S'_{ij} \subseteq S_{ij}$$

We get a capacitated regionalization problem by an additional constraint for each variable:

$$\lambda_i \leq x_i \leq \varkappa_i$$
$$\quad \dots\dots\dots 15$$
$$\lambda_{ij} \leq x_{ij} \leq \varkappa_{ij}$$

3. EXTENSIONS OF THE BASIC MODELS WITH RESPECT TO PRACTICAL ASPECTS OF DIMENSIONING PLANTS AND CANALS

The purpose of an economic analysis using operations research techniques is not a detailed design, but a general scheme. Therefore, with the basic model some problem types can be dealt with, such as, for instance, a planning area without important industrial pollutants. In this case dimensioning treatment plants as canals with the sewage flow without respect to sewage loading may be permissible. However, the actual importance of an optimization model and its solution used as a decision aid is its applicability to complex and different problems.

3.1 Different Decision Parameters

The basic condition for the refinement of the model is the introduction of different decision parameters.

An important additional parameter for example is the
population equivalent for dimensioning treatment
plants. Such an additional parameter and its way
through the network can be described by a second set
of constraints, i.e. node equations analog equations
(2). Both, the sewage flow x_i, x_{ij} and its population
equivalent y_i, y_{ij} must reach the treatment plant on
the same route. With the presupposition of the single
assignment property it is ensured if the parameters
of a specific network element are zero or not simultaneous.

Therefore, it follows:

$$
\begin{aligned}
x_i = 0 \quad &\leftrightarrow \quad y_i = 0 \\
x_i \neq 0 \quad &\leftrightarrow \quad y_i \neq 0 \\
x_{ij} = 0 \quad &\leftrightarrow \quad y_{ij} = 0 \\
x_{ij} \neq 0 \quad &\leftrightarrow \quad y_{ij} \neq 0
\end{aligned}
\qquad \text{......16}
$$

In a binary model the logical constraints (16) can
be transformed into algebraic equations

$$
\begin{aligned}
x^b_{i_l} - y^b_{i_l} = 0 \, , \, l = 1(1)\,k_i \\
x^b_{ij} - y^b_{ij} = 0 \, , \, l = 1(1)\,k_{ij}
\end{aligned}
\qquad \text{......17}
$$

It is clear that cost functions $\Phi_i(x_i)$ and $\Phi_{ij}(y_{ij})$
are set to zero.

3.2 Storm Water Retention Tanks and Storm Water Treatment Plants

For dimensioning storm water retention tanks we need
different parameters as the range of the run-off area,
coefficients of discharge, and so on. But if the runoff area and the provided location of the retention
tank is known, all these parameters are constant, except the tank outflow. Therefore, for a certain tank,
the dimensioning parameter is the tank outflow, and
costs can be described as a function of it. It follows
as a constraint that the outflow has to be smaller or
equal to the inflow:

$$
x_{out} - x_{in} \leq 0 \qquad \text{......18}
$$

$$
\Phi = \ldots + \Phi_k(x_{out}) + \ldots \rightarrow MIN \qquad \text{......19}
$$

Whilst all other terms in the objective function are
concave, this term for retention tanks is convex.
Therefore, the single assignment property is no longer

valid. In order to solve the problem, it is proposed to replace the variable X_{out} by a set of values $X_{out,i}$ (fig. 1). It is an approximation, but by a suitable choice of the $X_{out,i}$, it may be sufficient for practice.

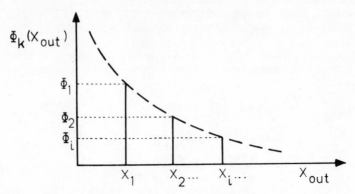

Figure 1: Approximation of the convex cost function of a retention tank by single points.

For storm water treatment plants there are two types of dimensioning methods. The first group considers the characteristics of the run-off area, the second is based on the surface loading and the time of passage. In the first case it can be handled for optimization as storage tanks, in the second case the costs are single functions of waste water flow, because a retention is not taken into account. Hence equation 1 and 2 are sufficient in order to describe the storm-water treatment plant.

3.3 Pumping Stations and Pressure Pipes

For pumping stations we need two parameters for the first time. The maximum flow determines largely the construction costs, the average flow the running costs. For the term in the objective function we obtain:

$$\Phi = \quad \dots \Phi_p(x_{max}) + \Phi_p(x_m) \dots \rightarrow MIN \dots\dots\dots 20$$

The constraints are in accordance with equation 2 the connection of both parameters corresponding to equation 16. If the pumping station is connected with a pressure pipe it will be linked into one system element. In dimensioning this system element the determination of the most economic diameter is included. Then this system element can be handled as pumping stations.

All mentioned system elements or their mathematical
formulations are handled as a so called 'offenes Modell' (open model). It means that on application not
all described formulations are necessary at once. The
planning engineer rather will compose a specific model with some of these formulations according to the
actual problem. In the specific case this leads to
a suitable model which is not too excessive.

With the shown formulations it is also possible to
formulate the various sewerage systems as separate
and combined systems or combinations of both.

4. SOLVING THE REGIONALIZATION PROBLEM

4.1 Solution Algorithms

Optimization algorithms to solve the problem (1)-(5)
have to take into account the properties of the problem. Gradient methods for instance are not helpful,
they would terminate at a local optimum.

An explicit enumeration of the basic solutions is
applicable only for small problems.

Implicit enumeration of local minima is another possibility for solving concave optimization problems.
The respective procedures use different cost functions, but are similar, e.g. the algorithm by Murty
(1968), by Cabot, Francis (197o) and Deininger, Su
(1971). For practical data the enumeration limiting
bounding-rule is hardly active. Algorithms that use
the analog network flow formulation proved to be more
effective by employing algorithms from graph theory,
for example the out-of-kilter algorithm to solve relaxed embedded subproblems (see Marks (1969)).

The binary model (8)-(10) can be solved by integer programming algorithms as the additive algorithm by
Balas (Balas (1965)), the pseudo-boolean-programming
(Hammer, Rudeanu (1968)), the cutting-plane-methods
and a lot of known procedures as well as optimization
packages of the computer centres (MPSX, FMPS etc.).

Experiences show that modified algorithms, modified
with respect to the properties of the problem, are
better with regard to the computation time. Hence, the
Balas-algorithm was adjusted to the given problem
structure, especially to the single assignment property. Numerous heuristic rules, in particular the
augmentation rules, show a different behaviour in

the enumeration process which can be used to reduce
computation time (see Ahrens (1975)).

An optimization package called REGIO was built-up
containing the explicit algorithm by Manas and Nedoma,
fixed charge algorithms based on Marks's algorithm
with different capacitated network flow algorithms
and different enumeration processes and last not
least binary optimization algorithms with and without considering the single assignment property. All
algorithms are modified with respect to the applicability of dynamic programming which means that these
algorithms can be used to optimize the stages within
the dynamic programming.

4.2 Decomposition Methods

Although the mentioned algorithms are partly effective computation time becomes quickly expensive with
increasing problem size. The computation time increases exponentially with the problem size respectively the number of variables in the model. Therefore, it can be reduced substantially by dividing
the network into smaller parts.

The first method is the exclusive decomposition: In
each network there are several system elements which
cannot appear in a solution or in the optimal solution simultaneously. Two explanatory examples are
given: On a node with discharge to different directions only one of these can appear in the optimal
solution. This is given by the single assignment
property. If the connection between two nodes enables
a flow in both directions, in the optimal solution
only one flow-direction can appear likewise. In these
cases the network can be devided into independant
subnetworks which contain exactly one of these system elements excluding one another. Then the optimal
solution is included in one of the subnetworks.

The second method, the dynamic decomposition, is
based on the principles of dynamic programming, and
therefore the basic presupposition is the existence
of a sequence of stages. Such a sequence is generally not present in a network. However, in the network
of a regionalization problem we often find a main
flow direction caused by the main dewatering direction of the planning area. From this, the opportunity arises for dividing the network into a sequence
of subnetworks. In this connection also the exclusive
decomposition is important. If the sequence of stages
is not present, it can be generated by the exclusive
decomposition. For example, if we have a network

with two stages, but a possible flow in both directions between the stages, we can decompose it into two networks with one flow direction at a time between the two stages.

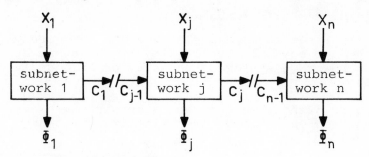

Figure 2: The regionalization problem as a n-stage decision problem.

In figure 2 the stages are any subnetworks, where the decision variable X_j is a vector including all the variables of the stage-network. The state parameter C_j also can be a vector. But it must be accentuated that very easily computational difficulties arise if C_j includes more than two or three vector elements.

With the notes of figure 2 we obtain the following dynamic programming problem:

$$\Phi = \sum_{j=1}^{n} \Phi_j(c_j, x_j) \rightarrow MIN \dots\dots 21$$

$$c_{j-1} = t_j(c_j, x_j) , j = 1(1) n \dots\dots 22$$

where the feasible values of X_j are defined by the constraints - generally the node equations - of the stage j.

For the optimization of the single stages as it is necessary for solving the recurrence relation

$$f_j^*(c_j) = \min_{x} (\Phi_j(c_j, x_j) + f_{j-1}^*(c_{j-1}))\dots\dots 23$$

any of the above mentioned optimization techniques is applicable. For each stage it may be another technique and for the selection of a suitable algorithm not only mathematical aspects should be considered. By the dynamic decomposition there is the possibility to consider also engineering aspects. For example it may be possible to calculate with a different accuracy in various parts of the planning area according to their different importance for a given problem.

5. EXAMPLES

5.1 Abidjan/Ivory Coast

A first realistic example is given by a study concerning the economic feasibility of the urban drainage and sewerage system of the city of Abidjan/Ivory Cost.

Figure 3 shows an abstract graph in which every treatment plant and sewer line is represented by an edge.

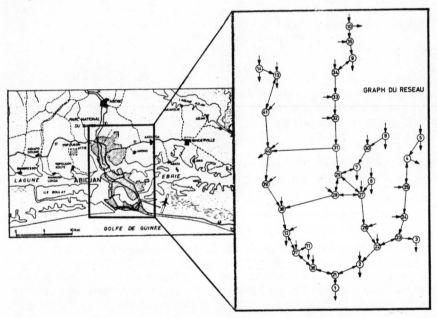

Figure 3: Map of Abidjan and the network of possible treatment plants and sewer lines.

Both, the exclusive decomposition and the dynamic programming technique are applied to solve the problem. The exclusive decomposition generates four separate problems, every problem is devided into four stages. The explicite enumeration by Manas and Nedoma was applied to optimize the first of the stages, binary optimization solved the last ones.

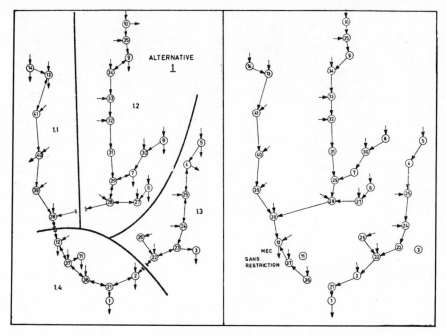

Figure 4 : One of the four subproblems with four stages and the optimal solution

The whole problem was solved in 28 minutes on a
UNIVAC 1108 computer (Computing Centre of the University of Karlsruhe). A sensitivity analysis executed with some water quality assumptions completed
the results.

5.2 Edenkoben/Germany

The planning area of the second example includes 16
communities. A speciality of this area is that the
conditions in the western part are of a wide variety
from those in the eastern one.

In the hilly western part there are many wine processing plants which produce such a sewage loading that
it cannot be neglected in dimensioning treatment
plants. Furthermore, because of the short distances between the communities it was not possible to allocate
a storm water treatment plant to each community in
advance. So in this part three parameters (sewage
flow, sewage loading and storm water flow) and a
high accuracy were necessary taking into account the
quantative share. On the other hand a very simple
network arose.

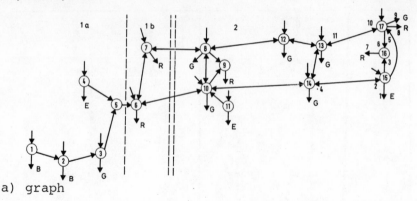

a) graph

b) arrangement of stages

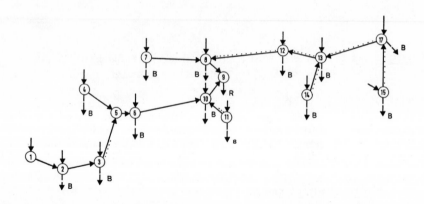

c) optimal solution

$\underset{\downarrow}{\bigcirc}$ = waste water source
.... = pressure pipe
feasible size for treatment plants:
  B = storm water treatment plant
  E = treatment plant for one community
  G = treatment plant for a small group of commu-
      nities
  R = regional treatment plant for all communities

Figure 5: Project Edenkoben

The other plane part produces only a quarter of the
whole pollution; wine-growing is not important.
Besides, the long distances between the communities
prevent a common storm water treatment plant for
several communities. Therefore, for dimensioning a
regional system one parameter was sufficient (sewage
flow). Otherwise for all sewer routes flow was possible in both directions and the network becomes
therefore more complicated.

Regarding the mentioned facts in the first part the
binary optimization technique was applied. This method is very accurate and suitable for different parameters. Its low computation velocity is in the present simple network without importance. In the eastern part with the more complicated network a fixed
charge model was applied.

The application of the different optimization techniques was possible by dividing the whole network
in the described parts. At first, it was divided into three sequential stages by the exclusive decomposition (fig. 5) and then solved via dynamic programming.

NOTATION

Φ = objective function
Φ_i = cost function for treatment plant at node i
Φ_{ij} = cost function for transportation between node i and j
Φ_k = cost function for storm water retention tank
Φ_p = cost function for pumping station
Φ_j = cost function for the stage j (dyn.progr.)
x_i = variable, size of treatment plant at node i
x_{ij} = variable, size of sewer line between i and j
x_{out} = outflow of a stormwater retention tank
x_{in} = inflow of a stormwater retention tank
x_{max} = maximum flow of a pumping station
x_m = average flow of a pumping station
$x_{i_1}^b$ = binary variable associated to the variable x_i
$x_{i j_1}^b$ = binary variable associated to the variable x_{ij}
y_i = variable, size of treatment plant at node i with respect to the pollution equivalent
y_{ij} = variable, size of sewer line between node i and j, pollution equivalent
$y_{i_1}^b$ = binary variable associated to y_i
$y_{i j_1}^b$ = binary variable associated to y_{ij}
m = number of nodes

E   = set of nodes,at which a waste water flow
      is given

W   = set of possible sewer lines

V   = set of nodes with possible treatment plant

κ_i, κ_{ij} = upper bounds of variables x_i, x_{ij}

λ_i, λ_{ij} = lower bounds of variables x_i, x_{ij}

α_i, α_{ij} = cost coefficients for treatment and trans-
      portation

β_i, β_{ij} = cost exponents for treatment and transpor-
      tation

c_{i_l}, c_{ij_l} = cost coefficients in a linear objective
      function

Q_{i_l}, Q_{ij_l}= possible values of flow for variables x_i,
      x_{ij}

k_i, k_{ij} = number of elements of the sets S_i, S_{ij}

c_j = state parameter (dyn.progr.)

t_j = transition function (dyn.progr.)

q_i = known amount of waste water at node i

LITERATURE

Ahrens, W.: Optimierungsverfahren zur Lösung nichtlinearer
    Investitionsprobleme - angewandt auf das Problem
    der Planung regionaler Abwasserentsorgungssysteme.
    Doctoral Thesis, University of Karlsruhe (1975),
    Anton Hain K.G., Meisenheim am Glan.

Balas, E.: An Additive Algorithm for Solving Linear Programs
    with Zero-One-Variables. Operations Research, Vol.13
    (1965), 517-546.

Cabot, A.W., Francis, R.L.: Solving Certain Non-Convex Quadratic
    Minimization Problems by Ranking the Extreme Points.
    Operations Research, Vol. 18 (197o), 82-86.

Deininger, R.A., Su, S.Y.: Regional Waste Water Treatment Sys-
    tems. ASCE Annual and National Environmental Engi-
    neering Meeting (1971), St. Louis, Miss.

Hahn, H., Meier, P.M., Orth, H.: Regional Wastewater Management
    Systems. In: Deininger (Ed.): Models for Environ-
    mental Pollution Control. Ann Arbor Science, Ann
    Arbor, Michigan (1973).

Hammer, P.L., Rudeanu, S.: Boolean Methods in Operations Re-
    search and Related Areas. Springer-Verlag, Berlin
    (1968).

Manas, M., Nedoma, J.: Finding All Vertices of a Convex Poly-
    hedron. Numerische Mathematik. Bd. 12 (1968),
    226-229.

Marks, D.H.: Facility Location and Routing Models in Solid
         Waste Collection Systems. Ph.D. Thesis. The Johns
         Hopkins University (1969).

Murty, K.G.: Solving the Fixed Charge Problem by Ranking the
         Extreme Points. Operations Research, Vol. 16 (1968),
         268-279.

Orth, H.: Verfahren zur Planung kostenminimaler regionaler Ab-
         wasserentsorgungssysteme. Doctoral Thesis, Univer-
         sity of Karlsruhe. Erich Schmidt Verlag Bielefeld
         (1975).

MODELLING OF AQUIFER BEHAVIOUR FOR LONG TIME PERIODS USING

INTERACTIVE ANALOGUE-DIGITAL COMPUTERS

K.R.Rushton and J.E.Ash

Department of Civil Engineering, University of Birmingham

ABSTRACT

An interactive analogue-digital computer system is used to
predict the flow of water through underground aquifers over
periods of hundreds of years. Applications include an
investigation of possible alternative flow mechanisms
within an aquifer and a study in which well discharge rates
are controlled according to the variations of water levels.

INTRODUCTION

Since groundwater flow through an aquifer can be adequately
described by a two-dimensional parabolic equation, many
methods of analysis are available. Analytical solutions
have only limited applicability since they are rarely
capable of representing the complicated aquifer geometry,
but numerical techniques widen considerably the range of
problems that can be considered.

Recent practical aquifer studies have required further
developments of the numerical techniques. Frequently long
time periods of hundreds of years need to be analysed, yet
the aquifer response is often so rapid that head variations
during short periods of less than a day may be significant.
Further, the magnitudes of the aquifer parameters may be
uncertain; these uncertainties can be resolved to some
extent by means of a sensitivity analysis which involves
many trial solutions. In addition, it has become
increasingly apparent that the infiltration into the aquifer
and the flow mechanism within the aquifer are governed by
more complex relationships than had been assumed hitherto.
The investigation of these possible flow mechanisms also
requires many trial solutions.

It follows that any numerical scheme selected for the
analysis of the regional groundwater problems must be capable
of analysing long time periods without loss of detail. Also
a large number of trial solutions must be economically
feasible. It is the contention of this paper that as an
alternative to the discrete time – discrete space digital
computer techniques (Thomas 1973, Pinder and Frind 1972) the
interactive analogue-digital computer system is worthy of
serious consideration.

FORMULATION OF GROUNDWATER PROBLEMS

Due to their relative simplicity, the equations for
groundwater flow in aquifers are well known (De Wiest 1965).
Considerations of continuity and Darcy's Law leads to a
differential equation for flow in an aquifer,

$$\frac{\partial}{\partial x} (T_x \frac{\partial h}{\partial x}) + \frac{\partial}{\partial y} (T_y \frac{\partial h}{\partial y}) = S \frac{\partial h}{\partial t} - Q(x,y,t). \tag{1}$$

In this equation the vertical components of flow are
neglected; therefore the piezometric head, h, remains
constant with depth. The transmissivities, T_x and T_y are
the integrals of the permeability over the saturated depth.
The storage coefficient, S, is the quantity of water, per
unit plan area, released from storage due to a unit fall in
head and Q is the infiltration per unit area. In
localities where the vertical flow is significant, special
techniques can be introduced (Rushton 1974).

An aquifer can be in one of two distinct states, either the
unconfined (water table) state or the confined (artesian)
state. In the unconfined state the free water surface lies
within the aquifer and the storage coefficient is of the order
of 1% to 10%. When the aquifer is under a confining pressure,
the piezometric head is the level to which water will rise
in a piezometer; the storage coefficient is then less than
0.1%. Equation (1) holds for both unconfined and confined
aquifers.

In defining a particular problem, the boundary and initial
conditions must be specified together with information about
inputs and outputs. Boundary conditions are ascertained
from geological information. The condition which occurs
most frequently in nature is that flow takes a known value
(often zero). In other situations such as at the coast or
on the edge of a lake the boundary condition is that the
piezometric head is known. Initial conditions are of great
importance since an error in the initial conditions may be
equivalent to a large volume of water positioned in the

wrong part of the aquifer. Sometimes accurate field
information is available which can be used as the initial
conditions; in other situations the solution is run
cyclically for a number of years with typical data until a
dynamic balance is achieved (Rushton and Wedderburn 1972).

Inadequacies and Uncertainties

The relatively simple formulation described above has been
critically reviewed recently and it has become apparent that
it leads to an inadequate representation of the behaviour of
many aquifers. For example Darcy's Law and therefore
equation (1) assumes that water is transmitted through and
released from pores within the aquifer whereas the majority
of the flow in chalk and limestone aquifers takes place
through fissures or solution channels (Foster and Milton
1974). Though it may be an acceptable approximation to
sum the highly variable permeability into the overall
transmissivity, yet the storage coefficient changes
significantly whenever the water surface coincides with the
fissures. Any solution which does not take into account this
variation in S is suspect.
Another major uncertainty in aquifer analysis is the
magnitude of the infiltration. Techniques are available
for estimating the infiltration from the rainfall,
evaporation, run-off and soil moisture deficit (Wales-Smith
1975). Since the infiltration is typically only 10 to 20%
of the rainfall, errors in any of the measurements can lead
to serious errors in the estimates of infiltration. A
further potential source of error is that no allowance is
made for the mechanism whereby the water reaches the
saturated regions of the aquifer.

These typical uncertainties are described here to indicate
that the predictions of a simple groundwater model may be
misleading. A sensitivity analysis, together with extensive
field data, can be used to investigate the uncertainties; a
typical example is described later.

Information Required from Model Investigation

The information required from an investigation reflects the
wide range of interest in aquifer behaviour. For instance
the water supply engineer wishes to know where boreholes
should be positioned to provide a reliable yield. He also
requires information about the day by day changes in
piezometric head and how the abstraction rates should be
modified in the light of these changes.

On the other hand the Water Resources Planner is interested
in the long term behaviour of the aquifer and requires
information such as the available resources within the
aquifer that can be exploited in times of severe drought or
the interaction of the aquifer with other sources of water

such as rivers.   Studies covering hundreds of years are
required.

Different questions are posed by farmers; what will be the
effect on springs, streams, shallow wells and crops?
Detailed local head variations are therefore of great
significance.

These three interests require significantly different
information.   Time periods from fractions of a day to
hundreds of years are important.   Head variations from many
metres at a pumped well to fractions of a metre remote from
abstraction sites must be predicted.

METHODS OF AQUIFER ANALYSIS

For the analysis of regional groundwater flow problems, some
form of mathematical model is required.   In reviewing the
available methods the following criteria should be
considered:

(a)   The model should be sufficiently flexible to obtain
the large number of solutions required for a sensitivity
analysis.

(b)   The model should be suitable for predicting aquifer
behaviour over long periods yet it should also be possible
to obtain detailed information during critical periods of
these long runs.

Analogue Model   Most of the early work in simulating time
variant aquifer behaviour was carried out using Resistance-
Capacitance analogue computers in which there is a direct
analogy between electrical and physical quantities.   When
assessing the value of this technique it must be remembered
that significant advances have been made in electronic
technology since the initial work.   The most important
advantage of the analogue method is that time is represented
as a continuous function; the disadvantages are that the
input parameters require complex function generators and
accurate measurement of voltages requires expensive
equipment.   The analogue model is well suited to sensitivity
analysis but it is not convenient for representing long
time periods.

Digital Computer Models   Extensive development of digital
computer models has taken place since 1968 (Thomas 1973).
Since long time periods have to be analysed, economy in
computing time is desirable.   The alternating direction
method (ADI) appeared to be a suitable method.   With the
ADI method, equation (1) is rearranged to form a series of
one-dimensional problems in the x and y directions

alternately. Since ADI is an implicit method it was thought
that it would be stable whatever the size of the time step.
However the stability analysis assumes that the function and
its derivatives should be smooth. This is clearly not the
case in an aquifer where sudden changes in pumping rate
cause sudden changes in head. Detailed studies have shown
that oscillations or other errors occur with the ADI solution
unless the time increment is sufficiently small (Rushton
1973).

However one implicit method, the backward difference method,
appears to give reliable results whatever the size of time
step. Unfortunately this method requires the solution of
a large number of simultaneous equations; iterative techniques
such as successive over-relaxation or a modified iterative
alternating direction implicit method (Prickett and Lonnquist
1971) are used.

When the backward difference method is used for aquifer
analysis, long computer runs are required. In practice this
restricts the number of variations included in a sensitivity
analysis. Long time periods can be included using large
time steps but the detailed changes occurring during critical
periods may not be modelled in sufficient detail.

Analogue-Digital Models In a third method a resistance-
capacitance analogue models the aquifer behaviour with a
small digital computer controlling the flows into and out of
the aquifer and recording the head variations. This is
different to the hybrid computer technique of Vemuri and
Karplus (1969) which uses a hybrid computer to solve the
discrete time - discrete space backward difference equations.
Full details are given later, but for comparison with the
other methods it should be noted that changes in parameters
can be made quickly and therefore the technique is well
suited for a sensitivity analysis. Periods of many hundreds
of years can be modelled, yet detailed head variations can
be monitored during critical periods.

ANALOGUE-DIGITAL COMPUTER SYSTEM

Typical Problem
The system will be described with reference to a particular
example, part of the Lincolnshire Limestone in Eastern
England (for further details of the aquifer see Downing and
Williams 1969). A plan and section of the aquifer is given
in Figure 1. The section shows that, in the western region,
the water table lies within the aquifer and typically the
storage coefficient is 0.05. To the East the aquifer is
under artesian pressure, such that the elastic properties
of aquifer and water lead to a storage coefficient of 0.0003.

Infiltration takes place in the West though some of the water returns to feed rivers. Water is pumped from the aquifer at a roughly constant rate from six major wells. Little is known about the eastern limit of the aquifer; at present it is apparent that a small eastwards flow does occur, though at a significant distance to the East the piezometric head remains effectively constant. It will be shown later that this is an over simplification of the flow mechanism and that flow enters the confined region directly and rapidly from fissures.

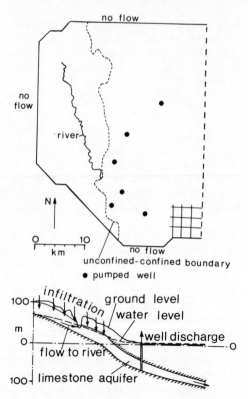

Figure 1.   Plan and typical section of the Lincolnshire Limestone aquifer.

Resistance-Capacitance Network

This hydraulic system can be modelled directly by a resistance-capacitance network. Direct relationships hold between physical and electrical properties; these are listed in Table 1. Typical values of the electrical quantities are also listed in the Table. In particular, it should be noted that 1 day is modelled by 10 msec, thus a month of 31 days is equivalent to 0.31 sec. of electrical time. The right hand side of Figure 2 contains a schematic diagram of the resistance-capacitance network; details of the choice of

components and construction of the networks are reported by
Rushton and Bannister (1970).

Table 1. Analogous physical and electrical quantities

Physical	Typical Value	Relationship	Electrical	Typical Value
head	3.2m	$V=C(1)h$	voltage	0.32volt
transmissivity	625m^2/d	$R_x = \dfrac{C(2)\Delta x}{T_x \Delta y}$	resistance	1.6MΩ
storage coefficient	0.05	$C=C(3)S\Delta x\Delta y$	capacitance	2μF
quantity	3,300m^3/d	$I=C(1)Q/C(2)$	current	0.33μA
time	1 day	$t_e=C(2)C(3)t$	electrical time	0.01sec

Note: In the above table values of the constants are

$$C(1) = 10^{-1}, \; C(2) = 10^{9}, \; C(3) = 10^{-10} \text{ with a}$$

mesh spacing $\Delta x = \Delta y = 2km$.

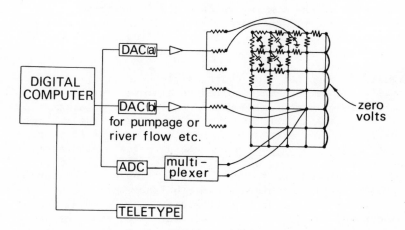

Figure 2. Resistance capacitance analogue computer with
connections to digital computer.
DAC = digital to analogue convertor,
ADC = analogue to digital convertor.

Digital Computer The digital computer attached to the
groundwater analogue consists of a 20K 16 bit machine
interfaced to a data logging console containing a high speed
voltmeter of high input impedance and a number of 12 bit
digital to analogue converters. Voltages may be read at
selected channels at speeds up to 265 per second. Timing
during an experiment is controlled by a real time clock
within the computer.

The major tasks in servicing the resistance-capacitance
network are as follows:

1. The calculation of infiltration to the aquifer
(derived from the rainfall, run-off and evaporation) and the.
conversion of these quantities to the appropriate binary
patterns for later conversion to voltages. These voltages
form the input data to the network and are changed every
month (280 - 310 msec).

2. The simulation of monthly changes in pumpage and
river run-off as voltages.

3. The recording of heads (voltages) as required. This
involves either measurement at frequent time intervals such
as once per day (every 10 msec) or scanning a selection of
nodal points at particular instants of time. The computer
can also be used to convert the information into a form
which can be assessed easily, such as identifying the
largest and smallest heads.

4. As the heads change, provision is made for the
modification of the pumping rates according to some
algorithm to control the water levels within the aquifer.
This involves measuring the voltages, noting the changes and
altering the pumping rates as appropriate.

A simplified computer flow chart is shown in Figure 3.
Initially the network is required to achieve a state of
dynamic balance using inflows and outflows for an average
year. When this dynamic balance is achieved in the analogue,
inflow and outflow data are changed to a sequence of years,
the nodal points are scanned and the pumpages manipulated
as appropriate. Output of results takes place after a run
has been completed; whilst this is occurring the computer
manipulates data to achieve dynamic balance once again.
The programme uses about 4K of computer store leaving the
remainder for data storage. Particular care was necessary
when developing the programme to ensure that timings are
strictly kept when the appropriate computer peripherals
are in use during the same period.

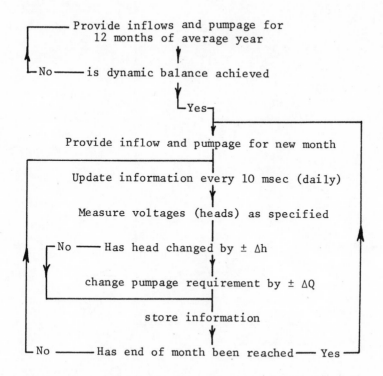

Figure 3. Flow chart of computer programme which
includes provision for modifying pumping
as changes in head occur.

TYPICAL EXAMPLES

Two typical examples are considered, one relates to a
sensitivity analysis into the flow mechanism within the
aquifer, whilst the second is concerned with an attempt
to control levels within the aquifer according to certain
criteria.

Sensitivity Analysis

If the flow mechanism of Figure 1 is assumed to apply for
the Lincolnshire Limestone, the <u>overall distribution</u> of heads,
as predicted by the numerical solution, is found to be
acceptable. However the <u>annual variation</u> of head at any
observation well within the confined portion of the aquifer
is found to be far too small. This is demonstrated in
Figure 4. The variation in the predicted heads (the broken
line) is typically 1m in a year whereas the observed head
variation (the chain dotted line) is around 10m. For clarity
the diagram contains only four years of fifteen years that
were included in this analysis.

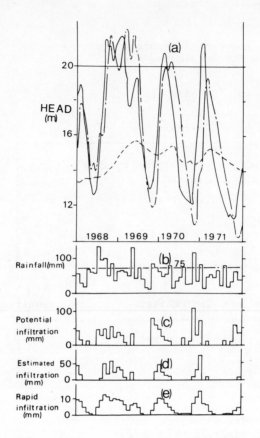

Figure 4. Head variation at a typical point within the
confined aquifer. Chain-dotted line, field
measurements; broken line, predicted heads
excluding rapid infiltration; full line,
predicted heads including rapid infiltration.

The above analysis assumes that the <u>potential</u> infiltration
can be calculated on a monthly basis as rainfall minus
evaporation and surface run-off. Only when this potential
infiltration exceeds the Soil Moisture Deficit is it assumed
that infiltration to the aquifer actually occurs. This
quantity is termed the <u>estimated</u> infiltration. One result
of this technique of calculating infiltration is that
infiltration hardly ever occurs during summer months; see
for example curve (d) of Figure 4. This is contrary to the
observed behaviour of piezometric heads in the confined
portion of the aquifer since heavy summer rainfall is
followed by a recovery in piezometric heads. This suggests
some form of rapid infiltration which is supported by
geological evidence and flow into swallow holes.

Direct measurement of infiltration over an extensive area is
not feasible at present. However, one possible approach is
to assume that rapid infiltration depends on three factors,
rainfall, potential infiltration and estimated infiltration.
There is also a delay between the occurrence of the rainfall
and its effect in the confined region. The term 'rapid'
indicates that the response time is a few months; this is
rapid compared with the normal aquifer response to recharge
of many years.

Many combinations of the above factors have been investigated
and by examining the sensitivity of the results to the
factors an adequate result has been obtained. <u>Rapid</u>
infiltration is calculated as 17.5% of the monthly rainfall
in excess of 75mm, 10% of the potential infiltration and
15% of the estimated infiltration distributed over a period
of 4 months. These quantities are plotted as (b), (c) and
(d) of Figure 4, and the rapid infiltration is plotted as
curve (e). With this rapid infiltration injected directly
into the western edge of the confined region and the
remainder of the normal infiltration entering the unconfined
region, the predicted piezometric head variation is shown as
the full line in Figure 4 (a). The agreement with observed
results is satisfactory. When other combinations of the
factors are used, better agreement is achieved at certain
times but poorer agreement at other times. Extensive field
investigations are presently being carried out to gain further
understanding of the actual mechanism.

Control of Aquifer Levels
The second application involves variations in the pumping
rates in an attempt to maintain the artesian pressures within
the confined portion of the aquifer at constant values. This
is of importance since low values of head may lead to saline
intrusions from the East whilst high heads can result in
losses of water from the aquifer through springs.

Many control rules could be introduced; the one described
below is very simple and is selected to demonstrate potential
difficulties. The rule is that if the increase (decrease)
in head exceeds Δh then the quantity pumped from the aquifer
increases (decreases) by ΔQ, see Figure 3. In applying this
control rule it is important to determine suitable magnitudes
of Δh, ΔQ and the frequency at which readings have to be
taken.

Certain results are included in Figure 5 which refers to the
years 1968 and 1969. The full line indicates the piezometric
head variations that would have occurred under a constant
pumpage of 61 ml/d. If the criterion, $\Delta h = 0.9m$,
$\Delta Q = 21$ ml/d, is selected with changes in pumpage occurring

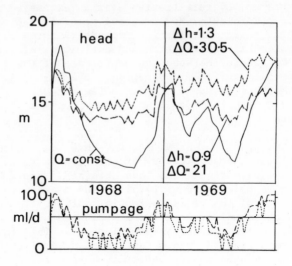

Figure 5. Modification of pumpage in an attempt to
maintain constant head.

every two days, then the range of head variation is reduced
from 8m to 2m. This would, however, require significant
variations in the pumping rate.

Improvements in the control could perhaps be achieved by
greater changes in the pumping rate. Therefore a change in
criteria to Δh = 1.3m, ΔQ = 30.5 ml/d was investigated. This
gives the same ratio of Δh/ΔQ as that for the first set of
values. The results, indicated by the dotted line, are less
satisfactory. Severe oscillations in the pumping rate result
and the insensitivity of the criterion leads to an upward
drift in heads.

Instead of attempting to control the aquifer levels by
monitoring the changes in head, it is possible to relate the
pumpage to the absolute head. Unless the right form of
relationship is selected insensitivity or instability can
easily occur.

CONCLUSION

This study has shown that the analogue-digital computer
system is well suited to the practical analysis of regional
groundwater flow problems. Particular advantages are
apparent when a large number of trial solutions are needed.
An extension of this present technique will allow the
simultaneous modelling of surface water and groundwater
systems. The analogue will be used to model the groundwater
regime whilst the digital computer models the surface water
and controls the analogue computer.

REFERENCES

De Wiest, R.J.M. (1965) Geohydrology. Wiley. Chapter 4.

Downing, R.A. and Williams, B.P.J. (1969) The Groundwater hydrology of the Lincolnshire Limestone, Water Resources Board, Reading.

Foster, S.S.D. and Milton, V.A. (1974) The Permeability and Storage of a Chalk Aquifer. Hydrological Sciences Bulletin, 19, 4: 485-500.

Pinder, G.F. and Frind, E.O. (1972) Application of Galerkin's Procedure to Aquifer Analysis. Water Resour.Res., 8, 1: 108-120.

Prickett, T.A. and Lonnquist, C.G. (1971) Selected Digital Computer Techniques for Groundwater Resources Evaluation. Illinois State Water Surv.Bull., 55, 1-60.

Rushton, K.R. and Bannister, R.G. (1970) Aquifer Simulation on Slow Time Resistance-Capacitance Networks. Groundwater, 8: 15-24.

Rushton, K.R. and Wedderburn, L.A. (1973) Starting Conditions for Aquifer Simulations. Groundwater, 11: 37-42.

Rushton, K.R. (1973) Critical Analysis of the Alternating Direction Implicit Method of Aquifer Analysis. Jnl. Hydrology, 21: 153-172.

Rushton, K.R. (1974) Extensive Pumping from Unconfined Aquifers. American Water Resources Bulletin, 10: 32-40.

Thomas, R.G. (1973) Groundwater Models, Irrigation and Drainage Paper 21, Food and Agricultural Organisation of the U.N. Rome.

Vemuri, V. and Karplus, W.J. (1969), Identification of Non-linear Parameters of Groundwater Basins by Hybrid Computation. Water Resour.Res., 5, 1: 172-185.

Wales-Smith, B.G. (1975) The Estimation of Irrigation Needs. Engineering Hydrology To-day, Paper 5, Instn.Civ.Eng.,London.

A STOCHASTIC MODEL OF LEVEE FAILURE

F. Szidarovszky
Professor, Dept. of Numerical Methods, Eötvös Univ., Budapest

L. Duckstein
Professor, Depts. of Systems & Industrial Engineering and
Hydrology & Water Resources, Univ. of Arizona, Tucson, Arizona

I. Bogárdi
Dept. Head, Water Resources Centre, Alkotmány u 29, Budapest

INTRODUCTION

Floods have been one of the most dangerous environmental hazards menacing a great part of the world [United Nations,
1975]. Further development of flood control systems is necessary in a number of river basins because of the following
reasons:
    (1) A steady increase of economical value in the flood-
plain accompanies the development of the national economy
[White 1969].
    (2) Due to human interference (deforestation, change in
agricultural land use, water regulation, etc.) the floods
occur more frequently and reach higher levels [Bogárdi 1972].
    (3) The earth material of the levees becomes "older"
due to physical and chemical effects (e.g., wetting and dry-
ing) and its resistance decreases [Szepesi 1969].

    In flood control development the available funds must be
utilized to provide the greatest benefit to the protected
area. The optimal development may be determined in the
following four steps:
    --establish the present degree of protection of the flood
      control system,
    --consider the different development alternatives,
    --estimate the optimal development in a reach,
    --calculate the optimal program of development of the
      flood control system.

    In the present paper, a method will be described for the

determination of the present degree of protection. It is emphasized that this approach is primarily applicable to flatland type rivers, where the most successful method of flood control is still the levee. Such flat land conditions hold in large river basins all over the world; the method, illustrated here by a Hungarian sample, may be used either to evaluate existing levee systems or to design new ones.

Hungary is surrounded from the west, north, and east by the Alps and the Carpathians. The rivers draining this mountainous area cross the Hungarian plains, one quarter of which was still inundated in the last century by unpredictable floods. About 25 percent of the country's area, almost 25,000 km^2, is below the flood level. This area comprises half of the population of the country as well as the capital, Budapest. Besides the many industrial establishments of Budapest, about 2,000 major industrial plants are located in the protected floodplains. Moreover, 3,000 km of railway lines, 4,500 km of highways, and much of the valuable agricultural land is situated in the flood plains.

The most economical method of flood control, i.e., the construction of reservoirs for the retention of flood peak is, unfortunately, not feasible in Hungary, because the potential reservoir sites are in the mountainous parts of the catchment in foreign territory. Then, the effectiveness of such reservoirs would be low because of their location several hundred kms away from the area to be protected. An alternative flood control method is river training, which is especially important for ice-carrying floods. Some reaches of the Danube River are especially liable to cause such floods; the river training operations carried out in the near past have significantly improved the situation. On the other hand, the beds of the great rivers, the Danube and the Tisza, in particular, are very wide, so flood levels cannot be significantly influenced by river training structures and dredging. Cheap transportation and the availability of water attracts industry into the levee-protected floodplains. Since the floodplains occupy a large proportion of the country, the introduction of zoning and restrictive measures for building is not feasible.

Thus, the only effective method for decreasing flood damages in Hungary consists of the construction, strengthening, and maintenance of flood levees. Presently, the flood endangered area of about 2.8 million hectares is protected by 4,200 km of flood levees. The inundation area between the flood levees, 660 km^2 of primarily agricultural area, is protected against floods during the growing season by so-called "summer dikes" of a total length of 500 km. Further, when floods occur, some sections of the system may offer lower protection than the actual flood level, so that in those

sections, flood-fighting operations become necessary. If the
flood level is higher than the protection offered jointly by
the system and the potential maximal flood-fighting effort,
the protected area is flooded, which often results in considerable damages.

FORMULATION OF THE MODEL

Definitions

The failure probability of a <u>levee reach</u> is investigated. The
reach refers to a levee line of several kilometers that pro-
tects a given area in the flood plain. The levee reach behaves as a structure: a levee rupture occurs at any point
of the reach, the structure fails and the whole area under
protection is inundated.

The <u>load on the levee reach</u> is the flood wave, whose
different parameters (peak level, duration, volume, etc.) can
be used as load characteristics. This load is a random
variable whose distribution function (DF) may be estimated
using observations taken at a gaging station along the
reach. If there is no effect from backwater or wind waves
along the reach, this load is the same in every cross
section of the levee. Otherwise, there is a spatial change
in load conditions, and a different DF of the load should be
estimated at every cross section [Bogárdi 1972; Szidarovszky
et al. 1974]. At any rate, the DF is estimated from a
finite sample, so that its parameters bear a parameter or
sample uncertainty [Haan 1972].

In the case of large flat rivers, failure of the levee
reach in any cross-section can be caused by one of the following effects (Figure 1): (1) overtopping caused by a flood
level higher than the levee crest; (2) sand boiling or sub-
soil failure due to adverse soil conditions; (3) failure of
levee slope due to seepage and wetting; (4) wind wave effects
(for example, erosion). The resistance or the protection
in one cross-section should be determined for each of the
four effects and should be expressed in terms of the flood
parameter that triggers the failure effect. Generally, there
is no single flood parameter governing all four effects: the
maximum flood level, the duration of the flood, the intensity
and duration of levee soaking, characterized by the value of
the so-called flood exposure [Bogárdi 1972], may trigger the
adverse phenomena.

Resistance values can be determined by direct measurements (e.g., levee crest height or soil properties), computations (e.g., seepage and slope stability analyses), or on
the basis of observations during flood occurrences (information on the location and time of adverse phenomena and on
the corresponding flood load). Further engineering and soil-

mechanical aspects of the safety analysis can be found elsewhere [Bogárdi et al. 1975].

PROBABILITY OF FAILURE IN A GIVEN CROSS-SECTION

The method takes into consideration (1) the stochastic character of flood load, (2) the various degrees of protection offered along the levee reach, and (3) the different modes of failure. Thus, it may be said that the levee reach is investigated as a stochastic system. There is a failure in the cross section if either

$h > H(1)$	:	overtopping
$h > H(2)$	:	subsoil failure
$[h > H(3)] \cap [w > W]$	:	slope stability failure
$h + x > X$	:	wind wave attack, erosion

Where the random loads are

h = peak flood level;

w = flood exposure, that is, the area of the stage hydrograph (m x day) above bankful capacity;

x = wave height and run-up [Bogárdi 1972];

and the random resistances are

$H(1)$: the highest flood level allowable with respect to overtopping;

$H(2)$: the highest flood level allowable with respect to boiling;

$H(3)$, $W(3)$: respectively, the smallest necessary flood level and the highest allowable flood exposure with respect to slope sliding. This threshold value, $H(3)$, is needed since a flood exposure, $W(3)$, might pertain to a low flood level $h < H(3)$, say 10 cm above bankful level for a few weeks, which is not likely to cause sliding.

X: the highest dynamic water level (peak static level + wave + run-up) allowable with respect to erosion failure.

Thus, a failure event in a cross-section is defined by

$$T = [(h + x) > X] \cup [h > H(1)] \cup [h > H(2)] \cup \{[h > H(3)]$$

$$\cap [w > W]\} \qquad (1)$$

In order to compute the probability of T, that is, the probability of failure (PF), the right side of Equation (1) should be divided into four disjoint events:

$$T = A \cup B \cup C \cup D$$

where

$A = [h \leq H(3)] \cap [(h + x) > X]$

$B = [h > H]$ where $H = \min [H(1), H(2)]$

$C = [H(3) < h \leq H] \cap [(h + x) > X]$

$D = [H(3) < h \leq H] \cap [(h + x) \leq X] \cap [w > W]$

Since events A, B, C, and D are mutually exclusive, the PF is:

$$PF = P(T) = P(A) + P(B) + P(C) + P(D)$$

If $H \geq H(3)$, the above relations may be transformed into the following expression for PF

$$PF = 1 - F(H) + \int_{H(3)}^{H} \int_{W.}^{\infty} f(h,w)\,dw\,dh + \int_{-\infty}^{H} [1-G(X-h)]g(h)\,dh \quad (2)$$

where

$$g(h) = \begin{cases} f(h) & \text{if } h \leq H(3) \\ W \\ \int_{-\infty}^{W} f(h,w)\,dw & \text{otherwise} \end{cases}$$

F is the DF of h, f the joint probability density (pdf) of h and w, and G is the DF of x.

If $H < H(3)$, events C and D are null, so that the last term of Equation (2), which accounts for the effect of waves, is zero. In the case when the distance between the levees is small, say less than 1 km, considerable waves cannot be generated for lack of enough fetch; then, the first three terms of Equation (2) are sufficient to calculate PF. Such will be the case for the practical example presented in this paper. On the other hand, the wave erosion can be a critical factor in large flat-land rivers or reservoirs.

PROBABILITY OF FAILURE OF A LEVEE REACH

For each failure mode, the levee reach is divided into sub-reaches, within which the mean value and variance of resistance for each failure mode is constant. The failure event for the whole reach is the union of the failure events T(i) of the subreaches, i = 1, ..., n. It is assumed that every subreach is characterized by one cross section.

$$T = T(1) \cup T(2) \cup T(i) \dots \cup T(n)$$

Let:
$$H = \min_{1 \leq i \leq n} [H(1,i), H(2,i)]$$

$$H(3) = \min_{1 \leq i \leq n} H(3,i)$$

$$t(h) = \min_{H(3,i)<h<H} W(i)$$

where $H(1,i)$, $H(2,i)$, $H(3,i)$, and $W(i)$ are the resistances of subreach i. The system PF can be calculated as:

$$PF = 1 - F(H) + \int_{H(3)}^{H} \int_{t(h)}^{\infty} f(h,w)\,dw\,dh \quad (3)$$

Note that PF is considered as a random variable itself because of the uncertainties in the resistances, $H(1)$, $H(2)$, $H(3)$, and W.

It is assumed that the resistances follow normal distributions with means equal to the deterministic values H(1), H(2), H(3), and W and standard deviations estimated as described in Bogárdi et al. [1975].

Often there is a spatial dependence between subsequent resistances. This spatial dependence may be characterized by a significant first order correlation coefficient. Naturally, in such cases, Equation (3) would not hold and the system resistance for each failure mode should be represented with an n-dimensional normal distribution. Principles and practical application of such an analysis can be found in another context in Szidarovszky et al. [1974].

Equation (3) can be solved in four different cases depending on the various uncertainties considered.

(1) No uncertainty in the resistances is assumed. Estimated mean values of resistances are substituted into Equation (3), which yields a single PF.

(2) Uncertainty in the resistances is assumed. Based on estimated means, variances, and assumed normal distributions of the resistances, a great number of possible system PF's are calculated using Equation (3). An expected value and variance of system PF can be computed; also a discrete or continuous distribution can be fitted to the simulated values of PF.

(3) Uncertainties in the estimated stochastic properties of the load are considered; namely, parameters of the joint pdf f(h,w) are estimated from a finite sample size. From a Bayesian viewpoint, these parameters may be regarded as random variables [Benjamin and Cornell 1970]: on this basis, equally likely samples and parameters can be generated. Again, with the help of Equation (3), possible values of PF can be calculated using the generated parameters. Statistical properties of the random values of PF are determined as in the preceding case.

(4) Uncertainties in the resistances and in the load parameters are considered: then simultaneous independent sets of resistances and load parameters are generated and used to perform the computations of cases (2) and (3).

A practical example is presented in the next section to illustrate the difference between the four cases.

PRACTICAL EXAMPLE

The PF of a levee reach, 14 km in length, of the Sebes-Körös

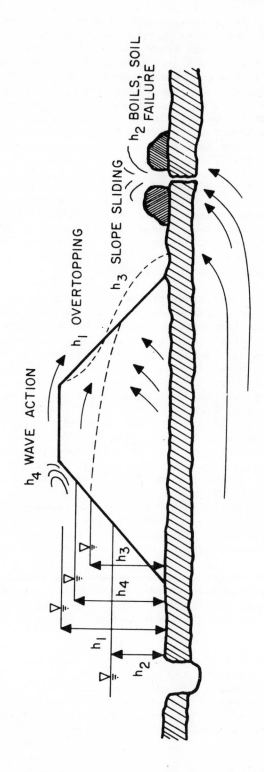

Figure 1: Modes of levee failure

River in Hungary is sought. A flood event occurs each time
the stage climbs above 500 cm. For each event, flood load is
given in terms of peak stage and flood exposure data taken in
the period 1901-1970 at the Körösladány gaging station, which
is located in the reach under study. During this period, 81
events have occurred. The hypothesis that h is lognormally
distributed cannot be rejected on the basis of a Kolmogorov-
Smirnov test at the 0.05 level. A similar result is found
for w. The mean M and standard deviation D of log h and log w,
respectively, are as follows:

$M(h)$ = 0.5132 $\qquad\qquad$ $M(w)$ = 0.7197

$D(h)$ = 1.1683 $\qquad\qquad$ $D(w)$ = 1.8417

The correlation coefficient between h and w is r = 0.97, which
is a fairly high value. As a result of this high correlation,
the difference between the PF of the system and that of the
weakest section is expected to be small, since failure caused
by h also causes failure by w, and vice-versa. Note that
this strong linear correlation between h and w cannot be
taken for granted in other examples.

Means and variances of resistance values of subsequent
subreaches are presented in Table 1. On the basis of the
Anderson test [Chow 1965], the hypothesis of significant
correlation between subsequent resistances has been rejected
at the 5% level. Results of system PF for the four cases
considered are as follows:

(1) A system PF of 0.0643 is found without considering
uncertainties in the resistances.

(2) A mean, $M(PF)$ = 0.0865, and a standard deviation,
$D(PF)$ = 0.0161, of system PF is obtained when considering
uncertainties in resistance. The coefficient of variation
was hypothesized to be 0.02 in $H(1)$ and 0.10 in $H(2)$, $H(3)$,
and W for all subreaches. The mean is significantly higher
than in case 1, but the coefficient of variation is of moderate value (0.25).

(3) A mean, $M(PF)$ = 0.0676, and a standard deviation,
$D(PF)$ = 0.0276, of system PF are obtained under uncertainty
of load parameters. The mean is not much higher than in case
1, but the coefficient of variation of 0.40 is higher than in
case 2.

(4) The effect of both uncertainties (resistance and load
parameter) results in larger values of the mean $M(PF)$ =
0.0887, and of the standard deviation, $D(PF)$ = 0.0395. This
corresponds to a coefficient of variation of 0.45, a somewhat
higher value than in case 3.

CONCLUSIONS

Historically, the safety of flood levees has been calculated
under the assumption that levee resistance or protection was
constant in space and in time. However, experience gained
during floods has shown, often tragically, that unpredictable

Table 1:   Average Resistance Values H(1), H(2), H(3), and W(3) of Subreaches

No.	Subreach Limits (km)	H(1) cm	H(2) cm	H(3) cm	W(3) m x day	PF Without Soil Uncertainties
1	0 - 0.5	816				.0485
2	1.0	782	782			.0571
3	1.5	834	774			.0446
4	2.0	789				.0571
5	2.5	826				.0465
6	3.0	784				.0560
7	3.5	807				.0505
8	4.0	754		600	47	.0622
9	4.5	800				.0516
10	5.0	778				.0571
11	5.5	839				.0505
12	6.0	781				.0571
13	6.5	846				.0428
14	7.0	818				.0485
15	7.5	780				.0571
16	8.0	769				.0606
17	8.5	830	800	530	44	.0603
18	9.0	766				.0606
19	9.5	803				.0516
20	10.0	765				.0618
21	10.5	855	785	550	40	.0611
22	11.0	769				.0606
23	11.5	762				.0618
24	12.0	847				.0428
25	12.5	850				.0428
26	13.0	832				.0455
27	13.5	835				.0446
28	14.0	771				.0594
		Coefficient of variation = 2%	Coefficient of variation = 10%	Coefficient of variation = 10%	Coefficient of variation = 10%	

failure phenomena can occur at different times along the levee.
This means that protection should not be taken as a certainty.
There is much data in that respect both in Hungary [Vízügyi
Közlemények 1966 and 1971] and elsewhere [White 1973]. In
the authors' opinion, the flood levee is a structure where the
random variation of both load and resistance should be considered in the safety analysis. In this spirit, a practical
design method has been developed in this paper. The following conclusions have been reached:

(1) Reliability of levee systems can be estimated by
considering uncertainties in the load and resistances, as well
as parameter uncertainty due to small sample size of loads
(e.g., floods).

(2) The mathematical model permits consideration of four
typical failure modes.

(3) Spatial dependence between resistance values should
be checked. In fact, the model is applicable to estimate
system reliability in the case of dependent resistance values;
however, the practical example was such that spatial
correlation between resistances could be disregarded.

(4) A realistic overall variance in resistance values
tends to increase the system PF.

(5) The main effect of uncertainty caused by small
sample size of floods is to increase considerably the variance
of PF. The mean PF also increases, but to a lesser extent.

(6) Such models point out the data (hydrological,
engineering, etc.) which have major influence on the performance of the system. Consequently, optimal data collection
systems may be designed.

(7) Similar mathematical analysis techniques can be
used in practice in order to gain more realistic information
on the performance of existing or planned environmental
protection systems.

ACKNOWLEDGMENTS

The research was effected in the framework of U.S.-Hungarian
cooperative research partially supported by National Science
Foundation Grant No. GF-38183 and the Hungarian National
Water Authority. The authors are indebted to Donald R. Davis
of the University of Arizona, Tucson, Arizona, for his
valuable comments.

REFERENCES

Benjamin, J. R. and C. A. Cornell (1970) Probability,
Statistics, and Decision for Civil Engineers. McGraw-Hill.

Bogárdi, I. (1972) Flood Control. Series of Subject Notes,
UNESCO Postgraduate Training Course in Water Management,
Budapest, Hungary.

Bogárdi, I., L. Duckstein, and F. Szidarovszky (1975) On the
Reliability of Flood Levee Systems. Paper prepared for 2nd
International Conf. on Statistics and Probability, Aachen,
W. Germany.

Szidarovszky, F., I. Bogárdi, L. Duckstein, and D. Davis (1974)
Economic Uncertainties in Hydrologic Design. Paper presented
at Fall Annual Meet. of American Geophysical Union, San
Francisco, California.

Chow, V. T. (ed.) (1965) Handbook of Applied Hydrology.
McGraw Hill, New York.

Haan, C. T. (1972) Adequacy of Hydrologic Records for
Parameter Estimation. Journal of the Hydraulics Division,
American Society of Civil Engineers, Vol. 98, No. HY8.

Szidarovszky, F., L. Duckstein, and I. Bogárdi (1974)
Reliability of a Levee Along a Confluence Reach. Paper
presented at 55th Annual Meet. of American Geophysical
Union, Washington, D. C.

Szepesi, K. (1969) The Change of Flood Levee Earth Materials
in Function of Time. (In Hungarian) Report of the Research
Institute for Water Resources.

United Nations (1975) Guidelines for Flood Loss Management
in Developing Countries. Dept. of Economic and Social
Affairs, New York.

Vizügyi Közlemények (Hydraulic Engineering) (1966) Danube
Flood 1965. Special number in Hungarian with English
summaries, Budapest, Hungary.

Vizügyi Közlemények (Hydraulic Engineering) (1971) Tisza
Valley Flood 1970. Special number in Hungarian with English
summaries, Budapest, Hungary.

White, G. (1969) Flood Damage Prevention Policies. U.N.
Interregional Seminar on Flood Damage Prevention Measures
and Management, Tbilisi, U.S.S.R.

White, G. (1973) Prospering with Uncertainty. In Floods
and Droughts, E. F. Schulz, V. A. Koelzer, and K. Mahmood.
Water Resources Publications, Inc., Fort Collins, Colorado.

NOTATIONS

A,B,C,D: failure events;
     DF: cumulative distribution function;
   F(h):   cumulative distribution function of h;
 f(h,w):   joint probability density function of h and W;
   G(x):   distribution function of x
      g: function in the correction term for wave effect;
 H(1,i):   resistance of levee subreach i to overtopping, cm;
 H(2,i):   resistance of levee subreach i to boiling, cm;
 H(3,i):   smallest flood level of levee subreach i for slope
            sliding;
      h: peak flood level, cm;
      n: number of subreaches;
     PF: probability of failure;
    pdf: probability density function;
      r: correlation coefficient;
   T(i):   failure event at time i;
   t(h):   a step function;
 W(1,i):   resistance of levee subreach i to slope sliding,
            m x day;
      w: flood exposure, m x day;
      X: resistance of a levee subreach to wave effect, cm;
      x: wave effect, that is, wave height plus run-up, cm;
      ∪ :   union of events;
      ∩ :   intersection of events.

Note: an italic symbol indicates a random variable. Unless
        otherwise specified, the corresponding regular type
        indicates arealization of that random variable.

FINITE ELEMENT MODELS FOR CIRCULATION STUDIES

by

C.A. Brebbia and P. Partridge.

INTRODUCTION

Mathematical simulation of the physical, chemical and biological aspects of marine and estuarial systems is an increasingly expanding field of research. This paper is concerned with the modelling of tidal effects, storm surges and current patterns in different natural systems.

The first stage of modelling consists of isolating the system and identifying its interactions with the natural environment. [1] In this way the inputs and outputs of the system are defined. Once this is done the governing equations to be used need to be formulated. These equations depend on the type of variables we are investigating which are called state variables. The state variables are related by a series of evolution equations (such as the momentum equations) and in general, some constraint equations (such as continuity). In addition the corresponding initial and boundary conditions need to be known.

The solution of these equations can be attempted by a numerical method. The method used is of fundamental importance. In a finite element or finite difference approach the grid size will determine the type of phenomenon which can be investigated. In addition, grid size relates to stability criterion and accuracy in evolutionary problems.

The refinement of a model though desirable in principle can give place to a larger number of parameters being needed, which represents more experimental data. The data can be difficult to obtain and produces a new type of error affecting the confidence one can have in the results. The engineer usually has to compromise between having a sophisticated model or a practical one, giving reliable results for the state variables under consideration. Large models also require substantial amount of computer time and storage.

Sometimes the system analyst does not spend enough time evaluating how well the model represents the physical conditions in the prototype, that is testing and adjusting the model. This is however, an important part of the analysis and can have far reaching consequences possibly calling for changes of state variables or modifications of the parameters.

In this paper the authors will describe some finite element models and modelling processes which have been applied to several circulation problems. Special consideration has been given to the adequacy of the models, and consequently all of them have been applied to regions for which some data was available. Nevertheless the models can be equally well applied to different regions and for other predictions than the ones described in the paper. They are based on the shallow water equations which are vertically averaged versions of Navier Stokes equations, and can take into consideration,

a) Tides.
b) Bottom friction.
c) Advective forces.
d) Coriolis.
e) Wind tangential forces.
f) Atmospheric pressure gradients effects.

Some of these effects involve the use of parameters which have not yet been properly defined (such as bottom friction and wind tangential stress). Their discussion is beyond the scope of this paper.

Two applications of the shallow water equations are shown, the first for the North Sea, the second for the Solent. The two problems are basically different but the same type of equations can be applied. Results are compared against prototype values and general guidelines on the type of mesh, elements and length of time step are given.

The Shallow Water Equations.

The evolutionary equations used in Marine and certain types of estuarial modelling are called the shallow water equations. They are a vertically averaged version of Navier Stokes momentum equations and have to satisfy the vertically averaged continuity equation which acts as a constraint condition. In addition initial and boundary conditions have to be fulfilled.

Starting with the Navier Stokes equations for incompressible flow one needs to make the following assumptions to obtain the shallow water equations (for a more rigorous deduction of shallow water equations see reference 2).

a)   One assumes that all components of vertical acceleration can be neglected in the third momentum equation. This gives

$$-\frac{\partial p}{\partial x_3} = -\rho g .$$

or, (1)

$$p = \rho g(\eta - x_3) + p_a .$$

where p_a is the atmospheric pressure and η the elevation of the free surface (figure 1). The problem is now governed by only two momentum equations.

b) Coriolis forces are given by $-\Omega v_2$ and Ωv_1 in the two remaining momentum equations which can now be written

$$\frac{\partial v_1}{\partial t} \quad \frac{\partial}{\partial x_1}(v_1{}^2) + \frac{\partial}{\partial x_2} (v_1 v_2) + \frac{\partial}{\partial x_3} (v_1 v_3) = \Omega v_2 + b_1$$

$$- \frac{\partial}{\partial x_1} (\frac{P_a}{\rho}) - g \frac{\partial \eta}{\partial x_1} + \nu \, \nabla^2 \, v_1$$

(2)

$$\frac{\partial v_2}{\partial t} + \frac{\partial}{\partial x_1} (v_1 v_2) + \frac{\partial}{\partial x_2} (v_2{}^2) + \frac{\partial}{\partial x_3} (v_2 v_3) = - \Omega v_1 + b_2$$

$$- \frac{\partial}{\partial x_2} (\frac{P_a}{\rho}) - g \frac{\partial \eta}{\partial x_2} + \nu \nabla^2 v_2$$

where $\nabla^2 = \frac{\partial^2}{\partial x_1{}^2} + \frac{\partial^2}{\partial x_2{}^2} + \frac{\partial^2}{\partial x_3{}^2}$, $\Omega = 2\omega \sin \phi$, where ϕ is

the latitude and ω the angular rotation of the earth. ν is dynamic viscosity for turbulent flow.

c) The classical method of integrating the momentum equations is to assume that the velocities are given by

$$v_i = V_i + v_i'$$ (3)

where V_i are the averaged velocities and v_i' the deviations from the mean in the x_3 direction. We define the depth average velocity as

$$V_i = \frac{1}{H} \int_{-h}^{\eta} v_i \, dx_3$$ (4)

where H is the total depth $H = h + \eta$. The average of the fluctuations is zero, i.e.

$$\int_{-h}^{\eta} v_i{}' \, dx_3 = 0 \qquad (5)$$

d)   In order to vertically integrate the momentum equations (2) one needs to use Leibnitz rule, i.e.

$$\frac{\partial}{\partial x_i} \int_{-h}^{\eta} v_j \, dx_3 = \int_{-h}^{\eta} \frac{\partial v_j}{\partial x_i} \, dx_3 + v_j \frac{\partial \eta}{\partial x_i}\bigg|_{x_3 = \eta} - v_j \frac{\partial h}{\partial x_i}\bigg|_{x_3 = -h}$$

$$(6)$$

Under these assumptions, the integration of the continuity equation over depth gives,

$$\frac{\partial H}{\partial t} + \frac{\partial}{\partial x_1} (HV_1) + \frac{\partial}{\partial x_2} (HV_2) = 0 \qquad (7)$$

The integration of the momentum equation produces nonlinear terms of the type,

$$\frac{1}{H} \int_{-h}^{\eta} v_i v_j \, dx_3 = V_i V_j + \frac{1}{H} \int_{-h}^{\eta} v_i{}' v_j{}' \, dx_3 \qquad (8)$$

The second of these nonlinear contributions are usually expressed in terms of the mean variables by introducing a diffusivity parameter ν'

$$\frac{1}{H} \int_{-h}^{\eta} v_i{}' v_j{}' \, dx_3 = \nu' \, \frac{V_i}{x_j} \qquad (9)$$

Friction terms in the vertically integrated version of (2) can now be written for instance as,

$$\frac{1}{H} \int_{-h}^{\eta} \left(\frac{\partial^2 v_1}{\partial x_1^2} + \frac{\partial^2 v_1}{\partial x_2^2} \right) dx_3 - \frac{1}{H} \left(\frac{\partial}{\partial x_1} \int_{-h}^{\eta} v_1{}' v_2{}' \, dx_3 + \right.$$

$$(10)$$

$$\left. \frac{\partial}{\partial x_2} \int_{-h}^{\eta} v_1{}' v_2{}' \, dx_3 \right) = \nu_T \left(\frac{\partial^2 V_1}{x_1^2} + \frac{\partial^2 V_1}{x_2^2} \right)$$

The bottom and surface stresses are given by,

$$\int_{-h}^{\eta} \nu \frac{\partial^2 v_1}{\partial x_3^{\,2}} \, dx_3 = \frac{1}{\rho} \left(\tau_s \Big|_1 - \tau_b \Big|_1 \right) =$$

$$= -\left(\frac{g}{c^2}\right) \frac{V_1}{H} \, (V_1^{\,2} + V_2^{\,2})^{\frac{1}{2}} + \frac{\gamma}{\rho} \frac{W_1}{H^2} \sqrt{W_1^{\,2} + W_2^{\,2}}$$

where c^2 is the Chezy coefficient and W_i the wind speed components. γ is a parameter relating to atmospheric density ρ_a. (usually given as a constant multiplied by ρ_a).

The final momentum equations are,

$$\frac{\partial V_1}{\partial t} + V_1 \frac{\partial V_1}{\partial x_1} + V_2 \frac{\partial V_1}{\partial x_2} = \Omega \, V_2 - g \frac{\partial \eta}{\partial x} - \frac{\partial}{\partial x_1} \left(\frac{P_a}{\rho}\right)$$

$$- \left(\frac{g}{c^2}\right) \frac{V_1}{H} \sqrt{V_1^{\,2} + V_2^{\,2}} + \frac{\gamma}{\rho} \frac{W_1}{H} \sqrt{W_1^{\,2} + W_2^{\,2}}$$

$$+ \nu_T \left(\frac{\partial^2 v_1}{\partial x_1^{\,2}} + \frac{\partial^2 v_1}{\partial x_2^{\,2}} \right) . \tag{12}$$

$$\frac{\partial V_2}{\partial t} + V_1 \frac{\partial V_2}{\partial x_1} + V_2 \frac{\partial V_2}{\partial x_2} = - \Omega V_1 - g \frac{\partial \eta}{\partial x_2} - \frac{\partial}{\partial x_2} \left(\frac{P_a}{\rho}\right)$$

$$- \left(\frac{g}{c^2}\right) \frac{V_2}{H} \sqrt{V_1^{\,2} + V_2^{\,2}} + \frac{\gamma}{\rho} \frac{W_2}{H} \sqrt{W_1^{\,2} + W_2^{\,2}}$$

$$+ \nu_T \left(\frac{\partial^2 v_2}{\partial x_1^{\,2}} + \frac{\partial^2 v_2}{\partial x_2^{\,2}} \right)$$

In what follows the terms in ν_T will be neglected. This assumption seems reasonable due to the difficulty of determining the ν_T parameter and it allows for an easier application of the boundary conditions.

Boundary and Initial Conditions

The solution of any set of differential equations can only
be attempted by knowing the corresponding boundary conditions.
If the problem is time dependent, the initial conditions are
needed as well, in this case, those corresponding to the
movement of large bodies of shallow water.

The factors affecting the movement are many - the shape and
position of the seabed, the shape and variations in shape of
the coastline, friction between the seabed and the water,
hence the material of the seabed, the meteorological conditions including wind, etc. Though the circulation of the
earth and the astronomical forces of the sun and the moon
act on the water as body forces, the main tidal cause of
water movement in areas such as the Solent and the North Sea
is the driving force caused by tidal motion of water on the
boundary of the area under consideration.

The shape of the land surface containing the body of water
is usually very complex, in some cases not even static though
the effects of erosion occur over too long a period of time
to be important.

Bottom friction will be introduced in the model via Chezy type
coefficients. The inadequacy of using constant Chezy coefficient for all or part of the model is evident. It must be
remembered that bottom friction, wind and other effects are
of great importance in the movement of shallow water. The
different materials making up the seabed have different
frictional resistances as the water depth and velocities
change.

The main meteorological conditions are wind forces and atmospheric pressure variations, the latter for large areas such as
the North Sea. They are the main cause of inaccuracies in
tidal prediction.

The boundary conditions of the model are of two types;
a) fixed or land boundaries such as those given by the coast
lines, where the normal velocities are zero and the tangent
velocity can be set free, b) open boundaries where the
elevation of the sea level (or the normal component of
velocity) is prescribed.

The determination of the initial conditions requires certain
knowledge of the free surface position at $t = 0$. Usually
this knowledge is not possible and the models have to be
started with zero elevation and velocity conditions. This is
called 'cold start'.

FINITE ELEMENT MODEL

In order to build finite element models the two momentum equations (12) and continuity (7), including influx type boundary conditions, can be written in the following weighted residual way,

$$\iint \{ \frac{\partial V_1}{\partial t} + V_1 \frac{\partial V_1}{\partial x_1} + V_2 \frac{\partial V_1}{\partial x_2} - B_1 \} \, \delta V_1 \, dA = 0$$

$$\iint \{ \frac{\partial V_2}{\partial t} + V_1 \frac{\partial V_2}{\partial x_1} + V_2 \frac{\partial V_2}{\partial x_2} - B_2 \} \, \delta V_2 \, dA = 0$$

(13)

$$\iint \{ \frac{\partial H}{\partial t} + \frac{\partial}{\partial x_1} (HV_1) + \frac{\partial}{\partial x_2} (HV_2) \} \, \delta H dA = \int (HV_n - H\bar{V}_n) \delta H dS$$

(14)

$H\bar{V}_n$ is the known flux coming into the system (e.g. due to rivers).

$$B_1 = \Omega V_2 - g \frac{\partial n}{\partial x_1} - \frac{\partial}{\partial x_1} (\frac{P_a}{\rho}) - \frac{1}{\rho} \tau_1 \Big|_b + \frac{1}{\rho} \tau_2 \Big|_s$$

(15)

$$B_2 = - \Omega V_1 - g \frac{\partial n}{\partial x_2} - \frac{\partial}{\partial x_2} (\frac{P_a}{\rho}) - \frac{1}{\rho} \tau_2 \Big|_b + \frac{1}{\rho} \tau_2 \Big|_s$$

The continuity equation is usually integrated by parts to render a simpler expression. This gives,

$$\iint \{ HV_1 \frac{\partial \delta H}{\partial x_1} + HV_2 \frac{\partial \delta H}{\partial x_2} - \frac{\partial H}{\partial t} \delta H \} \, dA = \int H\bar{V}_n \, \delta H dS$$

(16)

The above weighted residual statements (equations (13) and (16)) are the starting point for the finite element models. Assume that over an element the same interpolation function applies for the $V_1 V_2$ and H unknowns, i.e.

$$V_1 = \underset{\sim}{\phi} \, \underset{\sim}{V}_1^n , \qquad V_2 = \underset{\sim}{\phi} \, \underset{\sim}{V}_2^n , \qquad H = \underset{\sim}{\phi} \, \underset{\sim}{H}^n$$

(17)

ϕ are interpolation functions and $\underset{\sim}{V}_i^n$, $\underset{\sim}{H}^n$ are nodal values of V_i, H.

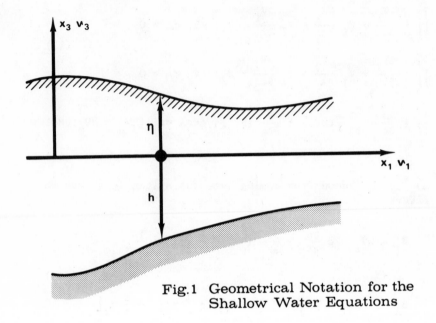

Fig.1   Geometrical Notation for the
Shallow Water Equations

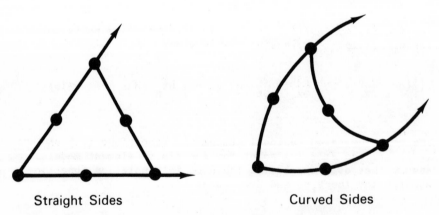

Straight Sides   Curved Sides

Fig.2 Six Node Elements

In what follows six nodes triangular finite elements with
curved boundaries were used in order to follow the boundaries
more carefully (figure 2). These elements are called isoparametric and can be formulated by a simple coordinate
transformation, the details of which can be seen in references
[2] and [3] . Curved elements have the important feature
that they tend to eliminate the spurious forces generated on
the boundaries by straight side elements joining at an angle.

Substituting equations (17) into (13) and (16) one obtains,

$$\underset{\sim}{M} \, \dot{\underset{\sim}{V}}_1^n + \underset{\sim}{K} \, \underset{\sim}{V}_1^n - \Omega \underset{\sim}{M} \, \underset{\sim}{V}_2^n + \underset{\sim}{G}_1 \, \underset{\sim}{H}^n + \underset{\sim}{F}_1 = \underset{\sim}{0}$$

$$\underset{\sim}{M} \, \dot{\underset{\sim}{V}}_2^n + \Omega \underset{\sim}{M} \, \underset{\sim}{V}_1^n + \underset{\sim}{K} \, \underset{\sim}{V}_2^n + \underset{\sim}{G}_2 \, \underset{\sim}{H}^n + \underset{\sim}{F}_2 = \underset{\sim}{0} \qquad (18)$$

plus,

$$\underset{\sim}{M} \, \dot{\underset{\sim}{H}}^n - \underset{\sim}{C}_1 \, \underset{\sim}{V}_1^n - \underset{\sim}{C}_2 \, \underset{\sim}{V}_2^n + \underset{\sim}{F}_H = \underset{\sim}{0}$$

where

$$\underset{\sim}{K} = \int \underset{\sim}{\phi}^T \, \underset{\sim}{\phi}_{,1} \, V_1 \, dA + \int \underset{\sim}{\phi}^T \, \underset{\sim}{\phi}_{,2} \, V_2 \, dA + \left(\frac{g}{c^2}\right) \int \underset{\sim}{\phi}^T \frac{\sqrt{V_1^2 + V_2^2}}{H} \, \underset{\sim}{\phi} \, dA$$

$$\underset{\sim}{G}_i = g \int \underset{\sim}{\phi}^T \, \underset{\sim}{\phi}_{,1} \, dA$$

$$\underset{\sim}{F}_i = \int \underset{\sim}{\phi}^T \left(\frac{P_a}{\rho}\right)_{,i} dA + \left(\frac{\gamma}{\rho}\right) \int \underset{\sim}{\phi}^T \frac{W_i}{H} \sqrt{W_1^2 + W_2^2} \, dA \ .$$

$$\underset{\sim}{C}_i = \int \underset{\sim}{\phi}_{,1}^T \, H \, \underset{\sim}{\phi} \, dA \ , \qquad \underset{\sim}{F}_H = \int H \, \bar{V}_n \, \underset{\sim}{\phi}^T \, dA \ .$$

and

$$( )_{,i} = \frac{\partial}{\partial x_i} \ , \qquad (\dot{\ }) = \frac{\partial}{\partial t} \ .$$

Equations (18) can be written as,

$$\begin{bmatrix} \underset{\sim}{M} & . & . \\ . & \underset{\sim}{M} & . \\ . & . & \underset{\sim}{M} \end{bmatrix} \begin{Bmatrix} \dot{\underset{\sim}{V}}_1^n \\ \dot{\underset{\sim}{V}}_2^n \\ \dot{\underset{\sim}{H}}^n \end{Bmatrix} + \begin{bmatrix} \underset{\sim}{K} & -\Omega\underset{\sim}{M} & \underset{\sim}{G}_1 \\ \Omega\underset{\sim}{M} & \underset{\sim}{K} & \underset{\sim}{G}_2 \\ -\underset{\sim}{C}_1 & -\underset{\sim}{C}_2 & 0 \end{bmatrix} \begin{Bmatrix} \underset{\sim}{V}_1^n \\ \underset{\sim}{V}_2^n \\ \underset{\sim}{H}^n \end{Bmatrix} + \begin{Bmatrix} \underset{\sim}{F}_1 \\ \underset{\sim}{F}_2 \\ \underset{\sim}{F}_H \end{Bmatrix} = \begin{Bmatrix} 0 \\ 0 \\ 0 \end{Bmatrix}$$

They can be represented as,

$$\underset{\sim}{M}\, \dot{\underset{\sim}{Q}} + \underset{\sim}{K}\, \underset{\sim}{Q} = \underset{\sim}{F} \tag{20}$$

Equation (20) is valid for each unconnected element. The next stage is to assemble all the element equations into a global system of equations for the continuum. To eliminate proliferation of notation the global system will be defined with the same notation as equation (20).

The time integration procedure used for the final system equations is the trapezoidal rule. Starting with

$$\underset{\sim}{M}\, \dot{\underset{\sim}{Q}} + \underset{\sim}{K}\, \underset{\sim}{Q} = \underset{\sim}{F} \tag{21}$$

one assumes

$$\dot{\underset{\sim}{Q}} = \frac{\underset{\sim}{Q}_t - \underset{\sim}{Q}_o}{\Delta t} \qquad \underset{\sim}{Q} = \frac{\underset{\sim}{Q}_t + \underset{\sim}{Q}_o}{2}$$

$$\underset{\sim}{F} = \frac{\underset{\sim}{F}_o + \underset{\sim}{F}_t}{2}$$

Hence (21) becomes,

$$\left(\frac{2}{\Delta t}\, \underset{\sim}{M} + \underset{\sim}{K}\right) \underset{\sim}{Q}_t = (\underset{\sim}{F}_o + \underset{\sim}{F}_t) + \left(\frac{2}{\Delta t}\, \underset{\sim}{M} - \underset{\sim}{K}\right) \underset{\sim}{Q}_o \tag{22}$$

or

$$\underset{\sim}{K}^* \, \underset{\sim}{Q}_t = \underset{\sim}{F}^*$$

The recurrence relationship is then,

$$\underset{\sim}{Q}_t = (\underset{\sim}{K}^*)^{-1} \, \underset{\sim}{F}^* \tag{23}$$

The $\underset{\sim}{K}^*$ matrix to be inverted in general is a large nonsymmetric banded matrix of side approximately three times the number of nodes by six times the element band width. (i.e. the maximum difference between nodal points numbers plus one).

The computer program has been optimized to solve the problem with a minimum of computer time. Boundary conditions have been taken into account and the corresponding rows and columns eliminated from the element matrices before assembling. This reduces significantly the maximum size of the global matrix.

The solution routine involves a large number of row operations on the global matrix. If the matrix is stored row by row as opposed to column by column in the computer it will reduce

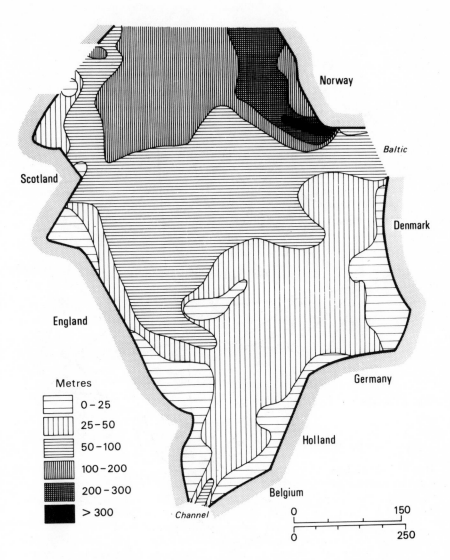

Fig.3a   Depth Contours for the North Sea

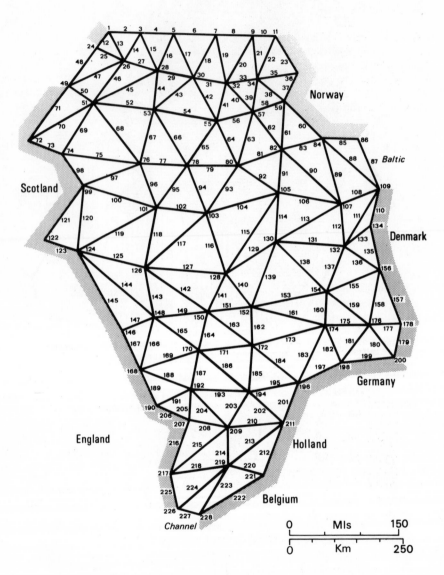

Fig.3b   Finite Element Mesh for the North Sea

the amount of time needed for the computer to handle it. It
is also advantageous to store the matrix in a 1 dimensional form such
that only one and not two addresses need to be evaluated each
time an element of the array is accessed.

The North Sea Model

The above finite element formulation has been applied to a
preliminary model of the North Sea. The mesh is shown in
Figure 3. The area has been discretized into 228 nodes and
97 six node elements - The depths and coordinates were
obtained from Admiralty Charts. Sections were drawn at
different angles across the whole region, in order to
determine the best locations for nodes and the best way of
representing the bottom topography. The mesh was checked
by plotting it on the lineprinter using a special plotting
routine.

At the tidal boundaries sinusoidal forcing functions with
different amplitudes and phase lags were applied, as shown
in Figure 4. This information was obtained from Admiralty
Charts. The wave fronts between Bergen and Lerwick and
between Kirkwall and Lerwick were linearly interpolated.

The general trends in the velocities compare reasonably against
the tidal stream atlases where these are available. In making
such comparison it must be taken into account that the velocities given by the tidal stress atlases are smoothed out,
the observations are made in only the top layer of the water,
the program yields depth averaged velocities given by

$$V_i = \frac{1}{(\eta+h)} \int_{-h}^{\eta} v_i \, dx_3$$

hence the currents worked out by the program are not on the
same smooth lines as those shown in the atlases, the program
being affected by local fluctuations in depth to a greater
degree than the figures in the atlases. The depths are continuously varying and never smooth. The overall trends are
not shown here.

Figure 5 shows the velocities obtained at 3 different mesh
points during the 6th tidal cycle from cold start. During
cycle 1 the Chezy value was 10 $m^{\frac{1}{2}}$/sec, during cycle 2 Chezy
was 15 and during the last four cycles Chezy equalled
20 $m^{\frac{1}{2}}$/sec. The Coriolis coefficient was 0.000119 and $\Delta t = 30$
min. For subsequent runs friction would be reduced to more realistic
values.
During the last four cycles at constant conditions of friction
the results assumed steady state values.

Figure 6 shows the wave heights obtained during the 6th cycle for
the same three points. These have reached steady state values.

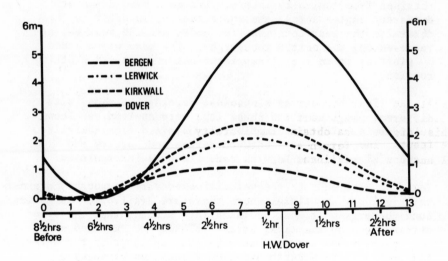

Fig.4 **Tidal Boundary Conditions for the North Sea**

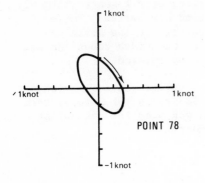

POINT 78

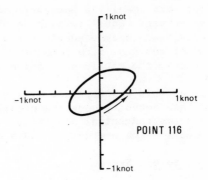

POINT 116

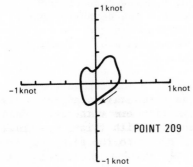

POINT 209

Fig.5 Steady state velocities at
3 points on N. Sea model
during 6th tide cycle

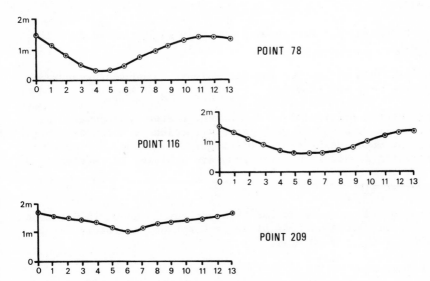

POINT 78

POINT 116

POINT 209

Fig.6 Steady state wave height at 3 points on N. Sea
model during 6th tide cycle

For this model the boundary conditions were taken as both velocities equal to zero on the land boundaries. These conditions seem adequate for a first try on the North sea model and save much computer time by bandwidth reduction and because the matrices do not have to be rotated.

Later this was replaced by a more accurate representation, at a land boundary node the normal velocity is taken to be zero and the tangential one free, which was used for the Solent models which use curved sided elements.

The Solent System

Figure 7 shows the 61 elements with 156 nodes mesh of the Solent using curved boundaries elements. The boundary conditions were $V_n = 0$ across the land boundaries and the tidal boundaries were specified at Hurst Point and Ryde (figure 10). The depth contours are shown in figure 8.

The Solent is a more complicated region to model than the North Sea due to the relatively large percentage changes in depth. This gives rise to problems with stability and accuracy. Various tests were run with this model. Tidal curves presented in figure 9 correspond to the sixth cycle from cold start, with Chezy's coefficient $c = 22 \ m^{\frac{1}{2}} \ s^{-1}$ through the model. It is necessary to decrease the friction gradually in order to maintain smooth results. The first 2 cycles were run with $c = 15$.

The time step for the results shown in figure 10 is $\Delta t = 15$ minutes.

Coriolis can be ignored for the Solent. Wind and pressure effects were not studied.

The readers interested in the Solent system can compare this model with the one of reference [4], which is a 3 node finite element model using explicit integration scheme. - Coliform pollution problems in the Solent are analysed in reference [5].

Computer Time

The computer time taken for this problem is about 1600 seconds on the ICL 1906A machine at Atlas Computer Laboratory for 2 cycles with $\Delta t = 30$ mins.

Conclusions

From the applications of shallow water models the following conclusion can be drawn,

1) Emphasis should be given to represent adequately the

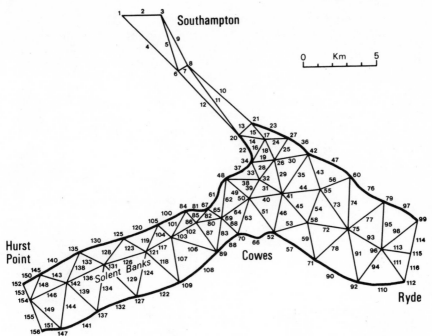

Fig.7   Finite Element Mesh for the Solent

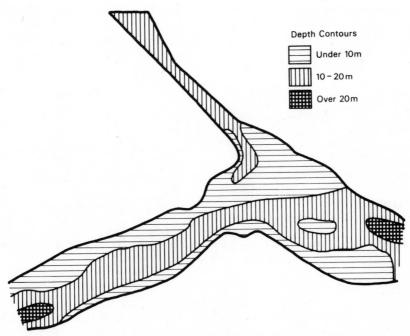

Fig.8   Depth Contours for the Solent

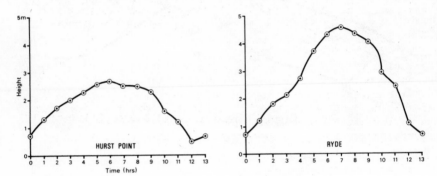

Fig.9 Applied Tidal Boundary Conditions for Solent Model

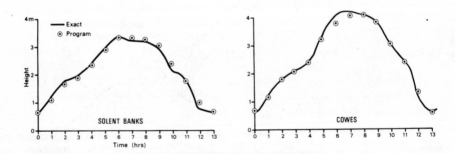

Fig.10 Wave Heights on Solent Model during One Tide Cycle

topography of the region - This is specially important in regions with rapidly changing characteristics, such as the Solent. Second order elements allow for a good approximation of depth.

2) Six nodes triangular elements can also be used to represent curved boundaries. This representation eliminates fictitious boundary forces which are the cause of inaccuracies if using linear three nodes elements.

3) Special care should be taken to check the input data adequately. In this respect it is desirable to have some form of graphical output facility.

4) For evolutionary process of this type, computer time can be very expensive and the program should be optimized before final runnings. In the process of writing the shallow water program described above the running time was cut by 40% by simple refinements in the programming.

5) Implicit schemes such as the trapezoidal rule, though in principle more expensive than simpler rules such as Runge-Kutta or Euler, allow for larger time steps. This can be of interest in problems such as the Solent, where the time step can be increased considerably over a simpler scheme without significantly affecting the accuracy of the results.

REFERENCES

1. Nihoul, J.C.J. (editor), "Modelling of Marine Systems". Elsevier Oceanography Series, Amsterdam, 1975.

2. Connor, J.J. and C.A. Brebbia, "Introduction to Finite Element Techniques for Fluid Flow". Butterworths, London, 1975.

3. Brebbia, C.A. and J.J. Connor, "Fundamentals of Finite Element Techniques for Structural Engineers". Butter-worths, London, 1973.

4. Brebbia, C.A. and R. Adey, "A Finite Element Circulation Model for the Solent". Atlas Computer Laboratory, SRC, Didcot, Oxfordshire, England, 1975.

5. Adey, R. and C.A. Brebbia, "Finite Element Solution for Effluent Dispersion" in "Numerical Methods in Fluid Dynamics (edited by C.A. Brebbia and J.J. Connor), Pentech Press, London, 1974.

ON THE CALCULATION OF OPTIMAL LONG-TERM AIR POLLUTION ABATEMENT STRATEGIES FOR MULTIPLE SOURCE AREAS

S.-Å. Gustafson[1] and K.O. Kortanek[2]

[1]Royal Institute of Technology, Stockholm, Sweden,
[2]Carnegie-Mellon University, Pittsburgh, USA

SUMMARY

Recent research has given us a rough picture of the physical
and chemical transformations taking place in the atmosphere.
The results indicate that the amount of carbondioxide and
particulate matter that can be released into the air, without
risk for unfavourable changes in world climate, is limited
and that the critical values soon may be reached. Further,
the amounts of pollutants that can be allowed to be deposited
on the ground per square unit is dependent on the soil and
other regional characteristics. Finally, sufficient air quality must be safe-guarded. Hence standards must be defined on
three levels: a world standard to protect global climate, a
regional standard to protect soil, vegetation and water and
local air quality standards to protect the population. In
this paper we discuss the problems arising by the selection
of these standards and indicate qualitatively their impact on
the mode of energy generation.

LOCAL, REGIONAL AND GLOBAL ENVIRONMENTAL POLLUTION PROBLEMS

Industrialization has brought prosperity to man since the output of goods and services per man hour has increased dramati-
cally over the levels attained in earlier ages. This has occurred since machine work has replaced human toil. Then the
energy - consumption per man-hour and also per capita has
steadily increased. Predominantly, this energy has been generated by means of the combustion of fossil fuels such as
coal and oil. Hereby waste products are released making the
air unhealthy and spoiling the neighbourhood of the industries. Foul city air is observed since hundreds of years ago
but not until the latest decades did effective measures
against this problem become instituted. Often the stacks of
the factories were built higher in order to disperse the pollutants over larger volumes of air, thus lowering the ambient

concentrations of pollutants. We notice that most air quality standards now in effect, give maximum values of permissible concentrations of various pollutants (see e.g. Yanagisawa, 1973) and hence it should normally be possible to meet these standards by building high stacks, for the contents of pollutants of rural air are generally low. A special problem is illustrated by Ruhr in Germany where the vegetation is damaged in vast areas due to the release of toxic gases from industries.

A remarkable fact is that damages have occurred also in relatively sparsely settled regions with good air quality. Here the decisive factor is, that pollutants are deposited on the ground or absorbed by lakes and rivers, damaging fish-life. Compare Air pollution across .. (1971) and Begränsning av .. (1974). It is clear that this problem cannot be solved by enforcing tough air quality standards which are met by building high stacks. Instead one must create *regional* standards which define the maximum amonts of various pollutants that might be deposited in a region. By a region we mean here a fairly large area, say 200 000 to 1 000 000 km^2, and many European countries may comprise only one such region. Later we shall discuss fixing of regional standards in the general situation when emissions in one region cause fall-outs in another.

It has been observed, that during the last decades the composition of the atmosphere has changed in the whole world. A small but significant increase of the concentration of carbon dioxide has been measured. Likewise, an increase in the amount of particulate matter contained in the air has been detected. There is reason to fear that unfavourable changes in world climate might take place, if the atmosphere is used as a recepient of pollutants in an ever-increasing rate. (See e.g. Freeman et al, 1974). However, much more research is needed before we can safely estimate how much waste products the earth, the water and the air can safely accomodate. It is quite likely that *global standards* can be constructed. Then the problem arises to determine how these totals of acceptable pollution shall be distributed among the nations of the world.

ENERGY PRODUCTION AND POLLUTION GENERATION

We note here that the intensity of pollution depends on how energy is generated and how it is used. Four sources of energy dominate in the industrialized countries: oil, coal, nuclear and hydro-electric power. Of these sources only the last one is renewable. It is also clean. On the other hand, the erection of dams causes dislocations in the environment and is often accompanied by the loss of scenic values. The yearly amount of available hydro-electric power is limited and governed by the rainfall. Hence long droughts have caused

rather serious energy shortages in countries relying to a
large extent on water power. If nuclear plants hold what their
proponents promise, they should be a reliable and rather clean
source of energy. The deposits of uranium are finite but
large and the radioactive emissions from plants are small. No
other pollutants are released. But break-downs in nuclear
plants are frequent and the economy of this technology is at
present not quite favourable . The possibility of unknown
hazards and the risk of large accidents has caused widely
spread concern. Coal is abundant in many countries and due
to the advancing prices for oil it has again become an attractive fuel for many industries which have recently switched
to oil. However, coal mining of the kind considered in the
Middle West of the US, may cause irreparable damages to the
landscape and loss of valuable farm land. Combustion of coal
will be accompanied by the release of several pollutants such
as sulfur dioxides, particulate matter and radioactive substances. The use of coal has caused the classical environmental problems of Ruhr and Great Britain. Oil has been a very
popular fuel but its draw-backs are well-known. The combustion of heavy oil in power plants causes the release of
sulfur dioxides and radioactive matters and cars release
among other things hydrocarbons and carbon monoxide. This
latter fact is the cause of the well-known air quality problems in Los Angeles.

Up to now the available supplies of the various fuels have
determined their prices. But if global standards of the maximum amounts of carbondioxide and particulate matter that may
be released into the atmosphere will be established, then
a ceiling of the total amounts of coal and oil that can be
burnt per annum will be defined. Then an increase in the use
of coal must be accompanied by a decrease in the consumption
of oil in order to meet the carbon dioxide condition. Hence
we get constraints which are mathematically representable as
linear inequalities. The present state of knowledge does not
warrant further detailed analysis of the many problems
spawned by the imposition of global standards. We mention only here that one should expect a larger emphasis on energy-
saving devices and greater efforts to develop clean and
renewable energy sources such as geothermal energy, hydro-
electric power and solar energy.

DETERMINATION OF REGIONAL STANDARDS

In this Section we discuss the selection of regional standards
defining the maximum amounts of sulfur which may be deposited
annually in the form of sulfuroxides within each region. The
argument can of course be applied to other pollutants as well.
We shall discuss the case when each region is a souveraign
state which may determine its pollution standards independently of other countries. Extension to the more general

situation when a country may comprise several regions for which different standards are chosen is straight-forward.

For definiteness let us consider n regions R_i, i = 1,2,...,n. In Region R_i the amount b_i of sulfur is deposited and the desired target quantity is c_i. If $b_i > c_i$ then a reduction of the total emissions in R_i by a fraction z_i, $0 \le z_i \le 1$ is called for. The goal should be reached by taking $z_i = 1 - \dfrac{c_i}{b_i}$ in the cases a) and b) below:

a) all sulfur deposited in R_i originates from sources inside R_i

b) all regions R_1, R_2, ..., R_n reduce their emissions with at least the fraction z_i.

Generally, case a) does not occur. As an example, a significant portion of the sulfur deposited in Sweden comes from foreign sources, Air pollution ... (1971).

Let a_{ij} denote the amount of sulfur originating from Region R_j and deposited in R_i. Then before regulation the relation holds

$$\sum_{j=1}^{n} a_{ij} = b_i, \ i = 1,2,...,n. \tag{1}$$

Assume now that each region R_i determines a reduction fraction z_i. Then the following conditions must be met

$$0 \le z_i \le 1, \ i = 1,2,...,n, \tag{2}$$

$$\sum_{j=1}^{n} (1-z_j) a_{ij} \le c_i, \ i = 1,2,...,n, \tag{3}$$

if all regions are to reach their targets. Conditions (2) and (3) are mathematically consistent, since we can always choose $z_i = 1$, i = 1,2,...,n. We note that Region R_i can reach its goal independently of the actions of other regions, if

$$\sum_{j \ne i} a_{ij} \le c_i$$

by choosing z_i such that

$$(1-z_i) \le (c_i - \sum_{j \ne i} a_{ij})/a_{ii} \tag{4}$$

But if z_i meets Condition (4) for i = 1,2,...,n, then all regions would have surpassed their goals c_i and the authorities would be under pressure to reduce z_i that is relax their emission standards. Let z_i^k, $i = 1,2,...,n$ be the standards prevailing during the year k. It seems natural to revise these standards according to the formula

$$(1 - z_i^{k+1}) = \left\{ c_i - \sum_{j \neq i} a_{ij}(1 - z_j^k) \right\} / a_{ii} \qquad (5)$$

If this is done for $k = 1,2,...,$ then convergence occurs under certain conditions. For example, if the equation

$$\sum_{j=1}^{n} a_{ij}(1 - z_j) = c_i, \quad i = 1,2,...,n \qquad (6)$$

has a solution z_i, $0 \le z_i \le 1$, then Equation (5) is a relaxation formula generating a sequence z^k, $k = 1,2,...$ Convergence results are given by Chazan-Miranker, 1969 also for the case when z_i^k are revised in an irregular fashion. It would be interesting to analyze the more general case when a_{ij} change with time.

From Equation (3) we conclude that it is easier for Region R_i to reach its goal, i.e. z_i can be taken smaller if the numbers z_j increase. Let $f_i(z_i)$ denote the cost for Region R_i to cut back its emissions with the fraction z_i. We shall assume that f_i is convex and increasing over $[0,1]$. (The cost curves computed in Begränsning ... (1974) are of this form). Then it is natural for Region R_j to consider the problem:

$$\text{Minimize } f_i(z_i)$$
$$z_i$$
$$\text{subject to } \sum_{j=1}^{n} (1 - z_j) a_{ij} \le c_i$$

$$\text{and } 0 \le z_i \le 1$$
(z_j fixed if $j \neq i$).

The optimum value of this convex program is a function of $z_1, z_2, ..., z_{i-1}, z_{i+1}, ..., z_n$) but these variables cannot be directly controlled by Region R_i. However, this Region may try, for example by offering side-payments, to persuade the other Regions to change their reduction fractions. This is advantageous for Region R_i as long as the necessary compensations are no greater than the gain in the value of $f_i(z_i)$. All other Regions may start similar negotiations.

We prove

Theorem 1. Let $z*$ be an optimal solution of the program

Minimize $F(z) = \sum_{i=1}^{n} f_i(z_i)$

subject to $\sum_{j=1}^{n} (1 - z_j) a_{ij} \leq c_i$, $i = 1,2,\ldots,n$,   (7)

and

$$0 \leq z_i \leq 1, \; i = 1,2,\ldots,n.$$ (8)

Then it is not possible for any Region to become better off by selecting a vector $\bar{z}$ with $F(\bar{z}) > F(z*)$ without making other Regions worse off by means of unsufficient sidepayments.

Proof $z*$ is a minimum point of a continuous convex function which is defined over a compact subset of R^n. Hence $z*$ is defined. If $f_i(\bar{z}) \leq f_i(z*)$, then Region R_i can pay $f_i(z*) - f_i(\bar{z})$ for moving from $z*$ to $\bar{z}$. Thus the total amount available for side payments is:

$$S_1 = \sum_{i=1}^{n} \max(0, f_i(z*) - f_i(\bar{z}))$$

But if $f_i(\bar{z}) \geq f_i(z*)$, then Region R_i needs at least the compensation $f_i(\bar{z}) - f_i(z*)$ in order not to loose by the transition from $z*$ to $\bar{z}$. The total need for compensations is:

$$S_2 = \sum_{i=1}^{n} \max(0, f_i(\bar{z}) - f_i(z*))$$

We find

$$S_1 - S_2 = \sum_{i=1}^{n} (f_i(z*) - f_i(\bar{z})) = F(z*) - F(\bar{z}) < 0$$

Hence the losses by the move from $z*$ to $\bar{z}$ cannot be compensated by the gains.   Q.E.D.
We note the implicit requirement for the use of Theorem 1 that all Regions agree on a common definition of the cost functions f_i. The standard c_i might be selected independently by Region R_i. The coefficients a_{ij} are physical variables. At present, no reliable methods of determining a_{ij} are known but research on this and similar problems has begun. See e.g. Air pollution .. (1971) and Bolin-Persson, (1974).

MEETING A REGIONAL STANDARD FOR SULFUR DEPOSITIONS

In this Section we treat the problem of determining an abatement strategy in order to meet a standard calling for a cut-
back in the total emission of sulfur in a region with a certain fraction z, $0 < z < 1$. The following approaches to the
problem of distributing the reduction among the sources in
the region have been discussed in the literature. (Gustafson,
1974).

Maximum control

All sources are required to reduce their emissions as much as
technically possible. This strategy has the apparent appeal
that everything possible is done to decrease the emissions
but in practice an (implicit) comparison between costs and
benefits must be undertaken in order to establish what is
"possible". The principle of maximum control does not give
any guidance in this decision.

Uniform roll-back

All sources are required to cut back their emissions with the
same fraction. One draw-back with this strategy is, that some
polluters perhaps cannot meet the requirement and hence must
close down their operations, another that the reduction in
sulfur emissions might be obtained in an unnecessarily expensive way. It might be that the same total reduction could
be obtained at less total cost if some sources were asked
to reduce their emission by a greater fraction than others.

Modified roll-back

The sources are divided into n groups G_r, $r = 1,2,\ldots,n$
and each group is required to reduce its emissions by a
fraction D_r where D_r, $r = 1,2,\ldots,n$ are selected such
that the total cost is minimized. Hence this strategy calls
for the solution of an optimization problem. We introduce:

Q_r,　　total emission by Group G_r before reduction

d_r,　　the highest possible fraction with which Group G_r
　　　　can reduce its emissions

$f_r(D_r)$, the cost incurred by Group G_r in order to reduce
　　　　its emission by the fraction D_r. f_r is a con-
　　　　tinuous and increasing function on $[0,1]$.

Q_0,　　the maximum permitted total emission of sulfur.

The reductions policy is defined by an optimal solution vector
of the problem

Minimize $\displaystyle\sum_{r=1}^{n} f_r(D)$

subject to $\displaystyle\sum_{r=1}^{n} (1 - D_r) Q_r \leq Q_0$

and $\qquad 0 \leq D_r \leq d_r, \; r = 1,2,\ldots,n$

The principal difficulty with this approach is, that the cost-functions f_r must all be known for a central decisionmaker. Inequities caused by prescribing different factors D_r must be compensated for, at least in a market economy.

Regulating the quality of fuels

Since the total consumption of energy in a region is known another approach is to limit the amount of sulfur that may be released for each unit of energy that is consumed. Such a regulation can be translated into requirements on the maximum content of sulfur in various fuels. This approach is advocated in Begränsning .. (1974).

Taxing released sulfur

A unit tax is levied on sulfur released into the environment. Then each source will cut back until the marginal cost for further emissions reductions surpasses the tax. Hence, if the tax is increased, the total emissions in a region go down. The problem is thus to determine the correct level of the tax. This cannot be computed apriori if the marginal costs are not known to the decision-maker. Compare Baumol (1971) and Begränsning (1974). There does not exist any general agreement on which method should be preferred. Begränsning .. (1974) advocates fuel regulation as a basic principle for future Swedish legislation but a strong minority of the authors fabours taxation.

MAINTAINING SATISFACTORY AIR QUALITY IN MULTIPLE SOURCE AREAS, E.G. CITIES.

Even if regional standards are met, the contents of sulfur dioxide and other pollutants of the air may rise to a dangerously high level in areas where many and/or large sources are present. Much work has been devoted to this problem. See e.g. Gustafson (1974) and Gustafson-Kortanek (1973b) and the further references given therein.

In order to protect public health special standards on the maximum permissible concentrations have been defined by many countries. Three main approaches are possible: A) further reductions of the emissions (beyond what is required by regional standards) B) increasing the height of stacks and thus dispersing effluents over larger volumes of air

C) moving sources away from the critical area or switching
fuels. Approach A) is discussed e.g. in Gustafson (1974).
The following approach is used. We consider an air quality
control area S. The sources are divided into n groups whose
concentration contributions are represented by the functions u_r.
Hence the total concentration (before reductions) is

$$\chi = \sum_{r=1}^{n} u_r$$

Let the maximum permissible concentration be φ. The air
quality is acceptable if

$$\chi(x) \leq \varphi(x) \ , \ x \in S \tag{9}$$

If Condition (9) is violated for at least one point x, one
must decrease the concentration. Let E_r be the fraction of
reduction. Then the remaining concentration is

$$\sum_{r=1}^{n} (1 - E_r) \, u_r(x)$$

If the stack-height are changed then the *form* of u_r is
influenced. We indicate this by replacing $u_r(x)$ with
$w_r(x,h^r)$ where h^r is a vector specifying the stack-heights.
w_r is assumed to be a continuous function of the arguments x
and h^r Condition (9) takes the form

$$\sum_{r=1}^{n} (1 - E_r) \, w_r(x,h^r) \leq \varphi(x), \ x \in S$$

An abatement policy is thus defined by E and $h^1, h^2, \ldots, h^n$
and we shall assume that the control cost G is also defined
by these entities. Hence an optimal abatement policy is an
optimal solution of *Program I*

$$\underset{E, h^1, \ldots, h^n}{\text{minimize}} \quad G(E, h^1, h^2, \ldots, h^n)$$

subject to $\qquad \displaystyle\sum_{r=1}^{n} (1 - E_r) \, w_r(x,h^r) \leq \varphi(x), \ x \in S$

and $\qquad 0 \leq E_r \leq e_r, \ r = 1,2,\ldots,n$

where $e_r \leq 1$ are given numbers which represent technical
constraints.

If h^r are kept fixed in Program I and we optimize over E,
then we get a semiinfinite program of the type considered in
Charnes-Cooper-Kortanek (1962), Gustafson (1973), (1974) and
Gustafson-Kortanek (1973a, 1973b). The computation may be

done using the codes in Fahlander (1973). For the more general problem when h^r are allowed to vary more advanced methods must be developed.

CONCLUSIONS

In principle, the environmental management problems can be formulated and solved within the framework of well-known mathematical theory. The most urgent tasks is to get a quantitative description of the transformation of pollutants in the atmosphere and their long-range transport over the continents and the oceans. The local air quality control problem is better known and effective measures to improve air quality have been taken in several countries. International cooperation is necessary for a successful attack on the regional problem. The environmental policy has its implications on the whole economy (See e.g. Koo (1971), Leontief (1970), Leontief-Ford (1971)) and hence even local standards should be looked upon in an international context.

Acknowledgement. This research was financially supported by the National Science Foundation (USA) under Grant GK-31833.

REFERENCES

Air pollution across national boundaries. Sweden's case study for the UN conference on the human environment (1971), P.A. Norstedt och Söner, Stockholm

Baumol, W.J. and W.E. Oates (1971), The use of standards and prices for protection of the environment, Swed. J. of Economics 73, 42-54.

Begränsning av svavelutsläpp - en studie av styrmedel (1974), SOU 1974:101, Allmänna Förlaget, Stockholm (Summary in English).

Bolin, B. and C. Persson (1974), Regional dispersion and deposition of atmospheric pollutants with particular application to sulfur pollution over Western Europe, Rep AC-28, International Meteorological Institute in Stockholm.

Bringfelt, B., T. Hjorth and S. Ring (1974), A numerical air pollution dispersion model for central Stockholm, Atmospheric Environment 8, 131-148.

Charnes, A., W.W. Cooper and K.O. Kortanek (1962), Duality, Haar programs and finite sequence spaces, Proc. Acad. Sci. U.S. 48, 783-786.

Chazan, D. and W. Miranker (1969), Chaotic relaxation, Linear Algebra and its Applications 2, 199-222.

Fahlander, K. (1973), Computer programs for semi-infinite optimization, Report TRITA-NA-7312, Dept of Numerical Analysis, Royal Institute of Technology, Stockholm.

Forrester, J.W. (1971), World dynamics, Wright Allen Press, Inc.

Freeman, S.D. et al (1974), A time to choose America's energy future. Final report by the Energy policy project of the Ford Foundation, Ballinger Publishing Co., Cambridge, Mass.

Gustafson, S.-Å. (1973), Nonlinear systems in semi-infinite programming in (G.B. Byrnes, and C.A. Hall, Eds), Numerical solution of systems of nonlinear algebraic equations, 63-99.

Gustafson, S.-Å. (1974), Optimization problems in air quality control, Methods of Operations Research (to appear)

Gustafson, S.-Å. and K.O. Kortanek (1973a), Numerical treatment of a class of semi-infinite programming problems, NRLO 20, 477-504.

Gustafson, S.-Å. and K.O. Kortanek (1973b), Mathematical models for air pollution control: determination of optimum abatement policies in (R.A. Deininger, ed) Models for environmental pollution control, Ann Arbor Science Publishers, inc.

Koo, Y.C. (1971), Environmental repercussions and trade theory, The Review of Economics and Statistics.

Kohn, R.E. (1971), Optimal air quality standards, Econometrica 39, 983-995.

Leontief, W. (1970), Environmental repercussions and the economic structure, an input - output approach, The Review of Economics and Statistics, 262-271.

Leontief, W. and D. Ford (1971), Air pollution and the economic structure: Empirical results of input - output computations, (mimeo)

Ring, S., T. Hjorth and L.E. Olsson (1975), Spridningsmodell för luftföroreningar i Malmö - Lund regionen, Swedish Meteorological and Hydrological Institute, Stockholm.

Strømsøe, S. (1973), The LRTAP emission survey. Cooperative technical programme to measure the long range transport of air pollutants, 250-260. Gausdal near Lillehammer, Norway.

Yanagisawa, S. (1973), Air quality standards, national and international, Journ. Air Poll. Contr. Assoc. 23, 945-948.

THE AIR POLLUTION ABATEMENT MASC-AP MODEL.

L.F. Escudero

Director, Environmental Sciences, IBM Sci. Cen., Madrid

INTRODUCTION

As a part of the preliminary work performed in the Nervion
River Valley Bilbao Air Pollution Study, the following method
has been developed for the evaluation and selection of
emission control policies and standards.

Escudero and Jimenez, 1975 describes a methodology used to
estimate the probability distribution of pollutant concentration in each receptor grid square of a studied area for a
seasonal time period, given the predicted pollutant emissions
due to the point and area sources with significant influence
on the pollutant concentration. This probability distribution
is estimated over the total range of different meteorological
conditions that affect the concentration significantly.

The probability distribution, which is estimated on the basis
of a stochastic diffusion model, gives the probability for
each meteorological condition and set of contributing
emissions that the concentration in each grid square will
exceed the maximum limit of concentration.

A polluted grid square is considered to be one in which this
probability is greater than the maximum probability allowed,
called the relative limit. A contributing area is the set of
point sources and area sources which affect the concentration
in the receptor polluted grid square. A polluted area is
defined as the set of contributing areas and polluted grid
squares which have at least one grid square or emitter source
in common.

GENERAL OBJECTIVE AND CONDITIONS FOR THE MASC-AP MODEL.

The objective of this model is to evaluate the alternatives
for reducing the emission at the point and area sources so

that the problem area will no longer be polluted area.

The reduction alternatives may be programmed for a single
seasonal period or for a set of these periods adapting the
reduction alternative for each emitter source to fixed and
constant abatement levels for the entire period programmed
(Escudero, 1973). This paper treats a single seasonal period,
and, in contrast to other types of models (Gorr and Kortanek,
1970; Kortanek and Gorr, 1971; Teller, 1968), the probabilistic limits of the real concentration are used, as it is
one of the principal characteristics of the reduction model.

The probabilistic limits of concentration include the new
average theoretical concentrations in the polluted grid square
when the emissions are reduced (Escudero and Jimenez, 1975).
These concentrations correspond to a given set of probabilities that the real concentration exceed the absolute
limit, so that once the new theoretical concentration has
been estimated it is assumed that it is the upper limit of the
interval which corresponds to it in the limit concentrations
relative to the given set of probabilities. In this way an
estimate is made of the probability of excess real concentration for each theoretical concentration, and therefore for
each emission reduction alternative.

The emission reduction alternatives are estimated such that
the emission reduction to be imposed on each influence source
be both the minimum possible and be in proportion to its
influence on the polluted area.

THE ELEMENTS OF THE EMISSIONS REDUCTION MODEL

The elements needed for using this mixed integer programming
model for each problem area are the following:

The receptor grid square $r \forall r \varepsilon R$ which makes up the polluted
area where the concentration is to be reduced.

The influence emitter grid square $e \forall e \varepsilon E$ within the problem
area.

The meteorological condition $m \forall m \varepsilon M$ in grid square $\underline{r}$ which,
given the set of emissions, causes the real concentration C_{rm}
to exceed the absolute limit AL in the seasonal period under
consideration.

The type of probability $p \forall p \varepsilon P$ which corresponds to the probability PAL_p of the limit concentration UC_{rmp}.

The predicted pollutant emission $AQA_e (\mu g/s)$ for the seasonal
period under consideration coming from the area sources
located in emitter grid square $\underline{e}$. Idem $(\mu g/s)$ for point

sources (AQP_e).

The theoretical unit influence KA_{rem} of the area emissions from emitter grid square $\underline{e}$ upon grid square $\underline{r}$ under meteorological condition $\underline{m}$, according to the stochastic diffusion model. Idem for the point source emissions (KP_{rem}).

The average theoretical pollutant concentration $TC_{rm}(\mu g/m^3)$ which, in the stochastic diffusion model, is found in grid square $\underline{r}$, under meteorological condition $\underline{m}$, given the actual set of emissions AQA_e and AQP_e.

The frequency MP_m of meteorological condition $\underline{m}$ during the seasonal period under consideration. Only those meteorological conditions are taken into account whose probability MP_m is significant. The maximum allowable probability (relative limit) RL that the real concentration C_r in any grid square exceed the absolute limit AL.

The theoretical concentration UC_{rmp} in grid square $\underline{r}$ under meteorological condition $\underline{m}$ corresponding to probability PAL_{rmp}.

The given set of probabilities PAL_{rmp} that the real concentration in each situation $\underline{rm}$ exceed the absolute limit AL. Using the stochastic diffusion model, the theoretical concentration is obtained for each possible set of emissions. It is assumed that the probability that the real concentration exceed the limit AL is the probability estimated by the UC_{rmp} value immediately above the corresponding theoretical concentration.

The probability that for the predicted set of emissions AQA_e and AQP_e the real concentration in grid square $\underline{r}$ under meteorological condition $\underline{m}$ exceed the maximum limit AL, taking into consideration the probability of the meteorological condition so that $PC_{rm} = MP_m \ PAL_{rm}$, therefore, $UC_{rmP} = TC_{rm}$.

The influence WA_e of the area sources in emitter grid square $\underline{e}$ during the seasonal period considered upon the pollutant concentration in all the grid squares which make up the polluted area under all of the meteorological conditions considered (Escudero and Jimenez, 1975). Idem for the point sources (WP_e).

The maximum percent MRA_e of reduction allowed of the predicted emission AQA_e in emitter grid square $\underline{e}$, based upon socioeconomic considerations. Idem for the point sources $AQP_e(MRP_e)$.

The variables used in the model are: The pollutant emission XQA_e to be reduced in the area source of emitter grid square $\underline{e}$ during the entire seasonal period being considered. Idem for the point sources (XAP_e). The new average theoretical concentration XC_{rm} in situation $\underline{rm}$ corresponding to the new emission from the emitter grid square $\underline{e}$. The binary variable Y_{rmp} whose value is 1 if the theoretical concentration UC_{rmp} is the upper limit of the concentration XC_{rm}. If not its value is 0.

THE FORMULATION OF THE MASC-AP MODEL

Using the elements described above, the model for the reduction of emissions that will eliminate the polluted area is the following:

Minimize in a weighted form the emissions reduction:

$$\text{Min. } QR = \sum_{e=1}^{E} \left(\frac{1}{WA_e} XQA_e + \frac{1}{WP_e} XQP_e \right) \tag{1}$$

such that with the conditions being the same, priority is given to the emission in the grid square that pollutes most.

Minimization of the Equation (1) is subject to the following conditions:

1) The estimation of the new theoretical average concentration XC_{rm} corresponding, according to the stochastic diffusion model, to the new set of emissions.

$$XC_{rm} = TC_{rm} - \sum_{e=1}^{E} (KA_{rem} XQA_e + KP_{rem} XQP_e) \quad \forall m\epsilon M, r\epsilon R \tag{2}$$

2) The necessity that only variable Y_{rmp} take on the value 1 if UC_{rmp} is the limit immediately above the new average theoretical concentration $XC_{rm} \; \forall m\epsilon M, r\epsilon R$.

$$XC_{rm} \leq \sum_{p=1}^{P} UC_{rmp} Y_{rmp} \quad \forall m\epsilon M, r\epsilon R \tag{3}$$

$$1 = \sum_{p=1}^{P} Y_{rmp} \quad \forall m\epsilon M, r\epsilon R \tag{4}$$

3) The Equation (6) is the principal condition of the model requiring the probability

$$\sum_{m=1}^{M} MP_m PAL_{rmp} Y_{rmp} \tag{5}$$

that the real concentration C_r exceed the absolute limit AL not be greater that the relative limit RL in any of the polluted grid square.

$$\sum_{m=1}^{M} \sum_{p=1}^{P} MP_m PAL_{rmp} Y_{rmp} \leq RL \quad \forall r\epsilon R \tag{6}$$

In this regard it is important to note that Equation (4) demands that each case have only one Equation (5) different from zero.

4) The variables for the amount of emission reduction are represented by:

$$XQA_e \leq MRA_e AQA_e \tag{7}$$

$$XQP_e \leq MRP_e AQP_e \tag{8}$$

The principal results of the reduction model are:
a) The reduction values, expressed in percentages, for the point and area sources of each grid square for the time period considered.
b) The values of the corresponding new emissions.
c) The new probabilistic distribution of concentration for each receptor grid square which makes up the polluted area
d) The probability that the new concentration exceed the limit established.

THE BRANCH AND BOUND POSSIBILITIES IN THE MASC-AP MODEL

The model for the reduction of the pollutant emissions needs the use of mixed integer programming techniques, since the Y variables are binary being able to take on only the values 0 and 1. Among the many algorithms existing for its solution (Geoffrion and Marsten, 1972) the MASC-AP reduction model is based on the IBM MPSX/MIP system using the following possibilities.

SOS conditions
A Special Order Set is a set (Beale and Tomlin, 1969) of binary variables of which one and only one has the value 1. In the emissions reduction model the SOS conditions are included in Equation (4) so that if one variable has the value 1 the others must be null. Accompanying each SOS row there must be another condition or some weighting that is responsible for the important attributed to it. For the SOS condition the corresponding weighting is the probability PC_{rm} that the concentration C_r exceed the maximum limit AL.

Quasi-integer variables
In the optimization models with integer variables, it is necessary, in the optimum, that these variables take on integer values (0 or 1 in this case), but often in the branching formation the candidate nodes have some variables with integer values and others with quasi-integer values (for example, 0.001; 0.995) which means having many successor nodes in order to make them integers (primarily if the number of integer variables is high and their coefficients in the objective function are not very different).

The need in our case for binary variables only is motivated by the requirement in Equation (6) that the probability that the concentration exceed the absolute limit not be higher than the relative limit. Thus, even though the binary variables had only quasi-integer values, the objective would also be achieved, since the quasi-integrality of the binary variables will really bring about the probability of exceeding the absolute limit, even though it were not the relative limit, but were a value very close to it. Given the probabilistic form of the model this would not ruin the plan adopted for the reduction of the emissions.

Pseudo-cost of the integer variables

There exist in the literature many controversies over the
strategy to be used in the branch and bound phase, mainly in
regard to the choice of the next branching node and the
choice of the branching variable. Although in the choice of
the branching node the criterium may be used of the best
functional value (Roy et al., 1970) or a mixed criterium, the
best functional value until the first integer solution and
then the best estimated value (Benichou et al., 1971), the
MASC-AP model uses the criterium of the best estimated value.
In regard to the branching variable, although the penalties
criterium may be adopted (Roy et al., 1970), the MASC-AP model
uses the criterium of the pseudo-costs (Benichou et al., 1971)
since it has been observed experimentally that it better
incorporates the influence of each variable upon the objective
function.

THE MASC-AP MODEL STRATEGY

The strategy of the MASC-AP model, since it has a large
percentage of binary variables and can thus be considered
"quasi-pure", is the following.

The selection of the branching variable and the branching node

The SOS row in Equation (4) to bifurcate will be that which
has not yet reached an integer or quasi-integer value, whose
associated value PC_{rm} is greater, since this is the most
difficult SOS condition to fulfill, and therefore the condition
which causes a greater deteriorization in the objective
function. Once the first integer solution is obtained, the
SOS row is chosen whose pseudo-cost is the one which offers
a greater deteriorization in the objective function.

These deteriorizations are classified in dynamic order such
that the "list" of the different deteriorizations is composed
by the actualized pseudo-costs. When the SOS row to bifurcate
has been selected, the criterium for creating the two
successor nodes is based on Equation (3).

Except in the node (0), before selecting the branching
variable it is necessary to select the branching node from
among all the candidate nodes. The criterium adopted by the
MASC-AP model is the choose the node with the best estimated
value so that, since the pseudo-costs are not expressly
calculated for the integer variables which are not yet branching variables, the estimated value in the first branches and
practically until some integer solution is reached, differs
very little from the functional value.

<u>Dropped nodes and selection of the candidate nodes</u>
Before obtaining the optimum continuous solution, the MASC-AP
model obtains a feasible integer solution such that in the
branch and bound phase those nodes are dropped whose functional value is worse than that of the previously obtained integer
solution.

Once the integer solution has been obtained, the branch and
bound phase drops the nodes whose functional value is greater
say by 10%, than that of the integer solution. Also, this
phase "postpones" nodes whose functional value even if it is
greater than the value of the integer solution does not have
a difference greater than the previous value (e.g., 10%), so
that once the optimality of the best integer solution has been
proved it is observed whether among the "postponed" successor
nodes there is some integer solution which differs from the
optimum solution by no more than 10%. In this way, different
alternatives for the reduction of emissions are produced.

Now, given that the alternatives for the emission are
estimated, since the effects of each emitter source on the
pollution of the problem area are estimated for only the
polluted area, a node is not admitted as candidate node if its
functional value is not better, say, as a minimum by 10%,
than the value of the best integer solution. In this way much
CPU time is saved, and at the same time little of the accuracy
of the quasi-optimum integer solution is lost.

CONCLUSION

The model presented in this paper must be considered an
effective tool for establishing bases for corrective alternatives for an abatement problem of air pollution. It should
also be considered a very useful instrument for qualifying,
within the development policies for a given area, the
standards that are more and more indispensible for protecting
our air environment.

It should be noted that the basic statistical parameter
considered in the formulation of the model is the maximum
probability allowed that the concentration in a given grid
square exceed the maximum limit allowed, in contrast to models
which use averages as their standards of quality. This method
avoids the danger of large concentrations being masked with
smaller concentrations. This probability depends conjointly on
the probabilistic matrix of the typology by which the different
meteorological factors have been stratified and the probability that for a theoretical concentration estimated on the
basis of a predicted set of emissions the real concentration
might exceed the maximum limit permitted.

It is of interest to point out that in order to estimate the

concentration in each grid square, stochastic diffusion models
have been used for each meteorological stratum, depending
on the emissions, so that the tabular form of the model is in
function with the emitter grid squares.

The criterium which minimize the model is the weighted
reduction of the emission levels for each contributing grid
square in accord with the effect it has on the pollutant
concentration in the sum of the grid squares wich make up the
polluted area.

REFERENCES

Beale, E.M.L. and J.A. Tomlin (1969) Special facilities in a
general mathematical programming system for non-convex
problem using ordered sets of variables. 5th Inter. Conf. on
O.R., North-Holland, 447-454.

Benichou, M. et al. (1971) Experiments in mixed-integer linear
programming. Mathematical Programming, 1, 1:76-94.

Escudero, L.F. (1973) Formulación matemática de un modelo pro-
babilístico de estimación y reducción de contaminantes atmos-
féricos. Centro de Investigación UAM-IBM, PCI-10.73, 71-78.

Escudero, L.F. and J. Jimenez (1975) Estimación de zonas con-
taminadas. I Congreso Iberoamericano del Medio Ambiente,
Madrid.

Fahlander, K. , S-A. Gustafson, and L.E. Olsson (1974)
Computing optimal air pollution abatement strategies-some
numerical experiments on field data. Proceedings of the Fifth
Meeting of the Expert Panel on Air pollution Modeling, Nato
Committee on the Challenges to Modern Society, 27.

Geoffrion, A.M. and R.E. Marsten (1972) Integer programming
algorithms: a framework and state-of-art-survey. Man. Sci.,
18, 9:465-491.

Gorr, W.I. and K.O. Kortanek (1970) Numerical aspect of
Pollution abatement problem: Constrained generalized moment
techniques. Inst. of Physical Planning, Carnegie-Mellon
University, 12.

Gorr, W.I., S-A. Gustafson and K.O. Kortanek (1972) Optimal
control strategies for air quality standards and regulatory
policies. Environment and Planning, 4:183-192.

Gustafson, S-A. and K.O. Kortanek (1972) Analytical properties
of some multiple-source urban diffusion models. Environment
and planning 4:31-34.

Gustafson, S-A. and K.O. Kortanek (1973) Mathematical Models
for air pollution control: determination of optimum abatement
policies. Models for Environmental pollution control (ed.R.A.
Deininger), Ann Arbor Science Publ., 251-265.

IBM (1975) MPSX/MIP/370, SH19-1094/1095/1099, N.Y.

Khon, R.E. (1970) Linear Programming Model for air pollution
control: a pilot study of the St. Louis airshed, Journ. Air
Poll. Contr. Assoc., 20: 78-82.

Kortanek, K.O. and W.I. Gorr (1971)Cost benefit measures for
regional air pollution abatement models, I. of P.P., 5.

Roy, B. at al. (1970) From SEP procedure to the mixed ophelie
program. Integer an non-linear programming (ed. J. Abadie),
North-Holland, 419-436.

Teller, A. (1968) The use of linear programming to estimate
the cost of some alternate air pollution abatement policies.
Proc. IBM 320-1953, N.Y., 345-354.

THE APPLICATION OF NUMERICAL MODELLING TO AIR POLLUTION IN
THE FORTH VALLEY

A.W.C. Keddie, G.H. Roberts, F.P. Williams

Air Pollution Division, Warren Spring Laboratory, Stevenage,
Herts, UK

INTRODUCTION

Surveys of pollution in themselves give only the current
distribution of the pollutant and a historical account of
the changes in the distribution. They provide little information on the relative contributions made by the various
types of source to the air pollutant concentrations or on
the likely impact of new sources. Such information is
essential in planning industrial, commercial and residential
developments in such a way as to ensure minimal environmental
impact and for identifying the most effective means of
ensuring that specified pollutant concentrations are not
exceeded. Both these aspects are growing in importance as
greater stress is placed on air quality objectives or
criteria. Indeed, some form of numerical diffusion modelling is the only practicable technique in multiple source
situations or in areas which are spatially large. Furthermore, because pollutant concentrations are highly dependent
on local sources, it is normally very difficult to provide
a reliable distribution map (e.g. in the form of isopleths)
without a very dense, and therefore expensive, network of
sites, particularly in urban areas. Provided the necessary
fuel consumption data are available, diffusion modelling can
assist in the spatial interpolation of measured concentrations and in many instances a model can provide an
acceptable indication of the distribution of a pollutant
much more quickly and cheaply than can a monitoring network.
This paper describes some of the practical aspects of
applying modelling techniques.

Warren Spring Laboratory has been commissioned by the
Scottish Development Department to undertake a study of the
distributions of smoke and SO_2, and their relationship to
emissions, in the Forth Valley (see Fig. 1). This area is
of particular interest because of the large scale industrial

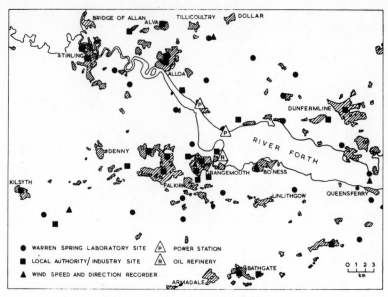

FIG.1 FORTH VALLEY SURVEY. POLLUTION MONITORING SITES

development already there (including two power stations and
an oil refinery) and because of the potential for further
large-scale industrial growth. The main objectives of the
study are:

  i)   To determine the existing spatial and temporal distri-
       butions of smoke and SO_2 concentrations in the area.
  ii) To provide emission inventories for those two pollu-
       tants.
  iii) Using numerical diffusion models, and other techniques,
       quantify the contributions to observed concentrations
       made by the different existing sources and predict
       the impact of future changes in the emission pattern.

THE DATA BASE

Observed Concentrations
A monitoring network is essential to provide baseline
information on the distribution of the pollutants in question
and to provide data for validation of the models.

The number and siting of monitoring stations have been
decided according to the type of area and use to which the
data will be put. The emphasis has been on obtaining the
greatest amount of useful data from a limited number of
"fixed" monitors. The instruments are located in areas of
differing emission characteristics having regard to the
likely spatial variability of the pollutant and, to a lesser
extent, the prevailing meteorological conditions. In rural

areas monitors are located in relation to the important
distant sources. Urban areas require a greater density of
monitoring sites than rural areas.

There are 40-45 monitors in operation in the Forth Valley
Survey at any one time. Nineteen of these monitors, one of
which is situated at a height of 160 m above sea level on the
north pier of the Forth Road Bridge, are operated by
Warren Spring Laboratory as a special survey of the area.
The remainder are operated by Local Authorities and Industry
as part of the National Survey of Air Pollution (HMSO, 1972).

The smoke (suspended particulate) and SO_2 concentrations are
determined by the British Standard methods (BS 1747, Parts 2
and 3), corrections being made for ammonia as necessary. The
sampling period is 24 hours.

Meteorological Data
Hourly wind-speed and direction are obtained from three
stations within the survey area (see Fig. 1): from Turnhouse
Airport and the Forth Road Bridge on the eastern perimeter,
and from Abbotsinch and Leuchars Airports, respectively 45 km
to the south-west and 65 km to the north-east of Grangemouth.
Cloud cover and rainfall are also obtained from Turnhouse and
daily minimum and maximum temperatures are obtained from
Turnhouse and several synoptic stations within the survey
area. Vertical temperature profiles are available from
Shanwell, some 70 km to the north-east of Grangemouth. The
relevant upper air observations are made daily at 1100 and
2300 hours, GMT. Additional information on the stability of
the atmosphere is obtained from solar radiation measurements
made by Warren Spring Laboratory in Grangemouth.

Emission Inventories
The distribution of fuel consumption forms the basis of any
emission inventory. The largest industrial consumers in the
Forth Valley are providing monthly fuel consumption rates.
Annual consumption rates have been obtained for all other
users, that is domestic, commercial and smaller industrial,
by sending questionnaires to the Local Authorities.

Domestic Emissions The basic source of information was the
percentage of the population, within each Ordnance Survey
(OS) 1 km grid square, burning coal, solid smokeless fuel or
oil. The annual emissions of smoke and SO_2 from each grid
square were then computed by applying the appropriate fuel
consumption-per-head factors and emission factors. For
example, for SO_2:

$$E = \sum_{i=1}^{3} 2 A_i S_i (1 - R_i)P_i \ \ldots\ldots\ldots\ (1)$$

where E is the SO_2 emission rate per grid square, A_i is the
annual consumption rate per head of population of the ith

fuel, S_i is the proportionate weight of sulphur contained in
the ith fuel, R_i is the proportion of the sulphur retained in
the ash (0.2 for coal and solid smokeless fuel, 0.0 for oil)
and P_i is the number of people within the grid square using
the ith fuel.

Corrections for seasonal variations are made using Equation
(4) in the next section.

Industrial/Commercial Emissions   The basic information supplied for each source was the grid reference, type of source,
fuel use (i.e. space heating or process), type of fuel and
annual consumption rate, sulphur content of the fuel, and the
stack height. The annual emission rates of smoke and SO_2 were
then computed for each source. For example, for smoke:

$$E = BF \qquad \dots\dots\dots\dots\dots\dots (2)$$

where E is the annual emission rate for the source, B is the
annual fuel consumption rate, and F is the proportionate
weight of the fuel emitted as smoke (i.e. particles <15 μm).

The value of F depends on the fuel (coal, coke, distillate
oil or residual oil) and on the size of the boilers in
question.

The large sources are always treated individually as elevated
point sources. The height of emission in each case is
corrected to give the effective height, that is, the physical
stack height plus the rise of the plume due to buoyancy. For
the power stations, oil refinery and a few of the other
larger sources, sufficient data has been provided to calculate
the buoyancy flux (or heat output) and the plume rise is
calculated directly using, for example, Briggs' (1969) plume
rise formula for neutral or unstable conditions:

$$\Delta H = 7.4 \ F^{1/3} \ H^{2/3} \ U^{-1} \qquad \dots\dots\dots\dots\dots (3)$$

where ΔH is the plume rise, m; F is the buoyancy flux parameter, m^4/s^3; H is stack height, m; and U is wind speed, m/s.

Where sufficient data on the characteristics of the effluents
are not available, plume rise is estimated from the capacity
of the boilers or nature of the process, the physical chimney
height and by comparison with similar units for which plume
rise is known.

Intermediate and small sources are generally aggregated by OS
kilometre grid squares, although separated into types of
source, for example, domestic, commercial and low level
industrial emissions and larger industrial/commercial sources.
Typical effective chimney heights for each type are computed

or estimated as outlined for the large industrial sources.
There may be a necessity to have greater spatial resolution in
the neighbourhood of, say, a monitoring site and intermediate-
sized sources may then be considered individually on the same
basis as the large sources.

One further segregation of the emission data is required, to
distinguish between space heating and process emissions.
Except for the largest industrial users who provide monthly
returns of fuel consumption, all other fuel consumption data
are on an annual basis. Process emissions are assumed to be
constant throughout the year but space heating emissions,
which are temperature dependent, are assumed to vary in
accordance with the Degree Day principle (Gas Council, 1965).
The simplest way of relating the primarily space heating
emissions, E_{sp}, to temperature is

$$E_{sp} = E_o \left[a + b\, (T_d - T) \right], \text{ if } T < T_d$$

$$\dots\dots\dots (4)$$

and $E_{sp} = a\, E_o,$ if $T > T_d$

where E_o is the annual average emission rate, T_d is the
datum temperature ($\approx 15^{o}C$ in the UK), T is the relevant daily,
monthly or seasonal mean temperature and 'a' and 'b' are
constants to be determined. The constant 'a' makes allowance
for any constant emission rate throughout the year due to
fuel consumption for water heating etc.

Relative Emission Rates   Some idea of the relative importance,
in terms of total emissions, of the various stationary source
categories in the Forth Valley can be gained from Table 1.

Table 1.   Relative Emission Rates in the Forth Valley

Source Category	Percentage of Total Smoke Emissions	Percentage of Total SO_2 Emissions
Domestic	62	1
Non-domestic space heating	1	1
Small industrial	1	2
Medium industrial	4	7
Oil refinery & power stations	32	89

That domestic premises are a major source of smoke is clear
and their contribution to ground-level concentrations will be
over 90% because of the inverse relationship between ground
level concentrations and effective chimney height. On the
other hand this inverse relationship means that although the
oil refinery and two power stations emit almost 90% of the
SO_2 their overall contribution to ground-level concentrations
is very much less.

ANALYSIS OF OBSERVED POLLUTANT CONCENTRATIONS

Analysis of the observed pollutant concentrations and their relationships to meteorological variables is not only import-ant from the point of view of describing the existing situa-tion but is also a valuable, if not essential, precursor to the detailed diffusion modelling. Interpretation of the data can shed light on the dispersion characteristics of the area which must therefore be encompassed within the model(s). Furthermore, various characteristics of the observed concen-trations, for example cumulative frequency distributions and pollution roses (directional dependence of concentrations), can be used in assessing the validity of the model(s).

Temporal Variations
Ambient pollutant concentrations observed at any monitoring site exhibit considerable fluctuations about the mean value (e.g. annual mean). It has been clearly demonstrated that ambient concentrations approximately satisfy the log-normal probability distribution:

$$f(C) = \frac{1}{C\sigma\sqrt{2\pi}} \exp\left[-(\ln C - \ln C_g)^2/2\sigma^2\right] \quad\ldots\ldots\ldots(5)$$

where $f(C)$ is the frequency of occurrence of concentration C, σ is the standard deviation of $\ln C$ and C_g is the geometric mean concentration (see, for example, Larsen, 1971). Ambient air-quality criteria or objectives are usually expressed in terms of period means (e.g. annual) and the frequency by which certain larger threshold values may be exceeded (e.g. WHO, 1972). In this latter respect it is the cumulative frequency of the observations:

$$F(C^*) = \int_{C^*}^{\infty} f(C) \, d C, \quad\ldots\ldots\ldots\ldots\ldots\ldots(6)$$

which is relevant. In the case of a log-normal distribution the statistics are simplified in that $F(C^*)$ plots as a straight line on log-probability paper, the line being uniquely defined by the median or geometric mean (C_g) and the standard geometric deviation $(S_g = \exp \sigma)$, which is the slope.

An interesting feature of the observations made in the Forth Valley is that the values of S_g for SO_2 are, on the whole, significantly smaller than the values for smoke. This implies that SO_2 is more uniformly distributed in time than is smoke, at least for sampling periods of 24 hours. The same is also true of the spatial distributions of the two pollut-ants but then this is to be expected in view of the more widespread distribution of SO_2 emissions and the greater effective heights of emission.

Diffusion models are still rather limited in their capacity to predict actual concentrations at a specific point at a specific time.   However, in relation to planning applications, this limitation is less severe than might first be assumed. What is important is that the model can predict, with reasonable accuracy, the mean concentration and the frequency distribution.   Consequently, a valuable test of a model (including the essential meteorological and emission input data) is its ability to reproduce observed frequency distributions at various monitoring points within the area in question.   For example, the mean SO_2 concentration at one site is almost 20 $\mu g/m^3$ greater than the mean at another site yet the value of S_g is much smaller.   The reason for this is almost certainly that the former site is surrounded by many small industrial sources, while the latter is primarily affected by one large source.   This is one feature of the observed statistics that a model must reproduce.   Even greater confidence can be placed on the model if it can reproduce the frequency distributions of both pollutants, with their different emission characteristics.

Pollution Roses

The mean pollution observed at a site is composed of contributions which are directionally dependent.   There are two principal reasons for the directional dependence: (i) The dispersion characteristics of the atmosphere are directionally dependent.   For example, easterly air streams tend to be more stable than westerlies.   (ii) The effective source strengths up-wind of the monitoring site may vary substantially.   This can be especially so in areas such as the Forth Valley where the urban areas are relatively small and there are strong sources within and beyond the survey perimeter (but see the section on regression analysis).

The observed pollution roses for the individual sites are another factor describing the observed pollution pattern and as such can be used as another test of the diffusion model(s) provided adequate account can be taken of pollution generated outside the survey area.   It is therefore important to have adequate monitoring coverage of the perimeter of the area in order to quantify what is being transported into the survey area on the different wind directions and which must be added to the concentrations computed by the model on the basis of local emissions.   As will be seen later, the pollution roses also provide essential information for any overall mass-balance calculations.

Correlations and Multiple Regression Analysis

Typical smoke/SO_2 correlation coefficients of observations made at individual sites and typical smoke/smoke and SO_2/SO_2 correlation coefficients of observations made at different sites throughout 1973-4 are respectively 0.7, 0.9 and 0.7. This shows that recorded values of smoke and SO_2 at individual sites tend to increase and decrease together from day-to-day and that these day-to-day variations tend to be common to the entire survey area. It can be concluded therefore, that, in general, meteorological conditions play a more important role in determining the relative day-to-day changes in pollutant concentrations than does the distribution of sources. Nevertheless, the lower SO_2/SO_2 correlation coefficient of 0.7, compared to the value of 0.9 for smoke, almost certainly reflects differences in the emission characteristics of the two pollutants; low level emissions of smoke and SO_2 can be expected to disperse similarly under most meteorological conditions but high level emission of SO_2, which make a major contribution to ground level concentrations of SO_2, will not necessarily disperse in the same way as the low level emissions. It must also be borne in mind that the correlation coefficients quoted are for daily data. The source configuration will play a more important role in determining shorter period fluctuations in concentrations.

Some feel for the importance of various meteorological variables in controlling ground level concentrations can be obtained from multiple regression analysis. Assuming a product relationship between the concentrations and the meteorological variables leads, for example, to an equation of the form:

$$\ln C = a + b\ln C' + c\ln T + d\ln U + e\ln P + f\ln I \ldots\ldots (7)$$

where C is the ambient concentration, T, U, P and I are respectively the corresponding ambient temperature, wind speed, precipitation intensity and cloud cover, and C' is the previous day's ambient concentration, included because of the observed strong serial correlation in pollution data. The constants a to f are the regression coefficients. Clearly additional or alternative parameters can be included such as relative humidity and intensity of atmospheric turbulence. The values of regression coefficients and of partial correlation coefficients for daily observations made in the Forth Valley and at Turnhouse Airport during 1973-4 and assuming the much simpler regression equation:

$$\ln C = a + b\ln T + c\ln U, \ldots\ldots\ldots (8)$$

are given in Table 2.

All coefficients are significant at the 1% level.

As would be expected concentrations exhibit inverse relationships with temperature and wind speed. The greater dependence of smoke concentrations (the major source of smoke is space-heating-type emissions), compared with those of SO_2, on temperature is clearly evident. One other feature of the data in Table 2 is to be expected; the values of the exponent (c)

of the wind speed for smoke is greater (in absolute terms)
than the values for SO_2. This is almost certainly due, in
part at least, to the fact that much of the SO_2 is emitted
from high stacks while the major contribution to ground level
concentrations of smoke is from the low-level emitters;
increasing the wind speed will increase the ventilation rate,
or advection rate, for both types of source but at the expense
of reduced plume rises, this latter effect being more important for the high-level emissions of SO_2 than for the low-level
emissions of smoke.

Table 2. Regression Coefficients and Partial
Correlation Coefficients for Equation (8)

Spatial Average and Pollutant	Coefficients					
			Temperature		Wind Speed	
	a	b	Partial Correlation	c	Partial Correlation	
WSL Urban Smoke	5.58	−0.60	−0.66	−0.58	−0.52	
" " SO_2	4.65	−0.23	−0.41	−0.50	−0.57	
WSL Rural Smoke	4.75	−0.47	−0.51	−0.83	−0.63	
" " SO_2	4.34	−0.14	−0.20	−0.62	−0.60	
National Survey Smoke	4.86	−0.46	−0.53	−0.71	−0.61	
" " SO_2	4.51	−0.11	−0.22	−0.32	−0.46	

In addition to identifying the important meteorological variables controlling concentrations in a particular area,
multiple regression analysis, together with simple correlation
coefficients, can be used to identify monitoring stations
which are returning observations which differ significantly
from the norm. Such differences can be genuine reflections of
local preculiarities in the emission pattern or dispersion
characteristics which must be taken into account in the
diffusion modelling but they can also be due to sampling
error.

Equations of type (7) and (8) are sometimes referred to as
regression (or statistical) models. Such models, provided
they are continually up-dated, can be used in short-period
forecasting schemes (e.g. in predicting the occurrence of a
pollution episode; see, for example, Smith and Jeffrey, 1971).
However, it is important to appreciate that their validity
extends only to the locality and range of values of dependent
and independent variables for which the regression coefficients were computed. Such an equation cannot be used for
predicting the effects of changing the emission characteristics of an area.

Smoke/SO_2 Ratios
The typical emission ratios (R_i) of smoke and SO_2 in the
Forth Valley vary from 3.0 for domestic coal through 0.3 for
domestic solid smokeless fuel to 0.02 for the large industrial

sources. Provided, therefore, that the two pollutants disperse similarly and have roughly the same life-times over the pollutant travel distances in question (a good approximation for most circumstances in the Forth Valley, the <u>observed concentration ratio</u> (R) of smoke and SO_2 at a site gives an indication of the relative contributions from, say, domestic and non-domestic sources. For example, assuming the major contributions are from domestic coal and solid smokeless fuel and industrial coal and oil, the concentration ratio (R) for any site can be approximated by:

$$R = \frac{R_1 + \beta R_2 + \alpha R_3}{1 + \beta + \alpha} \quad \dots\dots\dots\dots\dots (9)$$

where R_1, R_2 and R_3 are the respective emission ratios referred to above, β is the ratio of the contribution to ground level SO_2 concentrations from domestic coal and domestic solid smokeless fuel, and α is the corresponding ratio for the contribution from domestic coal and industrial coal and oil.

Because the domestic coal and solid smokeless fuel emissions are from similar source configurations and effective heights, a good approximation to β can be obtained directly from the emission inventories. Given the observed value of R, α can then be computed directly.

For the winter of 1973-4, typical values of R varied from about 1.5 in the mining communities to 0.5 in areas most affected by industry. These figures suggest that the industrial contribution to SO_2 concentrations ranged from being about the same as the domestic contribution in the mining communities to being 5 times the domestic contribution in other areas. At some sites the value of R on individual days was much less than 0.5 and on some days the industrial contribution to the SO_2 concentration at a site was probably as much as 20 times the domestic contribution. On other days the recorded value of R was much greater than 0.5 and the industrial contribution would then have been quite small.

Day-to-day variations in the observed smoke/SO_2 ratios provide another good practical test of the validity of a diffusion model.

DIFFUSION MODELLING

The basic diffusion equation relevant to most air pollution problems can be written in the form:

$$\frac{\partial C}{\partial t} + \underset{\sim}{V}\, \nabla C = \frac{\partial}{\partial x}\left(K_x \frac{\partial C}{\partial x}\right) + \frac{\partial}{\partial y}\left(K_y \frac{\partial C}{\partial y}\right) + \frac{\partial}{\partial z}\left(K_z \frac{\partial C}{\partial z}\right) + \text{sources}$$

$$+ \text{ sinks} \dots\dots\dots (10)$$

where C is the concentration, $\vec{V}$ the wind vector, and K_x, K_y and K_z are the components of diffusivity. Solutions of Equation (10) can be obtained using numerical (e.g. finite difference) or analytical techniques, the nature of the solutions depending on the simplifying assumptions and boundary conditions adopted. Our current applications involve only analytical solutions. These solutions have been preferred because of their convenience and speed in application and because, to date, there has not been a clear demonstration that the more complex and time-consuming numerical solutions provide, in practice, much more accurate or reliable predictions for essentially non-reactive pollutants such as smoke and SO_2. This should not be taken to mean that there is not a requirement for numerical solutions. There is considerable scope for developing such solutions for non-idealized situations where, for example, topography may have a significant influence on local dispersion characteristics.

The basis of the diffusion models currently being applied is the approximate steady-state solution for a continuous release (e.g. Fortak, 1970):

$$C(x, y) = \frac{Q}{\pi U \sigma_y \sigma_z} \exp\left[\frac{-y^2}{2\sigma_y^2}\right]\left[\exp\left(-\frac{H^2}{2\sigma_z^2}\right) + \exp\left(-\frac{(2L-H)^2}{2\sigma_z^2}\right)\right]$$

$$\dotfill (11)$$

where $C(x, y)$ is the ground level concentration, Q is the emission rate, U is the mean wind speed at height H, σ_y and σ_z are the cross-wind and vertical plume standard deviations and are functions of x, H is the effective source height, x, y and z are the down-wind, cross-wind and vertical co-ordinates and L is the height of the inversion (the equation is not valid for H>L). In deriving Equation (11), the statistical theory of turbulence has been used in preference to the gradient transfer approach expressed in Equation (10), the net vertical flux of pollutant is assumed to be zero at the ground and the elevated inversion, and it is assumed that there are no sinks. Corrections can be made to Equation (11) if necessary. For example, the effect of chemical transformations or absorption at the ground can be approximated by multiplying Equation (11) by exp $(-t/\tau)$, where t is the travel time and τ is the "life time", while in some cases it may be necessary to correct for topography by reducing the value of H.

Equation (11) is normally applicable to averaging times ranging from 3 minutes to 1 hour, depending on the values of σ_y and σ_z adopted. However, equations valid for long-period averages (e.g. month or year) can be derived by integrating Equation (11) with respect to y. Most of the problems with which we are concerned involve emissions from multiple sources such as urban areas. It is assumed that the contributions to

ground level concentrations from the individual point or area
sources are additive.

The sections which follow present some applications of
Equation (11) and simpler diffusion formulae to multiple
source configurations.

Overall Mass Balance Calculations

From the 1973-4 annual pollution roses for sites on the perimeter of the survey area estimates have been made of the
contributions to area average concentrations from sources
outside the area. These contributions amount to 15 µg/m^3 for
smoke and 25 µg/m^3 for SO_2, assuming no further dilution due
to diffusion and no losses as pollution is transported across
the area. Taking due account of the spatial representative-
ness and distribution of monitoring sites within the survey
area, the observed area averages are about 21 µg/m^3 of smoke,
and 33 µg/m^3 of SO_2. It might be deduced, therefore, that
sources within the survey area are contributing 6 µg/m^3, smoke
and 8 µg/m^3, SO_2 to the area averages. It must be stressed
that these are overall increments for the entire area. Many
of the urban and near-industry sites are returning annual
concentrations ranging from 45-70 µg/m^3, showing that the more
localised increments are in the range 20-55 µg/m^3.

For the domestic, commercial and smaller industrial sources an
approximation to their average contributions, C, can be
obtained from a simple "box" model. That is, the pollutant
is assumed uniformly distributed over the area and to some
height L*, which is a function of the area size. The relevant
equation is:

$$C = \frac{Q}{UaL^*} \quad \dots\dots\dots\dots\dots\dots\dots\dots (12)$$

where a is the length of the base side (assumed square), U is
the average wind speed, $L^* = \sigma_z(a/2)$ and Q is the total emission rate. Using the appropriate values of U, a and Q gives
annual average contributions of 3 µg/m^3, smoke and 7 µg/m^3,
SO_2.

The power stations and oil refinery contributions cannot be
computed on the above basis because of their high effective
heights of emission (250 m - 500 m). In this case the
average ground-level contributions were computed from:

$$C = \frac{1}{x_0} \int_0^{x_0} \frac{0.13\,Q}{U\sigma_z\,x} \exp\left(-H^2/2\sigma_z^2\right) dx \dots\dots (13)$$

the integrand having been obtained by integrating Equation
(11) with respect to y, letting L→∞, assuming equal wind-
direction frequencies and one wind speed and stability. The
distance x_0 is the typical distance from the source to the

edge of the survey area. Of course, account can be taken of the different wind-direction frequencies, wind speeds, stabilities and directional dependence of x_0 but Equation (13) will give the order of the contributions. Making some allowance for the periods when these emissions will be above the mixing layer (perhaps at least 30% of the time for the larger power station) the computed contributions for smoke are negligible and for SO_2 total about 7 $\mu g/m^3$. Added to the "box" model contributions, the computed total contributions to ground level concentrations from sources within the area are 3 $\mu g/m^3$ smoke, and 14 $\mu g/m^3$ SO_2. These can be compared with the corresponding estimates of 6 $\mu g/m^3$ and 8 $\mu g/m^3$ made from observations.

In view of the errors in sampling, the difficulties in obtaining truly representative spatial averages from a finite number of sites, the uncertainties in the emissions and simplifications incorporated in the "model" calculations, the two sets of figures can be regarded as being in broad agreement. However, loss mechanisms, at least for SO_2 are worth considering. Using recent estimates of the dry deposition velocity, taken together with the area average concentration of 33 $\mu g/m^3$, and of wet deposition rates, gives a loss equivalent to an area average of 4 $\mu g/m^3$. This effectively reduces the difference between the observed and calculated ground level SO_2 increments from 6 to 2 $\mu g/m^3$. This demonstrates the relative importance of loss mechanisms when modelling long period averages for a relatively large area, although it must be appreciated that, at least for dry deposition which is the more important mechanism in this situation, the main source of the SO_2 deposited over the Forth Valley is the area "background" due to external sources; it is unlikely that the typical percentage of SO_2 emitted within the survey area and lost within the same area exceeds 1 to 10%, the actual percentage increasing with decreasing effective height of emission.

These rather limited overall mass balance calculations for ground-level concentrations are now being extended to include more realistic representations of the vertical gradient of wind speed and concentration (e.g. in the vicinity of the Forth Road Bridge the westerly flux of SO_2 at 160 m is observed to be about twice that at ground-level while the corresponding smoke fluxes are about equal). Consideration is also being given to the directional fluxes and the relevant controlling parameters such as wind speed, stability and mixing depth. Variations in these almost certainly explain the following observations: on south-westerly air streams the ground-level fluxes of smoke and SO_2 leaving the survey area are respectively the same as, and marginally greater than, those entering while on north-easterly air streams there is a marginal increase in the corresponding smoke flux and a doubling of the SO_2 flux.

Box and Elevated Distributed Source Models

The "box" concept is also applicable to the modelling of multiple low-level emissions from small-scale urban areas. Table
3 gives a few examples for winter average smoke concentrations
and the agreement between observation and calculation is quite
good provided the local "background" concentration, C_0 is
taken into account, and, because of the relatively small areas
involved, L* is increased by an amount equal to the effective
height of emission (about 10 m for domestic sources).

Table 3. Computed and Observed Winter Average Smoke, $\mu g/m^3$

Town	Q(kg/h)	a(km)	L*(m)	C_0	$C_{calc} + C_0$	C_{obs}
Bo'ness	64.3	2	37	27	76	74
Falkirk	25.7	2	37	27	47	53
Grangemouth	12.1	2	37	27	36	40
Stirling	39.3	1.25	29	26	86	78

$$U = 5 \text{ m/s}; \quad \sigma_z = 0.15 \ (a/2)^{0.75}$$

Although the same model will work for the domestic (and
possibly other small sources) component of SO_2 it is not
realistic for the total SO_2 picture because of the much greater importance of the less diffuse sources and because the box
model cannot take adequate account of their greater values of
H.   A good approximation to the area average contribution
from these intermediate sources can be obtained from the
elevated distributed source model:

$$C = \frac{2Q_0}{\sqrt{2\pi} \ Ux_0} \int_0^{x_0} dx^* \int_0^{x^*} \frac{1}{\sigma_z} \exp \left(-H^2/2\sigma_z^2\right) dx \ldots (14)$$

provided the area is sufficiently large (e.g. see Turner et al
1972). $Q_0 (\equiv Q/a^2$ for a square based box model) is the
emission rate per unit area for the appropriate H category,
x^* is the down-wind distance from the up-wind edge of the
source area and x_0 is the distance over which the spatial mean
concentration is required. Equation (14) must be integrated
numerically. As an example of the different results produced
by Equations (14) and (12), corrected for H, consider
Grangemouth. The observed annual SO_2 average is 26 $\mu g/m^3$
(corrected for local background). The box model predicts a
total contribution of 43 $\mu g/m^3$ while Equation (14) predicts
only 18 $\mu g/m^3$, an underestimate but much closer to the
observed figure. Equation (14) could, of course, be used for
domestic sources and could also be used in place of Equation
(12) in the overall mass balance calculations.

Detailed Multiple Source Modelling

The modelling described in the previous two sections is of a
generalised nature and in order to predict the details of the
spatial and temporal distributions of ground-level concentrations, two models have been developed on the computer.

The first is used for predicting $\frac{1}{2}$-1 hourly contributions to concentrations. Equation (11) is the basic diffusion formula incorporated. The emission inventories are "fixed" in the OS 1 km grid frame-of-reference while the actual diffusion calculations are carried out in a frame of reference with the x-axis along the wind direction (e.g. see Turner, 1964). The standard deviations are expressed in the form:

$$\sigma_y = \sigma_{yo} + \alpha x^p \text{ and } \sigma_z = \sigma_{zo} + \beta x^q \ldots\ldots\ldots\ldots (15)$$

where α, β, p and q are constants depending on atmospheric stability. The value of σ_{yo} is taken as zero for elevated sources but for the low-level distributed sources, such as domestic, σ_{yo} is taken equal to s/2.4 where s is the length of the side of the emission inventory unit (normally s = 1km). The value of σ_{zo} is also taken as zero for plumes launched well clear of local buildings but again, say, for domestic sources in urban areas, is given a small value (say 3-5 m) to allow for any initial vertical spread due to building effects.

In practice, the computed contributions are highly sensitive to the values of σ_y and σ_z and therefore to the adopted values of α, β, p and q. In the absence of actual local measurements which would provide the appropriate values of the coefficients and exponents, we have adopted a range of published values (e.g. Singer and Smith, 1966). By choosing such a range of values we can get some idea of the magnitude of the errors in the computed contributions due to errors in σ_y and σ_z.

The contributions from individual point and area sources at specified receptor points can either be tabulated or the contributions can be displayed in "map" form for any prescribed spatial scale and resolution and concentration resolution. Fig. 2 illustrates such a "map" for domestic SO_2 emissions from Falkirk and SO_2 emissions from three hypothetical industrial sources. The low-range concentration resolution has been used in this example. Such a map presentation is invaluable in assessing the importance of plume overlap for various wind directions.

The second model is used for computing long-period averages and again the output can be by specified receptor point or in "map" form. Equation (13) is the basic diffusion formula in this case but with allowance for the frequency of wind direction, directional dependence of wind speed etc. The initial horizontal spread of emissions from an area source is allowed for by increasing the value of x on the denominator of Equation (13) (but note not the value of x used to compute σ_z) by an amount depending on the size of the area source and the angular size of the wind sector.

In both types of model the "box" concept is used to compute

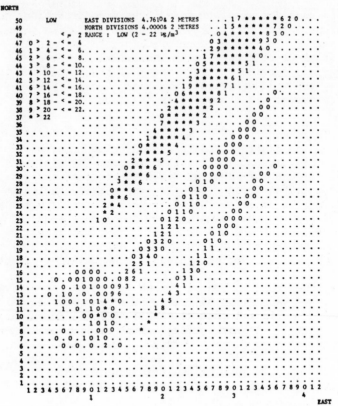

FIG.2 CONTRIBUTIONS TO HOURLY SO$_2$ CONCENTRATIONS FROM FALKIRK
(DOMESTIC) AND THREE HYPOTHETICAL INDUSTRIAL SOURCES

the relatively-important contribution from the diffuse low-
level sources in the immediate vicinity of a receptor or
"map" point.

SUMMARY

In this paper we have intentionally stressed the more practical aspects of a large-scale air pollution monitoring/
modelling project and some of the relatively simple techniques
by which one can readily gain considerable insight into the
characteristics of the area in question. It is all too
tempting to become immersed in the more sophisticated mathematical techniques of modelling without appreciating the
deficiencies of the available data and very often at the
expense of overlooking the more obvious significant features
of dispersion in the study area. Nevertheless, there is a
requirement for better models and, in the long run, numerical
solutions of the diffusion equation seem the only course by
which significant improvements will be made. It should be
appreciated, however, that such models are even more data-
hungry than the models described in this paper and in the
last analysis the predictions cannot be better than the input
data. There is an over-riding case for devoting more effort

to obtaining the <u>relevant</u> meteorological data and improving the quality of emission inventories.

ACKNOWLEDGEMENTS

This project is essentially a co-operative effort and leans heavily on the voluntary support of Local Authorities, Industry, the Meteorological Office and private individuals. All have given a generous response: Local Authorities and Industry through purchasing, installing and operating air pollution monitors and in helping to acquire the necessary emission data; the Meteorological Office, Edinburgh, in providing most of the required meteorological data; and private individuals in agreeing to Warren Spring Laboratory using their premises to house instruments.

We also acknowledge the major role played by our colleagues, R. Galbraith, H.L. Nicholson, D. Scott and A.B. Ward, who operate the monitoring network and carry out all of the sample analysis.

REFERENCES

Briggs, G. (1969) Plume Rise. US Atomic Energy Commission. Washington.
British Standard 1747 Parts 2 (1964) and 3 (1963), British Standards Institute, London.
Fortak, H.G. (1970) Numerical Simulation of Temporal and Spatial Distributions of Urban Air Pollution Concentration. Proceedings of Symposium on Multiple-Source Urban Diffusion Models, USEPA, North Carolina.
Gas Council (1965) Degree Days. Technical Handbook No. 101 London.
HMSO (1972) National Survey of Air Pollution 1961-71. London 1
Larsen, R.I. (1971) A Mathematical Model for Relating Air Quality Measurements to Air Quality Standards. USEPA, North Carolina, Report No. AP-89.
Smith, F.B. and Jeffrey, G.H. (1972) The Prediction of High Concentrations of Sulphur Dioxide in London Air. Meteorological Office Bracknell: Report No. TDN No. 19.
Smith, M.E. and Singer, I. A. (1966) An Improved Method of Estimating Concentrations and Related Phenomena from a Point Source Emission. J. Appl. Met., 5, 631-639.
Turner, D.B. (1964) A Diffusion Model for an Urban Area. J. Appl. Met., 3, 83-91.
WHO (1972) Air Quality Criteria and Guides for Urban Air Pollutants. Geneva: Technical Report No. 506.

SHALLOW-WATER APPROXIMATION FOR THE TRANSPORT OF POLLUTANTS
IN AN URBAN BASIN

C.Y. Liu and W.R. Goodin

University of California, Los Angeles

ABSTRACT

The distribution of an inert chemical species, carbon monoxide
(CO), emitted mainly from automobile exhaust and power plants
is investigated. The transport model, in analogy with the
shallow-water theory in fluid dynamics, considers variation
of all physical quantities in the horizontal direction below
the temperature inversion layer. Pollutants are found to be
carried primarily by the wind; turbulent diffusion on a normal
day plays only a minor role. The concentration of CO predicted by the present model for the entire Los Angeles basin
is compared with observed data at nine stations. Accuracy
of four different numerical schemes, the effect of turbulent
diffusivity, and the source strengths are examined.

1. INTRODUCTION

Air pollution models provide the capability for forecasting,
planning or monitoring of air quality on a regional or global
basis. With the advance of computers, recent models simulate
the transport and reactive processes of pollutants by numerical solution of the species continuity equation. (For a
review of current statistical and numerical models see Hoffert
(1972)). Two different methods of integration exist: the
moving-cell (Lagrangian) and the fixed-coordinate (Eulerian)
models. A moving-cell is an air parcel which may be viewed
as a vertical column of air moved by the instantaneous wind
vectors, thus tracing out a particular surface trajectory in
the airshed. By following a fixed mass of air, one may
neglect the horizontal diffusion and consider its chemical
kinetics as if the air parcel were a moving smog chamber. In
general, the moving-cell approach avoids the lengthy integration of the governing equation in three spatial dimensions and
time, it also permits the easy verification of pollutant distribution by tracing a given parcel from its source. However,

the concepts of an identifiable parcel of air, and that the
air at a specific location can be traced back to a single
source, are perhaps over-simplified. The early model of
Eschenroeder and Martinez (1970) and that of Wayne et. al.
(1973) are good illustrations.

A fixed-coordinate model generally involves the integration
of the coupled species concentration equations in a three-
dimensional Eulerian frame. They are often hampered by large
computer storage requirements, and large amounts of computer
time. But, one obtains solutions at each grid point and at
each time level, rather than only along a specific wind trajectory. Furthermore, numerical techniques for solving the
governing equation are well-known. In principle, the fixed-
coordinate model can consider the effects of ground absorption, arbitrary distribution of sources, rise and fall of the
inversion base, as well as arbitrary description of the photochemistry. Examples of the fixed-coordinate model are the
recent studies of Reynolds, et al. (1973, 1974) in which an
elaborate effort in source inventory and chemical modelling
are made, the work of Pandolfo and Jacobs (1973) where the
meteorological parameters are predicted, and the present
investigation.

2.   A TWO-DIMENSIONAL MODEL

Integration of the species concentration equation involves
considerable labor, and often prohibitive amounts of computer
time, particularly when chemical kinetics are included. The
present study formulates a simple two-dimensional model applicable to reactive pollutants. There are several basic assumptions:

1. The atmosphere below the inversion base is uniformly
    mixed in the vertical over a time scale on the order
    of an hour.

2. The atmosphere in this layer, below the inversion
    base, behaves like that in a well-mixed estuary where
    horizontal advection is large relative to vertical
    advection.

3. Horizontal diffusion is much less important than hori-
    zontal advection in the transport of pollutants.

These assumptions could simplify the species continuity
equation:

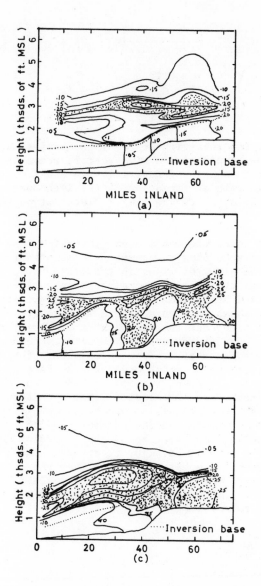

Figure 1. Contours of oxidant concentrations (ppm) in the
vertical cross section from Santa Monica to
Rialto-Miro, as observed by Edinger (1973). (a)
9:00 AM, (b) 12:00 noon, (c) 4:30 PM, 20 June
1970.

$$\frac{\partial C_i}{\partial t} + u \frac{\partial C_i}{\partial x} + v \frac{\partial C_i}{\partial y} + w \frac{\partial C_i}{\partial z} = \frac{\partial}{\partial x} \left(K_x \frac{\partial C_i}{\partial x} \right) + \frac{\partial}{\partial y} \left(K_y \frac{\partial C_i}{\partial y} \right) +$$

$$+ \frac{\partial}{\partial z} \left(K_z \frac{\partial C_i}{\partial z} \right) + R_i \ (C_1, C_2, \ldots C_N) + S_i (x,y,t)$$

$$i = 1, 2, \ldots N.$$

(1)

Here C_i is the concentration of the i-th species; u, v, w, are the x, y, z components of the wind vector, respectively; K_x, K_y, K_z are the turbulent diffusivities in the x, y, z direction; R_i is the rate of formation of the i-th species through chemical reactions; S_i is the source distribution for that species.

The atmosphere below the temperature inversion base is indeed very well-mixed according to a number of observations. The vertical profile of water vapor in the mixed layer is practically uniform; the constant concentration contours of oxidants observed by Edinger (1973) at three different hours of the day, as shown in Figure 1, are almost vertical. In Figure 1, we notice that the contours depart from being vertical in regions near the mountains. However, the horizontal and vertical gradients of concentration within the mixed layer are small compared to those observed at the base of the temperature inversion. Recent results of LARPP (The Los Angeles Reactive Pollutant Program) confirms that a uniform concentration profile in the vertical is correct except in the proximity of a strong ground source [Edinger (1975)]. The approximation of a well-mixed layer below the inversion seems justified. Since the concentration C_i is at most a weak function of vertical direction z, its variation over the entire thickness of the marine layer h could be characterized by (say) its mean value $\overline{C_i}$, in analogy with the shallow-water approximation for an estuary.

$$\overline{C_i} = \frac{1}{h} \int_0^h C_i \ dz$$

(2)

Within the same approximation, we shall find that the vertical advective velocity w is negligible in relation to horizontal advection. The value of w vanishes on the ground, but, in general, it assumes a non-trivial value at the top of the mixing layer, namely,

$$w(x,y,o,t) = 0,$$

and

(3)

$$w(x,y,h,t) = u\Big|_h \cdot \frac{\partial h}{\partial x} + v\Big|_h \cdot \frac{\partial h}{\partial y} + \frac{\partial h}{\partial t}$$

The gradients in h: $\partial h/\partial x$, $\partial h/\partial y$, and the temporal variation
of h, $\partial h/\partial t$ are on the order of 10^{-2} and 0.03 m $\sec^{-1}$,
respectively, in an urban basin such as Los Angeles; while u
or v on a normal day is about 5 - 10 m $\sec^{-1}$.   The value of w
evaluated by the second equation in (3) in on the order of
0.1 m $\sec^{-1}$, or virtually zero.   Vertical wind motion in the
marine layer is often observed to be cellular, yet its mean
motion over a period of one hour and a spatial resolution of
one kilometer is negligible.   Thus, the complete vanishing of
w, insofar as pollutant transport is concerned, seems well
justified.

Pollutants are transported in the horizontal direction mainly
by advection.   Horizontal diffusivity (K_x, K_y) is assumed to
have a constant value of 50 m^2 $\sec^{-1}$ in Reynolds et al. (1973)
analysis; while the vertical diffusivity (K_z) varies from
about 0.5 m^2 $\sec^{-1}$ under very stable conditions to about 100
m^2 $\sec^{-1}$.   Vertical diffusion plays a very important role in
mixing the marine layer, since vertical advection is negligible.   Based on the aforementioned value for the horizontal
diffusivity, and a typical wind speed of 10 m $\sec^{-1}$, we find
from observations that terms like $K_x \partial^2 C_i/\partial x^2$ (or $K_y \partial^2 C_i/\partial y^2$)
and $u\partial C_i/\partial x$ (or $v\partial C_i/\partial y$) are on the order of 10^{-4} ppm $\sec^{-1}$
and 10^{-2} ppm $\sec^{-1}$, respectively.   The horizontal wind is the
dominant agent in the transfer of pollutants, hence the search
for very accurate values of K_x or K_y, insofar as pollutants
transport is concerned, may be relaxed.

With the preceding assumptions, Eq. (1) can be integrated
vertically from the ground to the base of the temperature
inversion to yield

$$\frac{\partial \bar{C}_i h}{\partial t} + u\frac{\partial \bar{C}_i h}{\partial x} + v\frac{\partial \bar{C}_i h}{\partial y} =$$

$$= \frac{\partial}{\partial x}\left(K_x\frac{\partial \bar{C}_i h}{\partial x}\right) + \frac{\partial}{\partial y}\left(K_y\frac{\partial \bar{C}_i h}{\partial y}\right) + R_i h + S_i h$$

$$i = 1, 2, \ldots N . \qquad (4)$$

Equation (4) is the governing equation for the mean concentration $\bar{C}_i$ in the present two-dimensional model.   It has been a
assumed that the same chemical kinetics hold true for the mean
concentrations, namely

$$R_i(C_1, C_2\ldots,C_N) = R_i\,(\bar{C}_1, \bar{C}_2,\ldots\bar{C}_N)$$

The chemical species of concentration $\bar{C}_i$ is transfered in or
out of the computational region at the boundary by the local
wind, hence the boundary conditions for $\bar{C}_i$ are known once the
wind vectors are known at the boundary.   The shallow-water

approximation has, in effect, reduced the three spatial
dimensions [Eq. (1)] to two [Eq. (4)]. This reduction has
the following advantages:

1. Knowledge of the vertical wind component w, generally
    not recorded by existing wind stations, is not
    required.

2. Detailed correlations of all turbulent diffusivities
    can be avoided.

3. Boundary conditions for $\overline{C_i}$ on the ground and at the
    top of the mixing layer are no longer needed, hence
    we may bypass the difficult task of modelling ground
    absorption.

4. The time increment required for stable integration of
    Equation (4) is, in general, several orders of magni-
    tude larger than that for Equation (1). Consider, for
    instance, a horizontal grid size (Δx, or Δy) of 1 km,
    a vertical grid size* (Δz) of 20m, a vertical diffu-
    sivity K_z of 50 m^2 sec^{-1}, and a horizontal wind of
    10 m sec^{-1}, then the time-step allowed for the stable
    integration of Equation (1) is 4 sec; and it is 100
    sec for Equation (4).

5. The substantial reduction in computer storage and
    computer time seems clear.

3.   INPUTS

An air pollution model, in which Equation (4) is to be
integrated either using fixed-coordinates or tracing a
moving cell, requires three types of input information:
1. Meteorological data, such as the height of the inversion
base h, the wind field u, v, and turbulent diffusivities K_x,
K_y. 2. Source inventory for the i-th species S_i, and, in
general, 3. Mechanism of the chemical kinetics involving the
i-th species, R_i. In the present study of carbon monoxide
(CO) distribution in the Los Angeles basin, we shall consider
CO as a chemically inert species, so kinetic mechanisms need
not be considered.

Meteorological data is supplied to an air pollution model
either through direct measurement or by forecasting. A
mesoscale meteorological model, by which the aforementioned
variables including h, u, v, etc. are predicted, is being

---

*The minimum vertical mesh spacing of 20 m was employed by
 Reynolds (1973), and estimated by Lamb and Neiburger (1970).

formulated by many investigators:[*] Pandolfo and Jacobs (1973),
Goodin (1975). With few exceptions, meteorological inputs are
presently obtained through direct observation.

3.1   The Height of the Inversion Base, h.

The elevated temperature inversion lying on top of a well-
mixed marine layer is characteristic in a middle-latitude,
coastal basin such as Los Angeles. The variation of the
marine layer changes with location.

Neiburger (1974) correlated the diurnal variation of the
mixing depth h for the Los Angeles basin. His correlation
of h is separated into two components: one due to solar
heating at the surface (HQ) and a second due to wind field
divergence (HD). In other words,

$$h = h_0 + HQ + HD - (H_{Topo} - H_{Base})$$

where h_0 is the reference height (Figure 2a)

$$HQ = (HQ)_0 \sin (\pi t/\tau_H + \phi_1) \sin (\pi s/L)$$

$$HD = (HD)_0 \sin (2\pi t/\tau + \phi_2)$$

$(HQ)_0$, the amplitude of heating oscillation, about 400 m
        in Los Angeles.

$(HD)_0$, the amplitude of divergence oscillation, about 60 m.

ϕ_1, the phase shift that produces maximum h inland at
        1400 hours.

ϕ_2, the phase shift that produces maximum h at coast at
        0800 hours.

s, distance to the nearest coastline.

L, the length scale, it is taken to be 120 km.

τ_H, the heating period, exactly 12 hours.

τ, the diurnal period, 24 hours.

---

[*]The success of predictive mesoscale models would eliminate a
considerable amount of the uncertainty in the input data. A
complete mesoscale model, in which the Navier-Stokes equations, the energy equation and a set of turbulent model
equations are integrated, is being investigated by Dr. Paul
Swan at the National Aeronautics and Space Administration,
Ames Research Center.

H_{Topo} is the height of the actual land above sea level.

H_{Base} is the height of coastal plane above sea level, a linear function of the distance s.

Neiburger's correlation, supposedly valid for the entire year, is compared with the observations of Edinger in Figure 2b for three different hours on three consecutive days in June of 1970. The graphs in Figure 2b showing a transect from Santa Monica to Azusa, confirm the expected agreement despite the very simple sinusoidal approximations. The value of h, as given by Equation (5), is the input to the present investigation.

3.2   Wind field: u,v.

Wind vectors on the ground level are recorded at a finite number of locations. Based on those measured values, the complete wind field is extrapolated. Since wind is the prime carrier of air contaminants, a mass-consistent wind field is crucial in air pollution modelling. The use of objective analysis in the generation of a wind field from observed data succeeds in reducing wind divergence, but often produces a wind distribution that bears no resemblance to the observed one. An iterative technique, through which the divergence of the wind was minimized while the field of vorticity was retained, was proposed by Endlich (1967). Recently, Dickerson (1973) implemented Sasaki's variational formulation (1970) to generate a mass-consistent wind from data acquired in the San Francisco Bay area. An iterative algorithm, by which the wind divergence was reduced but the observed wind vectors were held fixed, was formulated by Goodin and Liu (1975). Results of these three methods for generating a mass-consistent wind field from the same set of initial conditions for 1500 hours, 5 January 1972 are presented in Figure 3. Qualitatively, the Dickerson-Sasaki algorithm yields a wind field (Figure 3a) showing a sea breeze heading inland uniformly, a similar observation can be made about the fixed-vorticity algorithm (Figure 3b). One observes that wind vectors at various locations in Figures 3a and 3b have little similarity to the observed values which are represented by heavy-lined vectors in Figure 3c. The fixed-velocity algorithm gives a wind field (Figure 3c) considerably more complex than a unidirectional sea breeze, particularly in the downtown Los Angeles area. Quantitatively, the mean-square-divergence of the wind field with an initial value of order unity (per second) remains practically the same in the Dickerson-Sasaki algorithm. It is reduced to a very low value, $0(10^{-6} \; sec^{-1})$ through the fixed-vorticity algorithm, and it becomes $0(10^{-4} \; sec^{-1})$ by the fixed-velocity method. The fixed-velocity scheme is adopted, in the present study, to produce wind fields from the hourly recording values obtained at some twenty stations in Los Angeles.

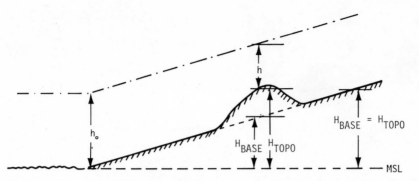

Figure 2a. Nomenclature used for inversion base calculation.

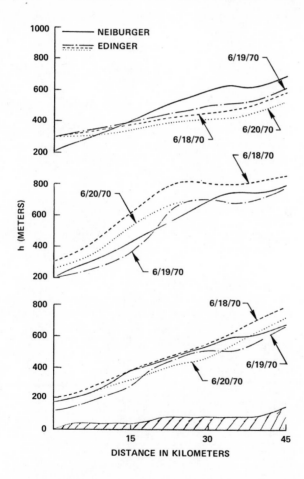

Figure 2b. Comparison of calculated and measured inversion
base at 3PM (bottom), noon (middle), 9AM (top).

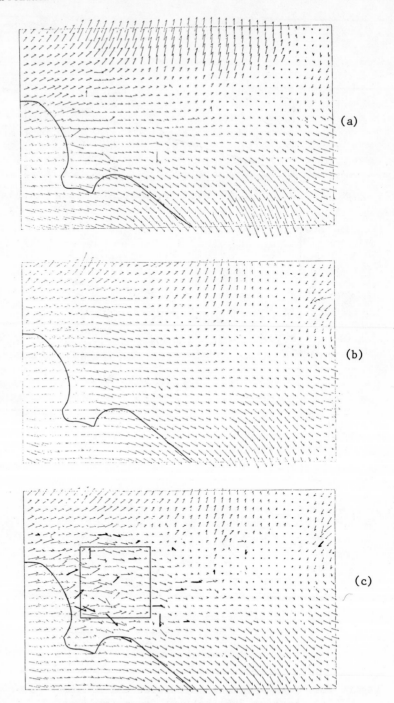

Figure 3.   Wind field produced by (a) Dickerson's algorithm,
            (b) fixed-vorticity algorithm, (c) fixed-station-
            velocity algorithm.

3.3   Turbulent Diffusivity: K_x, K_y, K_z.

Turbulent diffusivity in the lower atmosphere is most
difficult to predict, though various turbulence models have
been developed in recent years. Mixing in the atmosphere is
generally enhanced by an increase in surface wind speeds.
Hence, vertical diffusivity, K_z, is expected to increase from
a small value at the ground to a nearly constant value in the
middle of the mixed layer, then decrease as it approaches the
bottom of the temperature inversion layer. Correlations by
Eschenroeder and Martinez (1970), and Aleksandrova (1965),
all show the same qualitative behavior. One feature of the
present two-dimensional model is the complete independence of
the vertical diffusivity, and the minor role that horizontal
diffusivity plays in the transport of pollutants. For the
computation reported herein, the values of K_x and K_y were
zero, while a constant value of 50 m^2 sec^{-1} was used in the
analysis of Reynolds et al. (1973, 1974). The effects of
nonzero values in K_x and K_y were investigated separately.

3.4   Source Inventory: S_i.

Besides the wind field, the element which may significantly
affect the results of air pollution forecasting is the source
inventory. A fairly detailed inventory model, including not
just automobile emissions but also aircraft and stationary
sources, was developed by Roth, et al. (1974). Since the
present analysis is focused on the distribution of an inert
chemical species (CO), of which 99% is emitted by automobile
exhaust, the source inventory herein becomes quite simple.
On a two-dimensional grid, the traffic count in terms of
vehicle-miles per day on each grid square was calculated
using yearly-averaged traffic counts for the years 1964-1968
for streets and freeways in that square. The emission rates
of CO were then calculated from the formula:

$$CO[ppm/min] = \left(\begin{matrix} \text{Units Conversion} \\ \text{Constant} \end{matrix}\right) \left(\begin{matrix} \text{Vehicle-mile} \\ \text{/day} \end{matrix}\right)$$

$$\left(\begin{matrix} \text{Hourly traffic} \\ \text{percentage} \end{matrix}\right) \bigg/ \left(\begin{matrix} \text{Height of inversion} \\ \text{base} \end{matrix}\right)$$

where the hourly average was based on a smoothed version of
the bimodal traffic distribution used by Neiburger and Lamb
(1970), as given in Figure 4.

4.   RESULTS

The date of 29 August 1967, a moderately smoggy day in
Los Angeles was selected for computation, with wind, source
and CO observed data available [Neiburger (1974)]. A two-
dimensional grid, 70x60, each square one kilometer on a side,
was used for the finite difference integration. The wind-
field, inversion height, turbulent diffusivity, and source

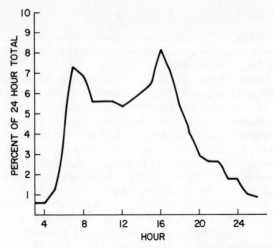

Figure 4.   Diurnal variation of average daily traffic
count, Los Angeles basin.

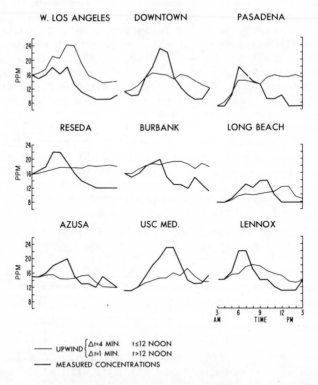

Figure 5.   Comparison of computer and measure concentrations at nine stations in Los Angeles basin, Δt
signifies time-step used in the integration.

distribution were obtained as described in the preceding section. The initial conditions were the measured values of CO at 3AM on that date interpolated to grid locations.

The upwind differencing scheme was used for Equation (4) because it displayed a large amount of pseudo-diffusion in a separate study of numerical schemes [Liu (1973)]. The numerical diffusion aids in smoothing the short wavelength components which dominate a numerical pollutant transport computation. Such a concentration distribution arises as a result of the discrete-valued source function. The diffusivity was set to zero; the effects of nonzero diffusivity were examined later.

The boundary conditions were specified as follows. The concentration gradient was held at zero everywhere except over the ocean. The concentration at the boundary points over the ocean were held fixed at the background values (3AM) since additional pollutants should not be advected into the field of interest from over the ocean.

The results of the computation along with the measured values are displayed in Figure 5 in the form of a time history. The computed curves are generally flatter than the measured ones since the peaks and valleys are smoothed by the large pseudo-diffusion. The computed results seem to be especially low during the morning rush hour. This may be due to inaccurate source values obtained from averaging five years of data. This problem may be accentuated by two additional factors. Source measuring errors, caused by sensors being too close to roads and freeways may produce unreasonable peaks in the measured curve. Second, the same bimodal traffic distribution may not be applicable to all sections of the Los Angeles basin as was assumed.

In order to understand the overall computed concentration pattern, isopleths were drawn on the map of the Los Angeles basin. Figures 6a, 6b, 6c show the hours of 3AM, 9AM and 3PM, respectively. The concentrations are in parts per million, with solid dots indicating the measured station values. The highest concentrations occur in the San Fernando and San Gabriel Valleys, while the lowest concentrations are in the southern half of the grid area. The isopleths show substantially better results than exhibited at each individual station. At 9AM (Figure 6b), the heavy concentration of CO at the center of the basin (north of the station VER, Vernon) is correctly predicted, and the moderate values of CO in the eastern part of the basin (Azusa) are also forecasted. At 3PM (Figure 6c), the almost uniform distribution of CO in the entire basin with relatively higher concentration in the downtown and West Los Angeles areas are also given. The

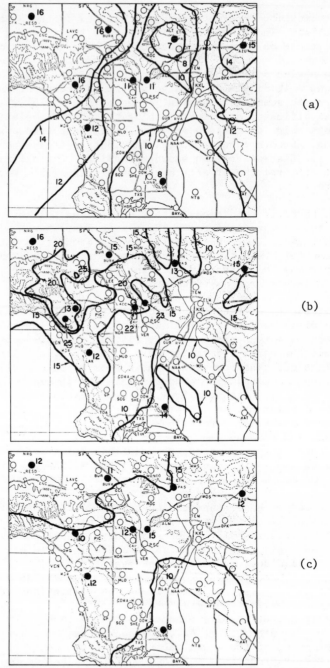

Figure 6.   Computed carbon monoxide concentration (isopleths) and measured values (numbers beside solid dots) for 29 August 1967. All values are in ppm. (a) 3:00AM, (b) 9:00AM, (c) 3:00PM.

two-dimensional model seems capable of preserving the basic physical mechanism of pollutant transport. Consequently, it predicts contaminant distribution better on a regional basis than at each grid point.

Because of the simplicity of the present formulation, a parametric analysis was carried to investigate the importance of the numerical scheme, turbulent diffusivity, and source strength. Conclusions of these experiments are summarized as follows.

In the first experiment, three additional advection schemes were examined for accuracy. They were leapfrog, Fromm's zero-average-phase-error (Fromm, 1969), and Peaceman-Rachford's alternating-direction-implicit (ADI) differencings. The diffusivity in all computations were all kept at zero in order to focus on the advective mechanism. Criteria for numerical stability of each scheme were satisfied at all times. The four schemes produced quite different solutions. [Figure 7] Fromm's zero-average-phase-error and upwind differencing produce generally similar results, since both have the transportive property. However, the upwind solution is more damped. The short wavelength Fourier components introduced into the computation by the discrete source input produce large oscillations in the ADI and leapfrog solutions. In general, the results of the experiment clearly indicate the importance of the numerical scheme in pollutant forecasting. In fact, the choice of numerical scheme is as important as the physical principles incorporated into the model.

The second experiment involved a test of the relative importance of diffusion. The upwind differencing scheme was used in this test because it produced the best results in the previous tests. A turbulent diffusivity of up to 800 m^2sec^{-1}, the highest value used by Lamb and Neiburger, was introduced into the computation. It did not significantly change the solution. Larger values of diffusivity, however, would cause the solution to exceed the scale of 25ppm. Thus, diffusion plays a varying role depending upon the amount of diffusion in the numerical scheme. In general, diffusion of moderate magnitude is much less important than advection.

As mentioned previously, at many of the stations, the concentrations computed using upwind differencing were consistently lower than the measured values. In addition to the obvious errors in yearly average traffic data, a possible explanation is that the general bimodal traffic distribution (Figure 5) is not accurate for all locations in the basin, since traffic peaks occur at different locations at different times.

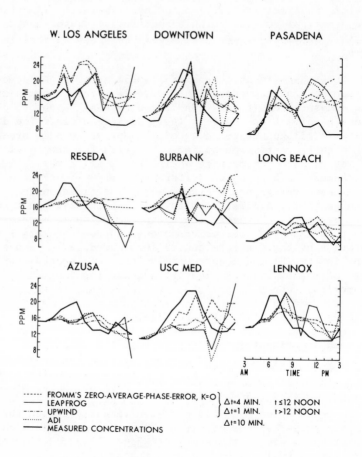

Figure 7.   Comparison of results from four different finite
difference schemes.

In the third numerical experiment, we increased the source strength for the hours 5-8AM by increasing the hourly percentages for those hours. The source adjustment produced better results at some stations (Downtown, USC Med, Lennox) while at others there was little change. At stations where there was indeed heavy morning traffic, the adjustment yielded closer prediction to the observed value. A station with little change may have had a small source strength to begin with or have slightly more divergent winds than its neighbors. In either case, source strength adjustment can only account for some of the discrepancy. Better knowledge of the inversion base heights to account for urban heat inland effects may also change the computed results.

5. SUMMARY

A number of experiments have been performed which show that the two-dimensional model yields reasonably good predictions to justify its basic assumption of a well-mixed marine layer. The advection scheme has been shown to be of great importance in determining the concentration values, while diffusion is small in comparison with advection. With the exception of extremely low wind speeds prevailing at morning hours, pollutants in an urban basin are dispersed almost totally by advection. It has also been shown that certain localized adjustments in source strength, inversion height, and diffusion coefficient can improve the calculated values.

The advantage of the present model lies not only in its simplicity in computation, but also the uncertainty regarding the appropriate boundary conditions for $\bar{C}_i$ on the ground and at the base of the inversion layer is avoided. In the future, photochemical reactions of pollutants could be readily incorporated, provided that a simple description of the chemical kinetics is found.

Acknowledgments - This work was supported by the National Aeronautics and Space Administration under UCL-302. The authors are grateful for their discussions with Professors M. Neiburger, J. Edinger of the University of California, Los Angeles, and Dr. Paul Swan of NASA-Ames.

REFERENCES

Aleksandrova, A.K., Byzova, N.L. and Mashkova, G.B., (1965) Experiments on the Spreading of Precipitating Admixture from a Point Source in the Bottom Layer of the Atmosphere, Investigation of the Bottom 300-Meter Layer of the Atmosphere ed. N. Byzova, translated by Israel Program for Scientific Translation, Jerusalem.

Dickerson, M.H. (1973) A Mass-Consistent Wind Field Model for the San Francisco Bay Area, Lawrence Livermore Laboratory, Livermore, California UCRL-74265.

Edinger, J.G. (1973) Vertical Distribution of Photochemical Smog in the Los Angeles Basin, Environ. Sci. Tech. 1, 247.

Edinger, J.G. (1975), Private communication.

Endlich, R.M. (1967) An Iterative Method for Altering the Kinematic Properties of Wind Fields, J. Appl. Met. 6, 837.

Eschenroeder, A.Q. and Martinez, J.R. (1970) Mathematical Modeling of Photochemical Smog, AIAA paper 70-116, New York, N.Y.

Fromm, J.E. (1969) Practical Investigation of Convective Difference Approximations of Reduced Dispersion. Phys. Fluids, 12, Supplement II, II-3.

Goodin, W. (1975) A Computational Study of Pollutant Transport in a Mixing Layer, Ph.D. Thesis, University of California, Los Angeles.

Goodin, W. and Liu, C.Y., (1975) An Iterative Algorithm for Mass-Consistent Wind Field Analysis, paper to be presented at the 2nd U.S. National Conference on Wind Engineering Research, June 23-25, 1975, Fort Collins, Colorado.

Hoffert, M.I. (1972) Atmospheric Transport, Dispersion, and Chemical Reactions in Air Pollution: A Review, AIAA Journal, 10, 377.

Lamb, R.G. and Neiburger, M. (1970) Mathematical Model of the Diffusion and Reactions of Pollutants Emitted over an Urban Area. Project Clean Air Research Reports, 4, University of California, Los Angeles.

Liu, C.Y. (1973) Numerical Problems in the Prediction of Pollutant Distribution in the Lower Atmosphere, paper presented at the 2nd Conference on Numerical Prediction of the American Meteorological Society, 54, No. 7, 755.

Neiburger, M. (1974) Private Communication.

Pandolfo, J.P. and Jacobs, C.A. (1973) Tests of an Urban Meteorological-Pollution Model using CO Validation Data in the Los Angeles Metropolitan Area, The Center for the Environment and Man Inc. CEM 4124-490a.

Sasaki, Y. (1970) Some Basic Formalisms in Numerical Variational Analysis, Monthly Weather Rev. 98, 875.

Reynolds, S.D., Roth, P.M., and Seinfeld, J.H. (1973) Mathematical Modelling of Photochemical Air Pollution - I. Atm. Envir. 7, 1033. Parts II (1974) and III (1974) appeared in Atm. Envir. 8, 97 and 563 respectively.

Wayne, L.G., Kokin, A., and Weisburd, M.I. (1973) Controlled Evaluation of the Reactive Environmental Simulation Model, Pacific Environment Services, Final Report, Santa Monica, California.

CHANGES IN ATMOSPHERIC POLLUTION CONCENTRATIONS

R.J.Bennett, W.J.Campbell, R.A.Maughan

Department of Geography, University College London

This paper examines changes in the level and structure of smoke and sulphur dioxide (SO_2) pollution concentrations at Kew between 1952 and 1971. A time series model of periodic and persistence components is used to relate observed variation in concentrations to changes in the level, nature and pattern of emissions, and to modifications in photochemical processes due to nonlinearities, by applying spectral analysis and adaptive parameter estimation derived from Kalman filtering.

PROCESSES CONTROLLING ATMOSPHERIC POLLUTION CONCENTRATIONS

Concentration of pollution in the atmosphere as indicated by measurements made at ground level depends upon two principal factors, emissions and meteorological conditions, and also, where the pollutant is photochemically active, upon reaction rates.

Emissions relate to the rate, height and temperature of discharge of a pollutant in the atmosphere, and to the pattern of discharge around the measuring point. Emissions are subject to periodic variation, for example to weekly and annual cycles of concentration which are attributable to economic activity (the working week) or to seasonal patterns of heating (Summers, 1966). Once emitted, the movement of pollution is controlled by the weather.

Meteorological conditions, for example vertical temperature gradient, eddy, mean wind speeds and wind direction, control the extent to which pollution is diffused in the atmosphere and carried away from the measurement point, and also the extent to which pollution from other sources is advected into the measurement area. Short-term variations in pollution concentration depend mainly on the diurnal cycle of meteorological variables for a given synoptic situation, while longer-term variations depend on whether or not the synoptic situation is conducive to pollution stagnation over the area. Anticyclonic weather patterns, most common in the winter months in Britain, cause local or regional build-up of pollution whilst cyclonic conditions are most favourable to pollution dispersion. These weather types follow recognized regimes through the year, and therefore contribute to seasonal variations in pollution concentrations.

When the pollutant in question is photochemically active, a third factor can be thought of as a control upon concent-rations, namely rates of reaction of the pollutant which determine how long the pollutant remains in its initial form. There are several photochemically active pollutants in the air and the number of possible reactions involving them is very large, so the precise effect of this control is difficult to determine. In the present case the control is relevant only to SO_2 which is known to react with several substances in the air (Goetz and Pueschel, 1967). For example, SO_2 reacts with metallic oxides, which may be responsible for its oxidation to SO_3, and with water, the end result being H_2SO_4, usually in the form of a fine aerosol mist causing marked reduction in visibility. The addition of SO_2 to the NO_2-olefin mixture of car exhausts leads to an increase in aerosol formation (Leighton, 1961). The exact nature and rates of these reactions are not well known, but their effects will be to reduce the amount of SO_2 in the atmosphere and so lower recorded concentrations.

These three factors interreact to produce variations in measured pollution concentrations, variations which may have a periodic form such as the annual cycle, or a form of persistence due to daily similarities in emissions or weather patterns, or other more complex forms.

Observed pollution series

The daily totals of smoke pollution, measured at Kew, from April 1952 to December 1971, and of SO_2 pollution from June 1960 to December 1971, are shown as monthly mean values in Figure 1. These data were collected as part of the National Survey of Air Pollution (Department of Trade and Industry, 1972). For the smoke series the most striking initial observ-ations are of the seasonal periodicity and the reduction of winter concentrations from the 1950s to the 1970s. Within the whole series there appear to be three recognizable periods:

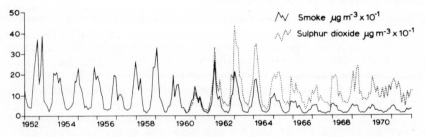

Figure 1 Monthly mean values for smoke and SO_2 pollution

(1) 1952 to 1959, characterized by high winter peaks and great seasonal variation, (2) 1959 to 1965, a transition period showing overall decrease in mean concentrations, and (3) 1965 to 1971, a low mean concentration period with little between-year variation. The seasonal component results from both emission and weather patterns over the year, but the overall reduction in level is probably the result of decreased emissions alone. The reasons for this are two-fold; first, changing fuel use, in particular the switch from coal to oil, and second, governmental legislation, embodied in the Clean Air Act, 1956. The latter did not begin to take effect in the Kew area until about 1960 to 1962 (Brazell, 1964) and its effects are the subject of controversy.

The SO_2 series shows no obvious divisions. After the initially high winter peaks of the early 1960s, concentrations for the winter months drop; in later years the initially smooth form of the seasonal cycle is disrupted, particularly over the summer months. For reasons of photochemical activity, variations in SO_2 concentrations are more complex.

Time series model of variations in pollution concentrations
In assessing change in both series over the period and in attempting to attribute changes to variations in the control variables, it is proposed to equate components of the series with those of the classical time series model, given by

$$Y_t = T_t + P_t + S_t + f_t \tag{1}$$

where the pollution series $\{Y_t\}$ can be broken down into four components given by the trend contribution $\{T_t\}$, the periodic element $\{P_t\}$, the stochastic component $\{S_t\}$ and a residual error component f_t. The trend element may be modelled by a polynomial model, by the use of moving averages, or by a number of other devices, the periodic component is often reproduced by elements of fourier series, whilst the stochastic component is itself usually broken down into further elements of autoregressive and moving average contributions, i.e. $\{S_t\}$ can be defined as:

$$S_t = \sum_{i=1}^{p} a_i Y_{t-i} + \sum_{j=1}^{q} c_j e_{t-j} \tag{2}$$

where the $\{a_i\}$ terms represent autoregressive parameters or memory terms of the past pollution levels given by lags on $\{Y_t\}$. The length of maximum lag defines the order of this autoregressive process. The $\{c_j\}$ terms represent the moving average elements of order q, the maximum lag, and define the dependence of the pollution series upon a set of unknown variables generated by $\{e_t\}$. Equation 2 can be rewritten as Equation 3 where the underbar denotes matrix or vector form and T denotes the transpose. This autoregressive, moving average model is often written as ARMA(p,q) (Box and Jenkins, 1970).

$$S_t = \underline{X}_t^T \underline{\theta}_t \quad \text{where} \quad \underline{\theta}_t^T = [a_1, \ldots, a_p; c_1, \ldots, c_q] \quad (3)$$

$$\underline{X}_t^T = [Y_{t-1}, \ldots, Y_{t-p}; e_{t-1}, \ldots, e_{t-q}]$$

CHANGES IN THE PROCESSES GOVERNING POLLUTION CONCENTRATIONS

Determination of the structure of the classical time series model given by Equation 1 permits the study of changes in the pollution process in terms of three systematic components of trend, periodicity and stochastic element. In this paper trend effects are studied by splitting the study period into three sections, identified above; periodic components are identified by spectral analysis; and the stochastic or persistence components are examined by the use of autocorrelation and partial autocorrelation functions.

Types of change

Central to any study of concentration of pollutants in the atmosphere is the problem of determining whether observed variations result from changes in meteorological conditions and in the level of pollution emission, or whether they are the result of changes in internal photochemical processes and in the timing, duration and frequency (collectively defined here as pattern) of emissions. Such changes in emission pattern and photochemical processes (due to nonlinear effects induced by variations in emission levels) are probably as important as changes in level themselves. Thus in searching for underlying mechanisms which have generated observed changes in pollution concentrations at Kew, attention is directed at three possible types of change: first, changes only in level, second, changes in level which have induced nonlinear effects, and third, changes in the pattern of control variables.

For the purposes of the following discussion, it is useful to define the nature of the controls on pollution concentrations in terms of three submodels:

$$e_t = \sum_k d_{tk} e_{t-k} \quad (4)$$

$$S_t = \underline{X}_t^T \underline{\theta}_t + f_t \quad (5)$$

$$\underline{\theta}_t = \emptyset \underline{\theta}_{t-1} + n_t \quad (6)$$

Equation 4 is an input submodel which controls the pattern of persistence and periodicity in the control variables governing the generation of pollution concentrations. Equation 5 is the process submodel defined in Equation 2 which governs the way in which internal pollution mechanisms (structural effects) operate. Periodic components enter this system of equations through the correlation properties of the $\{e_t\}$ sequence.

Equation 6 is a parameter submodel in which the evolution of
the parameter vector $\underline{\theta}_t$ is adjusted from one time instant t to
the next by a matrix $\emptyset$; $\{n_t\}$ is an independent zero mean
sequence with variance σ_n^2 representing parameter noise. The
first set of changes in the variables controlling the levels
of smoke and SO_2, which do not affect the pollution structure,
will be achieved only if no change in parameter structure
occurs, i.e. $\emptyset=I$, an identity matrix, and if σ_n^2 and σ_f^2 are
constant over the study period. In this case changes in
pollution levels are the result of uniform modulation by a
function $e_t = f(t)e_{t-1}$.

The second set of changes, in the structure of photochemical mechanisms induced by nonlinear effects, result from
the parameter vector $\underline{\theta}_t$ in Equation 5 being dependent upon the
magnitude of the input control variables (emission levels and
climate), i.e. the parameters are a function of the input
sequence $\underline{\theta}_t = f(e_t)$. Since the SO_2 sequence under study has
been split into two periods of high and transitional levels of
emissions (comparable with the smoke series) we can write $\underline{\theta}_t$,
(t=1960-1965) $\neq \underline{\theta}_t$, (t=1965-1971). These nonlinear effects are
confined to particular periods and represent a special form of
nonstationarity.

The third possible pattern of change, modification of the
pattern of emissions (duration, periodicity and persistent
effects) and climatic controls, will affect the correlation
and spectral properties of the observed pollution series. The
effect of these changes will be to induce non-uniform
modulation of the observed smoke and SO_2 levels through change
to the input submodel, i.e. $d_{tk} \neq d_{t+gk}$ ($-\infty < g < \infty$; g=0).
Since the input model is unknown in the present study, changes
of this form cannot be detected directly, but will be regist-
ered through changes in $\underline{\theta}_t$.

In the third case, $\underline{\theta}_t$ will have a transitional pattern
with any trends registering the effects of changes in the
emission and climatic control variables. In the second case
there will be two separate regimes of parameter values
conforming to the periods of high and low emission levels.
The results of the two sets of changes will be identical only
if the pattern of persistence and periodicity of the controls
has changed in exact conformity with the changes in levels.
The smoke and SO_2 series are examined below to see how far
they reveal evidence for these three types of change. The
periodic components of each series are first examined,
followed by the persistence components.

Changes in periodic components
The relative importance of the contributions of the periodic
components within the smoke and SO_2 series can be determined
from examination of the spectrum of each sequence. The
spectral estimates of each pollution series for each of the
time periods are given in Figure 2. These estimates were
derived using the autocovariance approach and a Hamming

smoothing window.

The spectrum of the smoke series shows the expected marked decline in overall magnitudes. The annual cycle is dominant in all periods and there seem to be no other significant periodicities present, except, perhaps, a weak seven-day peak. The overall shape of the spectrum becomes relatively more spread for the later periods, with the annual component contributing less to the overall variance. This is to be expected since decreased emissions will have most marked effect over the winter period. The smoke spectra therefore give some evidence for non-uniform modulations with respect to the annual and adjacent frequencies, but elsewhere changes to the smoke process would seem to be mainly ones of level. Since nonlinear effects are assumed not to be present in the smoke process, the non-uniform modulation must be the result of changed emission patterns and weather regimes, the latter discussed elsewhere (Lamb, 1972).

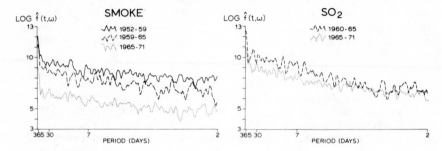

Figure 2   Spectral estimates ($\log_e$ values) for smoke and SO_2

The spectrum of the SO_2 series shows that the annual cycle is again the most important periodic component, but there are other contributions to process variance at frequencies of 45 days in the early spectrum, and at 30 and 75 days in the later spectrum, though these are difficult to interpret. Changes affect the annual component which increases relatively over the study period, as does the contribution of the monthly cycle. The overall shape of the spectrum is generally similar for the two periods, with greater complexity present in the later spectrum, but there is more evidence for non-uniform modulation at a larger number of frequencies than with the smoke spectra.

From this first analysis of the spectra it is difficult to know whether the observed changes are significant, and if significant, to what causes they can be attributed. In order to assess the significance and causes of the changes a further analysis was undertaken using estimates of the evolutionary spectra of the smoke and SO_2 series. Priestley and Rao (1969) have suggested the use of evolutionary spectral analysis for the detection of changes in stochastic processes similar to those under study here, and have given a test procedure based

upon analysis of variance (ANOVA) by which the significance of
the various contributions to changes in an evolutionary
spectrum can be assessed. Priestley suggests estimating the
spectrum of a process for a discrete set of time periods,
giving $\hat{f}(t,\omega)$ as an estimate of the spectrum at time t and
frequency ω. Assuming that the time periods do not overlap,
and that other assumptions of the ANOVA method can be
satisfied, it is then possible to split the variance of the
evolutionary spectrum into four components defined by the
classical ANOVA model as:

$$Y_{ij} = \mu + \alpha_i + \beta_j + \gamma_{ij} + \varepsilon_{ij} \quad (7)$$

$$\text{(mean) (time} \quad \text{(frequency (interaction (residual)}$$
$$\text{effects)} \quad \text{effects)} \quad \text{effects)}$$

where $Y_{ij} = \log_e \hat{f}(t,\omega)$ \hfill (8)

Equation 8 represents the log of the original spectrum, defined
for time effects i (i=1,2, ... ,I) and frequency effects j
(j=1,2, ... ,J) for I time periods and J frequency bands (where
the zeroeth and final frequency bands cannot be used).

Two problems arise in satisfying the assumptions of the
ANOVA model. First, it is assumed that each observation in the
experimental design is independent of each other observation.
Since the spectrum is a measure of the contribution of each
orthogonal (independent) component to the overall variance at
each frequency, this assumption will normally be satisfied.
But since smoothing of the spectrum is necessary in any finite
data problem, some leakage between adjacent frequencies will
occur, especially due to side lobes in the spectral window.
Each frequency element used in the ANOVA method should
therefore be separated by a significant gap from the other
elements in order to render the residual sequence uncorrelated.
Second, it is assumed that each observation is drawn from a
normally distributed population. The log transformation of the
spectrum values is designed to reduce the variability of the
spectrum, but complete normality is unlikely to be achieved.
This will increase the magnitude of the interaction term. In
the present analysis, using the Hamming window and seven-year
time periods, the residual variance σ^2 is known theoretically
(cf. Priestley and Rao, 1969):

$$\sigma^2 = 4.h/3.T' = 4\times3/3\times2556 = 0.00156 \quad (9)$$

where h is the width of the smoothing window adopted and T' is
the subset of original data used in the calculation of each
time element in the evolutionary spectrum. The ANOVA procedure
commences by first testing the additivity assumption, i.e.
testing the null hypothesis:

$$H_0 : Y_{ij} = \mu + \gamma_{ij} + \varepsilon_{ij} \quad (10)$$

that the interaction between components of the spectrum at
different times and frequencies is not significantly different

from random. Dependent .upon the outcome of this test, two
separate routes are followed. If the interaction term is not
significant then the null hypothesis is accepted and the
additivity assumption confirmed. Subsequent tests depend upon
determining whether differences between time periods are
significant, whether the spectrum is significantly different
from random, and whether particular subsets of times t are
characterised by spectra that could have resulted from a
random process. Rejection of the presence of interaction
effects requires that changes between time periods are
characterised only by changes in level. The shape of the
spectrum is unaffected and amplification up or down results
from changes in the levels of control variables, which does
not affect parameter structure or correlation properties.

   If the null hypothesis with respect to interaction effects
is rejected, then the additivity assumption is violated, and
sources of multiplicative non-uniformly modulated changes in
pollution levels are present. If the interaction term is non-
random the $\{Y_t\}$ process has different frequency contributions
at different time periods. The between time and between
frequency variation can be tested for significance, but more
useful than this is a test which determines if a significant
change has occurred within a subset of frequencies over all
time periods.

	SMOKE			SULPHUR DIOXIDE		
variance estimate	df	sum of squares	χ^2	df	sum of squares	χ^2
between times	2	296.8	190,000	1	14.4	9,200
between frequencies	60	112.7	72,100	60	144.0	92,000
interaction plus residual	120	14.3	9,000	60	9.3	5,900
total	182	423.7	271,000	121	167.7	107,000

Table 1   ANOVA of pollution series for every third frequency

   The results of the ANOVA for the three smoke time periods
and two SO_2 periods are given in Table 1. These results show
that although the interaction is small relative to the other
variance components, the small value of the variance of the
spectral estimate from Equation 9 gives a very high χ^2 value
in each case. The χ^2 test is obviously not very critical for
the present analysis, but if these results are accepted, then
both the smoke and SO_2 series have been non-uniformly
modulated over the study period. Examination of subsets of
frequency bands show that the smoke was non-uniformly
modulated over all frequencies, but the SO_2 spectrum had a
number of unchanging contributions at the quarterly, 10 day
and many higher frequency bands.   From the relative

contributions of the between time and between frequency components we may conclude from this analysis that the smoke series is mainly governed by a change of scale of the spectrum, but that some modulation effects attributable to modified emission patterns affect the shape of the spectrum. For the SO_2 series, the magnitude of the spectrum changes little over the study period, but the relative frequency content changes markedly around the annual component, and around middle range frequencies.

<u>Changes in persistence components</u>
Persistence components of the time series model are examined by the use of block estimates for the entire time period and by adaptive parameter estimation techniques based on the succession of observations over time.

<u>Block estimates</u> The form of adjustment in the persistence components over the study period can be judged from estimates of the autocorrelation function for each of the pollution series. The significance of autocorrelations within each sequence can be determined by calculating the partial auto-correlation function which tests the increment in explanation at each successive lag, taking into account the variation explained at the previous lags. The combination of these sets of information can be used to specify an initial hypothesis as to the most appropriate model order in terms of autoregressive or moving-average lags. The method is described by Box and Jenkins (1970), who show that for an AR(p) process, the auto-correlation function tails off, whilst the partial auto-correlation function is cut off after lag p. For the MA(q) process the autocorrelation function is cut off after lag q, whilst the partial autocorrelation function tails off. For the mixed ARMA (p,q) process both functions tail off, after the first q-p lags for the autocorrelations and after the first p-q lags for the partial autocorrelations. Thus a symmetry between the autocorrelation and partial auto-correlation functions of the smoke and SO_2 series, and the persistence effects of these theoretical models, can be used

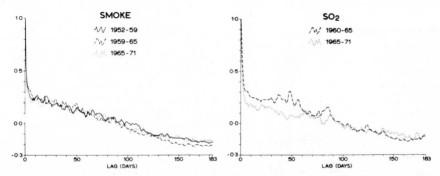

Figure 3   Autocorrelation function estimates for smoke and SO_2

to identify a suitable model of the stochastic component in
the overall time series model. Figure 3 shows estimates of the
autocorrelation functions for the smoke and SO_2 series for each
time period.

For the smoke series the forms of the estimates indicate a
first order autoregressive process at each time period. Only
the first lag value of the autocorrelation function is
significant as judged by the partial autocorrelation function.
Estimates of the partial autocorrelation function cut off as
would be expected from an autoregressive process. Whilst the
same AR(1) model seems to govern the stochastic component of
the smoke series at each period, there is some variability in
the magnitude of the persistence component for each period.
The persistence in smoke levels from one day to the next must
be due to the overall pattern of operation of · control
variables. It would seem, from the evidence shown here, that
this persistence has been increasing up to 1965 and decreasing
for later periods.

For the SO_2 series, the estimates of the autocorrelations
displayed in Figure 3 indicate a second order autoregressive
process for each time period. Only the first two lags of the
autocorrelation function are significant as judged by the
partial autocorrelations which are cut off after lag two. The
overall controls of SO_2 levels are again climate and emission
patterns. The longer, two-day, period of persistence which
characterises the SO_2 levels may be due either to different
emissions patterns, or to different behaviour of the
pollutants. Since SO_2 derives mainly from industrial
emissions, whilst smoke has a much larger domestic component,
a difference in persistence patterns might be expected. SO_2,
unlike smoke, however enters into photochemical reactions,
and the longer period of persistence may be a result of these
processes. Once again, the AR(2) process diagnostic is
confirmed by reference to the spectral estimate. The decrease
in persistence over the study period is shown in the
autocorrelations by the decrease in the first autocorrelation
coefficient from 0.76 to 0.6, and in the second coefficient
from 0.5 to 0.3. This is also confirmed by the decreasing
spread of the spectrum.

Adaptive parameter estimates   These estimation procedures are
concerned with identifying the nature of changes in the
parameter submodel (Equation 6), and with determining if these
changes can be described by the matrix function $\emptyset$. Estimation
can be undertaken by many methods, and an evaluation of a
number of these by Bennett (1974) showed that for conditions
in which noise levels were low and rapid parameter variation
occurred, estimation based upon a random walk model gave the
best parameter tracking. In conditions in which parameter
changes were slow, and in which high noise levels were present
(σ_f^2), a method proposed by Sage and Husa (1969) proved of most
utility. Since the speed of parameter variation and noise

conditions are not known here a priori, it was decided to
utilise both methods in the subsequent analysis. In each case
a recursive least-squares (ROLS) estimation algorithm deriving
from Plackett (1950) was used, in which predictions of
parameter changes were given at time t on the basis of
information available up to time t-1 by the equations:

$$\hat{\underline{\theta}}_{t/t-1} = \emptyset\hat{\underline{\theta}}_{t-1} + \Gamma n_{t-1} \tag{11}$$

$$P_{t/t-1} = \emptyset P_{t-1}\emptyset^T + \Gamma\sigma_n^2\Gamma^T \tag{12}$$

where $\hat{\underline{\theta}}_{t-1}$ denotes the estimate. Corrections to these
estimates on the basis of information available at time t are
made by the equations:

$$\hat{\underline{\theta}}_t = \hat{\underline{\theta}}_{t/t-1} - P_{t/t-1}\underline{X}_t[\sigma_f^2 + \underline{X}_t^T P_{t/t-1}\underline{X}_t]^{-1}(\underline{X}_t^T\hat{\underline{\theta}}_{t/t-1} - S_t) \tag{13}$$

$$P_t = P_{t/t-1} - P_{t/t-1}\underline{X}_t[\sigma_f^2 + \underline{X}_t^T P_{t/t-1}\underline{X}_t]^{-1}\underline{X}_t^T P_{t/t-1} \tag{14}$$

where $P_t = [\underline{X}_t^T\underline{X}_t]^{-1}$ and where the parameter vector $\hat{\theta}_t$, variable
vector $\underline{X}_t$, and S_t are defined in Equation 3. This   is
effectively the Kalman Filter applied to estimating a dynamic
parameter model (cf. Kalman and Bucy, 1961). Using these
equations, the random walk parameter estimates derive from
making the assumption that $\emptyset=\Gamma=I$, an identity matrix, and from
prespecifying σ_n^2, the expected level of variance of the
parameters. Sage and Husa (1969) give the equations for the
adaptive filter used below. The method is an extension of
Equations 11 to 14, requires no prior specifications, and
generates estimates of σ_f^2 and σ_n^2 . Both the random walk and
the Sage-Husa algorithms were applied to the smoke and SO_2
sequences, using least-squares estimates as starting values.
A number of general conclusions might be drawn from the
resulting parameter estimates, relating to the three sources
of behaviour or patterns of change identified earlier, namely,
changes in level, changes resulting from nonlinear effects,
and changes resulting from control variable effects.

   The pattern of parameter variation from the random walk
model and the evolution of the parameter a_1 and estimates of
σ_f^2 and σ_n^2 from the Sage-Husa filter are shown for the smoke
series in Figure 4. The random walk estimates of the
autoregressive parameter show considerable variation, damping
through the study period, with perhaps a slight discontinuity
to a lower mean value for the parameter around mid-1965. This
pattern of parameter variation is confirmed by the Sage-Husa
estimates where a change in parameter value post-1965 seems
more certain. This discontinuity does not seem to affect
either the process variance σ_f^2 or the parameter variance σ_n^2.
The adaptive parameter estimates allow a more detailed picture
of the variation within the series to be formed, and on the
basis of these results would seem to indicate a minor decrease

RANDOM WALK ESTIMATE

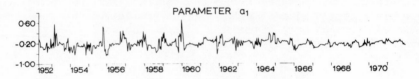

SAGE-HUSA ESTIMATES

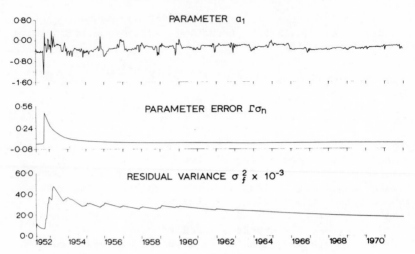

Figure 4   Adaptive parameter estimates for smoke series

in persistence for the post–1965 period, which is not
indicated by the block estimates of the autocorrelation
function for smoke given in Figure 3.

The pattern of parameter and variance behaviour derived
from the adaptive estimation methods for the SO_2 series is
shown in Figure 5. The random walk estimates of the two
autoregressive parameters display an approximate 'cyclic'
form for the first parameter, and a constant but varying
pattern for the second parameter. The 'cyclic' variation in
the first parameter is confirmed by the Sage–Husa estimates
which display a broadly increasing trend up to mid–1965, a
decrease up to 1967, and even level or slight increase from
1967 onwards. For the second parameter the Sage–Husa
estimates show a high degree of variation, with evidence of a
general decline in persistence. The estimates of both the
parameter variance and the process variance both show some
degree of variation over the 1960–62 period, with a
stabilization to a new level after 1962 or 1963. This overall
pattern would seem to evidence a general variability in the
SO_2 parameters and variance governing persistence up to about
1963, with a stabilization to a new regime after that time.
This result is consistent with the belief that the SO_2 series

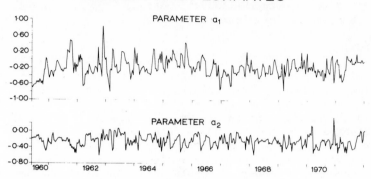

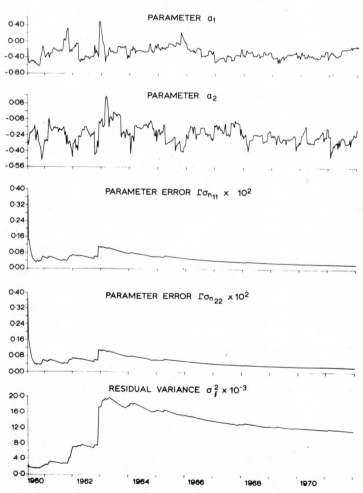

Figure 5 Adaptive parameter estimates for SO_2 series

might be subject to changed emission patterns similar to those governing smoke over the 1959-65 period, with the establishment of a new regime after that time.

CONCLUSION

In summarizing the general findings of the work, two cautionary comments are necessary. First, the method adopted in the study is a black-box technique which represents but one possible avenue of approach. Only certain types of result of an autopredictive nature can be detected and there are inherent limitations in attempting to infer the behaviour of control variables in the absence of direct measurements of them. Second, a number of points should be made relating to the data set employed. Changes in definition of the 24-hour collection period for smoke data and in the measurement method occurred during the period 1952-1971, but it is not thought that these have any significant effect on the analysis. The SO_2 series is shorter than desirable and, beginning near a time of high pollution levels in general, gives rise to some difficulty in deciding whether or not the first SO_2 period corresponds to the 'transitional' smoke period. Because of the length of the data series, hypothesis testing based on statistical inference procedures is to some degree invalidated; the large number of observations makes acceptance of the null hypothesis most unlikely.

Nevertheless, on the basis of the limited evidence available, the following conclusions are in order. For the smoke series, spectral estimates show the main source of variation to be the annual component, with some non-uniform modulation as a result of changed emission patterns and weather conditions. Intuitive recognition of a distinct change in level is confirmed. These features are reinforced by variance analysis, demonstrating further that modulation is not confined to any particular subset of frequencies. Adaptive parameter estimates show a dampening of variation in parameter values toward the later part of the series, with a slight discontinuity at about 1965. For the SO_2 series changes in the spectrum are concentrated in particular frequency bands, especially the annual and frequencies between quarterly and 10-day. There is no marked change in level, but there is evidence again of non-uniform modulation. Persistence in the SO_2 series has decreased markedly by a factor of between one-half and one-third, as measured by the autocorrelation functions, a finding confirmed, though less strongly, by adaptive parameter estimates. In general, variation in the SO_2 parameters points to stabilization to a new regime at about 1963, though it has not proved possible to isolate the effects of nonlinearities in the behaviour of SO_2 concentrations, perhaps because of an inappropriate scale and type of analysis.

In summary, the study demonstrates the possibilities of identifying and interpreting the magnitude and form of the effects of changed emission patterns and weather conditions on pollution concentrations, and of reproducing these effects in the form of a classical time series model.

REFERENCES

Bennett, R.J. (1974) Methods of dynamic modelling of spatial systems, unpublished Ph.D., Cambridge.

Box, G.E.P. and Jenkins, G.M. (1970) Time series analysis, forecasting and control, Holden-Day, San Francisco.

Brazell, J.H. (1964) Frequency of dense and thick fog in central London as compared with frequency in outer London, Met. Mag., 93, 129-135.

Department of Trade and Industry (1972) National Survey of Air Pollution 1961-1971, Warren Spring Laboratory, HMSO, (London).

Goetz, A. and Pueschel, R. (1967) Basic mechanisms of photo-chemical aerosol formation, Atmos. Environ., 1, 287-306.

Kalman, R.E. and Bucy, R.S. (1961) New results in linear filtering and prediction theory, Trans. ASME, J. Basic Engineering, D 83, 95-108.

Lamb, H.H. (1972) British Isles weather types and a register of the daily sequence of circulation patterns 1861-1971, Met. Office, Geophysical Memoirs, 116.

Leighton, P.A. (1961) Photochemistry of air pollution, Academic Press, New York.

Plackett, R.L. (1950) Some theorems in least-squares, Biometrika, 37, 149-157.

Priestley, M.B. and Subba Rao, T. (1969) A test for non-stationarity of time-series, J.R. Statist. Soc., B 31, 140-149.

Sage, A.P. and Husa, G.W. (1969) Algorithms for sequential adaptive estimation of prior statistics, Proc. 8th IEEE Symposium on Adaptive Processes.

Summers, P.W. (1966) The seasonal, weekly and daily cycles of atmospheric smoke content in central Montreal, J. Air Pollut. Control Ass., 16, 432-438.

Acknowledgements
The data were kindly provided by the Department of Trade and Industry, Warren Spring Laboratory. The figures were produced by Valerie Cawley and Chris Cromarty of the Cartographic Unit, and the manuscript typed by Annabel Swindells, Department of Geography, University College London.

COMPUTER MODELLING OF POLLUTANT TRANSPORTS IN LAKE ERIE

D. C. L. Lam

Canada Centre for Inland Waters, Burlington, Ontario, Canada

Abstract   The large scale lakewide advective and diffusive
transports of pollutants or nutrients in Lake Erie are simulated by mathematical models. A discussion will be presented
on the computational techniques for treatment of the advective
and diffusive terms and the boundary conditions. Some
verification results for stratified and nonstratified lake
conditions are included.

INTRODUCTION

Lake Erie is the southernmost lake in the Laurentian Great
Lakes System in North America. It is a relatively shallow
lake. The western part is about 10 m in depth, the central
part is about 20 m and the maximum depth of the eastern part
is about 65 m. It has a general orientation from west-south-
west to east-north-east, with a length of about 400 km and a
width of 70 km. Prevailing winds are from the south and south-
west.
The present paper describes the development of a mathematical
model for the lakewide transports of pollutants or nutrients
in Lake Erie, as part of the modelling programme at the
Canada Centre for Inland Waters. One important feature of the
model is its capability to simulate the time-dependent large
scale physical transports as well as biochemical processes
occurring in the lake. The present paper centres mainly on
the computational techniques and physical concepts associated
with the modelling of such large scale lakewide transports in
an Eulerian frame of reference.

MATHEMATICAL MODEL

In the Eulerian description of mass conservation in a
turbulent flow field, the following concept is frequently used.
Consider the one-dimensional equation for some concentration c

$$\partial c/\partial t = -u\partial c/\partial x + D\partial^2 c/\partial x^2 \qquad (1)$$

where x is the spatial variable, t is time, u is the instantaneous turbulent velocity and D is the molecular diffusivity.
It is difficult to model the instantaneous value c from
equation (1) itself, since u and c have random components.
Most numerical models are designed to predict the mean value
of c averaged over some length and time scales. Thus u and c
are written as $u = \bar{u} + u'$ and $c = \bar{c} + c'$ where the bar notation denotes the averaged values and the prime notation the
fluctuation components. If both u and c are averaged over the
same length and time scales, substitution into equation (1)
gives

$$\partial\bar{c}/\partial t = - \bar{u}\ \partial\bar{c}/\partial x - \partial(\overline{u'c'})/\partial x + D\partial^2 \bar{c}/\partial x^2 \ . \qquad (2)$$

Here, the fluctuation term $(\overline{u'c'})$ can be brought into closed
form by various turbulence models. One simple model is the
gradient hypothesis which states that the turbulent exchange
is proportional to the mean concentration gradient, i.e. $\overline{u'c'}=$
$-\nu\partial c/\partial x$ where ν is an effective turbulent eddy diffusion coefficient. This coefficient is usually several orders of
magnitude larger than the molecular diffusivity D, and hence
equation (2) can be written as

$$\partial\bar{c}/\partial t = - \bar{u}\partial\bar{c}/\partial x + \nu\partial^2 \bar{c}/\partial x^2 \ . \qquad (3)$$

From this point on, only mean values will be dealt with and
the bar notation can be left out.

Many expressions have been proposed for the turbulent eddy
diffusivity, e.g. in Fickian diffusion, ν is a constant.
Recently, Murthy et al (1974) performed a number of large
scale dye-diffusion experiments in Lake Ontario. Statistical
analysis of the data shows that it is possible to write $\nu = $
$5.6\times10^{-3} L^{1.3}$ cm^2/sec in the epilimnion of the lake, where ν is
the horizontal turbulent eddy diffusivity for a length scale
of L cm. For the present large scale (several km) transport
model, therefore, it is essential to assume that, in the
spectrum of different scales of motions in the lake, it is
possible to distinguish motions on scales larger than the
numerical grid-length (i.e. mean advection) from sub-grid-
scale motions (i.e. eddy diffusion). Furthermore, to be consistent with the assumption, mean values of velocities and
concentrations averaged or smoothed over the same numerical
grid-cells must be used. In other words, to compute again the
transports on a finer grid-mesh, the velocities and concentrations must be smoothed over this finer grid-mesh and a
smaller diffusivity ν must be used as suggested by the expression of Murthy et al. For very small grid-lengths, the
gradient hypothesis may not be applicable and some stochastic
models must be used instead. For large scale lakewide
simulation, the gradient hypothesis with a diffusion coefficient varying with the grid-length is a reasonable first

approximation.

The governing equations for the present model are the time-dependent two-dimensional equations, integrated over a layer of water of depth H contained between two arbitrary surfaces (Simons 1973):

$$\partial(Hc)/\partial t = - \nabla \cdot (\vec{v}Hc) + \nabla \cdot (\nu H \nabla c) + (wc)_2 - (wc)_1$$
$$+ (K\partial c/\partial z)_1 - (K\partial c/\partial z)_2 + S \ , \qquad (4)$$

where ∇ is the horizontal gradient operator, z is the vertical coordinate, $\vec{v}$ is the horizontal velocity vector, w is the vertical velocity at the top and bottom surfaces (denoted by 1 and 2 respectively), ν and K are the horizontal and vertical diffusivities and S is the source term. For a one-layer representation of a nonstratified lake, the right hand side of the equation reduces to the first two terms plus the source term. For a two-layer stratified model, vertical advection (i.e. upwelling and downwelling) and vertical diffusion (which is very small) occur only at the thermocline which is conveniently taken as the separating interface of the two layers. The velocities in the model are approximated by the computed currents from a hydrodynamic model, which is based on actual wind data inputs (Simons 1975). The transport model uses the same 6.67 x 6.67 km^2 grid-squares as in the hydrodynamic model, totalling 596 cells over the lake. For this length scale of 6.67 km, Murthy et al (1974) suggest ν = 2.5 x 10^5 cm^2/sec in the epilimnion; ν = 10^3 cm^2/sec in the hypolimnion; and K = 0.1 cm^2/sec. Some of the model results will be presented in the final section of this paper.

The assumption that the diffusion coefficient is a function of the grid length scale complicates the analysis of methods for solving equation (4). However, the following simpler cases can be examined.

NUMERICAL TREATMENT OF ADVECTION-DIFFUSION TERMS

It has long been known that the use of central differences for the advection terms in the mass conservation equation for flows with high Reynolds number would lead to oscillations in the numerical solutions (e.g. Courant et al 1952;Price et al 1966). These oscillations are due to the finite difference approximation of the spatial derivative in the advection terms and are not related to the usual dynamic instability caused by approximation of the time derivative. In fact, they also occur in steady state problems (Thom and Apelt 1961). These oscillations may disappear if sufficiently small grid spacings are used. For low Reynolds-number flows, the requirement can be easily met. For high Reynolds-number flows, however, one may need prohibitively small grid spacings.

Several methods have been proposed to circumvent this problem. The upwind-or upstream-differencing scheme has been one of the more economical methods (Courant et al 1952; Blair et al 1957). It does not put any restriction on the grid spacings, but may suffer loss of accuracy due to false-diffusion effects (Roache 1972). However, a recent investigation of the use of upstream differencing (Raithby 1975) shows that the false-diffusion effects may be small for the case when advection is the dominant factor in the direction considered. Meanwhile, other improved upstream differencing schemes have been developed (Torrance 1968; Spalding 1972; Raithby et al 1974).

Another school of thought, however, aims at developing methods that use central differences but do not produce oscillations, at least with less severe restriction on the grid spacings. These include the alternating-direction-implicit (ADI) methods (Denny et al 1974) and the box scheme (Keller 1971; Blottner 1974). The box scheme, in particular, resembles certain finite element methods, when applied to the one-dimensional advection diffusion equation (see later).

Thus, to select an appropriate scheme for the lakewide transport model, it is desirable to compare the performance of some of these schemes, particularly at higher cell Reynolds numbers. The comparison test should be able to answer, perhaps indirectly, why some central difference schemes are better than others, and why the first order accurate upstream-differencing scheme may be better than the second order accurate central differencing scheme. In this connection, the central differencing scheme (CDS), the upstream-differencing scheme (UDS) and the box scheme (BOX) have been chosen as examples in the following test. Consider the simple, one-dimensional, time-dependent advection diffusion equation again,

$$\partial c/\partial \tau = - u\partial c/\partial x + v\partial^2 c/\partial x^2 \quad , \qquad (5)$$

or, putting $b = u/v$, $t = v\tau$,

$$\partial c/\partial t = - b\partial c/\partial x + \partial^2 c/\partial x^2 \ , \qquad (6)$$

where u and v are constants, $0 \leqslant x \leqslant 1$ and $0 \leqslant t \leqslant T$, and let the boundary conditions be

$$c(0,t) = c(1,t) = 0 \ . \qquad (7)$$

Let F_m (L) be the eigenfunctions of the spatial operator,

$L = - b \partial/\partial x + \partial^2/\partial x^2$. For any initial condition $c(x,0) =$

$\sum_{m=0}^{\infty} a_m F_m(L)$, i.e. $c(x,0)$ is spanned by the eigenfunctions, the solution of (6) can be written as

$$c(x,t) = \sum_{m=0}^{\infty} a_m F_m(L) \exp(\lambda_m(L)t) \qquad (8)$$

where $\lambda_m(L)$ is the eigenvalue associated with $F_m(L)$.

Suppose the x-domain is partitioned into N equal spacings, $h=1/N$, so that $X_0 = 0$, $x_j = x_{j-1} + h$, $j=1,2,...,N$. Replacing the operator L by finite difference spatial approximations for the three methods, the following semi-discrete problems of systems of ordinary differential equations are obtained

$$\text{CDS:} \qquad dc/dt = Ac \qquad\qquad (9)$$

$$\text{UDS:} \qquad dc/dt = Bc \qquad\qquad (10)$$

$$\text{BOX:} \qquad C^{-1}dc/dt = Ac \qquad\qquad (11)$$

The description of the matrices A, B and C^{-1} will be given in the Appendix of this paper. Note that in (11), the matrix C^{-1} resembles the "mass inertia matrix" in some finite element formulations (Whiteman,1972). The purpose of considering these semi-discrete problems is that the effects of the spatial dis-cretization can be isolated. Thus, the solutions to the equations (9) - (11) can again be written as a finite sum of the eigenfunctions of the matrices and exponential decay terms in the eigenvalues similar to (8). The correspondence between the eigenfunctions or eigenvalues of the schemes to the exact eigenfunctions or eigenvalues, particularly the lower order ones (i.e. for small m), will be a measure of the effects of the spatial discretization.

	λ_m	F_m
L - EXACT	$-\{ m^2\pi^2 + b^2/4\}$	$\{\exp(2\beta)\}^{j/2}\sin(j\theta_m)$
A - CDS	$-\bar{h}^2\{4\sin^2(\theta_m/2) + 2\cos\theta_m(1 - \sqrt{1 - \beta^2})\}$	$\{(1+\beta)/(1-\beta)\}^{j/2}\sin(j\theta_m)$
B - UDS	$-\bar{h}^2\{4\sin^2(\theta_m/2) + 2\beta + 2\cos\theta_m(1 - \sqrt{1+2\beta})\}$	$\{1 + 2\beta\}^{j/2}\sin(j\theta_m)$
CA- BOX	$-\bar{h}^2\{4\tan^2(\theta_m/2) + 2\cos\theta_m(1 - \sqrt{16-4\beta^2\sin^2\theta_m})/\sin^2\theta_m\}$	$\{(1+\beta-h^2\lambda_m(CA)/4)/(1-\beta-h^2\lambda_m(CA)/4)\}^{j/2}\sin(j\theta_m)$

Table 1. Eigenvalues λ_m and eigenfunctions F_m of L,A,B and CA. ($\theta_m = m\pi h$; $\beta = bh/2$; $j,m = 1,2...,N-1$)

Table 1 shows the exact eigenfunctions $F_m(L)$ and eigenvalues $\lambda_m(L)$, together with the eigenfunctions $F_m(A)$, $F_m(B)$ and $F_m(CA)$ and the eigenvalues $\lambda_m(A)$, $\lambda_m(B)$, $\lambda_m(CA)$ for CDS, UDS and BOX schemes respectively. These expressions can be derived from the eigenvalues and eigenvectors for a tridiagonal Toeplitz matrix (Jorden 1950).

Note that the eigenfunctions of the three finite difference schemes differ from the exact eigenfunction only in the exponential factor, exp (2β). Figure 1 shows exp(2β) and the corresponding factors $(1+\beta)/(1-\beta)$, $1+2\beta$ and $\{1 + \beta - h^2 \lambda_1 (CA)/4\}/\{1 - \beta - h^2\lambda_1(CA)/4\}$ for CDS, UDS and BOX schemes respectively. In the case of the BOX scheme, h = 1/50 and m = 1 are used.

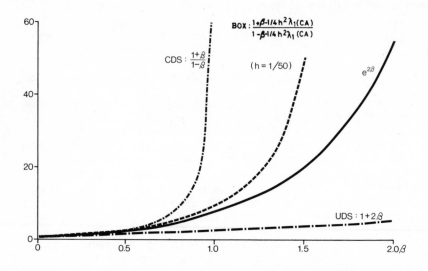

Fig. 1   Comparison of spatial factors in $F_m(L)$, $F_m(A)$, $F_m(B)$ and $F_1(CA)$.

For b >0 (the case b<0 follows easily by putting x =-x), the performance of the three schemes depends on the range of the values of β= bh/2 = 1/2(uh/ν), i.e. half of the cell Reynolds number. Thus, for the central difference scheme, if β>1, then $(1 +\beta)/(1 - \beta)$ is negative and $F_m(A)$ becomes complex for all m. For the upwind difference scheme, $1 + 2\beta$ stays positive and hence $F_m(B)$ is always real. For the box scheme, there is also a break-point, which occurs, however, less drastically than for the CDS and the eigenfunctions turn complex in pairs, one by one, as β grows beyond the value of 2 (Lam 1973). The breakdown of resemblance of eigenfunctions is accompanied by oscillations in the numerical solutions. Thus, the CDS solution becomes oscillatory if β>1. The BOX scheme solution becomes oscillatory if β > 2. In practice, however, these restrictions on β, particularly for the box scheme, are not so stringent. As an example to illustrate this, the numerical solutions of equation (6) by the three methods are examined with the initial condition, c(x,0) = exp(bx/2). sin(πx) = $F_1(L)$, choosing b = 100, h = 1/40, i.e. β = 1.25. The Crank-Nicolson implicit scheme is used in treating the time derivative, to achieve reasonable accuracy in the time discretization.

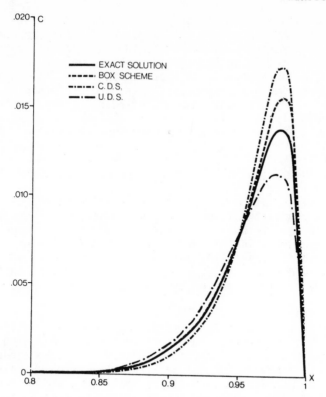

Fig. 2   Numerical solutions of equation (6), b = 100,
h = 1/40, $\Delta t = 2 \times 10^{-6}$, $t = 2 \times 10^{-4}$, m = 1.

Figure 2 shows the exact and computed solutions. The box scheme
provides the best solution, with some errors in the amplitude
but little phase-shifts. The CDS solution is not oscillatory,
since β is still close to the critical value of 1. However,
it does show a very large overshooting with considerable
phase-shifts. The UDS solution is not as bad as the CDS
solution and shows some damping and phase-shifts.Although the
above analysis is based on a simple one-dimensional equation
with constant velocity and diffusion coefficients for a
simple boundary condition, several fundamental characteristics
about these numerical schemes have been demonstrated. A
similar analysis of the central difference scheme for other
boundary conditions and variable coefficients can be found in
Price et al (1966).

To summarize, therefore, the oscillations are due to spatial
discretization and too large cell Reynolds numbers for some
schemes. These oscillations are different from the usual
dynamic instability due to time discretization with too large
time steps; in fact, they will still occur even if very small
time steps are used. To avoid them, the use of central

difference scheme must be restricted to cell Reynolds-numbers less than 2 (i.e. β < 1). This restriction can be relaxed to some extent, by introducing some spatial averaging or smoothing matrix on the time derivative vector, as in the case of the box scheme. Such type of matrix is also known as "mass inertia matrix" for some finite element methods (Whiteman 1972). The upstream-differencing scheme, on the other hand, allows a wider range of cell Reynolds numbers and can be used in the present transport model because of its simplicity.

COMPUTATIONAL TECHNIQUES FOR THE LAKEWIDE TRANSPORT MODEL

In the actual implementation of the model, a number of practical computational problems must also be considered. Here the aim is to develop a model which should achieve a certain level of accuracy in the numerical computations, and also allow for uncertainties in the input data for the initial and boundary conditions. Thus, these problems are to be solved preferably by simple methods instead of by complicated ones.

Time Derivative
One such example is the treatment of the time derivative. In the analysis of the one-dimensional diffusion-advection equation, we used the implicit Crank-Nicolson scheme for the time discretization. The ADI and fractional-step methods are examples of unconditionally stable implicit methods for two spatial variables. However, for an irregular region, they are very complicated to program and require large computer storage. This becomes more difficult if one wants to model the transports of several interacting variables at the same time. On the other hand, the explicit methods are much easier to program. Recently, Morton (1971) showed many desirable features of the explicit, unconditionally stable, three-level Leapfrog scheme (with DuFort-Frankel treatment of the diffusion term). A simpler three-level explicit but conditionally stable method is to compute the unknowns at the advanced (n+1) time-level with the advection term evaluated at the middle (n) time-level and the diffusion term at the old (n-1) time-level. For sufficiently small diffusion, the latter method may give $O(\Delta t^2)$ accurate solutions as in the case of the leapfrog scheme (Roache 1972). This method for the time discretization is used in the present model, with a time step of six hours.

Spatial Discretization
The upstream-differencing scheme was chosen because of its simplicity and its applicability for high Reynolds-number flows, as demonstrated in the analysis of the one-dimensional equation. Indeed, the central difference scheme has been tested using the same three-level time discretization scheme as described above. Oscillatory results were obtained over the

entire region in the two-dimensional transport model, as
expected. Perhaps, the use of ADI methods with the central
differencing scheme or fractional-step methods with the box
scheme may improve the results. However, some local oscillations may still occur in CDS solutions, if inconsistent boundary conditions are used.

Conservation Property

In the model, to maintain mass conservation in the numerical
procedure, the horizontal two-dimensional grid mesh is
arranged in such a way that, for each grid cell, the velocities
u are specified at the corners of the cell and the concentration c at the centre of the cell. The upstream-differencing
scheme is then applied to find the advective flux uc at each
side of the cell, so that u is approximated by the average of
the velocities at the two corners of the side whereas c is
always taken to be the concentration on the upstream side.
Since a three time-level scheme is used, care should be taken
with the starting procedure so that conservation is ensured.
In this connection, half time-steps are used to start the
solution, using the same initial condition for both the first
and second time-levels at the beginning.

Boundary Conditions

Boundary conditions that are inconsistent with the numerical
scheme may lead to instability in the solution (e.g. Taylor
1970). To be consistent with the present numerical scheme,
the boundary condition used in the transport model naturally
requires that no advective and diffusive fluxes occur across
the interface of land and water at the lake boundaries. As
for the river inputs, each of them is treated as a source
term in the grid-cell closest to the location of the river.
Thus, these input cells may contain concentrations much higher
than the neighbouring grid-cells. In fact, in extreme cases,
such conditions cause discontinuity problems for some finite
difference schemes. For example, if central difference scheme
is used for the advection terms, the advective flux across
any one of the four sides of a grid-cell is approximated by
the velocity times the average of the concentration in the two
adjacent cells sharing the same side. For a river input cell
with very high concentration, the averaged concentration at
the side will be also high. If the flow condition at the side
is such that the water flows from the neighbouring cell sharing the same side to the river input cell, the central
difference approximation will be over-estimating the advective
flux so much that it often causes a negative concentration to
appear in the neighbouring cell. The disturbance will gradually propagate into the interior points and eventually lead to
unstable solutions. On the other hand, the upstream differencing scheme is consistent with this boundary condition treatment and presents a problem for only one river source in the
Lake Erie model.

Time Smoothing

This one exception is the Detroit River source in the
Western Basin. Two river-input cells are involved here and
both have very high aspect ratios of cell grid-length over
cell depth. The velocities at the sides of the cells are
among the fastest in the whole region and the river source
is usually the greatest. Possibly due to the concurrence of
such unusual factors, oscillatory solutions sometimes occur
in these two cells and propagate to the neighbouring cells.
If the aspect ratio is lowered by increasing the cell depths,
these oscillations disappear. However, this is not as good
as the following time smoothing procedure which also smooths
out the oscillations. First, the unknown c_j^{n+1} is computed at
the n+1 time-level. Next, the values at the middle level is
smoothed by the substitution:

$$c_j^n = 1/4 \ c_j^{n+1} + 1/2 \ c_j^n + 1/4 \ c_j^{n-1} \ . \ \text{Then } c_j^{n+1} \text{ is computed}$$

again, using this new c_j^n.

SOME RESULTS

The numerical model has been applied to the simulation of the
transports of the conservative substance, chloride, and the
nonconservative substance, phosphorus, in Lake Erie (Lam et al
1974; 1975). Two examples are given of the chloride computations, one for the one-layer (fall) model and the other for the
two-layer (summer) model, to illustrate some of the points
mentioned in this paper. Figure 3 shows the mean computed
currents (Simons, 1975) for the period October 23 - November
19, 1970, in the one-layer model, and the mean computed
currents for the period July 16 - August 16, 1970, for both
the epilimnion and the hypolimnion layers. Some observed
currents for the summer period are also shown. These computed
currents are stored on magnetic tapes in the form of 12-hourly
averaged velocities for the whole cruise period April -
December, 1970. For the same cruise period, observed chloride
data from ten ship cruises have been collected by the Canada
Centre for Inland Waters.
The observed chloride data were interpolated over these cells.
Figure 4 shows the observed data of cruise 8 and cruise 9.
In the computation, observed cruise 8 is used as the initial
condition and actual time-dependent river sources from 21
rivers in the water basin were used as boundary conditions.
Three computed chloride distributions for cruise 9 are shown
in Figure 4, using horizontal diffusion coefficients of 10^4,
2.5×10^5 and 10^6 cm^2/sec respectively. The relative root-mean-
square errors for these three computed distributions as compared to the observed cruise 9 data were 7.4%, 6.3% and 6.6%
respectively. This shows that $\nu = 2.5 \times 10^5$ cm^2/sec, which
agrees with the large scale dye-diffusion experimental findings by Murthy et al (1974), should be a better choice.

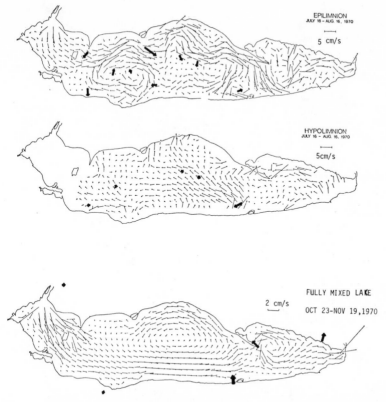

Fig. 3   Computed and observed currents. (Heavy arrows denote
wind vector for the fall period, and denote observed
currents for the summer period).

Figure 5 shows the mean advective and diffusive fluxes per
unit length across the dividing section between the Western
and Central Basins and also across the section between the
Central and Eastern Basins. The diffusive flux which is
estimated by using $\nu = 2.5 \times 10^5$ cm^2/sec is about two orders
of magnitude less than the advective flux.
Finally, Figure 6 shows the observed chloride distributions
of cruises 4 and 5, and the computed cruise 5 using the two-
layer model. The 650 μmoles/ℓ contours in the epilimnion of
the Central Basin in the observed cruises 4 and 5 show a
reversal during the cruise interval. The computed cruise 5
also shows such reversal. This phenomenon is related to the
clockwise-gyre circulation pattern, as shown in the same
region for approximately the same time in both the computed
and observed currents in Fig. 3.

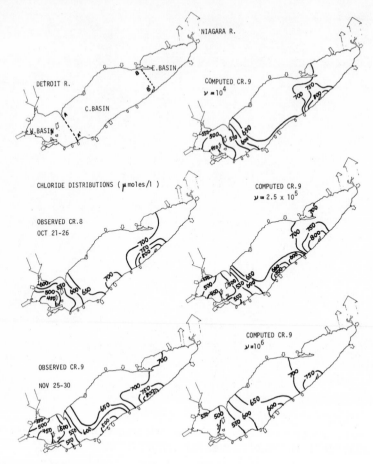

Fig. 4   Testing of the horizontal diffusion coefficient ν in
the one-layer model.

CONCLUSION

The development of the present one-layer and two-layer lakewide transport models has been based upon the physical
assumptions emphasized in the present paper and a number of
numerical methods. The preliminary test of the model shows
that the results are reasonably good. However, a more
rigorous verification of the model is being carried out by
means of developing and implementing an objective criterion
for comparing computed and observed data.

ACKNOWLEDGEMENT

The author wishes to thank Drs. T.J. Simons, C.R. Murthy and
N.M. Burns at the Canada Centre for Inland Waters for helpful
suggestions and discussions.

Fig. 5 Computed mean
        advective and
diffusive fluxes per
unit length across AA'
and BB' (see Fig. 4)

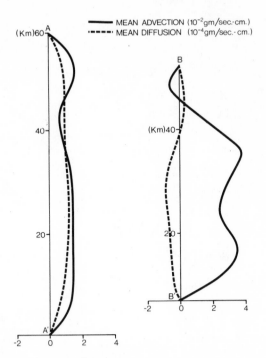

Appendix The matrices A, B and C^{-1} in equations [9]-[11] are
all (N-1) x (N-1) tridiagonal Toeplitz matrices and the
solution vector c is an (N-1)-vector augmented with $c_0 = c_N$ =
0 to satisfy the boundary condition [7]. Thus, equation [9]
refers to the central differencing scheme, with the tridiagonal elements in the i-th row of A as $A_{i,i-1} = (1+\beta)/h^2$, A_{ii} =
$-2/h^2$, $A_{i, i+1} = (1-\beta)/h^2$, $\beta = bh/2 = uh/2\nu$ = half cell
Reynolds number. Equation[10] refers to a scheme using upstream differencing for the advection term and central differencing for the diffusion terms, so that the tridiagonal
elements of B are $B_{i, i-1} = (1+2\beta)/h^2$, $B_{ii} = (-2-2\beta)/h^2$, $B_{i, i+1} = 1/h^2$. Equation [11] can be derived from the box scheme
by considering coupling between three adjacent grid points
(Lam, 1973). Here, matrix A is identical to that in the
central differences scheme and C^{-1} is a weighting matrix with
$C^{-1}_{i,i-1} = 1/4$, $C^{-1}_{ii} = 1/2$ and $C^{-1}_{i,i+1} = 1/4$.

References
Blair, A., N. Metropolis, A.H. Taub and M. Tsingon.(1957) A
study of a numerical solution to a two-dimensional hydrodynamic problem, Physics and Mathematics, LA-2165.
Blottner, F.G. (1974). Variable grid scheme applied to
turbulent boundary layers. Computer methods in Appl. Mech.
and Eng., 4, pp. 179-194.
Courant, R., E. Isaacson and M. Rees(1952). On the solution of
nonlinear hyperbolic differential equations by finite

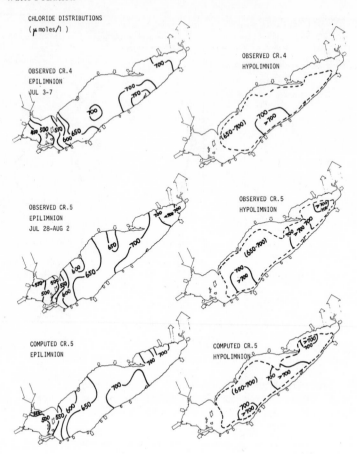

Fig. 6   Computed and observed chloride distributions using the
two-layer transport model.

References (cont'd)

differences. Commun. Pure Appl. Maths., Vol. V, pp. 243-255.
Denny, V.E. and R.M. Clever (1974). Comparisons of Galerkin and
finite difference methods for solving highly nonlinear
thermally driven flows. J. Comp. Phys., 16, pp 271-284.
Jordan, C. (1950). Calculus of finite differences. Chelsea, N.Y.
Keller, H.B. (1971). A new difference scheme for parabolic
problems. SYNSPADE 1970, B. Hubbard ed., Acad. Press, N.Y.
pp 327-350.
Lam, D.C.L. (1973). Modal analysis of semidiscrete problems
for the diffusion-convection equation. Proc. Third Manitoba
Conf. on Numerical Math., Winnipeg, pp 277-286.
Lam, D.C.L. and T.J. Simons (1974). Numerical computations of
advective and diffusive transports of chloride in Lake Erie
for the year 1970. Presented at the 17th Conf. Great Lakes
Res., IAGLR.
Lam, D.C.L. and J.M. Jaquet (1975). Computations of physical
transport and regeneration of phosphorus in Lake Erie in fall,

1970. To be presented at the 18th Conf. Great Lakes Res., IAGLR.

Morton, K.W. (1971). Stability and convergence in flow problems. Proc. Roy. Soc. London, A323, pp. 237-253.

Murthy, C.R., G. Kullenberg, H. Westerberg and K.C. Miners (1974). Large scale diffusion studies. CCIW Paper No. 14.

Price, H.S., R.S. Varga and J.E. Warren (1966). Application of oscillation matrices to diffusion-convection equation. J. Maths. Phys., Vol. 45.

Raithby, G.D. and K.E. Torrance (1974). Upstream-weighted schemes and their application to elliptic problems involving fluid flow. Computers and Fluids, Vol. 2, pp. 191-206.

Raithby, G.D. (1975). An evaluation of upstream differencing for problems involving fluid flow. To be published. 28 pp.

Roache, P.J. (1972). Computational fluid dynamics. Albuquerque, Hermosa, 434 pp.

Spalding, D.B. (1972). A novel finite difference formulation for differential expressions involving both first and second derivatives. Int. J. Num. Math. Eng., 4, pp. 551-559.

Simons, T.J. (1973). Development of three dimensional numerical models of the Great Lakes. Scientific Series No.12, CCIW.

Simons, T.J. (1975). Continuous dynamical computations of water transports in Lake Erie for the year 1970. CCIW Report.

Taylor, P.J. (1970). The stability of the DuFort-Frankel method for the diffusion equation with boundary conditions involving space derivative. Computer J., 13, pp. 92-97.

Thom, A. and C.J. Apelt (1961). Field computation in engineering and physics. Van Nostrand, London.

Torrance, K.E. (1968). Comparison of finite difference computations of natural convection. J. of Res. Vol. 72B, No. 4, pp. 281-301.

Whiteman, J.R. (1972). The mathematics of finite elements and applications. Academic Press, London.

A WATER QUALITY OPTIMIZATION MODEL FOR NONSERIAL RIVER SYSTEMS

M. B. Bayer

The University of Calgary, Calgary, Canada.

INTRODUCTION

This paper describes a modelling method for evaluating policies
for achieving specified water quality standards in a nonserial
river system. To simplify the presentation, the river system
is assumed to be a closed economic system to avoid the problem
of taking into account the external diseconomies of internal
pollution abatement decisions. Moreover, the river system is
assumed to be under the management of a single agency which
has the legal authority to specify and codify river water
quality standards. These standards are designated as lower
limits on dissolved oxygen (DO) concentration, upper limits on
biochemical oxygen demand (BOD) concentration and upper limits
on water temperature in the various reaches of the river
system. It is the agency's purpose to control the amount of
bio-degradable materials and waste heat introduced into the
receiving waters in order that these standards be met. Only
bio-degradable and thermal wastes are considered in this paper
since they constitute the major portion of industrial and
domestic wastes.

The water quality model is formulated as a set of interdependent mathematical programming problems with nonlinear
objective functions and linear constraints. The model is
developed on the assumption that the following are known for
each tributary branch and the mainstream:
(a) Minimum allowable DO and maximum allowable BOD
     concentrations,
(b) Maximum allowable water temperature,
(c) Equilibrium air temperatures in the river basin,
(d) Rate constants for the physical phenomena in the river
     system,
(e) Minimum mean period mainstream and tributary flows, and
(f) Construction costs for pollution abatement structures
     throughout the operating ranges for these structures.

WATER   QUALITY   TRANSFER   FUNCTIONS

The original Streeter-Phelps equation describing the oxygen
balance in water courses (Streeter and Phelps,1925) was
developed for steady-state conditions and assumed that oxygen
uptake was a first order reaction. More recently several
researchers (Woodward, 1953; Thomas, 1957; Young and Clark,
1965; Zanoni, 1967; Hartmann and Wilderer, 1968; Marske and
Polkowski, 1972) have experimented with fitting second order
reactions to BOD data. Although no single mathematical
expression has been found to describe the complete BOD
reaction, Zanoni observed that the second order equation gave
excellent fit in the region of rapid oxygen uptake. Hartmann
and Wilderer in their study of first and second order
reactions concluded that the second order reaction is a
better estimator of the true BOD kinetics at low BOD load
levels. Marske and Polkowski determined that the second order
model describes BOD data better than the first order model
when the first order deoxygenation rate constant is greater
than .20. In this paper a second order reaction for BOD is
assumed because the BOD loads are low (4ppm or less) and
the deoxygenation rate constants for all reaches are above
.20.

The second order reaction for oxygen uptake is described by
the differential equation

$$\frac{dB_t}{dt} = k_1 (B_o - B_t)^2 \tag{1}$$

which integrates to

$$B_t = \frac{B_o k_1 t}{1/B_o + k_1 t} \tag{2}$$

where:
t is time, days,
B_t is the cumulative BOD concentration exerted from time
    t = 0 to t, mg/litre,
B_o is the ultimate BOD concentration, mg/litre, and
k_1 is the deoxygenation rate constant at equilibrium
    temperature, days $^{-1}$.

It is noted that equation (2) is nonlinear in the unknown
B_o and would cause the constraints to be nonlinear in the
model. Therefore $1/B_o$ is replaced by a constant, k_o, which
is a median value of $1/B_o$ in the range of values $1/B_o$ in
the model.

The differential equation describing the reaeration reaction is

$$\frac{dD_t}{dt} = -k_2 D_t \tag{3}$$

where:
t is time, days,
D_t is the DO deficit concentration at time t, mg/litre, and
k_2 is the reaeration rate constant at equilibrium temperature, days^{-1}.

The temperature response is described by the differential equation

$$\frac{d(T_t - T_\varepsilon)}{dt} = k_3 (T_t - T_\varepsilon) \tag{4}$$

which integrates to

$$T_t = (T_o - T_\varepsilon) e^{-k_3 t} + T_\varepsilon \tag{5}$$

where:
t is time, days,
T_t is the water temperature at time t, $^\circ$C,
T_o is the water temperature at time t = 0, $^\circ$C,
T_ε is the equilibrium air temperature of the river basin, $^\circ$C, and
k_3 is the thermal decay rate constant, days^{-1}.

The rate constants for the deoxygenation and reaeration reactions are affected by temperature as follows (Keshaven et al., 1973)

$$k_1 (T_t) = k_1 \theta_1^{(T_t - T_\varepsilon)} \tag{6}$$

$$k_2 (T_t) = k_2 \theta_2^{(T_t - T_\varepsilon)} \tag{7}$$

where:
$k_1 (T_t)$ is the deoxygenation rate constant at temperature T_t $^\circ$C, days^{-1},
$k_2 (T_t)$ is the reaeration rate constant at temperature T_t $^\circ$C, days^{-1},
θ_1 is the temperature activity constant for k_1,
θ_2 is the temperature activity constant for k_2, and
k_1, k_2, T_t and T_ε are defined as above.

Substituting the expressions for T_t from equation (5) into

equations (6) and (7) gives the temperature dependent expressions for the deoxygenation and reaeration rates in terms of
the unknown T_0 as

$$k_1 (T_t) = k_1 \, \theta_1 \,^{(T_0 - T_\varepsilon)} \, e^{-k_3 t} \tag{8}$$

$$k_2 (T_t) = k_2 \, \theta_2 \,^{(T_0 - T_\varepsilon)} \, e^{-k_3 t} \tag{9}$$

The saturation value of oxygen in water is also affected by
temperature. As heat from thermal wastes dissipates, the
saturation value of DO concentration changes from its value at
the point where the thermal wastes enter the river to the value
of DO concentration for the ambient temperature of the water
at some point downstream. The saturation value of DO
concentration, O_s, at some water temperature, T_t, may be
estimated by the empirical function (Dysart,1970)

$$O_s = 14.652 - .41022 \, T_t + .007991 \, T_t^2 - .000077774 \, T_t^3 \tag{10}$$

and the DO concentration at time t, O_t, is

$$O_t = O_s - D_t \tag{11}$$

Incorporating both organic and thermal pollution, the differential equation describing the DO deficit concentration is

$$\frac{dD_t}{dt} = \frac{dB_t}{dt} - k_2(T_t)D_t \tag{12}$$

where B_t is given by

$$B_t = \frac{B_o \, t \, k_1(T_t)}{k_o + t \, k_1 \, (T_t)} \tag{13}$$

and B_o, B_t, D_t, k_o, $k_1(T_t)$, $k_2(T_t)$ and t are defined as above.

Equation (12) is a linear first order differential equation
for which the solution is

$$D_t = e^{\int k_2(T_x)dx} \int \frac{dB_t}{dt} \, e^{\int k_2(T_x)dx} \, dt$$

$$+ \, D_o \, e^{- \int k_2(T_x)dx} \tag{14}$$

Equation (14) is simplified by setting

$$\int \frac{dB_t}{dt} \, e^{\int k_2(T_x)dx} \, dt = \int \frac{d}{dt} (B_t \, e^{\rho \int k_2(T_x)dx}) dt \tag{15}$$

where ρ is a constant unique for each t and is obtained through
numerical methods. The resulting expression for equation

(14) is

$$D_t = B_t \ e^{(\rho-1) \int k_2(T_x)dx} + D_o e^{-\int k_2(T_x)dx} \qquad (16)$$

By letting $\pi = 1-\rho$ and substituting $p = \int k_2(T_x)dx$, equation (16) is simplified to

$$D_t = B_t \ e^{-\pi p} + D_o e^{-p} \qquad (17)$$

The expression for p integrates to an infinite power series with alternating signs. Because numerical evaluation of such power series is susceptible to rounding errors, p was evaluated using numerical integration.

STRUCTURE OF THE MODEL

The river system consists of a mainstream and several major tributaries called tributary branches. The mainstream and tributary branches may each be divided into n reaches with n+1 points such that the section of a branch between two consecutive points i and i+1 is called reach i. Associated with each reach are activities which are assumed to occur at the ends of the reaches. These activities may include one or more of the following:
(a)   Consumptive and non-consumptive outflows,
(b)   Effluent inflows from waste treatment plants,
(c)   Inflows from major tributaries,
(d)   Inflows from runoff, minor tributaries and seepage along the reach, and
(e)   Flow losses along the reach due to evaporation and percolation.

It is not possible to measure the continuous inflows and losses for (d) and (e) along a reach, but the net increase or decrease in the flow from the top to the bottom of the reach may be measured. In the model these continuous activities along a reach are approximated as discrete activities at the ends of the reaches and are included in the tributary inflows without loss of generality. Moreover, the reaches are made sufficiently short so that effects due to variations in flow rates, in values of rate constants for the physical phenomena, and in channel configuration are minimized and therefore neglected. Also, for a short reach the minimum point of the oxygen sag curve occurs at or very near to its end points, thereby eliminating the requirement for a constraint on DO deficit effective between the end points of the reach (Arbabi, et al.,1974) and thus simplifies the model considerably.

The equations for DO deficit and BOD concentrations effective at the ends of the reaches are obtained using the response function given by equation (17). The DO deficit concentration at the upper end of reach i is given by

$$D_i' = (D_{i-1}'' \, z_{i-1} + \phi_i \, y_i + \phi_i' \, y_i')/z_i \tag{18}$$

where:

$$z_i = z_{i-1} + y_i + y_i' - g_i \tag{19}$$

$$z_{i-1}' = x_{i-1} - g_i \tag{20}$$

and where:

z_i is the river flow in reach i, litres/day,

g_i is the total outflow from the lower end of reach i-1, litres/day,

y_i is the effluent inflow from the waste treatment plant into the upper end of reach i, litres/day,

y_i' is the tributary inflow into the upper end of the reach i, litres/day,

ϕ_i is the DO deficit concentration of the effluent from waste treatment plant i, mg/litre,

ϕ_i' is the DO deficit concentration of the inflow from tributary i, mg/litre,

D_{i-1}'' is the DO deficit concentration at the lower end of reach i-1, mg/litre, and

D_i' is the DO deficit concentration at the upper end of reach i, mg/litre.

The DO deficit concentration at the lower end of reach i is given by

$$D_i'' = \psi_i^{\pi_i} (b_i + b_i' + B_{i-1})(u_i - w_i \, g_{i+1}/z_i)/z_i + \psi_i \, D_i' \tag{21}$$

where:

$$\psi_i = e^{-p_i} \tag{22}$$

$$\psi_i^{\pi_i} = e^{-\pi_i p_i} \tag{23}$$

$$K_i' = k_i' \, t_i \, \theta_i' \, (T_i' - T_*^*) \, e^{-k_i''' t_i} \tag{24}$$

$$u_i = K_i'/(k_i + K_i') \tag{25}$$

$$w_i = 1 - u_i \tag{26}$$

$$b_i = B_i^o \, x_i \tag{27}$$

$$x_i = 1 - \eta_i$$

$$B_i = w_i (b_i + b_i' + B_{i-1}) \tag{29}$$

$$T_i' = (\tau_i \, y_i + \tau_i' \, y_i' + T_{i-1}'' \, z_{i-1}')/z_i \tag{30}$$

$$K_i'' = k_i'' \, \theta_i'' \;^{(T_i' - T_i^*)} \, e^{-k_i''' \, t_i} \tag{31}$$

$$P_i = \int_o^{t_i} K_i'' \, dt \tag{32}$$

and where:

B_i^o is the ultimate BOD of the effluent inflow to waste treatment plant i, mg/day,

B_i is the ultimate BOD remaining at the lower end of reach i, mg/day,

b_i is the ultimate BOD of the effluent from waste treatment plant i, mg/day,

b_i' is the ultimate BOD of the inflow from tributary i, mg/day,

k_i is a constant associated with the second order BOD uptake reaction for reach i,

k_i' is the deoxygenation rate constant, at equilibrium temperature, for reach i, days^{-1},

k_i'' is the reaeration rate constant at equilibrium temperature for reach i, days^{-1},

k_i''' is the thermal decay rate constant for reach i, days^{-1},

T_i' is the water temperature at upper end of reach i, ^oC,

T_i'' is the water temperature at lower end of reach i, ^oC,

T_i^* is the equilibrium air temperature for reach i, ^oC,

x_i is the effluent residual level, which is the ratio of BOD (or waste heat) in the outflow from to BOD (or waste heat) of the inflow to waste treatment plant i,

η_i is the waste removal ratio (efficiency) of waste treatment plant i,

θ_i' is the temperature activity constant for k_i',

θ_i'' is the temperature activity constant for k_i'',

π_i is the numerical integration proportionality constant for reach i,

τ_i is the temperature of the effluent from waste treatment plant i, ^oC,

τ_i' is the temperature of the inflow from tributary i, ^oC, and

D_i', D_i'', g_i, t_i, y_i, y_i', z_i and z_i' are defined as above.

The BOD concentration at the upper end of reach i is given by

$$B_i' = (b_i + b_i' + B_{i-1}'' \, z_{i-1}'')/z_i \tag{33}$$

where:

B_i' is the ultimate BOD concentration at the upper end of reach i, mg/litre,

B_i'' is the ultimate BOD concentration at the lower end of
       reach i, mg/litre, and

b_i, b_i', z_{i-1}'', and z_i are defiend as above.

The BOD concentration at the lower end of reach i is given by

$$B_i'' = w_i \, B_i' \quad (1 + g_{i+1}/z_i)/z_i \qquad (34)$$

where B_i'', B_i', w_i, g_{i+1} and z_i are defined as above.

The constraints on DO and BOD involve maximum allowable levels
of DO deficit and BOD concentrations at the upper and lower
ends of each reach for a given probability Θ of violating the
specified DO and BOD standards (Bayer, 1974). The probability
distributions of DO and BOD concentrations are assumed to be
approximately normally distributed with means and standard
deviations known for each reach. The DO and BOD standards
adjusted by the appropriate numbers of standard deviations
to reflect the desired probability Θ are called adjusted
standards. The adjusted standards for DO deficit concentration
D_i^* and D_i^{**} at the upper and lower ends of reach i

respectively, are

$$D_i^* \;=\; 0_i' \,-\, 0_i^* \qquad (35)$$

$$D_i^{**} \;=\; 0_i'' \,-\, 0_i^{**} \qquad (36)$$

where:

$0_i'$ is the saturation value for DO concentration at the upper
       end of reach i, mg/litre,

$0_i''$ is the saturation value for DO concentration at the lower
       end of reach i, mg/litre,

0_i^* is the adjusted standard for DO concentration at the upper
       end of reach i, mg/litre, and

0_i^{**} is the adjusted standard for DO concentration at the
       lower end of reach i, mg/litre.

The adjusted standards for BOD concentration at the upper and
lower ends of reach i are B_i^* and B_i^{**} respectively. Then the
constraints on the DO and BOD concentrations at the ends of
reach i are

$$D_i^* \;-\; D_i' \;\geq\; 0 \qquad (37)$$

$$D_i^{**} \;-\; D_i'' \;\geq\; 0 \qquad (38)$$

$$B_i^* \;-\; B_i' \;\geq\; 0 \qquad (39)$$

$$B_i^{**} \;-\; B_i'' \;\geq\; 0 \qquad (40)$$

The maximum allowable water temperatures, T_i^* and T_i^{**}, at the

upper and lower ends of reach i are used in specifying the
temperature constraints.

$$T^*_i - T'_i \geq 0 \qquad (41)$$

$$T^{**}_i - T''_i \geq 0 \qquad (42)$$

where T'_i and T''_i are defined as above.

Additional constraints on each reach are the upper and lower
bounds on the fraction of the waste heat, or BOD, entering
a waste treatment plant which is allowed to enter the reach
by way of the treatment plant effluent. Thus

$$X''_i \leq x_i \leq X'_i \qquad (43)$$

where:

X''_i is the minimum required level of waste treatment for
treatment plant i,

X'_i is the practical upper limit to the level of waste
treatment for treatment plant i, and

x_i is defined as above.

The annualized cost function for the expansion of waste
treatment plant i to provide for increased waste removal is
of the form

$$f(x_i) = \alpha_i \, x_i^{(\beta_i + \gamma_i x_i + \delta_i x_i^2)} \qquad (44)$$

where:

x_i is defined as above, and

α_i, β_i, γ_i, and δ_i are constants unique to waste treatment
plant i.

Equation (44) along with inequalities (37) to (43) are used
to construct the water quality model for the series of reaches
which make up a tributary branch. The model, a problem in
nonlinear programming, may be solved for the set of effluent
residual levels necessary to achieve desired standards of DO,
BOD and temperature for the branch. The mainstream is
modelled in much the same way as the tributary branches except
for the way in which its major tributaries are handled. At
the point where a tributary enters the mainstream, the
tributary is replaced by an equivalent pseudo-facility which
embodies both the natural and structural activities on the
tributary. The tributary flow into the mainstream becomes the
effluent of the pseudo-facility, and solution of the
mainstream system determines the allowable temperature, BOD
concentration, and consequently the DO concentration for this
effluent. The efficiency of the pseudo-facility is a surrogate
for the efficiencies of the waste treatment plants along

the tributary, and given the conditions at the end of the tributary, the efficiencies of the tributary treatment plants are then obtained by solving the tributary branch model.

For a mainstream reach j which contains a pseudo-facility, the DO deficit concentration at the upper end of the reach is given by

$$D'_j = (D''_{j-1} z'_{j-1} + \phi_j y_j + \phi_j^+ y_j^+)/z_j \qquad (45)$$

where:

ϕ_j^+ is the DO deficit concentration of the effluent from pseudo-facility j, mg/litre,

y_j^+ is the effluent outflow from pseudo-facility j, litres/day, and

D'_j, D''_j, ϕ_j, y_j, z'_{j-1} and z_j are defined as above for a tributary reach.

The DO deficit concentration at the lower end of reach j is given by

$$D''_j = \psi_j{}^{\pi_j} (b_j + b_j^+ + B_{j-1})(u_j - w_j\, g_{j+1}/z_j)/z_j + \psi_j\, D'_j \qquad (46)$$

where:

b_j^+ is the ultimate BOD of the effluent from pseudo-facility j, mg/day, and

D'_j, D''_j, b_j, B_{j-1}, ψ_j, π_j, g_{j+1}, u_j, w_j, and z_j are defined as above for a tributary reach.

The BOD concentration at the upper end of reach j is given by

$$B'_j = (b_j + b_j^+ + B''_{j-1} z''_{j-1})/z_j \qquad (47)$$

where:

b_j^+ is defiend as above, and

B'_j, b_j, B''_j, z''_{j-1} and z_j are defined as above for a tributary reach.

The BOD concentration at the lower end of reach j is given by

$$B''_j = w_j\, B'_j\, (1 + g_{j+1}/z_j)/z_j \qquad (48)$$

where:

B'_j, B''_j, g_{j+1}, w_j and z_j are defined as above for a tributary reach.

The constraints on DO deficit and BOD concentrations and

temperature for the mainstream reach are formulated in the same manner as for a tributary reach. The cost function for the pseudo-facility is of the form

$$f(x_j^*) = \alpha_j^* \; x_j^* \;^{(\beta_j^* + \gamma_j^* \; x_j^* + \delta_j^* \; x_j^{*2})} \tag{49}$$

where:

x_j^* is the effluent residual level provided by pseudo-facility j, and

α_j^*, β_j^*, γ_j^* and δ_j^* are constants unique to pseudo-facility j.

NUMERICAL RESULTS

The modelling method was applied to a river system which has a major tributary branch of 5 reaches and a mainstream of 5 reaches. The tributary has a waste treatment plant located at the upper end of reaches 1, 3, 4, and 5 to treat industrial or municipal organic wastes, and a cooling tower at the upper end of reach 2 to treat thermal wastes. The mainstream has a waste treatment plant located at the upper end of reaches 1, 2, 3 and 5 to treat industrial or municipal organic wastes, and a pseudo-facility located at the upper end of reach 4 to replace the major tributary at the point where it enters the mainstream. There are also minor tributaries entering reaches on both the major tributary and the mainstream. The physical data pertaining to the system are assumed data and are given in Table 1.

The maximum water temperature allowed in the river system was 20°C, and the adjusted standards for DO and BOD in each reach were 6.5 mg/litre and 4.0 mg/litre respectively. The DO and BOD constraints for the tributary and mainstream effective for the optimal solution are given in Table 2. The co-efficients for the annual cost functions and the bounds on the decision variable x for the facilities on the tributary and the mainstream are given in Table 3. To obtain the objective function cost coefficients for the pseudo-facility, the tributary branch model was run for five DO concentrations from 6.5 to 8.5 mg/litre effective at the lower end of reach 5 for each of four effluent temperatures from 21 to 24°C for the· thermal polluter. The cost coefficients for a given temperature were obtained using least-squares regression, with the overall BOD removal ratio of the tributary system (efficiency of the pseudo-facility) as the independent variable. The annual costs of meeting the water quality standards, along with the removal ratios (efficiencies) for the waste treatment plants and the pseudo-facility, are also given in Table 3.

The mainstream and tributary branch models, formulated as non-linear programming problems, were solved using the differential algorithm (Bayer and Cross, 1972) on a CDC 7600 machine.

Reach	k_o days^{-1}	k_1 days^{-1}	k_2 days^{-1}	k_3 days^{-1}	Flow Time days	Equil. Temp. °C	Trib. Temp. °C	Waste Temp. °C	Trib. Flow 10^9 l/d	Waste Flow 10^8 l/d	Trib. DO mg/l	Waste DO mg/l	Trib. BOD mg/l	Waste BOD mg/l
1T[a]	.333	.304	.795	.346	.225	19.5	15.5	22.0	2.924	.642	9.90	1.00	.154	542.0
2T	.333	.318	.760	.325	.480	20.0	16.0	24.0	1.710	1.280	9.79	1.00	.223	0.0
3T	.333	.332	.726	.305	.735	20.5	16.5	22.0	2.154	.694	9.68	1.00	.289	619.0
4T	.333	.346	.691	.284	1.020	21.0	17.0	22.0	2.446	.368	9.58	1.00	.351	767.0
5T	.333	.360	.656	.263	1.316	21.5	17.5	22.0	2.714	.936	9.48	1.00	.410	838.0
1M[b]	.333	.311	.778	.336	.351	20.0	16.0	22.0	2.573	.392	9.79	1.00	.188	597.0
2M	.333	.325	.743	.315	.608	20.5	16.5	22.0	1.966	.584	9.68	1.00	.256	638.0
3M	.333	.339	.708	.294	.882	21.0	17.0	22.0	2.007	.403	0.58	1.00	.320	783.0
4M[c]	.333	.353	.673	.273	1.170	21.5	-	19.12	-	123.6	-	6.70	-	15.2
5M	.333	.367	.638	.252	1.485	22.0	18.0	22.0	1.894	1.021	9.38	1.00	.474	917.0

a. T = Tributary reach.   b. M = Mainstream reach.   c. Contains pseudo-facility

Table 1. Physical data for the river system

ACKNOWLEDGEMENTS

The research for this paper was carried out while the author
was a Visiting Fellow with the Department of Economics,
University of Southampton, Southampton, England. The author
is thankful for the secreterial and computer services without
which this paper could not have been written. Financial
support was provided by the Canada Council through a Leave
Fellowship.

Const. Number	Constraint Coefficients					R.H.S. Vector
1T	3.0251	0.0				1.0
2T	.78629	0.0	1.5894			1.0
3T	.35430	0.0	.71621	.77058		1.0
4T	.38512	0.0	.55434	.34536		1.0
5T	.14114	0.0	.28531	.30698	1.6509	1.0
6T	.25120	0.0	.41184	.33564	1.0100	1.0
1M	2.2776					1.0
2M	1.0027	2.1091				1.0
3M	.46639	.79220	.59862			1.0
4M	.45974	.96684	1.2370			1.0
5M	.19790	.36745	.36291	2.2075		1.0
6M	.087256	.18350	.23476	2.4888		1.0
7M	.090097	.17452	.19037	1.5150	.88888	1.0
8M	.037291	.078423	.10033	1.0636	1.1288	1.0

Table 2. DO and BOD constraints

Facility	Objective Function Coefficients				Bounds on x		Effluent Residual Level	Treatment Plant Efficiency	Annual Cost £ (10⁵)
	$\alpha(10^5)$	$\beta(10^{-1})$	$\gamma(10^{-3})$	$\delta(10^{-5})$	Upper Limit	Lower Limit			
1T	1.6247	-2.5853	6.1237	-6.7257	.70	.01	.3306	.6694	2.15819
2T	1.1090	-4.0420	-8.5984	8.2889	.40	.10	.4000	.6000	1.61117
3T	1.8365	-1.9269	9.0541	-6.8454	.70	.01	.4656	.5344	2.12110
4T	1.5357	-4.5273	-8.2436	5.3749	.70	.01	.7000	.3000	1.80853
5T	2.9413	-3.5184	7.7826	-6.4087	.70	.01	.3668	.6332	4.17384
1M	1.5387	-2.8476	5.3542	-7.6163	.70	.01	.3896	.6104	2.00857
2M	1.8413	-3.2355	-9.4723	8.5240	.70	.01	.2889	.7111	2.76107
3M	1.1439	-3.6391	7.5683	-5.1239	.70	.01	.4378	.5622	1.54077
4M*	2.6369	-4.9463	-1810.9	39576.0	.1157	.0363	.1157	.8843	11.90337
5M	2.7491	-4.0728	8.2407	-6.0135	.70	.01	.7000	.3000	3.17242
								Total Annual Cost	£21.38620

* Refers to the pseudo-facility

Table 3.   Objective function coefficients, plant efficiencies and annual costs

REFERENCES

Arbabi, M., Elzinga, J., and ReVelle, C. (1974)   The Oxygen Sag Equation: New Properties and a Linear Equation for the Critical Deficit.   Water Resources Research, 10, 5: 921-27.

Bayer, M. B. (1974) Applying Probabilistic Water Quality Standards in River Basin Water Quality Optimization Models. Proceedings, Ninth Canadian Symposium on Water Pollution Reserach, University of Western Ontario, London, Canada.

Bayer, M. B., and Cross, G. W. (1972) A Nonlinear Programming Algorithm for Programming Problems with Nonlinear Objective Functions and Linear Constraints.   The University of Calgary, Calgary, Canada.

Dysart, B. C.(1970) Water Quality Planning in the Presence of Interacting Pollutants.   Water Pollution Control Federation Journal, 42, 8: 1515-29.

Hartmann, L., and Wilderer, P. (1968) Physical and Biochemical Aspects of BOD Kinetics.   Water Research, 2, 30-40.

Keshaven, K., Sornberger,G. C., and Kirshberg, C. I.(1973) Oxygen Sag Curve with Thermal Overload.   Journal of the Environmental Engineering Division, Proceedings of the ASCE, 99, EE5: 569-75 .

Marske, D. M., and Polkowski, L. B. (1972) Evaluation of Methods for Estimating Biochemical Oxgyen Demand Parameters. Water Pollution Control Federation Journal, 44, 10: 1987-2000.

Streeter, H. W., and Phelps, E. B. (1925) A Study of Pollution and Natural Purification of the Ohio River.   Public Health Bulletin No. 146, U.S. Public Health Service, Washington.

Thomas, H. A., Jr. (1957) The Dissolved Oxgyen Balance in Streams.   Boston Society of Civil Engineers, Sanitary Engineering Division, Seminar on Waste Water Treatment and Disposal, Lecture No. 4 .

Woodward,R. L. (1953) Deoxygenation of Sewage - A Discussion. Sewage and Industrial Wastes, 91, 8: 43-57.

Young, J.C., and Clark, J. W. (1965) Second Order Equation for BOD.   Journal of the Sanitary Engineering Division, Proceedings of the ASCE, 91, SA1: 43-57 .

Zanoni, A. E. (1967) Waste Water Deoxygenation at Different Temperatures.   Water Research, 2, 543-66.

SIMULATION OF NONLINEAR STOCHASTIC EQUATIONS WITH APPLICATIONS IN MODELLING WATER POLLUTION

C. J. Harris

Control Systems Centre, U.M.I.S.T., Manchester.

INTRODUCTION TO STOCHASTIC MODELS

A wide variety of complex engineering, econometric and biological dynamical systems with stochastic (random) inputs and/or parametric disturbances can be modelled by nonlinear stochastic differential/integral equations. For example continuous stirred tank reactors (CSTR) with random perturbations in concentrations and feedrates, and the dynamics of structures subject to wind gusts. The conventional engineering modelling approach to such systems is to represent them by the vector differential equation,

$$\frac{d\underline{x}}{dt} = \underline{f}(\underline{x}, t) + \underline{G}(\underline{x}, t)\, \underline{\xi}(t) \qquad (1)$$

where $\underline{x} = \{x_i\}$ and $\underline{f} = \{f_j\}$ are n-vectors, and $\underline{G} = \{g_{ij}\}$ is a n x m matrix. f_i and g_{ij} are assumed known and to have continuous partial derivatives with respect to t and $\underline{x}$ at least up to second order. $\underline{\xi}(t)$ is an m-vector white noise process, with $E(\underline{\xi}(t)) = 0$ and $E\{\underline{\xi}(t) \cdot \underline{\xi}(t+s)\} = \delta(s)\, \underline{Q}$, $\underline{Q} = \text{diag}\{q_{ii}\}$.

Alternatively since white noise is formally defined as the time derivative of the Wiener Process $\underline{W}(t)$, ie $d\underline{W}(t) = \underline{\xi}(t)dt$. Then equation (1) can be written as

$$d\underline{x}(t) = \underline{f}(\underline{x}, t)\, dt + \underline{G}(\underline{x}, t)\, d\underline{W}(t) \qquad (2)$$

with $E[d\underline{W}(t)] = 0$ and $E[d\underline{W}(t) \cdot d\underline{W}(t)^T] = \underline{Q}\, dt$ and a solution

$$\underline{x}(t) = x(t_0) + \int_{t_0}^{t} \underline{f}(\underline{x}, s)ds + \int_{t_0}^{t} \underline{G}(\underline{x}, s)\, d\underline{W}(s) \qquad (3)$$

It would appear that equations (1) and (2) are identical, however white noise although a convenient tool in modelling, does not exist either mathematically nor physically. Since the Wiener process is non-differentiable (Jazwinski, 1970), and white noise has infinite power! The so called Itô

269

stochastic differential equations (SDE) (2) are
mathematically rigorous idealisations of physical processes
with random perturbations. The second integral of equation
(3) is not well defined, since a Wiener process may be of
unbounded variation therefore the integral cannot be dealt
with by ordinary Riemann or Lebesgue-Stieltjes integration.
In consequence the rules of Itô calculus (Jazwinski, 1970)
are somewhat different from ordinary calculus. For example,
for a scalar differentiable function $\varphi(\underline{x},t)$ its Itô
derivative is

$$d\varphi = \frac{\partial \varphi}{\partial t}.dt + \text{grad}\,\varphi.dt + \tfrac{1}{2}\text{tr}(\underline{GQ}.\underline{G}^T)\text{grad}(\text{grad}\,\varphi)dt + O(dt) \quad (4)$$

The additional term is caused by the property of Wiener
processes: $d\underline{W}(t) = \underline{Q}.(dt)^{\frac{1}{2}}$. Failure to include this term
would lead to erroneous solution of SDE. In general Itô SDE
are impossible to solve analytically, except in the simplest
linear cases, and then only by solving a second order partial
differential equation (the Fokker-Planck equation, Fuller,
1969). A simulation algorithm for Itô random integral
equations would be very useful in validating nonlinear models
of physical phenomena which are subject to random disturbances
and in investigating various control schemes.

SIMULATION ALGORITHM

Returning to the Itô SDE(2), divide the interval of interest
T, up into equal subintervals $t_{r+1} - t_r = h$, a constant, for
$r = 1,2,\ldots,N - 1$, with $T = [t_N,t_1]$, then the solution to
equation (2) over the interval (t_r,t_{r+1}) is

$$x_i(t_{r+1}) = x_i(t_r) + \int_{t_r}^{t_{r+1}} f_i(\underline{x},t)\ dt$$

$$+ \sum_{j=1}^{m} \int_{t_r}^{t_{r+1}} g_{ij}(\underline{x},t)\ dW_j(t) \quad (5)$$

for $i = 1,2,\ldots n.$

Now expand f_i and g_{ij} in a Taylor's series about $(t_r,\underline{x}(t_r))$
(up to second order) for $t \in (t_{r+1},t_r)$

$$f_j(\underline{x},t) = f_i^r + \frac{\partial f_i^r}{\partial t}.(t - t_r) + \sum_{s=1}^{n} \frac{\partial f_i^r}{\partial x_s} \cdot (x_s(t) - x_s^r)$$

$$+ \tfrac{1}{2} \frac{\partial^2}{\partial t^2} f_i^r.(t - t_r)^2 + \sum_{k=1}^{n} \frac{\partial^2 f_i^r}{\partial x_k \partial t}\cdot(x_k(t) - x_k^r)(t - t_r)$$

$$+ \frac{1}{2} \sum_{j,k=1}^{n} \frac{\partial^2 f_i^r}{\partial x_k \partial x_j} \cdot (x_k(t) - x_k^r)(x_j(t) - x_j^r) \qquad (6)$$

$$g_{ij}(\underline{x}, t) = g_{ij}^r + \frac{\partial g_{ij}^r}{\partial t} \cdot (t - t_r) + \sum_{k=1}^{n} \frac{\partial g_{ij}^r}{\partial x_k} \cdot (x_k(t) - x_k^r)$$

$$+ \frac{1}{2} \frac{\partial^2 g_{ij}^r}{\partial t^2} \cdot (t - t_r)^2 + \sum_{k=1}^{n} \frac{\partial^2 g_{ij}^r}{\partial x_k \partial t} \cdot (x_k(t) - x_k^r)(t - t_r)$$

$$+ \frac{1}{2} \sum_{k,j=1}^{n} \frac{\partial^2 g_{ij}}{\partial x_k \partial x_j} \cdot (x_k(t) - x_k^r)(x_j(t) - x_j^r) \qquad (7)$$

for $i = 1, 2, \ldots n$, and $j = 1, 2, \ldots m$. The superscript r refers to the evaluation of the variable at time t_r.

These expressions are then substituted into equation (5) to discreteise it. Terms involving $(x_k(t) - x_k^r)$ which arise in the above expressions are successively replaced by equation (6), evaluated between (t_r, t). The number of successive substitutions are governed by the desired order of truncation error in the increment time h. After lengthy substitutions and simplifications based on various lemmas (Skorokhod, 1965) relating to Itô and Wiener integrals, a first order [O(h)] simulation algorithm for SDE of the form of equation (2) results as

$$x_i^{r+1} = x_i^r + f_i^r \cdot h + \sum_{j=1}^{m} g_{ij}^r \cdot Z_j^r + \frac{1}{2} \sum_{j=1}^{m} \sum_{s=1}^{n} \frac{\partial g_{ij}^r}{\partial x_s} \cdot g_{sj}^r ((Z_j^r)^2 - h)$$

$$+ \frac{1}{2} \sum_{\substack{j=1 \\ j \neq i}}^{m} \sum_{s=1}^{n} \sum_{\substack{k=1 \\ k \neq 1}}^{m} \frac{\partial g_{ij}^r}{\partial x_s} \cdot g_{sk}^r \cdot Z_k^r \cdot Z_j^r + O(h) \qquad (8)$$

for $i = 1, 2, \ldots n$; and where $Z_j^r \triangleq \int_{t_r}^{t_{r+1}} dW_j(t) = W_j^{r+1} - W_j^r$, is

a normally distributed random variable, which has a zero mean and variance $h.q_{jj}, (h = t_{r+1} - t_r)$.

The algorithm is readily implemented on a digital computer, since the normal random variable Z_j^r (for $r = 1, 2, \ldots N-1$) is easily generated by a random number generator within the computer. The algorithm (8) has been derived for SDE driven by an uncorrelated vector Wiener process $\underline{W}(t)$; in practice this is an unrealistic restriction, the following modification allows the algorithm the widest applicability. Consider the vector incremental Wiener process with independent elements $d\underline{W}'(t) = \{dW_j'\}$ and a covariance matrix $\underline{Q}$ which is diagonal.

Now transform the actual correlated incremental Wiener process $d\underline{W}(t)$, with covariance matrix $\underline{D}$, by the linear transform

$$d\underline{W}(t) = \underline{A}\ d\underline{W}'(t) \tag{9}$$

then owing to the properties of normally distributed random variables $\underline{D} = \underline{A}.\underline{Q}\ \underline{A}^T$. There are many transforming matrices $\underline{A}$ which satisfy this equality. In particular, in the time invariant case, since $\underline{Q}$ is diagonal its elements can be considered as the eigenvalues of the actual covariance matrix $\underline{D}$. In which case the unknown matrix $\underline{A}$ is a similarity transforming matrix or modal matrix, which contains the eigenvectors of $\underline{D}$ as columns. The generation of the eigenvalues and eigenvectors of $\underline{D}$ is a standard subroutine of most computing facilities. Hence the SDE(2) can be written as

$$d\underline{x} = \underline{f}(\underline{x},t) + G(\underline{x},t)\underline{A}.d\underline{W}'(t) \tag{10}$$

with g_{ij}^r in the simulation algorithm (8) replaced by

$$\sum_{k=1}^{m} g_{ik}^r.a_{kj}^r \quad \text{where } \underline{A} = \{a_{ij}\}.$$

For a particular SDE algorithm (8) is repeatedly solved to produce different discretised sample paths of $\underline{x}(t)$; each time using different realisations of x_i^r and Z_j^r for $r = 1,2,...N-1$. From these sample paths the moments of the solution $\underline{x}$ are found by averaging over all the realisations. The convergence of the proposed algorithm is at least of order h faster than conventional numerical integration procedures such as Euler's and Runge-Kutta's methods which ignore the special properties of SDE, (see Appendix).

BIOLOGICAL WASTE TREATMENT: ACTIVE SLUDGE REACTOR MODELS

A problem of increasing importance is that of achieving improved regulation of effluent discharge into rivers/seas from biological waste treatment plants. In most cases the primary concern is in controlling the concentration of biologically oxygen demanding (BOD) materials below some threshold or upper limit. BOD can be considered as an aggregate of the oxygen absorbing potential of substrate in the effluent. Waste waters entering sewage plants vary in mass flow rate as well as in concentration and in composition of dissolved and suspended materials. These include sludge loads of toxic materials and variable substrate (organic carbon) or nutrient concentrations. Various mechanisms of

effluent control are possible; one approach is to regulate
microbial concentration in the reactors (digestors) by
adaptively varying sludge recycle rates. Current practice
is to set the recycle rate at that for maximum loading.
Consequently during low loading periods, the microorganisms
are subject to severe nutrient substrate (pollutant) limiting
growth concentrations of organisms in the effluent over that
of the influent (Busch, 1971) and produces what might be
termed deactivated sludge.

The continuous flow cultivation of micro-organisms for
biological treatment of urban waste water has attracted
considerable attention (see D'Ans et al, 1971 for survey).
Many mathematical models of microbial growth in current use,
orginate from a single strain bacterial growth in a single
substrate model due to Monod (1950). The model of an
anaerobic digester is an idealisation of the digestion of
sludge from the primary clarification process in waste
treatment plants, and is based upon the following
assumptions: (i) the rate of multiplication of the pollutant
removing bacterial population is proportional to the present
population, (ii) when the nutrient substrate is in unlimited
supply then the rate of bacterial growth is constant,
otherwise it is dependent upon the substrate concentration,
giving a growth limiting concentration, (iii) in each
micro-organism formed a fixed fraction (the yield constant)
of substrate is incorporated.

The state equations for biomass (c_b) and substrate (c_s)
concentrations can be derived most easily using the perfect
mixing model of CSTR and writing the time varying state mass
balances for micro-organisms and substrate in the reaction
vessel. For modelling purposes the flow schematic of fig.1
is assumed; flow equalisation prior to reaction is used to
contribute to process stability.

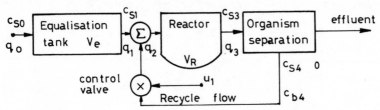

fig.1 Flow scheme of active sludge control

Nomenclature c_{so} = incoming substrate (pollutant)
concentration; c_b = micro-organism concentration;
u_1 = recycle flow rate; q_o = incoming sludge flow rate;
V_e = equalisation tank volume; V_R = reactor tank volume;

K_1 = growth rate constant for micro-organisms;

Y = yield constant.

The influent flow rate and pollutant concentration are subject to sudden and varied intensity perturbations due to rainfall, industrial waste discharge and domestic waste. This turbulent flow/concentration pattern is best modelled by the pair of SDE,

$$dq_o = (\alpha_1 + 1 - \beta_1 q_o V_e^{-1})dt + (2\gamma_1 q_o V_e^{-1})^{\frac{1}{2}}.dW_1 \qquad (11)$$

$$V_e dc_{so} = (\alpha_2 + 1 - \beta_2 c_{so} V_e)dt + (2\gamma_2 c_{so} V_e)^{\frac{1}{2}}.dW_2 \qquad (12)$$

where q_o and $\dot{c}_{so}$ are modelled such that they always remain non-negative (for physical compatibility) and are subject to band limited perturbations (filtered white noise). It can be demonstrated for the above models that q_o and c_{so} are stationary Markov processes with decay parameter β_i $(i=1,2)$, mean value $(\alpha_i + 1)\beta_i^{-1}$ and variance $\gamma_i(\alpha_i + 1)\beta_i^{-1}$. These parameters allow adequate modelling for a particular physical plant/environmental configuration, and may be found by standard statistical estimation techniques. In general, the influent feedrate and substrate concentration are related, this is reflected in the model equations (11), (12) by the correlation between the Wiener noise processes W_1 and W_2.

Mass balance for the equalisation tank yields

$$dV_e = (q_1 - q_o)dt \qquad (13)$$

$$V_e.dc_{sl} = q_o(c_{so} - c_{sl})dt \qquad (14)$$

Similarly, mass balance for the reactor yields

$$V_R.dc_{s3} = \{q_2(c_{sl} - c_{s3}) - K_1 V_R[(c_{b1}q_1 + c_{b4}u_1)(u_1 + q_1)^{-1}$$
$$+ Y(c_{sl} - c_{s3})]\} dt \qquad (15)$$

where $q_2 = q_1 + u_1$, $q_1 = E(q_o) = (\alpha_1 + 1)\beta_1^{-1}$ and $Y = \Delta c_b.(\Delta c_s)^{-1}$.

These equations do not contain differentials of the Wiener processes W_1, W_2 and could be written as ordinary differential equations, however their solutions are random since they are functions of q_o and c_{so}.

Defining the state variables $V_e = x_1$, $q_o = x_2$, $c_{so} = x_3$, $c_{sl} = x_4$, $c_{s3} = x_5$, the above model SDE becomes

$$dx_1 = ((\alpha_1 + 1)\beta_1^{-1} - x_2)dt$$

$$dx_2 = (\alpha_1 + 1 - \beta_1 x_2 x_1^{-1})dt + (2\delta_1 x_2 x_1^{-1})^{\frac{1}{2}}dW_1$$

$$dx_3 = x_1^{-1}(\alpha_2 + 1 - \beta_2 x_3)dt + (2\gamma_2 x_3 x_1^{-1})^{\frac{1}{2}}dW_2$$

$$dx_4 = x_1^{-1}x_2(x_3 - x_4)dt$$

$$dx_5 = (\alpha_1 + 1 + u_1\beta_1)(V_R\beta_1)^{-1}(x_4 - x_5)dt$$

$$- K_1[(c_{b1}q_1 + c_{b4} \cdot u_1)\beta_1(\beta_1 u_1 + \alpha_1)^{-1}$$

$$+ Y(x_4 - x_5)]dt \qquad (16)$$

Typical parameter values and the results of the simulator are shown in fig. 3 in conjunction with the results of the river pollution model.

RIVER POLLUTION MODELS

Some of the major problems in water quality control is the development of techniques for monitoring water quality variations and evaluating the concentration of pollutants and associated variables such as dissolved oxygen at various points in a river system, as a function of various conditioning factors such as sewage plant outfalls, effluent runoff from adjoining land, rainfall and the volume of river flow (Kneese, 1964).

A dynamic model for the interaction of biologically oxygen demanding (BOD) pollutants and dissolved oxygen (DO) is necessary, since it is the transients of water quality that cause the problems in water quality management, in particular at points adjacent to effluent discharges. Physico-Chemical modelling of DO-BOD interaction in a non-tidal river is based upon the classical work of Streeter and Phelps (1925) and results in 2nd order partial differential equations. Recently it has been shown (Beck and Young, 1974) that simple models based on lumped parameter first order SDE with associated transportation delay to allow for distributed effects between spatial points, can describe the observed temporal variations in DO and BOD in a single reach of a river. If a reach is defined as a stretch of a river which receives one major controlled effluent discharge from a sewage plant. Each reach can be considered as an ideal CSTR with parameters and variables uniform throughout the reach. With the upstream reach acting as input into the next reach.

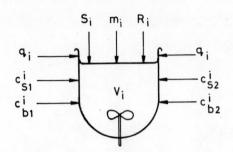

<u>fig.2</u> An ideal CSTR model for the ith reach of a river

<u>Nomenclature</u>; c_b^i = DO concentration in i^{th} reach,

c_s^i = BOD concentration in the ith reach, q_i = volume flow rate of ith reach, V_i = volume of ith reach,

c_{bs}^i = saturation concentration of DO in i^{th} reach,

K_2^i = DO reaeration rate, K_3^i = BOD decay rate,

$\delta_1^i(S_i - S_i^T), \delta_2^i(S_i - S_i^T)$ are terms that account for photosynthetic effects on algae populations in the reach, $(S_i - S_i^T)$ = effective sunlight, m_i = net rate of removal of DO by mud deposits, $R_i = q_e^i \cdot c_{s3}^i (V_i)^{-1}$ = the addition of BOD due to local runoff from adjoining land and effluent discharge from sewage plants, q_e = effluent flow rate, c_{s3}^i = BOD conc. of effluent.

Taking mass balances for the ideal CSTR model for the ith river reach, yields similarly to the active sludge reactor models

$$\frac{dc_b^i}{dt} = \frac{q_i}{V_i}(c_b^{i-1} - c_b^i) - K_2^i(c_b^i - c_{bs}^i) - K_3^i c_s^i + m_i$$
$$+ \delta_1^i(S_i - S_i^T) \qquad (17)$$

$$\frac{dc_s^i}{dt} = \frac{q_i}{V_i}(c_s^{i-1} - c_s^i) - K_3^i(c_s^{i-1} - c_s^i) - K_2^i c_b^i$$
$$+ R_i + \delta_2^i(S_i - S_i^T) \qquad (18)$$

The reach holding time $q_i \cdot V_i^{-1}$ is a function of rainfall, localised land water runoff, tributaries, and the particular physical shape of the reach (weir's will for example produce turbulent flow patterns). Then $q_i \cdot V_i^{-1}$ can be modelled as a non-negative random variable given by the SDE

$$\frac{dq_i}{V_i} = (\alpha_3^i + 1 - \beta_3^i \cdot \frac{q_i}{V_i})dt + (2\delta_3^i \cdot \frac{q_i}{V_i})^{\frac{1}{2}}dW_3 \qquad (19)$$

The mean reach flow rate is $(\alpha_3^i + 1)\beta_3^{-1}$, parameters are estimated from observation data for each reach.

Define the state variables $x_6^i = c_b^i$, $x_7^i = c_s^i$, $x_8^i = q_i \cdot V_i^{-1}$ then equations (17), (18) and (19) can be written as

$$dx_6^i = \{x_8^i(x_6^{i-1} - x_6^i) - K_2^i(x_6^i - x_{6s}^i) - K_3^i x_7^i + m_i$$
$$+ \delta_1^i(S_i - S_i^T)\} dt$$

$$dx_7^i = \{x_8^i(x_7^{i-1} - x_7^i) - K_3^i(x_7^{i-1} - x_7^i) - K_2^i x_7^i$$
$$+ R_i + \delta_2^i(S_i - S_i^T)\} dt$$

$$dx_8^i = (\alpha_3^i + 1 - \beta_3^i \cdot x_8)dt + (2\delta_3^i x_8)^{\frac{1}{2}}dW_3 \qquad (20)$$

Equations (17) and (18) are ordinary differential equations but are modelled as SDE in the above, due to their functional relationships with the random reciprocal holding time x_8^i. To account for transportation between various spatial points, a pure delay term precedes the above dynamics.

Since each reach has a major effluent discharge from a sewage plant (see term R_i in equation (20)), a complete water pollution/quality models for each reach of the river can be obtained by combining the state equations (16) of the Active Sludge Reactor together with equations (20) of the river water quality model.

SIMULATION OF WATER QUALITY MODELS

To illustrate the dynamics of the above water quality models, the simulation algorithm (8) has been used with the following set of estimated parameters and initial values.

$V_r = 3.0 \times 10^4$ gal; $E(V_e) = 1.2 \times 10^5$ gal; $E(q_i V_i^{-1}) = 0.9 \, \text{day}^{-1}$;

$q_1 = 4.0 \times 10^4$ gal.hr^{-1}; $u_1 = 0.5 q_1$; $q_e V_i^{-1} = 0.1 \, \text{day}^{-1}$;

$R_i = 2.5 \times 10^{-6}$ lb. gal^{-1}.day^{-1}; $m_i = 1.0 \times 10^{-6}$ lb.gal^{-1}.day^{-1};

$x_{6s}^i = 3.5 \times 10^{-3}$ lb. gal^{-1}; $c_{b1} = 6.3 \times 10^{-4}$ lb. gal^{-1};

$c_{b4} = 2.0 \times 10^{-3}$ lb. gal^{-1}; $E(c_{so}) = 3.3 \times 10^{-4}$ lb. gal^{-1};

$K_1 = 6.0 \times 10^{-3}$ hr^{-1}; $K_2^i = 0.3 \, \text{day}^{-1}$; $K_3^i = 0.2 \, \text{day}^{-1}$;

$\underline{x}(0) = (1.2 \times 10^5, \, 3.0, \, 3.0 \times 10^{-4}, \, 3.2 \times 10^{-4}, \, 0,$
$\qquad 3.2 \times 10^{-5}, \, 1.5 \times 10^{-5}, \, 0.9)^T$; $\delta_1 = \delta_2 = 0.2$.

Some of these parameters were estimated by Young and Beck (1974) from observations taken over an extensive period on the River Cam. Six thousand realisations of each of the above SDE (equations (16) and (20)) were made over a computational time interval of 2 days. The transient and steady state water quality gains are given in the next section.

Results and discussion
Figure 3 shows the transient response of the BOD gain of the Active Sludge Reactor as a function of the perturbation intensity of the influent substrate concentration (at constant feedrate q_o). This figure clearly demonstrates that large variations in the input (influent) concentration levels leads to a reduction in the effective BOD removal of the active sludge reactor and a consequent increase in river pollution. (see next page for figures 3 and 4).

Figure 4 shows how the steady state average influent feedrate and perturbation intensity affects the concentration yield (effective DO gain) of micro-organisms from the pollutant; a similar set of curves results for the pollutant average concentration, noise intensity and the expected gain of micro-organisms (at constant influent feedrate).

In Figure 5, the average DO and BOD gains as functions of the influent concentration variance (at constant influent feedrate) are shown. These curves are of potential importance in water quality management, since they demonstrate the adequacy (or inadequacy) of a particular sewage control policy on the adjoining river reach DO and BOD levels.

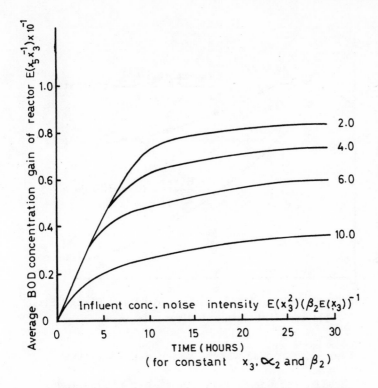

FIG.3 BOD GAIN OF ACTIVE SLUDGE REACTOR

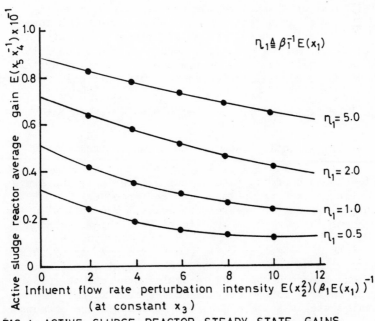

FIG.4 ACTIVE SLUDGE REACTOR STEADY STATE GAINS

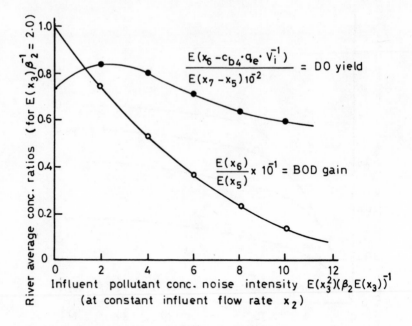

fig.5 River Reach steady state water quality gains

The above results are based upon the simple proportional
control $u_1 = 0.5q_1$ in the sewage plant, the proposed
simulation algorithm allows the possibility of investigating
optimal control laws that maximise DO yield and BOD loss
and that satisfies environmental and financial constraints.
For example a control recycle feedrate u_1 can be used to
regulate the water quality of the above composite system
by finding the u_1 that minimises the quadratic cost function,

$$J = \tfrac{1}{2}E(\int_0^T (\mu_1(x_6 - x_6(d))^2 + \mu_2(x_7 - x_7(d))^2 + \mu_3 u_1^2)dt) \quad (21)$$

where μ_i are weighting factors and $x_i(d)$ is the desired
value for the variable x_i. A quadratic cost function is
selected because of its analytical tractability and since
it enables an exchange between the variances of
concentrations and the recycle feedrate. The optimal u_1 is
found numerically by Rosenbrock's hill climbing technique
together with the SDE simulator (8) and the dynamic
constraints of equations (16), (20). The results of this
approach will be reported later. A somewhat simpler (and
realistic) approach would be to employ proportional plus
integral control in the recycle feedrate, this not only
eliminates steady state errors but attenuates the effects of
noise by the filtering characteristic of the integral action.

REFERENCES

Beck, M.B., (1973), Ph.D. Thesis, Department of Engineering, Cambridge University.

Bharucha-Reid, A.T., (1960) Elements of the theory of Markov processes and their applications. McGraw-Hill, N.Y. 143.

Busch, A.W., (1971), Aerobic Biological treatment of waste waters, Oligodynamics Press, Houston, USA.

Clements, D.J., and Anderson, B.D.O.; (1973), Well behaved Ito equations with simulations that always misbehave, Trans. IEEE. AC-18, No. 12, 676.

D'Ans, G., Kokotovic, P.V., and Gottlieb, D., (1971), A nonlinear regulator problem for a model of biological waste treatment, Trans. IEEE, AC-16, No. 4.

Fuller, A.T., (1969), Analysis of nonlinear stochastic systems, Int. J. Control, 9, 603.

Jazwinski, A.H., (1970), Stochastic Processes and Filtering theory, Academic Press, N.Y.

Kneese, A.V., (1964), The economics of regional water quality management, J. Hopkins Press, Baltimore, USA.

Monod, J., (1950), La technique de cultures continues, théorie et applications, Ann. Inst. Pasteur, 79, nr.4.

Skorokhod, A.V., (1965), Studies in the theory of Random Processes, Addison-Wesley, Reading-Mass, USA.

Streeter, H.W. and Phelps, E.B., (1925), A study in the pollution and natural purification of the Ohio river, Bull. No. 146, US public health service.

Young, P.C., and Beck, M.B. (1974), the modelling and control of pollution in a river system, Automatica, 10, No.5 455.

APPENDIX

It has been shown (Clements and Anderson, 1973) that some
Ito SDE have solutions which are bounded, yet may have
digital simulations that are unbounded. This is because
the discretisation effectively converts the unforced SDE
into discrete versions that are unstable outside certain
parameter and time increment (h) intervals. To demonstrate
this, consider the scalar SDE,

$$dx = x\,dt + x\,dW \tag{A1}$$

It can be shown (Bharucha-Reid, 1960) that the solution $x(t)$
has an inaccessible boundary at $x = 0$, ie $x(t)$ must be
positive for all t   0. From equation (8) the simulator
for this SDE is

$$x^{r+1} = x^r(1 + h + Z_1^r + \tfrac{1}{2}((Z_1^r)^2 - h)) \tag{A2}$$

Also the Euler simulator for equation (A1) is

$$x^{r+1} = x^r(1 + h + Z_1^r) \tag{A3}$$

where $Z_1^r \sim N(0,h)$ with $E((Z_1^r)^k) = \begin{cases} 1.3\ldots(k-1)h^{\frac{k}{2}}, & \text{for k even} \\ 0, & \text{otherwise} \end{cases}$

The probability that $x^{r+1} \leq 0$ given $x^r > 0$ (ie the simulator
violates the boundary condition) is required; then from
Tchebychev's inequality

$$\text{Prob}(x^{r+1} \leq 0/x^r > 0) = \text{Prob}(Y \leq - (1 = h))$$

$$\leq E(Y^{2k}).(1 + h)^{-2k} \tag{A4}$$

for $k = 1,2,\ldots$ and where $Y = \{Z_1^r + \tfrac{1}{2}((Z_1^r)^2 - h)\}$ or Z_1^r for the
simulator (A2) and the Euler simulator (A4) respectively.
Hence for $k = 2$ the simulator (A2) and Eulers method (A3)
for the SDE (A1) give respectively

$$\text{Prob}(x^{r+1} \leq 0/x^r > 0) \leq \begin{cases} 15h^3(1 + 0.25h)(1 + h)^{-4} \\ 3h^2(1 + h)^{-4} \end{cases} \tag{A5}$$

The simulation interval h can be selected such as to make
this probability as small as desired. Inequalities (A5)
illustrate that the probability of violation of the boundary
condition of SDE (A1) (or the probability of the instability
of simulation) for the proposed simulator (8) is of order h
smaller than the deterministic Euler simulator. (Typically
$h = 0.002$ sec. for an integration period T of 0.3 sec. for
the above example).

A MATHEMATICAL MODEL FOR ESTIMATING POLLUTION LOADINGS IN
      RUNOFF FROM URBAN STREETS

Roger Sutherland, Harza Engineering Company, Chicago Illinois
      60606
Richard McCuen, Department of Civil Engineering, University of
      Maryland, College Park, Maryland 20742

INTRODUCTION

Urban storm water runoff is a major source of water pollution
and degrades the quality of flow in receiving rivers and streams.
In the past decade, several studies have concluded that at certain times the quality of urban runoff is comparable to that of
raw sewage. Storm water runoff is a non-point source of pollution. Therefore, it is not easily identified and characterized,
which adds significantly to the problem of adequate control and
treatment. Nevertheless, many planning agencies now require
that non-point sources of pollution be considered in the development of water quality management proposals for both local and
regional planning.

Studies have shown that urban storm water pollution results
primarily from debris and contaminants from streets, contaminants from open land areas, publicly used chemicals, air-
deposited substances, ice control chemicals, and dirt and contaminants washed from vehicles. Debris and contaminants from
streets are the most readily controllable source of storm
water pollution. The most significant component of street
debris, in terms of producing water pollution by runoff, is the
"dust and dirt fraction" or that fraction of street refuse
passing an 1/8 inch hardware cloth (1). A 1972 study prepared
for the United States Environmental Protection Agency (E.P.A.)
by Sartor and Boyd (2) sampled the total solids accumulation on
the streets of eight American cities and further defined the
physical and chemical characteristics of the "dust and dirt
fraction.

Working with the data collected and published by the E.P.A.
study and numerous other sources, this paper discusses the
development and application of a computer simulation model that
estimates the accumulation of eight pollutants on urban streets,
their removal by rainfall, and their removal by street sweeping

operations. The eight pollutants considered are: total solids
volatile solids, five-day biochemical oxygen demand, chemical
oxygen demand, Kjeldahl nitrogen, nitrates, phosphates, and
total heavy metals. The model has three primary components.
The first component computes the accumulation of the eight
pollutants on the street. This component deals specifically
with the pollutants accumulating and
residing on the street and does not include pollutants accumulating on the surrounding watershed. The pollutant loadings
are developed as a function of time between rainfall or street
sweeping, land use, pavement type and condition, population
density, and traffic volume. The second component estimates the
removal of street contaminants by rainfall. The model estimates
the amount of pollutants originally residing on the street that
enter the storm sewer inlets during a storm event. The removal of pollutants by rainfall is developed as a function of
the initial amount of total solids in each particle size range,
the total volume of rainfall, the percentage of impervious area
in the watershed, the slope of the gutter, and the length of
the gutter. The third component of the model determines the
removal of accumulated pollutants by street sweeping. The
effectiveness of street sweeping in removing pollutants is developed as a function of the particle size range of the accumulated loadings, the type of street sweeper, the pavement type,
and the forward speed of the street sweeper.

Knowing the type of street sweepers available, a city's public
works department can use the model to obtain the optimum street
sweeping operation. Data from the Washington D.C. area were
used to illustrate this application of the model. The model
could also be used by an urban planner to estimate the total
pollution loading from urban streets that enters surface water-
ways. Thus, the planner could identify those parts of a city
that are contributing the greatest non-point source pollution.
Through the adjustment of input data to correspond to future
forecasts of population and land use changes, the planner
could also obtain an estimate of future pollution loadings.

REVIEW OF THE LITERATURE

In 1962, an extensive study of a 27 acre residential and light
commercial, urban watershed located in the Mt. Washington section of Cincinnati, Ohio was initiated (3,4,5). The watershed
was gauged and for a two year period the rainfall volume, runoff quantity, and runoff quality were continuously monitored.
Using the average pollutant concentrations, the constituent
loads in the runoff were determined both on an annual basis
and on the basis of daily discharges during storms(5). These
figures were compared to those representative of sanitary sewage production based upon the actual watershed population density. The results indicated that the weight of suspended
solids discharged annually in the runoff equalled 160 percent

of that produced as sanitary sewage; COD, 33 percent; BOD, 7
percent; total hydrolyzable phosphate, 5 percent; and total
nitrogen, 14 percent. During a storm event the average weight
of suspended solids discharged daily in the runoff equalled
2,400 percent of that produced daily as sanitary sewage; COD,
520 percent; BOD, 110 percent; total hydrolyzable phosphate,
70 percent; and total nitrogen, 200 percent (5).

Several attempts have been made to correlate the concentration
of pollutants found in storm water runoff to variables that
describe the degree of urbanization of a watershed. Land use,
impervious area, vehicular and pedestrian traffic volumes,
population density, and socio-economic differences within an
area are some of the factors that can be related to the degree
of urbanization. Pravoshinsky and Gatillo (6) found that the
intensity of auto and pedestrain traffic, the catchment cover
type, the duration and intensity of rainfall, the amount of
dust deposition, the length of the antecedent dry period, and
the quality and technology of town cleaning were the major
factors which influenced the pollution of surface runoff from
streets in Minsk, U.S.S.R.

The condition prior to a storm event appears to have a major
affect on the quality of the storm water runoff. Wilkinson
(7) noted that the BOD concentration of storm water from a 611
acre estate at Oxney, England, tended to increase with the
length of the antecedent dry weather period up to 8 to 10 days,
after which little further change occurred.

MODEL FORMULATION

The model developed herein contains three components, which
estimate the accumulation of pollutants on a street, the
amount of pollutants removed as a result of rainfall, and the
amount of pollutants removed by street sweepers.

The Accumulation Component
Data published by Sartor and Boyd (2) were used to formulate
the accumulation component. In the model, accumulation is a
function of land use (i.e., industrial, commercial, and residential), pavement type and condition, traffic volume, and
the length of time since rainfall or street sweeping. For each
of the three land use categories, a mathematical relationship
whose functional form closely resembled the assumed shape of
the accumulation function were empirically fitted using a least
squares criterion to provide the best initial estimate of total
solids as a function of time since the last significant rainfall or sweeping.

Throughout the development of the planning model, a computer
program that utilizes the pattern search method of numerical
optimization to obtain optimum mathematical equations was used

quite extensively. Using the pattern search program, optimum equations were obtained for each of the selected functional forms in each of the three land use categories; the resulting equations are summarized in Table 1.

Table 1. Preliminary Equations for Accumulation Component

Land Use	Correlation Coefficient	Standard Error (lbs/curb mile)	Equation*	Equation Number
Industrial	0.91	194	$P_I=1388(1-e^{-.19t})$	(1)
Commercial	0.71	165	$P_C=500(1-e^{-.335t})$	(2)
Residential	0.49	268	$P_R=1089t/(1.0+1.3t)$	(3)

*t = time, in days, since rainfall or street sweeping
P = accumulation of total solids in pounds/curb mile

The measures of goodness-of-fit reported in Table 1 are not representative of the final accumulation component because the equations do not consider variation in other factors that effect the accumulation.

The unit of pounds per curb mile as a measurement of total solids accumulation should be clarified. The E.P.A. study (2) found that the distribution of total solids across the width of the street was not uniform. Most of the material was concentrated along the curb due to the tendency of traffic to blow material out of the traveled lanes. This non-uniformity makes it difficult to discuss loading intensities on the basis of weight per unit area. For this reason, the unit of pounds per curb mile was used as a measurement of pollutant loadings in the model instead of pounds per unit area.

The second step in the development of the accumulation function was to determine the effect of the remaining four variables (i.e., pavement type, pavement condition, traffic density, and population density) on each of the three accumulation equations of Table 1. For a given land use, it was assumed that the coefficients of the accumulation equations presented in Table 1 were a function of the four variables mentioned above. The analysis was designed to systematically evaluate the change in the value of each of the four variables.

In the development of the final accumulation functions, it was necessary to quantify various qualitative variables such as heavy vs. moderate traffic volume, fair vs. good pavement condition, etc. The various traffic volumes were assigned AADT (annual average daily traffic) values that were estimated from the reported range of traffic volumes. And the reported qualitative estimates of pavement condition were related to the established standard Present Serviceability Index, (PSI), which is used throughout the United States to classify pavement condition (8).

The pattern search optimization technique was used to relate the coefficients of Table 1 and the remaining predictor variables. Equations were provided for two forms of residential housing (i.e., single-family and multi-family); the equations relate the coefficients to the pavement condition. The equations for industrial and commercial land uses are a function of the traffic volume and pavement condition. The computed coefficients P were evaluated for asphalt pavements and must be modified for concrete pavement with residential and industrial land uses.

Table 2. Final Accumulation Equations

Land Use	Residential	Industrial	Commercial
General Form	$P_R = Pt/(1+Kt)$	$P_I = P(1-e^{-Kt})$ C_p	$P_C = P(1-e^{-.335t})$
Housing Type			
Single-family	$P = e^{(.722-.172C_p)}$ $K = 1.173 + .0384C_p^{1.176}$	0.5 $P = 731 + .02T^{1.101}$ $K = .2 + .00003T^{.859}$	$P = 452 + .046T^{.892}$
Multi-family	$P = e^{(7.55-.185C_p)}$ $K = 1.125 + .0384C_p^{1.264}$	1.5 $P = 680 + .021T^{1.091}$ $K = .187 + .00001T^{.937}$	$P = 372 + .050T^{.872}$
		2.5 $P = 631 + .021T^{1.084}$ $K = .156 + .00003T^{.834}$	$P = 291 + .085T^{.803}$
		3.5 $P = 580 + .022T^{1.07}$ $K = .131 + .00003T^{.818}$	$P = 222 + .049T^{.837}$
		4.5 $P = 532 + .021T^{1.063}$ $K = .118 + .00003T^{.780}$	$P = 154 + .051T^{.803}$

T = traffic volume (AADT)
C_p = pavement condition (PSI)
t = time (days) since rainfall or sweeping
P_R, P_I, P_C = The accumulation of total solids (lbs/curb mile)

Note: for residential land use and concrete pavement decrease P by 8%

for industrial land use and concrete pavement decrease P by 10%

The Rainfall Component

The removal of particulate matter is primarily a function of rainfall intensity, street surface characteristics, and partical size. Due to the lack of qualifications in the empirical work of Sartor and Boyd (2), a theoretical approach to the material transport problem was used in the development of the rainfall component.

In 1946, W.D. Ellison defined soil erosion as "a process of detachment and transportation of soil materials by erosive agents" (9), and explained that the erosive agents involved were rainfall and runoff. Each of the erosive agents have both a detachment and transport component associated with them. Thus, in an effort to develop a mathematical model that estimates soil erosion by water, Meyer and Wischmeier (10) separated the process into four interrelated phases: 1) soil detachment by rainfall, 2) soil transport by rainfall, 3) soil detachment by runoff, and 4) soil transport by runoff. When dealing with an impervious surface such as an asphalt or concrete street, which is the case here, it seems reasonable to assume that all of the accumulated solid material are available for transport. It also seems reasonable to assume that the amount of material transported by rainfall is insignificant when compared to the amount of material transported by runoff. Sartor and Boyd (2) found that on the average 88% of the accumulated total solids loadings were located within one foot of the curb and 97% of the available material was located within forty inches of the curb. The problem, therefore, becomes one of material transport due to shallow, open channel, gutter flow.

The Yalin (11) equation, as modified by Foster and Meyer (12), was used in the development of the rainfall component of the planning model. Yalin (11) assumed that sediment motion begins when the lift force of flow exceeds a critical lift force. Once a particle is lifted from the bed, the drag force of the flow moves it downstream until the weight of the particle forces it back to the bed.

The modified Yalin equation is extremely sensitive to local flow parameters (12). Therefore, it was necessary to use a hydrologic model to accurately predict the hydraulic radius of the gutter flow (i.e., an important input to the modified Yalin equation) throughout the duration of a given rainfall event. The Basic Inlet Hydrograph Model (BIHM) developed by Ragan and Root (13) was used in conjunction with the modified Yalin equation. The gutter flow component of the BIHM uses the method of characteristics to obtain an explicit solution for both the continuity and momentum equations.

The rate of transport of soil particles estimated by the modified Yalin equation is a function of many variables. One of the more important variables is particle size. For the development of the rainfall function, the following six particle size ranges, which were defined and investigated by Sartor and Boyd (2), were selected: 1) $D \leq 43$ microns, 2) $43 \leq D < 104$, 3) $104 < D \leq 246$, 4) $246 < D \leq 840$, 5) $840 < D \leq 2000$, 6) $2000 < D$, where D is the particle diameter in microns. Because of the nature of material transport, it is important to know the amount of material that is initially available for transport in each reach of the gutter. When the capacity of the runoff to transport a given particle size range exceeds the amount of material in that particle size range available for transport, the particle size range is elimated from further consideration by the Yalin equation, thus increasing the capacity of the runoff to transport the remaining material.

Given the length and slope of the gutter, the percentage of impervious area, the initial total solids loadings in the gutter, and a rainfall-time relationship, the modified BIHM was used to estimate the percentage of total solids removed in each of the six particle size ranges. The pattern search optimization method was used with the output from the BIHM to derive six equations that estimate the percentage of total solids removed in each particle size range as a result of a 1/2 inch total volume design storm. The six equations and the goodness-of-fit statistics associated with each equation are given in Table 3.

Table 3. Table Solids Removal by Rainfall

Range	R	S_e(%)	Equation
1	.92	2.29	$T_1 = 91.4 + .757\ G^{1.92} + .104I - .0101S - .00319L$
2	.89	1.49	$T_2 = 95.6 + .647\ G^{1.55} + .0608I - .00575S - .00278L$
3	.94	3.74	$T_3 = 83.6 + 1.03\ G^{2.14} + .201I - .0192S - .00628L$
4	.95	6.60	$T_4 = 64.2 + 1.35\ G^{2.45} + .369I - .0364S - .0073L$
5	.96	9.59	$T_5 = 33.6 + 1.58\ G^{2.70} + 1.02I^{.903} - .0616S$
6	.99	3.40	$T_6 = (G_1 - 1.44)(-3.7 + .502I^{.952} - .0201S + .0258L)$

where R=correlation coefficient, S_e=standard error of estimate, T_i=removal percentage for particle size range i, G=slope of gutter in percent, I=impervious area in percent, S=initial total solids loading in lbs/curb mile, L=length of gutter in feet.

The effect of rainfall intensity and rainfall volume on removal percentages is presented in Table 4. It should be noted that for particle size ranges 1 through 5 the change in predicted removal percentages for storms of equal volumes due to the change in rainfall intensity is not very significant. Therefore, it was decided that total rainfall volume of a storm would be included as a variable in the rainfall function while rainfall intensity would not be included. The amount of pollutants associated with range 6, which is the only particle size range that demonstrated sensitivity to rainfall intensity, is not very significant. The actual amount of pollutants associated with range 6 rarely exceeds 10% of any of the pollutants residing on the street (2).

The effect of total rainfall volume on removal percentages
was analyzed with the data presented in Table 4 and data obtained from additional runs of the BIHM. Removal percentages
due to eleven different total rainfall volumes occurring over
a duration of one hour were obtained for each of the specific
cases shown in Table 4. The removal percentages were related
to rainfall of different volumes by the following equation:

$$TS_{V=V_o} = K_{V_o} (TS_{1/2})$$

where $TS_{V=V_o}$ is the percentage removal of total solids in a
particle size range due to a total rainfall volume V_o in
inches, $TS_{1/2}$ is the percentage removal of total solids in a
particle size range due to total rainfall volume of 1/2 inch,
and K_{V_o} is some factor that relates TS_{V_o} to $TS_{1/2}$ and is a
function of $TS_{1/2}$ and V_o. K_{V_o} will always be less than 1.0

Table 4.   Fraction of Total Solids Removed by Rainfall

Specific Case	Particle Size Range	1/2 Inch Total Rainfall Volume			1 Inch Total Rainfall Volume		
		1/2"/hr for 1 hr.	1/8"/hr. for 4 hr.	1/12"/hr for 6 hrs.	1"/hr. for 1 hr	1/4"/hr. for 4 hrs	1/6"/hr. for 6 hrs.
CASE 1	1	.850	.853	.831	.939	.927	.930
Slope 1.5%	2	.914	.914	.905	.969	.962	.962
Imperv 45%	3	.717	.746	.698	.875	.869	.875
Solid 800	4	.448	.481	.426	.750	.732	.730
#/crb. mi.	5	.148	.108	.078	.587	.504	.445
Length 600'	6	.000	.000	.000	.023	.000	.000
CASE 2	1	.941	.943	1.00	.980	.980	.977
Slope 1.5%	2	.970	.970	1.00	.999	.991	.991
Imperv 75%	3	.884	.897	.996	.956	.959	.955
Solid 600	4	.768	.776	.801	.901	.897	.889
#/crb. mi.	5	.615	.540	.391	.826	.782	.738
Length 600'	6	.016	.000	.028	.224	.001	.000
CASE 3	1	1.00	1.00	1.00	1.00	1.00	1.00
Slope 3.5%	2	1.00	1.00	1.00	1.00	1.00	1.00
Imperv 75%	3	1.00	1.00	1.00	1.00	1.00	1.00
Solid 600	4	1.00	1.00	1.00	1.00	1.00	1.00
#/crb. mi.	5	.934	.947	.934	1.00	1.00	.995
Length 200'	6	.447	.012	.000	.758	.328	.097

for rainfall volumes less than 1/2 inch. If the rainfall volume is exactly 1/2 inch, K_{V_O} will have a constant value of 1.0. For rainfall volumes greater than 1/2 inch, K_{V_O} is greater than 1.0. Using all the data obtained with the BIHM, equations relating K_{V_O} to $TS_{1/2}$ for specific rainfall volumes (V_O) were developed.

Given the initial total solids loading obtained from the accumulation function, the length and slope of the gutter, and the percent impervious area, the rainfall component of the planning model uses the equations presented in Table 3 to estimate the removal percentage in each of the six particle size ranges that can be expected from a rainfall of 1/2 inch total volume. If the actual rainfall volume is not 1/2 inch, an equation corresponding to the rainfall volume (i.e., equations not presented) is used to obtain K_{V_O} values for each particle size. The removal percentages in each of the six size ranges due to the actual rainfall volume are estimated. The fainfall component of the planning model estimates the amount of total solids in each of the six particle size ranges that are transported to the storm sewer system for any rainfall event.

The Street Sweeping Component

A third component of the planning model estimates the removal of pollutants from the urban streets as a result of a street sweeping operation. The U.S. Naval Radiological Defense Laboratory (NRDL) (14,15) conducted a series of tests designed to evaluate the efficiency of motorized and vacuumized street sweepers in removing particulate material from asphalt and concrete pavements, and reported street sweeping efficiencies as high as 98%. Sartor and Boyd (2) conducted a series of controlled sweeper tests in which a newly constructed asphalt paved street was loaded with a synthetic street surface contaminant and reported total removal percentages ranging from 36% to 78% of the initial loading. Sartor and Boyd (2) also conducted a series of in situ sweeper tests on the streets of six American cities. The removal percentages reported for the in situ tests ranged from 11% to 62% of the initial total solids loading.

The NRDL data published by Clark and Cobbin (15) were used to develop the street sweeping component of the planning model. For both motorized and vacuumized street sweepers, the researchers (15) obtained the mass remaining due to different relative efforts, particle size ranges, and pavement types. The authors (15) defined relative effort as inversely proportional to sweeper speed or 1200 divided by the forward speed of the street sweeper in feet per minute.

After the conversion of the particle size ranges to those used in the model and the units of measurement from grams per square

foot to pounds per surb mile, the NRDL data was used to develop
the equations that are used by the street sweeping function of
the planning model (see Table 5).

Table 5. Street Sweeping Equations

Pavement Type	PS	Equation for Motorized Sweeper	Equations for Vacuumized Sweeper
Asphalt	1-2	$M=192 \, RE^{-.711}$	$M=227 \, RE^{-.771}$
	3	$M=108 \, RE^{-.851}$	$M=198 \, RE^{-1.47}$
	4-6	$M=86.8 \, RE^{-1.19}$	$M=102 \, RE^{-2.33}$
Concrete	1-2	$M=130 \, RE^{-.75}$	$M=35.2 \, RE^{-.421}$
	3	$M=86.8 \, RE^{-1.19}$	$M=25.5 \, RE^{-.559}$
	4-6	$M=19.8 \, RE^{-.667}$	$M=10.6 \, RE^{-.667}$

where PS is the particle size range, M is the mass remaining
in pounds per curb mile, and RE is the relative effort of the
sweeper.

The street sweeping component of the planning model uses the
equations of Table 5 to estimate the mass remaining in each
of the six particles size ranges. The mass remaining is then
compared to the mass available obtained from the accumulation
function. If the mass available in any particle size range
is less than the mass remaining, it is assumed that the street
sweeping operation did not remove any total solids in that
particle size range. If the mass available in any particle
size range is greater than the estimated mass that remains, it
is assumed that the street sweeping operation removed a mass
of total solids in that particle size range equal to the
difference of the two values.

Model Synthesis
The equations of Tables 2, 3, and 5 describe the accumulation
and removal of total solids on the urban streets. The model
uses hourly precipitation in determining the amount of total
solids in each of the six particle size ranges being removed
by rainfall. The amount removed by sweeping or rainfall is
computed and summed throughout the duration of the precipitation records. When the end of the historic record is encountered, the planning model uses computed information and
reported relationships (2) to estimate the amounts of the
other seven pollutants that have been removed by rainfall and
street sweeping. Table 6 gives the mean total amount of the
eight pollutants in pounds per curb mile that were found by
Sartor and Boyd (2) for each of the three land use categories.
These values were used in computing the pollution loadings
for the other seven pollutants. Table 47 of the E.P.A. report (2) gives the fraction of a pollutant associated with

each particle size range for each of the eight pollutants.

Table 6*

DISTRIBUTION OF CONTAMINANT LOAD
BY LAND-USE CATEGORY

(lb/curb mile)

	RESIDENTIAL	INDUSTRIAL	COMMERCIAL
Total Solids	1,200	2,800	360
Volatile Solids	86	150	28
BOD_5	11	21	3
COD	25	100	7
Kjeldahl Nitrogen	2.0	3.9	0.4
Nitrates	0.06	0.18	0.18
Phosphates	1.1	3.4	0.3
Total Heavy Metals	0.58	0.76	0.18

MODEL APPLICATION

Using over thirteen years of hourly precipitation data for the
Washington, D.C. area, the planning model was used to examine
the effect of pavement condition on the amount of pollutants
accumulating on urban streets. Factors that were constant for
the four land uses included gutter slope (2%), gutter length
(400 feet), sweeper type (motorized), sweeper speed (4 mph),
sweeping frequency (4 days), pavement type (asphalt) and
traffic volume (10,000 ADT). The results of the analyses are
shown in Table 7; the accumulation of total solids are shown
for two pavement conditions: excellent (PSI=4.5) and poor
(PSI=1.0).

From the data presented in Table 7, it appears that the amount
of pollutants accumulating on pavements in poor condition is
2 1/2 to 2 times the expected accumulation of pavements in
excellent condition. This observation appears to be consistant
with an earlier conclusion by Sartor and Boyd (2) which is as
follows:

Streets whose pavement condition was rated "fair to poor"
were found to have total solids loadings about 2 1/2
times as heavy as those rated "good to excellent".

---

*Table 45, p. 144 of Reference 2.

It should be noted that the total amounts of pollutants accumulating in each of the four hypothetical areas are rational
and very significant. Studies of dustfall in seven cities
throughout the United States have found average accumulations
of 495 tons per square mile per year with a maximum accumulation of 765 tons per square mile per year (16). The computer
planning model estimates an average total solids accumulation
of 763 tons per square mile per year (i.e., assuming 630 foot
square blocks and an average total solids accumulation of
50,000 pounds per curb mile per year).

Table 7.

Effect of Pavement Condition on Accumulation

Land Use	Impervious Area (%)	PSI = 4.5	PSI = 1.0
Industrial	70	37,940	78,205
Commercial	95	14,940	39,124
Residential (Multi-family)	60	63,592	124,988
Residential (Single-family)	40	47,851	88,755

CONCLUSIONS

A computer planning model that estimates the accumulation of
eight pollutants on urban streets, their removal by rainfall,
and their removal by street sweeping operations has been developed and presented. Over thirteen years of hourly precipitation data from Washington, D.C. were used to demonstrate
some of the model's capabilities (17). This research led to
the following conclusions:

1. Under good operating procedures and conditions occuring
    over an extended period of time, street sweepers can remove
    approximately 50% of the pollutants accumulating on urban
    streets. Actual removal percentages vary considerably with
    the type of pollutant, the frequency of street sweeping,
    the type of street sweeper, and the forward speed of the
    street sweeper. The statement "good operating procedures
    and conditions" means frequent sweepings on smooth, un-
    cracked pavement by vacuumized street sweepers operating at
    slow forward speeds. Since "good operating procedures and
    conditions" are rarely found, a more realistic removal
    efficiency of 33% should be adopted by any model that
    assumes a constant street sweeping removal efficiency.
    The ineffectiveness of street sweepers in removing pollu-
    tants from the street is the result of their inability to
    remove the smaller particles which contain the greater bulk
    of the pollutants.

2. The amounts of pollutants accumulating on the street over
    an extended period of time were very significant. And, it
    appears that the accumulated amounts of pollutants estim-
    ated by the planning model are reasonable. Actual pollutant
    magnitudes vary considerably with the type of pollutant,
    the land use of the area being investigated, the pavement
    type, the pavement condition, the traffic volume, and the
    frequency of street sweepings.

3. Total rainfall volume was found to be the most important
    variable in estimating the amount of pollutants removed by
    a storm event. A linked-process hydrologic model modified
    to include a material transport equation was used to devel-
    op the rainfall component of the computer planning model.
    Results indicate that the actual amount of pollutants re-
    moved by rainfall is a function of the total rainfall
    volume, the type of pollutant, the amount and particle size
    range of the total solids residing on the street, the im-
    pervious area, and the slope and length of the gutter. On
    the average, a rainfall of 1/2 inch total volume removes
    approximately 78.5% of the pollutants accumulated on the
    street. Thus, the ability to intercept, store, and eventu-
    ally treat the flow from a low volume storm such as a 1/2
    inch total rainfall would significantly reduce the amount
    of pollutants entering the surface waterways.

References

1. American Public Works Association, Water Pollution Aspects of Urban Runoff, U.S. Department of the Interior, Federal Water Pollution Control Administration WP-20-15, January, 1969.

2. Sartor, J.D., and Boyd, G.B., Water Pollution Aspects of Street Surface Contaminants, U.S. Environmental Protection Agency, EPA-R2-72-081, November, 1972.

3. Weibel, S.R., Weidner, R.B., Cohen, J.M., and Christianson, A.G., "Pesticides and Other Contaminants in Rainfall and Runoff," American Water Works Association Journal, Vol. 58, No. 8, p. 1075, August, 1966.

4. Weibel, S.R., Anderson, R.J., and Woodward, R.L., "Urban Land Runoff as a Factor in Stream Pollution," Water Pollution Control Federation Journal, Vol. 36, No. 7, p. 914, July, 1964.

5. Weibel, S.R., Weidner, R.B., Christianson, A.G., and Anderson, R.J., "Characterization, Treatment, and Disposal of Urban Stormwater," Water Pollution Control Federation Journal, Vol. 38, No. 3, p. 337, March, 1966.

6. Pravoshinsky, N.A., and Gatillo, P.D., "Determination of the Pollutional Effect of Surface Runoff," Advances in Water Pollution Research, International Association on Water Pollution Research, Prague, pp. 187-195, 1969.

7. Wilkinson, R., "The Quality of Rainfall Runoff Water from a Housing Estate," Institution of Public Health Engineers (London), Vol. 55, Part 2, pp. 70-78, April, 1956.

8. American Association of State Highway Officials, Interim Guide for Design of Pavement Structures, Chapter 1, p. 5, 1972.

9. Ellison, W.D., "Soil Detachment and Transportation," Soil Conservation, Vol. 11, No. 8, p. 179, 1946.

10. Meyer, L.D. and Wischmeier, W.H., "Mathematical Simulation of the Process of Soil Erosion by Water," Transactions of the ASAE, Vol. 12, No. 6, pp. 754-762, 1969.

11. Yalin, M.S., "An Expression for Bed-load Transportation," Journal of the Hydraulics Division, ASCE, Vol. 89, No. HY3 Part 1, p. 221, May, 1963.

12. Foster, G.R., and Meyer, L.D., "Transport of Soil Particles by Shallow Flow," Transactions of the ASAE, Vol. 15, No. 1,

pp. 99-102, 1972.

13 Ragan, R.M., and Root, M.J., A Linked System Model for the
Synthesis of Hydrographs in Urban Areas, A report to the
Maryland State Highway Administration and Federal Highway
Administration, June, 1974.

14 Lee, H., Sartor, J.D., and VanHorn, W.H., Stoneman II Tests
of Reclamation Performance, Volume III, Performance Characteristics of Dry Decontamination Procedures, U.S. Naval
Radiological Defense Laboratory, USNRDL-TR-336, June 6,
1959.

15 Clark, D.E.,Jr. and Cobbin, W.C., Removal Effectiveness of
Simulated Dry Fallout from Paved Areas by Motorized and
Vacuumized Street Sweepers, U.S. Naval Radiological Defense
Laboratory, USNRDL-TR-746, August 8, 1963.

16 Johnson, R.E., Rosano, A.T., Jr., and Sylvester, R.O.,
"Dustfall as a Source of Water Quality Impairment," Journal
of the Sanitary Engineering Division, ASCE, Vol. 92, No.
SA1, pp. 245-267, February, 1966.

17 Sutherland, R.C., A Mathematical Model For Estimating
Pollution Loadings and Removals from Urban Streets ,
M.S.C.E. Thesis, University of Maryland, January, 1975.

THE ADVECTION-DISPERSION EQUATION FOR AN AN-ISOTROPIC MEDIUM
SOLVED BY FRACTIONAL-STEP METHODS

G.K. Verboom

Head Mathematical Branch, Delft Hydraulics Laboratory, Delft

INTRODUCTION

This paper is concerned with the numerical solution of the advection-diffusion equation. This parabolic equation, describing
the transport of any scalar quantity, is given by

$$\frac{\partial C}{\partial t} + \text{div } (\vec{u}C) = \text{div } (\vec{D}.\text{grad } C) + P \ , \tag{1}$$

where C is the concentration of the scalar, u is the velocity
vector with components (u,v,w), $\vec{D}$ is a tensor, commonly of
diagonal form, containing the turbulent and molecular diffusion
coefficients, and P represents loss and production terms. In a
bounded region appropriate initial and boundary conditions must
be given in addition to Equation (1).

In aquatic environments as rivers, lakes, estuaries, and coastal seas the characteristic length in the vertical direction is
usually much smaller than the horizontal ones, so Equation (1)
is averaged over the depth. In rivers often the same is true
for the transversal length scale and Equation (1) is averaged
over the cross-section.
With $\overline{uC} = \overline{u}\,\overline{C} + \overline{(u-\overline{u})(C-\overline{C})}$, where an overbar means a depth, or a
cross-sectional averaging, usually a Fickian-type formulation
is used to express the last term in known quantities, or

$$\overline{(u-\overline{u})(C-\overline{C})} = -FD_x \frac{\partial \overline{C}}{\partial x} \ ,$$

where F is either the depth, h, or the cross-sectional area, A.
The dispersion coefficient, D_x, is known theoretically in
simple cases only, Elder 1965, and must be taken from measurements otherwise.
In an aquatic environment the molecular and turbulent diffusion
coefficients can be neglected as they are at least an order of
magnitude smaller than the dispersion coefficients, Fischer
1973.

Numerical solution

If Equation (1), or an averaged version of it, is solved numerically special attention must be given to the following features:
- the advection is usually predominant in one direction, in coastal seas and rivers parallel to the shore and banks. In this direction the disperion is often small compared to the advection, but not negligible (salt intrusion in tidal rivers, transport of wastes along the shore).
- in the transversal direction the advection and dispersion are of the same order of magnitude, but an order of magnitude smaller than in the predominant direction.

In literature hardly any reference is made to the particular problems that are encountered if these large an-isotropies are present.

As in explicit computations the time step is more or less determined by the largest transport mechanism, the time step becomes often very small. The use of implicit schemes eliminates this problem only to some extent as the time step is still bounded, but now because of accuracy instead of stability reasons.

In view of the two principle errors, i.e. amplitude and phase errors, it is advection that causes the problems: when solving a pure dispersion equation only amplitude errors are encountered, but solving an advection equation both errors are present. The amplitude error can be eliminated by using non-dissipative schemes, such as Crank-Nicolson, leap-frog, angled derivative, but as shown by Fromm 1969, the phase errors of these schemes are even larger than that of the explicit second order Lax-Wendroff scheme and an order of magnitude larger than the phase error of an explicit fourth order scheme proposed by Fromm 1968.

As the number of grid points used in a fourth order scheme is 5 at least, rather complicated formulas result if such a scheme is used for the advection-dispersion equation, even if it is a one-dimensional equation.

In this paper we call attention to the fractional-step methods, which eliminate these problems, and we will present some ideas to select the numerical scheme that is adequate to solve each fractional step.

FRACTIONAL-STEP METHODS

To illustrate the fractional-step methods we use the one dimensional advection-dispersion equation

$$\frac{\partial C}{\partial t} + u \frac{\partial C}{\partial x} = \frac{1}{A} \frac{\partial}{\partial x} \{AD_x \frac{\partial C}{\partial x}\} , \qquad (2)$$

or

$$\frac{\partial C}{\partial t} = LC , \qquad (3)$$

where the operator L contains the space derivatives.
All two time-level finite difference schemes can be derived
from a Taylor-expansion in time, which can be written as

$$C^{n+1}(x) = \exp \left(\Delta t \, \frac{\partial}{\partial t} \right) C^n(x) = \exp \left(\Delta t \, L \right) C^n(x) \, , \qquad (4)$$

where $C^n(x)$ is the finite difference approximation to
$C(x, t = n\Delta t)$. To derive Equation (4) the coefficients of L are
treated locally as constant in time.
If L is written as $L = L_1 + L_2$, where $L_1 = -u \, \frac{\partial}{\partial x}$ and

$L_2 = \frac{1}{A} \, \frac{\partial}{\partial x} \left\{ AD_x \, \frac{\partial}{\partial x} \right\}$, then Equation (4) can be solved in two
steps

$$C^x(x) = \exp \left(\Delta t \, L_1 \right) C^n(x) \qquad (5a)$$

$$C^{n+1}(x) = \exp \left(\Delta t \, L_2 \right) C^x(x) \, , \qquad (5b)$$

where $C^x(x)$ is some arbitrary quantity, having no physical
meaning.
If L_1 and L_2 do not commute, then Equation (5) must be used in
reversed sequence in the next time step in order to maintain
the order of the truncation error. The fact that $C^x(x)$ is an
arbitrary quantity presents some problems at the boundaries:
the boundary conditions of C^x must be evaluated from those of
C^n or C^{n+1} , Mitchell 1969; but this disadvantage is outweighed
by the advantages, such as
- the numerical scheme used can be chosen for each step separately; stability and consistency are assured if each step is
  stable and consistent,
- a complicated more dimensional problem is splitted in many,
  but simple steps.

Accuracy

To see whether a scheme is appropriate to solve a particular
step, i.e. whether certain accuracy criteria can be fulfilled,
we compare the theoretical and the numerical solution, where
the Fourier-series method is used to find the solutions.
The accuracy with which a sinusoidal wave is represented depends on the number of grid points per wave length; unfortunately the smallest wave length that contributes to the solution depends on the solution itself.
Daily and Harleman 1972, introduced the spectral density method
to find the smallest relevant wave length as a function of time
and place; but for simplicity we assume this wave length, L_s,
to be 10 times the space increment.
Now the error made in each step after a fixed time interval, T,
is investigated as a function of the time step, Δt, and the
space increment, Δx.
A scheme is said to be adequate to solve a particular step if
the following criteria are fulfilled:
for the advective step, i.e. Equation (5a)

- the difference between the distance covered by the numerical and the theoretical solution must be smaller than $L_s/10$,
- the amplitude error must be smaller than 10 percent, or the numerical diffusion coefficient, defined as the diffusion coefficient in a pure diffusion equation necessary to give the same decrease in amplitude after the same time interval, must be smaller than some percentage of the actual dispersion coefficient; in this paper 3 percent is used.

For the dispersive step, i.e. Equation (5b)
- the amplitude error must be smaller than 10 percent.

To both steps a stability criterion is added, if the scheme used is an explicit one.

As a result of applying these criteria the range of possible values of space and time increments is limited. If at the end of the analysis no area of possible values remains, then some or all numerical schemes used must be replaced by more appropriate schemes. If an area remains, then the next questions to be answered are whether these values are acceptable from a point of view of costs, and whether the geometry can be described adequately with the allowable space increment.

EXAMPLES

Constant coefficients

As a first example we use Equation (2) with constant coefficients; the values used are u = 1 m/s, D_x = 10 or 100 m^2/s, and T = 10 hr.

In view of the above given argument the advective step is treated with the explicit fourth-order scheme of Fromm 1968, and for comparison with the Crank-Nicolson formula. The dispersive step is treated with a simple explicit scheme and with the Crank-Nicolson formula.

The two finite difference approximations to Equation (5a) are

$$
\begin{aligned}
c_j^x = c_j^n &- \frac{\alpha}{12} \{8(c_{j+1}^n - c_{j-1}^n) - c_{j+2}^n + c_{j-2}^n\} - \\
&- \frac{\alpha^2}{24} \{30c_j^n - 16(c_{j+1}^n + c_{j-1}^n) + c_{j+2}^n + c_{j-2}^n\} - \\
&- \frac{\alpha^3}{12} \{-2(c_{j+1}^n - c_{j-1}^n) + c_{j+2}^n - c_{j-2}^n\} + \\
&+ \frac{\alpha^4}{24} \{6 c_j^n - 4(c_{j+1}^n + c_{j-1}^n) + c_{j+2}^n + c_{j-2}^n\} ,
\end{aligned}
\tag{6}
$$

where $\alpha = u\Delta t/\Delta x$; this is a fourth-order scheme, $O(\Delta t^4, \Delta x^4)$, and

$$
c_j^x = c_j^n - \frac{u\Delta t}{4\Delta x} \{c_{j+1}^n - c_{j-1}^n + c_{j+1}^x - c_{j-1}^x\} ,
\tag{7}
$$

the Crank-Nicolson formula, $O(\Delta t^2, \Delta x^2)$.

The two finite difference approximations to Equation (5b) are

$$C_j^{n+1} = C_j^* + \frac{D_x \Delta t}{\Delta x^2} \{C_{j+1}^* - 2 C_j^* + C_{j-1}^*\} , \tag{8}$$

a simple explicit formula, $0(\Delta t, \Delta x^2)$, and

$$C_j^{n+1} = C_j^* + \frac{D_x \Delta t}{2\Delta x^2} \{C_{j+1}^* - 2 C_j^* + C_{j-1}^* + C_{j+1}^{n+1} - 2 C_j^{n+1} + C_{j-1}^{n+1}\} \tag{9}$$

the Crank-Nicolson formula, $0(\Delta t^2, \Delta x^2)$

It is a simple matter to show that

$$C_T \equiv C(x,t) = C_o \exp \{- k^2 D_x t + ik(x - ut)\} ,$$

is a solution of Equation (2), where k is the (real) wave number, C_o is a constant, and the subscript T refers to the theoretical solution.
The numerical solutions of Equation (6) to (9) are found after substituting

$$C_N \equiv C_j^n = C_o \exp \{i\omega n\Delta t + ikj\Delta x\} , \tag{10}$$

where ω is the complex circular frequency and the subscript N refers to the numerical solution.

Stability. The same procedure is used to find stability crite-ria, i.e. Equation (10) is substituted in Equations (6) to (9): for stability the imaginary part of ω must be positive, or $|\exp(i\omega\Delta t)| \leq 1$.
The range of possible values of Δt and Δx is limited for the explicit equations only; for Equation (6) and (8) the stability criteria are, approximately

$$\Delta t \lesssim \frac{\Delta x}{|u|} \quad \text{and} \quad \Delta t \lesssim \frac{\Delta x^2}{2D_x} , \text{ respectively.}$$

Results. The influence of the criteria concerning the advective and the dispersive step are given in Figure 1 for $D_x = 10$ m²/s and in Figure 2 for $D_x = 100$ m²/s, where Δt is given as a function of Δx. The values of Δt and Δx investigated are given by $\Delta t \in [10,300]$ s and $\Delta x \in [100,1000]$ m. The results shown are valid for a real time period of 10 hrs.
Each figure consists of four parts, the first three parts cor-respond to the solution obtained with Equation (6), (8) or (9) and the fourth part gives the allowable area if the two "best" schemes are combined. (The figure corresponding to Equation (7) is a trivial one in both cases and is left out.)

In Figure 1a, where Equation (6) is used to solve the advective step, three numbered lines are shown. Line number 1 results from the stability criterion $\Delta t \leq \Delta x/|u|$; only the area to the right of this line is allowed. Line number 2 results because of the fase error criterion, i.e.
$$\Delta S \equiv | uT - u_N T | \leq L_s/10,$$

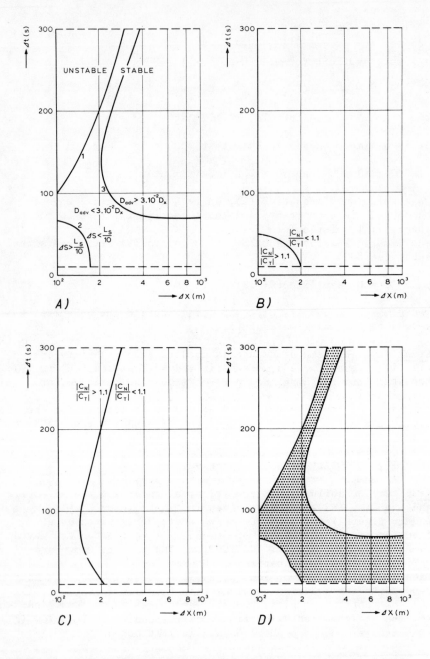

Figure 1   Allowable values of Δt and Δx; 1-d advection-dispersion equation, u = 1 m/s and D_x = 10 m²/s.
A) advective step, Equation (6); B) dispersive step, Equation (8); C) dispersive step, Equation (9); D) result of A) + B).

where u_N is the advective velocity, as it is represented in the numerical solution: only the area to the right of this line is allowed. The third line is due to the criterion that the numerical diffusion coefficient, Dadv, must be smaller than 3 per cent of D_x, or Dadv $\leq 3\times10^{-2}D_x$: only in the area to the left this criterion is fulfilled. As a result of these three criteria only the area between the lines is allowed.

Note that no line is found due to the criterion that the amplitude error is less than 10 per cent: this means that although Dadv $\leq 3\times10^{-2}D_x$ in the area to the right of line 3 the amplitude error is still less than 10 per cent, so one can doubt whether the third criterion is worthwhile, especially as it limits the area appreciably.

If Equation (7) is used to solve the advective step no combination of Δt and Δx of the values investigated is allowed and this is solely due to the large phase error.

In Figures 1b and 1c only one line shows up, due to the amplitude-error criterion. Only the area to the right is allowed. Note that the area is much smaller in case of Equation (9): the Crank-Nicolson formula presents no stability criterion, such as the explicit scheme does, but the amplitude error is not necessarily smaller. With a dispersion coefficient of 10 m²/s the line due to the stability criterion falls outside the figure; so there is no need to use the Crank-Nicolson formula, not for stability and even to the contrary because of accuracy reasons.

From these figures it is obvious that for the advective step the explicit fourth order scheme and for the dispersive step the explicit scheme suffice to find accurate results after 10 hrs real time. The resulting area is given in Figure 1d.

In Figures 2a to 2c the results are given for $D_x = 100$ m²/s. The differences compared to Figures 1a to 1c are mainly in Figures 2a and 2b.

In Figure 2a the criterion due to the numerical dispersion coefficient disappears; this is obvious as Dadv remains the same, whereas D_x is now 10 times larger.

Figure 2b is much more complicated than Figure 1b; the area is bounded by three lines instead of one. Line number 1 represents the stability criterion; only the area to the right is allowed. Line numbers 2 and 3 are due to the amplitude-error criterion. To the left of line 2 the amplitude of the numerical solution is more than 10 per cent smaller and beneath line 3 more than 10 per cent larger than the theoretical solution.

Note that the stability criterion is still overruled by the accuracy criterion. The conclusion that can be drawn from Figure 2 is essentially the same as that from Figure 1, i.e. there is no need to use implicit schemes or other more advantaged schemes to solve Equation (2), if the values of the coefficients are as indicated. The area that results if Figures 2a and 2b are combined is given in Figure 2d.

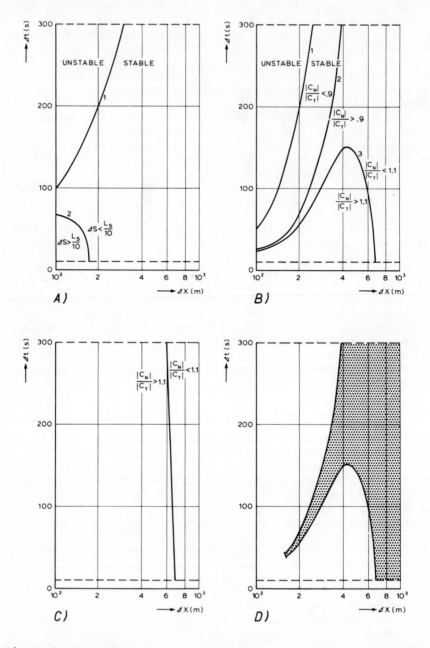

<u>Figure 2</u> Allowable values of Δt and Δx; 1-d advection-disper-
sion equation, u = 1 m/s and D_x = 100 m^2/s.
A) advective step, Equation (6); B) dispersive step, Equation
(8); C) dispersive step, Equation (9); D) result of A) + B).

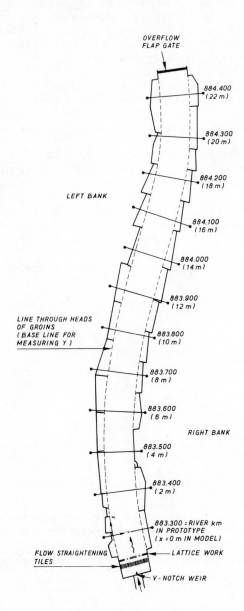

<u>Figure 3</u> Lay-out of IJssel model

Variable coefficients

In the preceding section the coefficients were constants; in
actual situations they are functions of space and time, in
these cases the above demonstrated criteria are applied
locally. In Figures 1 and 2 this would result in lines corresponding to the upper and lower limit of the coefficients.
An example of this kind is described below.

In a hydraulic model of the IJssel-river, scale 1/50 undistort-
ed, a conservative tracer is released continuously, see Figure
3 for the lay-out of the model. The area between the groins is
filled with concrete to eliminate additional mixing near and
behind the groins.
The longitudinal velocity component, u, is known from measurements and the transversal velocity component, v, is calculated
by solving the continuity equation of water. The concentration
profile is measured at various stations along the river, from
the measurements the transversal dispersion coefficient, D_y,
is calculated, Holley 1973. (The longitudinal dispersive transport is neglected compared to the longitudinal advective transport.)
To close the circle we solve the two-dimensional advection-dispersion equation

$$\frac{\partial C}{\partial t} + u \frac{\partial C}{\partial x} + v \frac{\partial C}{\partial y} = \frac{1}{h} \frac{\partial}{\partial y} \{hD_y \frac{\partial C}{\partial y}\} \ , \tag{11}$$

in three steps

$$\frac{\partial C}{\partial t} + u \frac{\partial C}{\partial x} = 0 \ , \tag{12}$$

$$\frac{\partial C}{\partial t} + v \frac{\partial C}{\partial y} = 0 \ , \tag{13}$$

$$\frac{\partial C}{\partial t} = \frac{1}{h} \frac{\partial}{\partial y} \{hD_y \frac{\partial C}{\partial y}\} \ . \tag{14}$$

The boundary conditions used are
- zero flux normal to the banks
- inflow: the concentration is given
- outflow: because of the parabolic character a boundary condition must be given: as a harmless condition the second
  derivative normal to the outflow was set equal to zero.

Except in a small area near the banks, the various coefficients
are given by
$u \in [0.08, 0.12]$ m/s, $v \in [0.005, 0.02]$ m/s, $h \in [0.05, 0.15]$ m, and
$D_y \in [0.4, 2.4] \times 10^{-4}$ m^2/s. To apply the procedure described above
we have to neglect the variation in h, but not, of course, in
the actual computation.
For the time interval T we used the time necessary to reach the
far end of the model by longitudinal advection, i.e. T $\approx$ 200 s.
In view of the results of the previous section we used Equations (6) and (8) to solve the advective and dispersive steps,

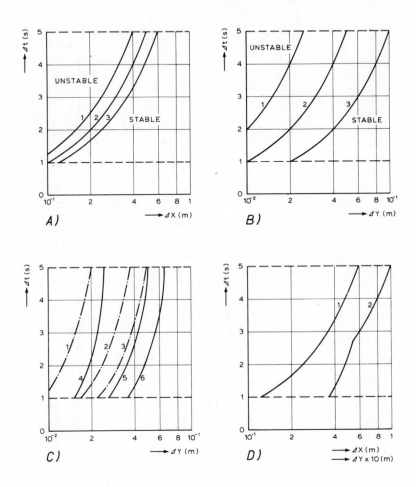

<u>Figure 4</u>   Allowable values of Δt, Δx and Δy; 2-d advection-dispersion equation with variable coefficients.
A) advective step x-direction; B) advective step y-direction;
C) dispersive step y-direction; D) result of A) and B) + C).

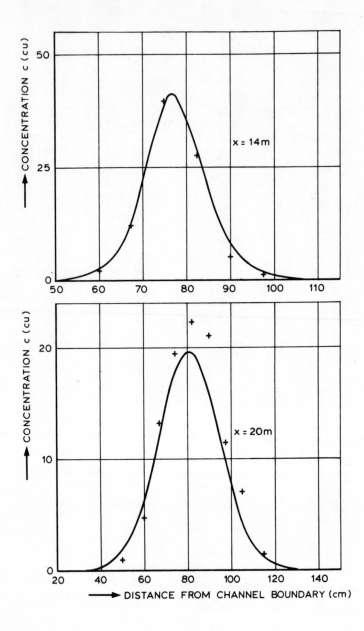

Figure 5 Measured (+) and calculated (−) concentration. Central injection at x = 12 m.

respectively. The time and space increments that are used in this analysis are:
$\Delta t \epsilon [1,5]$ s, $\Delta x \epsilon [0.1, 1]$ m, and $\Delta y \epsilon [0.01, 0.1]$ m. For both advective steps only the stability criterion limits the allowable values of Δt and Δx, or Δy; Figures 4a and 4b. The lines 1 to 3 in these figures correspond in Figure 4a to a longitudinal velocity of 0.08, 0.1 and 0.12 m/s, respectively and in Figure 4b to a transversal velocity of 0.005, 0.01 and 0.02 m/s respectively.
For the dispersive step both the stability and the amplitude error limit the area of possible values of Δt and Δy; Figure 4c. The lines 1 to 3 are due to the stability criterion, $\Delta t \leq \Delta y^2/2D_y$, with D_y equals 4×10^{-5}, 1.4×10^{-4} and 2.4×10^{-4} m^2/s, respectively, whereas lines 4 to 6 are due to the amplitude error with D_y in the same sequence. In Figure 4d the three figures are shown together for the worst situation, i.e. the largest velocities and dispersion coefficient; only the areas to the right are allowed. In the actual computation we used $\Delta x = 0.2$ m, $\Delta y = 0.064$ m, and $\Delta t = 1.5$ s; the space increments were chosen as small as possible because of geometrical resolution and the value of Δt chosen is a compromise between costs and accuracy. The results at two stations along the river are shown in Figures 5a and 5b together with measurements: the correspondence is quite satisfactory.

CONCLUSION

In this paper it is demonstrated that the fractional-step method is very suitable to solve the one- and more-dimensional advection-dispersion equation. One of the essential features of the method is, that the numerical scheme used to solve a particular step is independent of the schemes used for the other steps. As a consequence the method can be used with great advantage if some coefficients are an order of magnitude larger than other coefficients, whereas the transport mechanism cannot be neglected.
In the examples used the explicit schemes are to be prefered to the implicit Crank-Nicolson formula, this because of accuracy only.
The idea to use accuracy to select a particular scheme is well-known, but not as presented in this paper or in combination with the fractional-step method.

References

Daily, J.E., Harleman, D.R.L.(1972) Numerical model for the prediction of transient water quality in estuary networks. Cambridge, M.I.T., Dept. Civ. Eng., Ralph M. Parson Lab., Rep. no. 158.

Elder, J.W. (1965) Diffusion and mixing.
J. Boston Soc. Civ. Eng., 52, 108-128.

Fischer, H.B. (1973) Longitudinal dispersion and turbulent mixing in open channel flow.
Ann. Rev. Fluid Mech., 5, 59-78.

Fromm, J.E. (1968) A method for reducing dispersion in convective difference schemes.
J. Comp. Phys., 3, 176-189.

Fromm, J.E. (1969) Practical investigation of convective difference approximations of reduced dispersion.
Phys. Fluids Suppl. II, 3-12.

Holley, E.R., Karelse, M. (1973) Model-prototype comparisons for transverse mixing in rivers.
Istanbul, Proc. XV Congr. IAHR, Vol. 1, A40.

SOLUTION OF THE ADVECTIVE-DIFFUSION EQUATION BY THE METHOD OF MOVING COORDINATE SYSTEMS WITH PARTICULAR REFERENCE TO THE MODELLING OF ESTUARINE POLLUTION

B. M. Mollowney

WATER RESEARCH CENTRE, STEVENAGE, U.K.

Effective control of pollution in the estuarine environment
requires the ability to predict quantitatively the effect of
discharges of pollution on the water quality in an estuary.
Mathematical models applying the principle of conservation of
mass to the various substances or parameters relating to water
quality are widely used for this purpose. The equation of
ass balance for a substance is usually called the advection-
diffusion equation and, as well as specifying the rate at
which the substance is changed by advection and diffusion, it
contains terms for the time rate of addition of the substance
from outfalls, the rate of decay by biological or chemical
degradation, and the rate of formation as a result of breakdown of other substances. The equation is usually referred
to a coordinate system (reference frame) which is fixed in
space, and the solution, whether analytical or numerical, is
given in terms of these fixed coordinates and time. It is
well known thst much of the variation of the solution during
a tidal period at a fixed point is caused by the oscillatory
advective term simulating the horizontal and vertical tidal
flow. For a realistic numerical solution the time step Δt
must be less than or equal to the ratio of the element length
Δx to the velocity u. Furthermore, the length of the elements
must be kept small to reduce numerical dispersion effects.
For typical estuarine velocities Δt is of the order of a few
minutes, so the calculation of the periodic equilibrium solution corresponding to a steady discharge of the substance and
a periodic tide is very time consuming. Clearly, if it were
possible by some means to reduce the size of the advective
terms the time step could be increased and a more efficient
algorithm obtained. The method suggested in this paper is to
solve the equation in a moving coordinate system.

For many of the problems encountered in the management of
estuaries a time average of the periodic solution over a tidal
cycle is sufficient. It might be thought that the equation
which this average solution obeys could be obtained by averaging the time-varying equation over a tidal period. However,
the resulting equation is not of closed form because the terms
representing the time averages of the advective flux are
unknown. Attempts to express them in terms of other time-
averaged quantities, for example by introducing virtual diffusion coefficients (Okubo, 1964), have not been satisfactory
as the solutions given by these steady-state equations do not
compare well with the time averages of real time solutions
(Harleman, 1971). Again, these difficulties can be alleviated
by changing from a fixed to a moving coordinate system in
which the advectove terms are smaller. O'Kane (1974) has
given an excellent mathematical description of an oscillating
reference frame for one-dimensional estuaries. The reference
frame chosen was one which moved with the tidal velocity so
that there was a constant volume of water between any observer
on the frame and the head of the estuary at all times. In
effect, Mollowney (1973) used the same moving frame in the
numerical solution of the mass balance equations in a series
of oscillating segments (elements) for temperature, dissolved
oxygen, and associated substances. He also suggested that
steady-state equations could be derived by time averaging in
the moving frame. In this paper the method is extended to two
and three dimensions. The equations of conservation of mass
of substance and volume of water in a coordinate system moving
with an arbitrary velocity relative to the fixed system are
derived and the benefits discussed. In particular it is shown
that steady-state models can be derived more rigorously in a
moving frame than in a fixed frame.

The equations of conservation of a substance in a fixed
coordinate system will first be derived as it will be needed
for the transformation to a moving frame.

FIXED COORDINATE SYSTEMS

Conservation Equations
Consider an arbitrary closed volume V with surface S in a
fixed coordinate system. The equation of conservation of mass
of the substance in the Volume V is

$$\frac{d}{dt} \int_V \rho c \ dV = - \int_S \rho c \underline{u} \cdot \underline{n} \ dS + \int_S \rho \underline{F} \cdot \underline{n} \ dS + \int_V (m - k\rho c) dV \qquad (1)$$

where ρ is the fluid density, c the concentration expressed in
terms of mass of substance per unit mass of solution, u the
fluid velocity vector, $\underline{n}$ the outward unit vector normal to the

surface, $\underline{F}$ the vector expressing flux by diffusion, m the time rate at which the substance is being added from outfalls per unit volume and k is a decay coefficient. In general, density gradients are small compared with concentration gradients in estuaries so that, to a good approximation, ρ is constant. It is assumed throughout that units are such as to make the density, ρ, of the receiving water equal to unity. Using Green's Theorem (Aris 1962) to convert surface integrals to volume integrals Equation 1 becomes

$$\int_V \frac{\partial c}{\partial t}\, dV = \int_V (div\ \underline{F} - div(\underline{u}c) + m - kc)dV. \tag{2}$$

Because V is arbitrary, the equation

$$\frac{\partial c}{\partial t} + div(\underline{u}c) = div\ \underline{F} + m - kc \tag{3}$$

holds at any point.

The equation of conservation of volume which is obtained from Equation 3 by putting $k = 0$, $c = 1$, $\underline{F} = 0$, and $m = q$ is

$$div(\underline{u}) = q\ , \tag{4}$$

where q is the time rate of addition of water per unit volume.

Rectangular Cartesian Coordinate System
In a rectangular Cartesian coordinate system with coordinates x^1, x^2, x^3 and velocity u^1, u^2, u^3, Equations 3 and 4 take the form

$$\frac{\partial c}{\partial t} + \frac{\partial}{\partial x^i}(u^i c) = \frac{\partial F^i}{\partial x^i} + m - kc \tag{5}$$

and

$$\frac{\partial u^i}{\partial x^i} = q \tag{6}$$

respectively, where

$$F^i = D^{ij} \frac{\partial c}{\partial x^j} \tag{7}$$

and D^{ij} is the diffusion tensor. It should be noted that D^{ij} D^{ij} cannot be represented as a diagonal matrix here as, in general the coordinate axes will not coincide with the principal axes of diffusion.

Meandering Coordinate System

The location of a point in an estuary can also be expressed using a -eandering coordinate system in which the longitudinal axis y^1 is along the centre of the channel, the depth axis y^3 coincides with the depth axis x^3 and the axis y^2 is normal to the y^1 and y^3 axis. The same point can be determined by the three Cartesian coordinates x^1, x^2, x^3 or by the three curvilinear coordinates y^1, y^2, y^3. The relationship between the two systems can be represented as

$$x^i = x^i(y^1, y^2, y^3). \tag{8}$$

The equations can also be interpreted as defining a mapping from the x-space in which the estuary follows a meandering path to the y-space in which it is 'straight'. This coordinate system may be considered to be a special case of a moving coordinate system.

MOVING COORDINATE SYSTEMS

Equations of Transformation

Let the equations of the transformation from a curvilinear coordinate system, where a point P has coordinates a^1, a^2, a^3, moving relative to a rectangular Cartesian coordinate system where the coordinates of P are x^1, x^2, x^3, be

$$x^i = x^i(a^1, a^2, a^3, t) \tag{9}$$

where i takes the successive values 1, 2, 3. This can be expressed more succinctly as

$$x^i = x^i(a^j, t). \tag{10}$$

Equation 9 can be inverted to give

$$a^i = a^i(x^j, t) \tag{11}$$

which is valid provided that the Jacobian determinant

$$J' = \frac{\partial(x^1, x^2, x^3)}{\partial(a^1, a^2, a^3)} \tag{12}$$

exists and does not vanish (Aris 1962).

Similarly Equations 11 may be inverted if

$$J = \frac{\partial(a^1, a^2, a^3)}{\partial(x^1, x^2, x^3)} \tag{13}$$

does not vanish. It can be shown that $JJ' = 1$.

As well as considering Equations 9 to define a coordinate transformation they can also be thought of as defining a point transformation or mapping, carrying certain points from the a-space into points of the x-space. From this point of view the Jacobain, J', is the ratio of the volume of an element in the x-space to that in the a-space. Thus

$$dV = |J'| \, da^1 \, da^2 \, da^3 \tag{14}$$

where dV is the volume element in the x-space. In this paper J' is assumed to be positive so that $J' = |J'|$. A simple example may help to make the above ideas clearer.

Example of a Transformation to a Moving Frame
Let

$$a^1 = x^1, \; a^2 = x^2, \; a^3 = (d_2 + x^3)/D, \tag{15}$$

where, as shown in the upper part of Fig. 1, $d_2(x^1, x^2, t)$ is the height of the water surface above the reference plane defined by $x^3 = 0$, $d_1(x^1, x^2)$ the depth of the bottom below this plane, and $D = d_1 + d_2$ is the total depth of water, in the rectangular coordinate system. The coordinate a^3 is the fractional depth often used for plotting observations made over the depth in stratified estuaries. As viewed from the x-frame, the a-frame oscillates vertically so that the equations of the surface and bottom are $a^3 = 0$ and $a^3 = 1$, respectively. The transformation can also be considered (lower part of Fig. 1) as mapping the estuary into a slab of unit thickness in the a-space.

The equations of the inverse transformation are

$$x^1 = a^1, \; x^2 = a^2, \; x^3 = D'a^3 - d_2' \tag{16}$$

where $D'(a^1, a^2, t) = D(x^1, x^2, t)$ and $d_2'(a^1, a^2, t) = d_2(x^1, x^2, t)$. By direct calculation J' is found to be equal to D' and J equal to $1/D$.

Application of Tensor Calculus
Before transforming the conservation equations it is necessary to introduce some basic definitions and theorems from tensor calculus.

Scalar functions If $f(x^i, t)$ is a function in the x-space, the equivalent function in the a-space may be written as $f'(a^i, t)$. We also define $f*(a^i, t)$ to be the function obtained by substituting $x^j(a^i, t)$ into $f(x^j, t)$. That is,

$$f*(a^i,t) = f(x^j(a^i,t),t) \tag{17}$$

If

$$f' = f*J'^W \tag{18}$$

where W is an integer, then f is called a relative scalar of weight W (Sokolnikoff 1951). If $W = 0$, the function f is called an absolute scalar or invariant. An example of a relative scalar is the function $m(x^i,t)$ representing the time rate of addition of mass per unit volume of the x-space. The equivalent in the a-frame is the function expressing the time rate of addition per unit volume of the a-space and since J' is the ratio of volume elements we obtain

$$m' = m*J' \tag{19}$$

m is therefore a relative scalar of weight 1. Concentration is an absolute scalar so that

$$c'(a^i,t) = c*(a^i,t) = c(x^i,t) \tag{20}$$

Vectors   The components of an absolute vector $\underline{A}$, which in the x-frame are A^i, transform according to the equation

$$A'^i = \frac{\partial a^i}{\partial x^j} A*^j \tag{21}$$

where $A*^j(a^i,t) = A^j(x^i,t)$.

Divergence   The equation for the divergence of a vector $\underline{A}$, which in the rectangular coordinate system is

$$\text{div } \underline{A} = \frac{\partial A^i}{\partial x^i}, \tag{22}$$

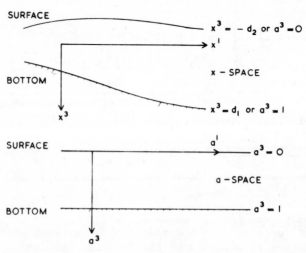

Figure 1. Elevation view of estuary in x-space and a-space.

becomes, in the new system (Sokolnikoff 1951),

$$\text{div } \underline{A} = \frac{1}{\sqrt{g'}} \; \frac{\partial}{\partial a^i} \; (\sqrt{g'} \; A'^i), \tag{23}$$

where g' is the determinant of the metric tensor g'_{ij} in the a-space. Now

$$g'_{ij} = \frac{\partial x^k}{\partial a^i} \frac{\partial x^\ell}{\partial a^j} \; g_k \tag{24}$$

and taking determinants of both sides gives

$$g' = J'^2 g \tag{25}$$

where g is the determinant of the metric tensor in the x-space. Since g is unity

$$\sqrt{g'} = J' \tag{26}$$

and substituting into Equation 23 gives

$$\text{div } \underline{A} = \frac{1}{J'} \frac{\partial}{\partial a^i} \; (J'A'^i). \tag{27}$$

Useful Identities   (i) If it is assumed that $\underline{A} = (1,0,0)$ then $\text{div } \underline{A} = 0$ and, since

$$A'^i = A^j \frac{\partial a^i}{\partial x^j} = \frac{\partial a^i}{\partial x^1} \tag{28}$$

substituting Equation 27 gives

$$\frac{\partial}{\partial a^i} \; (J' \frac{\partial a^i}{\partial x^1}) = 0. \tag{29}$$

Similarly it can be shown for $j = 2,3$ that

$$\frac{\partial}{\partial a^i} \; (J' \frac{\partial a^i}{\partial x^j}) = 0. \tag{30}$$

(ii) We now define

$$u_T^j(x^i,t) = u*_T^j(a^i,t) = \frac{\partial x^j}{\partial t}\,, \tag{31}$$

where u_T^j are the components of the velocity of the moving frame relative to the fixed frame. The components of $\underline{u}_T$ in the a-frame are

$$u_T'^{\,i} = u*_T^j \frac{\partial a^i}{\partial x^j}\,. \tag{32}$$

We now wish to prove that

$$u_T'^{\,i} = - \frac{\partial a^i}{\partial t} \tag{33}$$

or, in a more useful form, that

$$\frac{\partial a^i}{\partial t} + \frac{\partial a^i}{\partial x^j} \frac{\partial x^j}{\partial t} = 0. \tag{34}$$

Let $f(x^i,t) = f*(a^i,t)$, be an arbitrary scalar function. Then

$$\frac{\partial f}{\partial t} = \frac{\partial f*}{\partial t} + \frac{\partial f*}{\partial a^i} \frac{\partial a^i}{\partial t}\,, \tag{35}$$

and

$$\frac{\partial f}{\partial x^j} = \frac{\partial f*}{\partial a^i} \frac{\partial a^i}{\partial x^j}\,. \tag{36}$$

Also since $f*(a^i,t) = f(x^i,t)$,

$$\frac{\partial f*}{\partial t} = \frac{\partial f}{\partial t} + \frac{\partial f}{\partial x^j} \frac{\partial x^j}{\partial t} \tag{37}$$

Substituting Equations 36 and 37 into 35 gives

$$\frac{\partial f*}{\partial a^i} \left(\frac{\partial a^i}{\partial t} + \frac{\partial a^i}{\partial x^j} \frac{\partial x^j}{\partial t}\right) = 0. \tag{38}$$

Since f* is an arbitrary function, the individual coefficients of $\frac{\partial f*}{\partial a^i}$ in the sum must vanish which proves Equation 34.

Similarly it can be shown that

$$\frac{\partial x^i}{\partial t} + \frac{\partial x^i}{\partial a^j} \frac{\partial a^j}{\partial t} = 0 \ . \tag{39}$$

(iii) Another useful result, which is known as Euler's Expansion Formula (Aris 1962) is that

$$\text{div } \underline{u}_T = \frac{1}{J'} \frac{\partial J'}{\partial t} \ . \tag{40}$$

(iv) By using Equations 27 and 33, div $\underline{u}_T$ may also be written as

$$\text{div } \underline{u}_T = - \frac{1}{J'} \frac{\partial}{\partial a^i} \left(J' \frac{\partial a^i}{\partial t} \right), \tag{41}$$

which together with Equation 40 gives

$$\frac{\partial J'}{\partial t} + \frac{\partial}{\partial a^i} \left(J' \frac{\partial a^i}{\partial t} \right) = 0. \tag{42}$$

It should be noted that the identities given in Equations 30, 34, 39, 40, and 42 are true for values of N equal to one, two, or three, where the summation is from 1 to N, and J' is the N-dimensional Jacobian.

We are now ready to transform the conservation equations.

Transformation of the Conservation Equations
Each term of Equation 3 is transformed separately.

(i)

$$\frac{\partial c}{\partial t} = \frac{\partial c'}{\partial t} + \frac{\partial c'}{\partial a^i} \frac{\partial a^i}{\partial t} \tag{43}$$

$$= \frac{1}{J'} \frac{\partial}{\partial t} (J'c') + \frac{1}{J'} \frac{\partial}{\partial a^i} (J' \frac{\partial a^i}{\partial t} c')8 \tag{44}$$

after using Equation 42.

(ii)

$$\text{div}(\underline{u}c) = \frac{1}{J'} \frac{\partial}{\partial a^i} (J'u'^i c') \tag{45}$$

using the formula for the divergence of a vector, Equation 27.

(iii)

Also

$$\text{div } \underline{F} = \frac{1}{J'} \frac{\partial}{\partial a^i} (J'F'^i).$$

(46)

Since

$$F^{\ell} = D^{\ell m} \frac{\partial c}{\partial x^m}$$

(47)

it can be shown that

$$F'^i = D'^{ij} \frac{\partial c'}{\partial a^j}$$

(48)

where

$$D'^{ij} = D^{\ell m} \frac{\partial a^i}{\partial x^{\ell}} \frac{\partial a^j}{\partial x^m} .$$

(49)

(iv)

$$m = m'/J'$$

(50)

from Equation 19.

(v)

$$kc = k'c'$$

(51)

since k and c are invariants.

Taking these together the transformed equation is

$$\frac{\partial}{\partial t}(J'c') + \frac{\partial}{\partial a^i}(J'\Omega'^i c') = \frac{\partial}{\partial a^i}(D'^{ij}J' \frac{c'}{\partial a^j}) + m' - k'J'c'$$

(52)

where

$$\Omega'^i = u'^i + \frac{\partial a^i}{\partial t} .$$

(53)

Combining with Equation 33 this becomes

$$\Omega'^i = u'^i - u_T'^i ,$$

(54)

or in the x-frame

$$\Omega^i = u^i - u_T^i .$$

(55)

That is, $\underline{\Omega}$ is the water velocity relative to the moving frame.

The equation of conservation of volume obtained by setting

$k' = 0$, $c' = 1$, and $q' = m'$ in Equation 52 is

$$\frac{\partial J'}{\partial t} + \frac{\partial}{\partial a^i}(J'\Omega'^i) = q'. \tag{56}$$

Equations 52 and 56 are the required three-dimensional conservation equations in a reference frame moving with an arbitrary velocity $\underline{u}_T$ relative to the fixed frame.

Numerical Solution

The advective term is smaller in the moving frame, so that larger time steps may be used in the numerical solution. If we choose to move the frame with the same velocity as the water, the advective term disappears completely; in practice however, this is not a good procedure because the element mesh becomes very distorted, when viewed from the fixed frame, as time progresses (Adey and Brebbia 1974), whilst the Jacobian J' becomes pregressively more and more difficult to approximate accurately in the a-frame. A better approach is to assume that J' is constant so that

$$\frac{\partial J'}{\partial t} = 0 \tag{57}$$

and to make the velocity, $\underline{u}_T$, of the moving frame a periodic function of time. This gives a periodically oscillating mesh of constant volume viewed in the x-frame. If the velocity, $\underline{\Omega}$, at a point is of the same sign throughout a tidal cycle, we can further restrict the arbitrariness in the choice of $\underline{u}_T$. Essentially, the problem is to split the fluid velocity, $\underline{u}$, assumed known, into a sum of a periodic velocity, $\underline{u}_T$ and a residual velocity, $\underline{\Omega}$, subject to

$$\text{div } \underline{u}_T = 0 \tag{58}$$

and

$$\text{div } \underline{\Omega} = q. \tag{59}$$

Treatment of Boundaries

A further advantage of the moving frame is that the treatment of boundaries is simplified by choosing to move the frame with the boundary. Thus if the equation of the moving boundary in the x-frame is

$$F(x^i, t) = 0 \tag{60}$$

it can be shown that the corresponding equation in the moving frame is

$$F*(a^i) = 0 \tag{61}$$

where $F*(a^i) = F(x^i(a^j,t),t)$ so that the boundary is fixed in the a-frame. This is an advantage in numerical solutions as there is no need to add new elements as time progresses to take effect of the changing boundary.

Steady-state Equations

Steady-state equations can be obtained by averaging Equations 52 and 56 over a tidal period assuming that c is periodic. We define the time average $\bar{f}$ of a function $f(t)$ to be

$\frac{1}{T} \int_0^T f(t)dt$ where t is the time and T the tidal period.

Averaging Equation 52 in this way gives

$$\frac{J'}{T} \{c'(a^i,T) - c'(a^i,0)\} = \frac{1}{T} \int_0^T \frac{\partial}{\partial a^i} (D'^{ij}J' \frac{\partial c'}{\partial a^j} - J'\Omega'^i c')dt+$$

$$+ \frac{1}{T} \int_0^T (m' - k'J'c')dt \tag{62}$$

where it has been assumed that the a-frame is such that J' is constant in time. The left-hand side is zero since c' is periodic and, moreover, if c' is a slowly varying function then, to a good approximation,

$$\frac{1}{T} \int_0^T (D'^{ij} \frac{\partial c'}{\partial a^j} - \Omega'^i c')dt = \bar{D}'^{ij} \frac{\partial \bar{c}'}{\partial a^j} - \bar{\Omega}'^i \bar{c}'. \tag{63}$$

Equation 62 now becomes

$$\frac{\partial}{\partial a^i} (\bar{D}'^{ij} J' \frac{\partial \bar{c}'}{\partial a^j} - J'\bar{\Omega}'^i \bar{c}') - k'J'\bar{c}' + \bar{m}' = 0. \tag{64}$$

Similarly, combining Equations 56 and 57 and averaging gives

$$\frac{\partial}{\partial a^i} (J'\bar{\Omega}'^i) = \bar{q}'. \qquad\qquad \tag{65}$$

Source Terms

The source terms m' and q' are more complicated functions of time than their counterparts m and q in the x-frame. An outfall discharging a substance at a constant rate, M, at a point α^1, α^2, α^3 in the fixed frame can be represented mathematically by a delta function (see Van der Pol and Bremner, 1964, for properties of the delta function). Thus

$$m(x^i, t) = M\delta(x^1 - \alpha^1)\delta(x^2 - \alpha^2)\delta(x^3 - \alpha^3). \tag{66}$$

The corresponding representation in the a-frame is

$$m'(a^i, t) = M\delta|a^1 - a^1(\alpha^j, t)|\delta|a^2 - a^2(\alpha^j, t)|\delta|a^3 - a^3(a^j, t)| \tag{67}$$

where $a^i, (\alpha^j, t)$ is the variable position of the outfall in a the a-frame corresponding to the fixed point $\alpha^1, \alpha^2, \alpha^3$ in the x-frame. If $\underline{u}_T$ is a periodic function, then $a^i(\alpha^j, t)$ is also periodic and so the outfall follows a closed curve in a-space during a tidal cycle. The equation for q' is similar to Equation 67 with Q, the volume rate of addition, replacing M.

The source terms in the steady-state equations can be represented using the concept of the residence fucction, $R'(\underline{b}, \underline{\alpha})$, which is defined as the fraction of the tidal period that a point $\underline{b}$, in the moving frame, is 'downstream' of the outfall at $\underline{\alpha}$. For an observer in the moving frame at a point $\underline{b}, R$ can also be represented as the fraction of the tidal period that the variable outfall position, $a^i(\alpha^j, t)$, or in vector notation $\underline{a}(\underline{\alpha}, t)$, is 'upstream' of $\underline{b}$. Mathematically

$$R' = \frac{1}{T}\int_0^T H[\underline{b}^1 - a^1(\alpha^j, t)]\ H[\underline{b}^2 - a^2(\alpha^j, t)]H[\underline{b}^3 - a^3(\alpha^j, t)]\, dt \tag{68}$$

where

$$H(z) = 0 \text{ if } z < 0$$

$$= 1 \text{ if } z \not< 0 \tag{69}$$

is the Heaviside unit step function (Van der Pol and Bremner 1964).

From the definition of $\bar{m}'$ and using Equations 67 and 68 can be shown that

$$\bar{m}'(\underline{b}) = M\frac{\partial^3 R'}{\partial b^1\, \partial b^2\, \partial b^3}. \tag{70}$$

Similarly

$$\bar{q}'(\underline{b}) = Q\frac{\partial^3 R'}{\partial b^1\, \partial b^2\, \partial b^3}. \tag{71}$$

Substituting for $\bar{m}'$ and $\bar{q}'$ in Equations 64 and 65 we finally obtain

$$\frac{\partial}{\partial a^i}(\bar{D}'^{ij} J' \frac{\partial \bar{c}'}{\partial a^j} - J'\bar{\Omega}'^i \bar{c}') - k'J'\bar{c}' + M \frac{\partial 3_{R'}}{\partial a^1 \partial a^2 \partial a^3} = 0, \quad (72)$$

and

$$\frac{\partial}{\partial a^i} (J'\bar{\Omega}'^i) = Q \frac{\partial^3 R'}{\partial a^1 \partial a^2 \partial a^3} . \quad (73)$$

Although Equations 72 and 73 are of similar form to steady-state equations derived in the literature by averaging in the fixed frame, it is important to note that continuously discharging sources are represented here as closed-curve sources rather than point sources.

CONCLUSION

Two-dimensional and one-dimensional equations in the moving frame can also be derived by a simple modification of the method just described. The one-dimensional equations have been applied to both time varying (Barrett and Mollowney 1972) and steady-state problems (Mollowney 1973). Two-dimensional steady-state equations are currently being applied both to a wide vertically mixed estuary and to a narrow stratified estuary.

ACKNOWLEDGEMENTS

The author wishes to acknowledge many helpful discussions with Mr. D. Munro and the encouragement and criticism given by Mr. M. J. Barrett.

This paper is published by permission of the Director, Water Research Centre.

REFERENCES

Adey, R.A., and Brebbia, C.A. (1974).   Finite Element Solution for Effluent Dispersion.   In 'Numerical Methods in Fluid Dynamics'.   (Edited by C.A. Brebbia and J.J. Connor) Pentech Press, London, London, p.325.

Aris, R. (1962).   Vectors, Tensors, and the Basic Equations of Fluid Mechanics. Prentice-Hall, London, pp. 58, 83.

Barrett, M.J. and Mollowney, B.M. (1972).   Pollution problems in relation to the Thames Barrier.   Phil. Trans. R. Soc. London., A., 272, p.213.

Harleman, D.R.F. (1971).   One-Dimensional Models.   In 'Estuarine Modelling: An Assessment'. (Edited by G.H. Ward and W.H. Espey) Water Quality Office, Environmental protection

Agency, Austin, Texas, p.34.

Mollowney, B.M. (1973). One-Dimensional Models of Estuarine
Pollution. In 'Mathematical and Hydraulic Modelling of
Estuarine Pollution'. (Edited by A.L.H. Gameson) Water
Pollution Research Technical Paper No. 13. H.M. Stationery
Office, London, p. 73.

O'Kane, J.P.J. (1974). A kinematic reference frame for
estuaries of one dimension. Proc. International Symposium on
Mathematical Models in Hydrology, Warsaw, 1971. In
'Mathematical Models in Hydrology'. Int. Ass. Hydrol. Sci.,
Vol. 2, p. 797.

Okubo, A. (1964). Equations describing the diffusion of an
introduced pollutant in a one-dimensional estuary. In
Studies on Oceanography'. University of Tokyo Press, p. 126.

STOCHASTIC MODELING OF BI-HOURLY RIVER DISSOLVED OXYGEN
RECORDS MONITORED AT A FIXED CROSS-SECTION

Yoram J. Litwin

HYDROCOMP International, Palo Alto, California

Erhard F. Joeres

University of Wisconsin-Madison

ABSTRACT

Short term river dissolved oxygen forecasts are constructed
from data provided by a continuously operating monitoring network. The discrete time series approach used consists of the
ARIMA parametric time series modeling technique recently
developed by G.E.P. Box and G. Jenkins. The iterative procedure, results achieved for a case study, and implications for
water quality management programs are described.

SOMMAIRE

Des prévisions à court terme d'oxygène dissout dans les rivi-
ères sont établies à partir de données fournies par un reseau
de moniteurs fonctionnant en permanence. L'approche par
séries temporelles discrètes utilisée, consiste en la technique de modelage paramétrique de séries temporelles ARIMA
récemment développée par G.E.P. Box et G. Jenkins. Le procédé
iteratif, les résultats realisés au cours d'une étude de cas,
et les implications quant aux programmes de qestion de
qualité de l'eau sont décrits.

INTRODUCTION

Recent years have witnessed an increasing use of telemetric
monitoring networks capable of transmitting continuous information to a remote location on up to eight or more water quality variables recorded by sampling probes located at several
selected, fixed locations. Installation and operation of such
networks creates a variety of technical problems (Litwin and

Joeres, 1974b), but the main challenge from the water quality management point of view is to devise adequate software systems for effective analysis and interpretation of the vast quantity of information generated by the continuous monitoring of several variables of a number of locations. This includes long-term examination of trends and effects resulting from the introduction of abatement measures, the short term prediction of emerging water quality problems, and the more fundamental analysis for understanding the underlying physical phenomena. It is generally agreed that a meaningful analysis of such continuous records necessitates the use of modern data analysis techniques, which in turn could be integrated into a supplementing software system to augment the existing sophisticated hardware of the telemetric networks.

Initial investigations into aspects related to developing such software systems to deal with short-term emerging water quality problems were recently conducted by the writers (Litwin and Joeres (1974a, 1974c)). The viability and development of real-time control schemes based on data supplied by telemetric networks is predicated on the feasibility of being able to derive accurate and continuous forecast of expected water quality conditions several days into the future. The need for such short-term forecast is based on the lead-time necessary to initiate available corrective control measures (such as flow augmentation or artificial reaeration) to ameliorate the predicted degradation of water quality. The control schemes investigated by the writers (Litwin and Joeres (1974a, 1974c)) assume that it is possible to base such short-term forecasts on data provided by a continuously operating network using the discrete ARIMA time series modeling technique recently developed by Box and Jenkins (1970). It is the objective of this paper to present the ARIMA technique as a potential tool for short-term analysis of continuous dissolved oxygen records derived from telemetric monitoring stations, and to document the results achieved for a case study of the Lower Fox River in Wisconsin, including the possible implications of such tools for water quality management programs.

Available Data Base   The dissolved oxygen data used were obtained by the telemetric monitoring network on the Lower Fox River in Wisconsin (see Figure 1). This network, established in 1971 by the Wisconsin Department of Natural Resources (Weckwerth et. al., 1974), consists of five field stations and a central receiving station in Madison (150 miles away), where a computer center is available for data storage and processing. Each field station is equipped with a multiple analyzer unit with optional sensors for measuring up to seven water quality parameters. At present only the following five are measured: dissolved oxygen, temperature, pH, conductivity, and turbidity. All field stations are equipped with transmitters for transmitting data once every hour to Madison through regular telephone lines. The five field stations in this network (Menasha, Appleton, Rapid Croche Dam, DePere, and Green Bay) are reasonably evenly spaced over the 39-mile stretch of the Lower Fox River, providing a fairly accurate picture of water quality conditions on the river.

Preliminary examination of the data base indicated a rather frequent occurrence of misrecorded "data gaps". The misrecording of data occurs mainly as a result of (a) failures of the on-river monitoring equipment, (b) failures of the telemetric transmission lines, and (c) failures of the computer recording process. Since utilization of these data for the present investigation requires the availability of continuous portions of data, the records were scanned to select a large variety of continuous dissolved oxygen series. The 43 dissolved oxygen time series selected are listed in Table 1. The following guiding judgments were used in the selection of these series: (a) representation of the widest possible spectrum of river conditions; (b) the selection of time segments with the smallest possible amount of missing data; and (c) the availability of the largest possible number of time series from the same time periods at different locations along the river. As a result, all seasons were represented, with emphasis placed on the summer and fall months, during which pollution levels and their control are usually most crucial.

The Analyzed Dissolved Oxygen Series Each of the series listed in Table 1 is denoted by a label comprised of capital letters (DØ-Dissolved Oxygen), and a two digit number: the first digit indicates the monitoring station while the second follows a sequential count for each series from a given station. In some cases a small letter is appended as well, indicating that this time series was broken into one or more overlapping segments to test the effect of changes with time on the fitted model. Examination of data plots revealed that the various series differ among themselves, reflecting the wide spectrum of river conditions represented. Sample plots of the various types of series (classified into seasonal, nonseasonal, and mixed, depending on the extent of their diurnal variation) are shown in Figure 2. These sample data were chosen from different stations to show spring, summer, and fall dissolved oxygen series.

THEORETICAL BACKGROUND

The ARIMA model is essentially a device for transforming a highly dependent series z_t into a sequence of random deviates a_t, commonly called "white noise". The designation white noise derives from the fact that when white light is passed through a prism, it decomposes into a spectrum of equal, random intensity, while any other artificial source of light creates an unequal, or non-random spectrum. The operation of

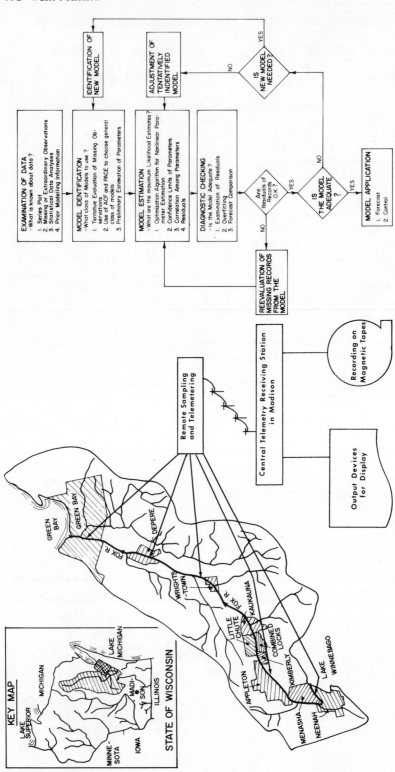

Figure 3   BLOCK DIAGRAM OF THE ITERATIVE ARIMA BUILDING PROCEDURE

Figure 1   THE LOWER FOX RIVER TELEMETRIC NETWORK

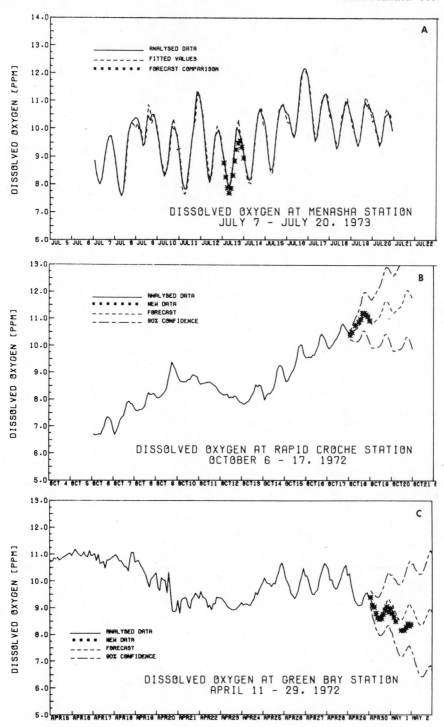

Figure 2
Sample Plots of Dissolved Oxygen Series DØ14a

Station	Sequence No.	Series Identification			Number of Days	Number of Observations	Number of Missing Observations	Basic Parameters [ppm]					
		Code	Time	Year				Max	Mean	Min	St. Dev.	St. Error of Mean	Initial Sum of Squares
(1)	(2)	(3)	(4)	(5)	(6)	(7)	(8)	(9)	(10)	(11)	(12)	(13)	(14)
Menasha (15)	1	DØ11	March 22	72	14	168	13	14.32	11.73	8.90	1.24	0.096	261.74
	2	DØ12a	October 6	72	12	144	6	11.37	8.96	7.16	0.96	0.080	132.37
	3	DØ12b	October 12	72	12	144	5	12.34	10.23	7.71	1.17	0.098	197.53
	4	DØ13	February 14	73	13	156	24	16.22	13.48	12.14	1.19	0.096	227.42
	5	DØ14a	July 7	73	14	167	17	12.20	9.75	7.57	0.99	0.077	167.50
	6	DØ14b	July 15	73	12	144	21	12.20	9.64	7.42	1.07	0.089	163.88
	7	DØ15	August 7	73	10	120	4	9.16	6.33	2.68	1.14	0.104	157.25
Appleton (18)	8	DØ21	May 18	71	11	132	7	8.44	7.42	6.26	0.44	0.038	25.60
	9	DØ22	September 3	71	12	144	14	9.85	4.08	2.20	1.01	0.084	146.31
	10	DØ23a	October 6	72	12	144	4	10.00	8.00	6.34	0.96	0.080	131.87
	11	DØ23b	October 12	72	12	144	4	10.32	9.02	6.34	1.08	0.090	167.59
	12	DØ24	May 14	73	14	167	16	8.80	7.82	6.76	0.66	0.051	72.54
	13	DØ25a	June 18	73	17	204	17	7.95	6.24	5.04	0.67	0.047	90.64
	14	DØ25b	June 25	73	17	204	25	9.44	7.07	5.04	1.06	0.074	222.77
	15	DØ26a	July 7	73	14	167	13	10.21	7.90	5.36	1.09	0.084	199.13
	16	DØ26b	July 15	73	12	144	15	10.21	6.50	3.13	1.87	0.156	501.85
Rapid Croche (21)	17	DØ31	May 18	71	11	132	8	6.26	4.85	3.69	0.66	0.058	58.00
	18	DØ32	September 3	72	12	144	12	8.13	0.87	0.00	1.82	0.152	479.08
	19	DØ33	October 6	72	12	144	5	10.83	8.57	6.67	1.01	0.083	144.23
	20	DØ34a	February 14	73	13	156	11	16.29	13.86	12.26	1.02	0.082	163.64
	21	DØ34b	February 19	73	14	168	16	14.64	12.80	11.08	0.91	0.070	138.30
	22	DØ34c	February 25	73	14	167	15	14.64	12.27	11.23	0.99	0.077	164.50
	23	DØ35a	June 18	73	17	204	18	7.65	5.73	3.88	0.76	0.054	119.11
	24	DØ35b	June 25	73	17	204	26	7.96	5.84	3.22	0.96	0.067	187.99
	25	DØ35c	July 7	73	14	167	15	7.71	4.87	1.11	1.47	0.114	360.54
	26	DØ36	August 7	73	10	120	6	2.74	1.15	0.07	0.69	0.063	57.15
De Pere (24)	27	DØ41	February 2	72	12	144	13	16.39	15.50	12.93	0.52	0.043	39.12
	28	DØ42	April 11	72	19	228	24	13.96	11.94	10.17	0.69	0.046	110.00
	29	DØ43	June 4	72	17	204	7	11.06	6.40	3.63	1.59	0.111	515.06
	30	DØ44	October 6	72	12	144	16	10.36	8.58	7.11	0.83	0.069	98.24
	31	DØ45a	February 19	73	14	168	18	14.90	12.49	9.33	1.11	0.085	206.11
	32	DØ45b	February 25	73	14	168	16	14.90	12.48	10.55	1.08	0.083	194.44
	33	DØ46	May 14	73	14	167	20	10.44	9.04	8.53	0.60	0.047	60.64
	34	DØ47a	July 7	73	14	167	13	9.27	7.70	5.77	0.76	0.059	97.08
	35	DO47b	July 15	73	12	144	16	8.98	7.02	5.05	0.85	0.071	103.36
	36	DØ48	August 7	73	10	120	4	8.67	6.26	5.19	0.85	0.077	86.19
Green Bay (27)	37	DØ51a	February 2	72	12	144	2	12.45	11.77	11.13	0.27	0.023	10.78
	38	DØ51b	February 9	72	18	216	17	12.02	11.13	10.16	0.44	0.031	42.76
	39	DØ52	April 11	72	19	228	22	11.61	10.14	8.83	0.81	0.053	149.59
	40	DØ53a	February 14	73	13	156	10	12.38	10.34	7.10	1.29	0.013	258.21
	41	DØ53b	February 19	73	13	156	17	12.84	10.73	7.10	1.23	0.099	237.46
	42	DØ53c	February 25	73	15	179	18	13.60	10.84	9.12	0.98	0.073	172.85
	43	DØ54	July 7	73	14	167	18	7.82	4.62	1.10	1.45	0.112	349.22

Table 1   The Analyzed Dissolved Oxygen Series

the ARIMA model is therefore analogous to a filter receiving
as an input a time series with imbedded sequential dependencies, and providing as output sequentially independent time
series.

If, for example, values of a time series at equispaced times
t, t-1, t-2, ... , are denoted by z_t, z_{t-1}, z_{t-2}, ... , and
represented in shorthand notation with the backward shift
operator B (defined to simplify algebraic notation as $Bz_t =
z_{t-1}$), then they may be related to the random deviates of
white noise a_t by means of the following autoregressive-moving
average (ARMA) model

$$\phi_p(B)z_t = \theta_q(B)a_t \tag{1}$$

where $\phi_p(B)$ and $\theta_q(B)$ are the autoregressive and moving average operators, respectively, defined as

$$\phi_p(B) = 1 - \phi_1 B - \phi_2 B^2 - ... - \phi_p B^p \tag{2}$$

$$\theta_q(B) = 1 - \theta_1 B - \theta_2 B^2 - ... - \theta_q B^q \tag{3}$$

When the input time series z_t, z_{t-1}, z_{t-2}, ... , show nonstationarity, i.e., the mean and the variance of the series are
changing with t, then they may still be related to the random
deviates a_t by means of the following model

$$\phi_p(B)\nabla^d z_t = \theta_o + \theta_q(B)a_t \tag{4}$$

where ∇ is the backward difference operator of order d ($\nabla z_t =
z_t - z_{t-1}$), and θ_o is a constant; for d>0 this implies the
existence of an underlying deterministic polynomial trend of
degree d. Equation (4) represents the so-called autoregressive integrated moving average ARIMA (p,d,q) model, with the
integers p,d,q, defining the order of the model.

When the input time series exhibit a periodicity or season-
ality every s units apart, a more general model must be
employed. Assuming that the seasonal effects may be modeled
in a similar way to the nonseasonal ones, it is possible to
introduce a seasonal backward shift operator B^s ($B^s z_t = z_{t-s}$)
and the seasonal backward difference operator ∇_s ($\nabla_s z_t = z_t - z_{t-s}$),
and to represent the "between period" parts of a seasonal
process by a model analogous to Equation (4)

$$\Phi_P(B^s)\nabla_s z_t = \Theta_Q(B^s)\alpha_t \tag{5}$$

where Φ_P and Θ_Q, respectively, are seasonal autoregressive and
moving average operators of order P and Q, and α_t is the
"between periods" error component. In general the α_t of such
seasonal time series are sequentially correlated, representing
a nonseasonal component "within periods", which can be modeled

by the nonseasonal ARIMA model described by Equation (4).
Combining Equations (4) and (5) yields the so-called multiplicative, or seasonal ARIMA model of order $(p,d,q) \times (P,D,Q)_s$

$$\Phi_P(B^s)\phi_p(B)\nabla_s\nabla z_t = \theta_o + \Theta_Q(B^s)\theta_q(B)a_t \tag{6}$$

Identification of both the nonseasonal and seasonal ARIMA
models is carried out in a similar fashion, essentially based
on a comparison of the characteristics of theoretical ARIMA
models with those of the analyzed data. A brief account of
the various steps involved in the identification process is
given in the subsequent section.

A wide range of time series taken from many different fields,
such as engineering, economics, etc., have successfully been
represented by ARIMA models. They provide a very attractive
and systematic approach toward time series analysis and have
already found their way into several applications to hydrological time series (Litwin and Joeres, 1975b). The main advantage of ARIMA models from the monitoring network point of view
lies in their capability to develop a forecasting function
based on the most recently available records. This function
projects future values from a given origin, as well as the
probability limits on either side of the forecast. It is
derived to minimize mean square error between the actual and
forecasted values. Whenever new values of the water quality
parameter become available from the monitoring network, the
model is capable of updating the forecast from the most recent
origin. Such an application of ARIMA models provides the
basis of an approach to enhance the efficiency and utilization
of telemetric monitoring networks.

A MODEL FITTING EXAMPLE

The process of ARIMA model building involves three basic steps,
namely: identification, estimation, and diagnostic checking.
In the present investigation this process was extended to
accommodate the handling of missing data and the effective
utilization of any relevant prior information about the analyzed series. This extended approach to ARIMA model building
is described by the block diagram in Figure 3. The following
description of ARIMA model building for dissolved oxygen
series DØ14a (see Table 1) is given to illustrate the
procedure.

Examination of Data   The data plot (see Figure 2a) indicates
strong seasonal variations (twelve observations apart) corresponding to the known diurnal variations of dissolved oxygen
caused by algea photosynthesis and respiration. The original
data set did not include any extraordinary measurement which
could suggest an erroneous observation. There are seventeen
missing observations (10% of total) rather evenly distributed
throughout the series, so that simple extrapolation between

existing values seems to be satisfactory for the initial iteration.   Prior information about dissolved oxygen series indicates that they are in general nonstationary (i.e., d>0 should be used), and that similar series had been successfully described by an ARIMA $(1,1,0)(0,1,1)_{12}$ seasonal model (see Equation 7).

Model Identification   The basic tools in this step are the autocorrelation and partial autocorrelation functions (denoted as ACF and PACF, respectively).   They are calculated for the original series (after filling in missing observations) and for the first and second differences (d=0,1,2).   The first two of these autocorrelation functions (see Figure 4) indicate the need to choose the first difference (d=1), since the first spike is close to a value of one (r_1=0.92) and it is evident that the ACF for d=0 is not decaying fast enough indicates the need to take a seasonal difference of lag 12.   Examination of the remaining ACF and PACF in Figure 4 (d=1, D=1) suggests a seasonal moving average term of lag 12 and order one for removing the remaining seasonal effects, and a regular auto-regressive term of order one for removing the remaining seasonal effects, and a regular autoregressive term of order one for removing the remaining autocorrelation within each of the seasons.   The tentatively identified model is therefore the ARIMA $(1,1,0)(0,1,1)_{12}$ seasonal model defined as

$$(1-\phi_1 B)\nabla^{12}\nabla z_t = (1-\theta B^{12})a_t \tag{7}$$

The initially estimated parameters ϕ_1 and θ of this model should in principle lie within the limits set by its stationarity and invertibility conditions (examples of developing such conditions for simple ARIMA models are given in Box and Jenkins, 1970).   This requirement is, however, almost completely relaxed because of the availability of a powerful, nonlinear optimization routine (Pack et. al., 1972) used for ARIMA model estimation, since it has been shown to converge for virtually any initial values of model parameters.

Model Estimation   This step involves the iterative determination of the maximum likelihood estimates and the approximate standard errors of the initial values of the tentatively identified model.   If, for example, the initially estimated parameters ϕ_1 and θ of Equation (7) will be denoted after (n-1) iterations as $\phi_1^{(n-1)}$ and $\theta^{(n-1)}$, respectively, then the residuals following this iteration will be given by:

$$a_t^{(n-1)} = (1-\phi_1^{(n-1)}B)(1-\theta^{(n-1)}B^{12})^{-1}\nabla^{12}\nabla z_t \tag{8}$$

which can be expressed as

$$a_t^{(n-1)} = (1-\phi_1^{(n-1)}B)(1-\phi_1 B)^{-1}(1-\theta B^{12})$$
$$(1-\theta^{(n-1)}B^{12})^{-1}a_t^{(n-1)} \tag{9}$$

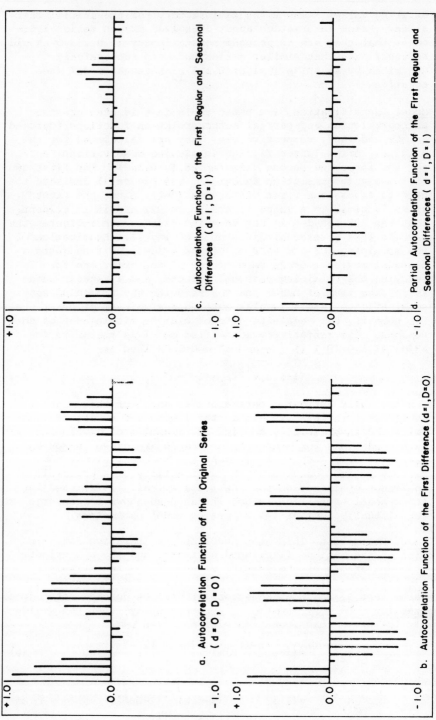

Figure 4   ACF and Partial ACF of Dissolved Oxygen Series DØ14a

a.   Autocorrelation Function of the Original Series (d = 0, D = 0)

b.   Autocorrelation Function of the First Difference (d = 1, D = 0)

c.   Autocorrelation Function of the First Regular and Seasonal Differences (d = 1, D = 1)

d.   Partial Autocorrelation Function of the First Regular and Seasonal Differences (d = 1, D = 1)

Equation (9) can be treated as a nonlinear equation with $a_t^{(n-1)}$ as the dependent variable and $\phi_1^{(n-1)}$ and $\Theta^{(n-1)}$ as independent variables. By using the nonlinear least squares optimization routine indicated above new estimates $\phi_1^{(n)}$ and $\Theta^{(n)}$ can be evaluated. These new values are then used in the next iteration, until satisfactory convergence to the least square value is achieved. In the example series DØ14a the convergence was achieved in only five iterations (for a relative change in the residuals sum of squares of less than 0.001).

Diagnostic Checking This is the next step in the ARIMA modeling procedure designed to detect model inadequacy and to suggest modifications if necessary. The tools of diagnostic checking are: (a) overfitting, i.e., examination if the model is not parsimonious; (b) examination of residuals for randomness; and (c) forecast comparison.

The first check for overfitting is to examine the correlation matrix among the estimated parameters. For the example case the correlation between ϕ_1 and Θ is low (r=-0.02). Whenever high correlation occurs, however, this is an indication that one of the parameters is superfluous and may be abandoned. The second check for overfitting is examination of the confidence limits of the parameters. The results for the DØ14a series do not indicate any need for model adjustment. In some cases, however, the confidence limits may include the value zero, indicating the need to disregard the corresponding moving average or autoregressive term; the confidence limit may also equal one, which suggests replacing the associated term by a difference operator (1-B). In either case, the need for model adjustment is clearly indicated. Other checks for overfitting may be applied as well, and they are discussed in more detail by Box and Jenkins (1970).

The second technique of diagnostic checking is the examination of residuals for randomness. The simplest approach is to plot the residuals and then to examine the plot visually. A more formal conclusion can be derived from examination of the autocorrelation function (ACF) of residuals (see Figure 5). To test whether this ACF is random, an χ^2 test is carried out. The null hypothesis that $r_k(a_t)$ represents white noise is acceptable for the example series because the calculated $\chi^2=44.2$ is less than the test value $\chi^2_{38,0.05}=55.8$. Since the χ^2 test applies only to the overall analysis, it is much more important to analyze the individual r_k's. The standard error of the r_k's is approximately given by (Bartlett, 1946):

$$\sigma_{r_k(a_t)}=\frac{1}{N} \tag{10}$$

where σ is the standard error of the autocorrelations r_k of the residuals a_t, and N is the number of analyzed residuals. For the example series $\sigma_{r_k(a_t)}=0.08$; it is indicated by confidence

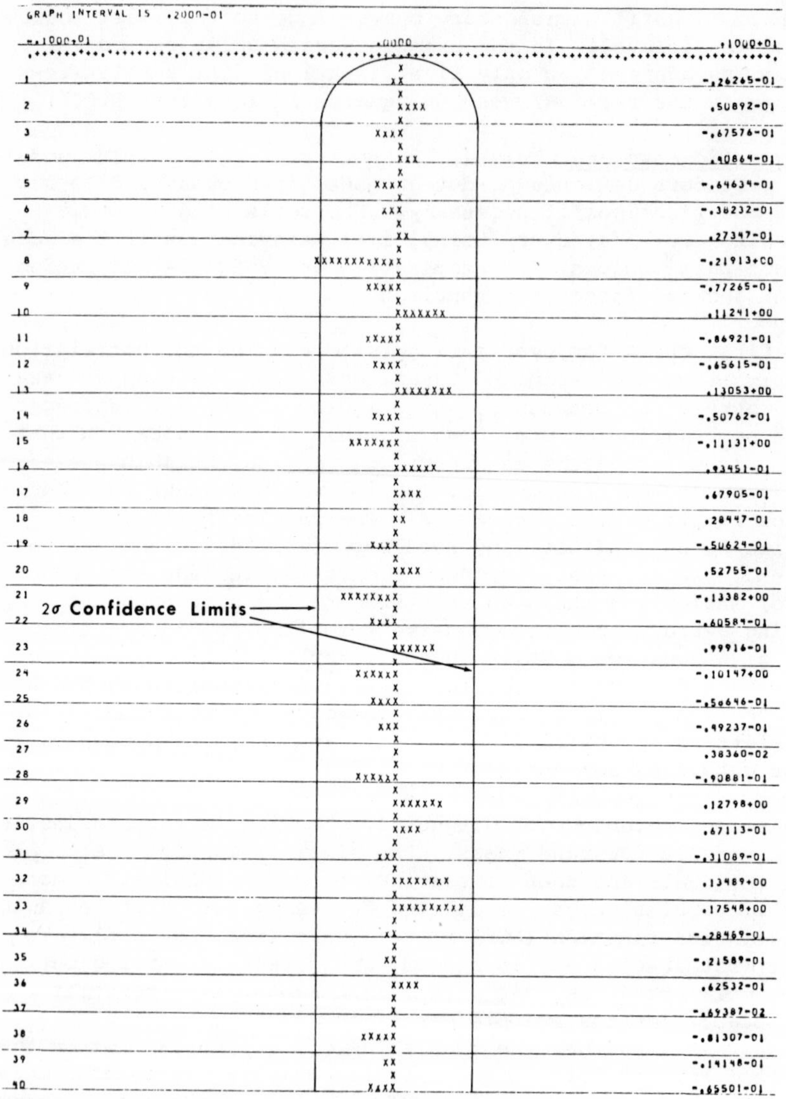

Figure 5
ACF of Residuals from the ARIMA $(1,1,0)(0,1,1)_{12}$ Model Fitted to the DØ14a Series

intervals in Figure 5. The fact that for k=8 the r_k value
exceeds these limits provides an indication of the need for
further improvement of the model.

The third technique of diagnostic checking is forecast comparison, i.e. for some known part of the series a forecast is
made and the results are compared with the actual subsequent
observations. Usually this technique of diagnostic checking
is used in the final stages of ARIMA model building as a tool
for discrimination among alternative models. For the example
DØ14a series, the results of forecast comparison are shown in
Figure 2a. Another comparison that can be made to test model
adequacy is to compare the fitted values from the model with
the original record. The dotted line in Figure 2a provides an
example of such a comparison.

Reevaluation of Missing Observation Examination of the residuals of the tentatively fitted in missing observations provides an indication whether new estimates are advisable.
Large values of these residuals call for reestimation of the
missing observations using the tentatively identified ARIMA
model. For the example dissolved oxygen series the preliminary estimates of missing data were good. To demonstrate the
application of this step, the missing values were nevertheless
replaced with fitted ones, and the parameters ϕ_1 and Θ of the
model were then reestimated. The results show that the new
values ($\phi_1'=0.48$, $\Theta'=0.92$) are almost identical to the initially estimated values ($\phi=0.50$, $\Theta=0.92$).

Iterative Reestimation and Reidentification Table 2 summarizes in detail all of the ARIMA modeling steps for series
DØ14a. As is evident, the best fitting model is the last one
shown. Because it is difficult to justify the $(1-\theta_8 B^8)$ moving
average term in this particular model, however, and because
other dissolved oxygen series were successfully described by
the ARIMA (1,1,0)(0,1,1) model (including the time overlapping
series DØ14b), the latter model (given by Equation 7) was
selected to represent series DØ14a. The small sacrifice in
accuracy seems justified by the generality and applicability
of the identified model to many other dissolved oxygen series.
Justification for selecting this model is demonstrated by the
good forecast of dissolved oxygen that was obtained for a lead
time of 36 hours. The plot of this forecast (which in separate comparisons was not significantly inferior to that
obtained by the model with the additional moving average term)
is shown in Figure 6a.

ANALYSIS AND INTERPRETATION OF RESULTS

Each of the dissolved oxygen time series selected for analysis
was modeled using the iterative ARIMA approach described in
the preceding section. Given the extent of conditions

Iteration	Model		Parameters			Residuals		Correlation Matrix
			Estimation		Confidence Limits	$s^2(a_t)$	χ^2	
			Preliminary	Final	Lower	Upper		
1	$\nabla z_t = a_t$							1515.4	
2	$\nabla^{12}\nabla z_t = a_t$							151.0	
3	$(1-\emptyset B)\nabla^{12}\nabla z_t = (1-\Theta B^{12})a_t$					4.29	44.2	∅ ⊖
		∅	0.48	0.50	0.36	0.64			∅ 1.00
		⊖	0.65	0.92	0.83	1.01			⊖ −0.02 1.00
4	$(1-\emptyset B)\nabla^{12}\nabla z_t = a_t$ $\emptyset_1$		0.50	0.44	0.29	0.59	9.42	91.1	
5	$(1-\emptyset B)(1-\Phi B^{12})\nabla z_t = a_t$						6.68	84.8	∅ Φ
		∅	−0.95	0.57	0.43	0.70			∅ 1.00
		Φ	−0.17	0.62	0.50	0.75			Φ −0.18 1.00
6	$(1-\emptyset B)(1-\Phi B^{12})\nabla z_t = (1-\Theta B^{12})a_t$						4.28	44.6	∅ Φ ⊖
		∅	0.76	0.50	0.36	0.64			∅ 1.00
		Φ	0.16	0.99	0.97	1.02			Φ 0.01 1.00
		⊖	−0.95	0.91	0.82	1.01			⊖ −0.01 0.47 1.00
7	$(1-\emptyset B)\nabla^{12}\nabla z_t = (1-\Theta B^{12})(1-\theta_8 B^8)a_t$						4.11	37.3	∅ θ_8 ⊖
		∅	0.50	0.49	0.35	0.63			∅ 1.00
		θ_8	0.22	0.20	0.04	0.35			θ_8 −0.04 1.00
		⊖	0.92	0.92	0.84	1.00			⊖ −0.01 0.00 1.00

Table 2   Iterative Steps of Identification of ARIMA Model for the DØ14a Series

represented in the data base, the basic overall conclusion is that the ARIMA time series modeling technique is capable of successfully modeling short segments (10-20 days) of bi-hourly dissolved oxygen data, and that it provides a generally reliable dissolved oxygen forecasting tool for time leads of up to 3 days (see Figures 2a, 2b and 6a). Although an earlier attempt to model dissolved oxygen series by means of the ARIMA approach has been reported (Huck and Farquhar, 1974), the lack of variety and range of series modeled was not sufficient to demonstrate the utility of the ARIMA approach as a useful water quality management tool (Litwin and Joeres, 1975a).

The general conclusion does not necessarily mean that all series were modeled equally well (as reflected mainly by the ACF of residuals and the forecasting capabilities of the fitted models). It provides, however, an important result for the present investigation which, in contrast to many other time series studies (where the primary interest lies in the analysis of an individual series), attempts to assess the overall adequacy of the ARIMA technique as a simple analytical tool for continuous modeling and forecasting of water quality. It is assumed that integration of short-term forecasting into the routine operation of telemetric monitoring networks will enhance the utility of such networks within the immediate decision-making framework.

The main criterum, therefore, to assess the adequacy of ARIMA modeling for this specific purpose is the success in representing prolonged time periods at a particular station (up to several months) by means of one class of ARIMA models. This is especially important from an implementation point of view for continuous forecasting and control, since if the fitted models differ frequently between successive time periods, their utilization would require frequent model identification and estimation and consequently become very cumbersome in their use. If, on the other hand, the same class of ARIMA models is found to be adequate for relatively long time periods, then the on-line computer connected to a monitoring network could be programmed with a specific set of forecasting and control equations, and continuous utilization would then be relatively simple. Although occasional adjustments of parameters in such a general model would be required at preselected time intervals (such as once or twice weekly or whenever a significant change in river or waste load conditions is observed), the related computational burden is considerably less. It could in fact be integrated into routine network operation, analogous to any other aspect of regular network maintenance.

Table 3 attempts to facilitate examination of the derived results in this light. Rather than presenting the modeling process which led to one or several best models, this table gives an overall summary of the attempts to fit one type of ARIMA model to a particular class of the analyzed time series. The earlier breakdown of the series into seasonal, nonseasonal and mixed (depending on diurnal variations) was used for this purpose. For each of the series, the summary in Table 3 lists the values of the fitted model parameters, the χ^2 test value of the overall randomness of the ACF of residuals from the fitted model, and the residuals sum of squares denoted by $s^2(a_t)$. In addition, two different measures of the adequacy of the corresponding general ARIMA model to represent each of the series are given:

(a) Efficiency of the model in removing the original sum of squares, ss_{in} (listed in Table 1)

$$\eta = (1 - \frac{s^2(a_t)}{ss_{in}}) \times 100\% \tag{11}$$

This measure was adopted from McMichael and Vigani (1972), where it was effectively used to assess the adequacy of the ARIMA models of organic loads from municipal treatment plants.

(b) A subjective classification of model fit into good, fair and poor, based on the model's ability to remove all spikes from the ACF of residuals, the range of model parameter confidence limits, and the comparison of the χ^2 and $s^2(a_t)$ values to a better fitting model. Whenever the fit of the general model was considered inadequate, or whenever spikes exceeding confidence limits of the ACF of

PART A - SERIES WITH STRONG DIURNAL VARIATIONS

Station	Sequence No.	Classification			ARIMA $(1,1,0)(0,1,1)_{12}$						A Better Fitting Model		
					Parameters					Fit G–Good F–Fair P–Poor			
		Code	Month	Year	ϕ_1	Θ_1	χ^2	$s^2(a_t)$	η		Model Type	χ^2	$s^2(a_t)$
(15)	1	Dφ11	March 22	72	0.24	0.81	43.1	11.80	95	G			
	2	Dφ12b	October 12	72	0.15	0.83	55.3	10.61	95	G			
	3	Dφ14a	July 7	73	0.48	0.92	44.2	4.29	97	G	$ARIMA(1,1,8)(0,1,1)_{12}$	32.3	4.11
	4	Dφ14b	July 15	73	0.41	0.74	38.8	3.32	98	G			
	5	Dφ15	August 7	73	0.16	0.93	14.8	34.60	78	F			
(18)	6	Dφ21	May 18	71	0.26	0.69	35.6	3.25	87	G			
	7	Dφ22	Sept. 3	72	0.47	0.69	46.7	13.00	91	G	$ARIMA(1,1,5)(0,0,1)_{12}$		
	8	Dφ26a	July 7	73	0.33	0.84	46.6	12.87	93	G	$ARIMA(1,1,6)(0,1,1)_{12}$	28.6	11.90
	9	Dφ26b	July 15	73	0.45	0.63	62.1	14.10	97	F	$ARIMA(1,1,6)(0,1,1)_{12}$		
(21)	10	Dφ31	May 18	71	0.36	0.82	34.5	3.13	91	G	$ARIMA(1,1,6)(0,1,1)_{12}$		
	11	Dφ33	October 6	72	0.36	0.78	25.2	1.22	99	G			
	12	Dφ35a	June 18	73	0.22	0.69	55.7	6.36	95	G	$ARIMA(1,1,3)(0,1,1)_{12}$		
	13	Dφ35b	June 25	73	0.32	0.65	45.9	6.26	97	G			
	14	Dφ35c	July 7	73	0.38	0.80	43.5	15.64	96	G	$ARIMA(1,1,3)(0,1,1)_{12}$		
(24)	15	Dφ44	October 6	72	0.47	0.74	32.3	1.11	99	G			
	16	Dφ47a	July 7	73	0.10	0.90	40.8	31.50	67	F	$ARIMA(1,1,4)(0,1,1)_{12}$		

Table 3   Summary of ARIMA Modelling of Dissolved Oxygen

PART B – SERIES WITH DUMPED DIURNAL VARIATIONS

Station	Sequence No.	Code	Month	Year	φ1	Φ1	χ²	s²(a_t)	n	Fit G-Good F-Fair P-Poor	Model Type	χ²	s²(a_t)
(15)	1	Dφ12a	October 6	72	0.42	0.27	51.0	7.15	95	F	ARIMA(1,1,0)(0,1,1)$_{12}$	32.0	6.70
	2	Dφ13	February 14	73	0.14	0.23	45.1	37.20	96	G			
(18)	3	Dφ23a	October 6	72	0.37	0.20	32.3	4.08	97	G			
	4	Dφ23b	October 12	72	0.36	0.17	40.3	2.52	95	G			
	5	Dφ24	May 14	73	0.26	0.18	40.8	1.15	96	G	ARIMA(1,1,0)(0,1,1)$_{12}$	26.5	8.30
	6	Dφ25a	June 18	73	0.19	0.35	33.0	6.80	92	G			
	7	Dφ25b	June 25	73	0.36	0.40	43.2	9.14	96	G			
(21)	8	Dφ36	August 7	73	0.14	0.23	42.4	9.12	84	G			
(24)	9	Dφ41	February 2	72	-0.07	0.39	37.0	5.51	86	F	ARIMA(0,1,7)(1,0,0)$_{12}$	21.8	77.60
	10	Dφ42	April 11	72	0.48	0.64	51.5	3.74	97	G			
	11	Dφ45a	February 19	73	-0.32	0.70	41.7	88.03	57	F	ARIMA(0,1,1)(1,0,0)$_{12}$		
	12	Dφ45b	February 25	73	-0.31	0.65	29.1	67.10	65	G	ARIMA(0,1,1)(1,0,0)$_{12}$		
	13	Dφ46	May 14	73	0.26	0.41	80.3	0.88	98	P	ARIMA(2,1,0)(1,0,0)$_{12}$	32.8	
	14	Dφ47b	July 15	73	-0.03	-0.08	35.3	19.12	82	P	ARIMA(0,1,0)		
	15	Dφ48	August 17	73	0.09	-0.05	38.4	23.90	72	P	ARIMA(0,1,3)		–

Table 3 (Contd.)

PART C - SERIES WITHOUT DIURNAL VARIATIONS

Station	Sequence No.	Classification			ARIMA (0,1,2) Parameters					Fit G-Good F-Fair P-Poor	A Better Fitting Model		
		Code	Month	Year	θ_1	θ_2	χ^2	$s^2(a_t)$	n		Model Type	χ^2	$s^2(a_t)$
(21)	1	Dϕ34a	February 14	73	0.24	0.14	43.8	16.10	90	G	ARIMA(2,1,0)(1,0,0)$_{12}$	47.3	2.37
	2	Dϕ34b	February 19	73	-0.18	-0.25	70.7	2.62	98	P	ARIMA(2,1,0)(1,0,0)$_{12}$		
	3	Dϕ34c	February 25	73	-0.17	-0.16	56.1	2.83	98	P			
(24)	4	Dϕ43	June 4	73	-0.19	0.03	46.7	31.50	94	F	ARIMA(1,1,0)	47.0	31.50
	5	Dϕ51a	February 2	72	0.48	0.15	43.2	2.30	79	G	ARIMA(1,1,0)(0,0,1)$_{12}$	43.1	
	6	Dϕ51b	February 9	72	0.28	0.27	59.4	5.70	87	G			
	7	Dϕ52	April 11	72	0.59	0.14	58.6	48.80	67	F			
(27)	8	Dϕ53a	February 14	73	0.22	0.07	35.2	59.80	77	G	ARIMA(0,1,0)		
	9	Dϕ53b	February 19	73	0.25	0.01	51.0	26.60	89	F			
	10	Dϕ53c	February 25	73	0.32	0.14	41.0	23.70	86	G			
	11	Dϕ54	July 7	73	0.48	0.17	27.2	107.80	69	G			

Table 3 (Contd.)

residuals remained unremoved, the better fitting model was also listed in Table 3.

The first part of Table 3 summarizes modeling of the seasonal series with the ARIMA $(1,1,0)(0,1,1)_{12}$ model defined by Equation (7). As shown in this table, most of the series come from the first three stations; none of them comes from the Green Bay station. Most of the series in this group represent the summer and fall months. The series at the various stations tend to correspond to the same time periods. Most of them were modeled very well with the general model chosen for the seasonal series. In some cases, small spikes in the ACF of residuals remained after fitting this model. Although they could always be removed by adding a regular moving average term of order k (k being equal to the location of the spike in the ACF), the minor improvement in accuracy gained generally could not be justified by the added complexity of the model.

The second part of Table 3 summarizes the mixed series. The most general model selected for this group of series was ARIMA $(1,1,0)(1,0,0)$ defined by:

$$(1-\phi_1 B)(1-\Phi B^{12})\nabla z_t = a_t \tag{12}$$

The fit of this model to the series from the first three stations was generally good. It was, however, less satisfactory for the remaining two stations. The fact that some of these series were represented well by the general model for the seasonal series, while others were more accurate by using the general model selected for nonseasonal series, emphasizes the subjectiveness of the series classification employed.

The third part of Table 3 summarizes modeling of the nonseasonal series. Most of the series in this group came from the Green Bay station, and they usually correspond to winter months. The most general model that could be chosen for series in this group was the ARIMA $(0,1,2)$

$$\nabla z_t = (1-\theta_1 B - \theta_2 B^2) a_t \tag{13}$$

which generally gave a fairly good fit.

The results presented in Table 3 indicate that a general model could be employed at any one of the stations for reasonably long time periods. Although results for data from the Green Bay station are less satisfactory, overall results do indicate that further efforts in applying ARIMA models to water quality data may yield very good results. In particular, implementation of this technique for continuous short-term forecasting of the measured data seems to be very timely, given the advent of continuously monitoring systems. This conclusion is reinforced by the fact that almost all of the overlapping series (designated by small letter suffixes) were well represented by the same type of ARIMA model. The structure of the results in Table 3 suggests that perhaps further classification of the series according to spatial and temporal distribution could possibly lead to still better fitting general models for some particular time of the year and for each of the monitored locations along the river. This, of course, would require examination of many more time series from less dispersed time periods. It should be pointed out as well that the less satisfactory results obtained with data from the Green Bay station, which is located at the mouth of the river (see Figure 1), could have been affected by the tidal influence of Lake Michigan "seiche waves".

SUMMARY AND CONCLUSIONS

Continuous monitoring of streams is now widely recognized as a necessary tool to document the improvements in water quality expected as pollution abatement programs are implemented and to identify locations where further abatement actions will be required. This continuous water quality monitoring objective does not of itself imply a need for telemetric facilities; the recent advent of the latter is motivated by the possibilities of achieving a higher reliability of the data collection system (failures of equipment are recognized quickly, thus reducing the amount of misrecorded data) and because the immediately available information enables identification and response to emerging water quality problems.

Effective reaction to problems recognized by means of the monitoring network requires a time lead of sufficient length for preventive measures to become effective. Since the telemetric network provides information on currently existing water quality conditions, its effectiveness and utility might be improved significantly if the continuous forecast of conditions expected in the next few days would be provided along with the actual observations.

The ARIMA technique investigated in this study appears to be particularly attractive for this purpose. Its basic feature of providing a forecast of water quality based on observed conditions only might give rise to the criticism that it does not directly account for the amounts of waste dumped into the stream and other factors affecting river quality; it may, however, still represent the most feasible approach available toward extending the utility of the telemetric monitors for effectively dealing with emerging water quality problems.

It might be argued that similar short term forecasts could be obtained with water quality models based on the Streeter-Phelps or similar causal equations. This would necessitate, however, that all of the numerous inputs required by these models (BOD of wastes dumped into the stream, solar radiation, etc...) could be fed continuously into the computer in a way similar to

(a) DISSØLVED ØXYGEN AT MENASHA STATIØN
JULY 7 - JULY 20. 1973

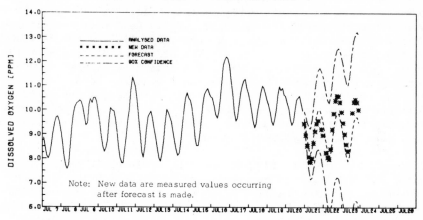

(b) DISSØLVED ØXYGEN AT MENASHA STATIØN - JULY 1973
FØRECAST AND ITS CØNTINUØUS UPDATE T HØURES LATER

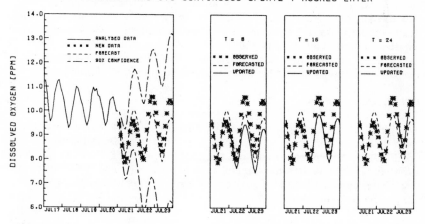

Figure 6
Forecast and Forcast Update for Dissolved Oxygen Series DØ14a

the data supplied by the telemetric monitoring network. Such
an operational assumption does not appear to be very realistic,
not only because five days are required to obtain BOD_5 measurements, but primarily because extending telemetric facilities to
monitor continuously in time all waste inputs and other factors
affecting river water quality does not appear feasible at the
present time. In addition the computer memory size required
and associated computational cost seems to preclude for the
moment the use of causal water quality models as forecast-
oriented software additions to be used in real-time for effective immediate utilization of the data supplied by telemetric
monitoring networks. The simplicity of the ARIMA models on the
other hand (which actually reflect a stream's "memory" structure as a function of the time variant boundary conditions),
and the good results obtained for both forecasting and continuous forecast updating (see Figure 6b), provide every positive
indication of their usefulness in developing telemetric network data analysis software systems.

The questions related to what would be included in such software, and how it could be integrated into the routine network
operation, will become clearer when a broader set of investigations on the applicability of the ARIMA approach will have been
carried out, and if those results are as promising as those
derived to date. Although such applications are only visual-
ized at this time, one can speculate about additional advantages which could be obtained by developing such software. The
first of these is related to the possibility of reconstructing
gaps in the observed data created by equipment malfunctions.
The second is related to the possibility of detecting faulty
records in the data. All of these uses would become particularly attractive if future telemetric networks would include
computer-connected display screens able to show not only the
most recent data, but also plots of the preceding records (for
example, 10 days) and the most recently updated forecast.

ACKNOWLEDGEMENT

This project was supported by the University of Wisconsin Sea
Grant Program under a grant from the National Oceanic and
Atmospheric Administration of the Department of Commerce. The
assistance of the Wisconsin Department of Natural Resources in
providing the data and other pertinent information is gratefully acknowledged.

REFERENCES

Bartlett, M.S. (1946) On the Theoretical Specifications of
Sampling Properties of Autocorrelated Time Series. Journal
Royal Stat. Soc. B8, 27.

Box, G.E.P. and G.M. Jenkins (1970) Time Series Analysis, Forecasting and Control. Holden Day.

Huck, P.M. and G.J. Farquhar (1974) Water Quality Models Using the Box-Jenkins Method. Jour. of Environmental Engr. Div. ASCE, Vol. 100, EE3.

Litwin, Y.J. and E.F. Joeres (1974a) Viability of Real-Time Water Quality Control Using Continuously Monitoring Stations. Paper No. H72, 55th Annual Meeting, American Geophysical Union, Washington, D.C.

Litwin, Y.J. and E.F. Joeres (1974b) Telemetric Surveillance System for Water Quality Management on the Lower Fox River. Proceedings: IWRA International Seminar on Water Resources Instrumentation, Chicago, Ill.

Litwin, Y.J. and E.F. Joeres (1974c) Stochastic Modeling for Real-Time Control. Project Report, Univ. of Wis. Sea Grant Program, Madison, Wis.

Litwin, Y.J. and E.F. Joeres (1975a) discussion of Water Quality Models Using the Box-Jenkins Method by Huck, et. al. Jour. of Sanitary Engr. Div. ASCE, Vol. 101, EE3.

Litwin, Y.J. and E.F. Joeres (1975b) ARIMA Modeling - a New Technique Applied to Hydrologic and Water Quality Control Studies. Proceedings of XVI International Congress of IAHR - Fundamental Tools to be Used in Environmental Problems, Sao Paulo, Brazil.

McMichael, F.C. and F.C. Vigani (1972) discussion of Characterization of Time Varying Organic Loads by A.T. Wallace and D.M. Zollman, Jour. of Sanitary Engr. Div. ASCE, Vol. 98, SA2.

Pack, D.J., M.L. Goodman and R.B. Miller (1972) Computer Programs for the Analysis of Univariate Time Series Using the Methods of Box and Jenkins. Tech. Report 296, Dept. of Statistics, Univ. of Wis., Madison.

MODELLING THE EFFECTS OF WEATHER, HEATING AND OCCUPANCY ON THE
THERMAL ENVIRONMENT INSIDE HOUSES

P. Basnett

Research Officer, Electricity Council Research Centre,
Capenhurst, Chester

INTRODUCTION

The Electricity Supply Industry has an interest in improving
the efficiency with which energy is used for domestic heating
purposes. In order to evaluate the design of heating equipment
it is useful to know how it will behave when installed in
houses of various types, and under standardised weather
conditions. As part of the research program in this field the
mathematical model which is reported here has been developed.
The model simulates the thermal interaction between a house
and a heating system.

At the Electricity Council Research Centre we have six full
size test houses. These houses are of four different
constructions, namely:- nine-inch solid brick wall with wet
plaster finish; thirteen-inch brick and block cavity wall with
wet plaster finish (two houses); timber frame construction
with one-inch mineral fibre insulation front and back, gable
wall of thirteen-inch brick and block cavity construction, all
with dry lining plasterboard finish (two houses); timber frame
as before but with three inches of mineral fibre insulation
and foam filled cavity in the gable wall. The houses thus
cover a range from an outdated type, a very large number of
which remain in current occupation, through two types
representing more modern construction, to a type which may
become more popular in the future. The houses are built as
three pairs of semi-detached houses, each pair consisting of
one brick-built and one timber frame house separated by a
cavity containing logging equipment for the extensive
instrumentation.

At each stage in the development of the model it was tested
and validated against measurements made in the test houses.
In the course of this validation it was found that the thermal
conductivity and capacity of many of the building materials

used in the test houses differ greatly from the figures
normally used by heating and ventilating engineers. Table I
shows the extent of these differences.

The model has also been used to predict the behaviour of houses
of types which have not yet been built. One result of these
predictions is an indication that when the insulation of a
house is greatly improved there is a danger that forced
ventilation or even air conditioning may be needed to preserve
acceptably low temperatures during the summer months.

CONSTRUCTION OF THE MODEL

Walls

The basic unit used in
building up the model is
the 'wall'. This notional
wall may correspond to a
wall, or to the floor,
ceiling or a window in the
building which is being
modelled. The heat flow
through the wall is assumed
to be one-dimensional, i.e.
each surface of the wall is
assumed to be at a uniform
temperature. This is not
an important restriction
since, in cases where it is
believed that large
temperature variations
exist across a single
physical wall, it may be
represented by two or more
sections of wall in the
model.

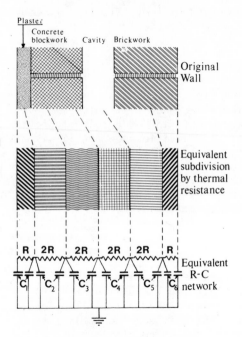

FIGURE I - Model of a Wall

Each wall is modelled by a
network of thermal
resistances and capacitances
as shown in Figure I. At the
stage of the validation exercise in which internal wall
temperatures were compared, some of the nodes in the network
were arranged to correspond with thermocouple positions in the
actual wall. However, in the final model the positions of the
nodes are adjusted in such a way that all the internal thermal
resistances are equal, while the resistances nearest to the
two surfaces have half the value of the internal ones. This
method of subdivision was suggested by Waters (1970) and
permits a smaller number of subdivisions to be used for the
same accuracy than if other methods of subdivision are used.
In the model we normally use six subdivisions (seven nodes).

Surface temperatures calculated using this subdivision were
found to agree within ± 0.IK with those calculated using
twenty subdivisions.

The outer surface of an external wall is subject to heat
transfer to the ambient air, using a constant heat transfer
coefficient, and to heating by solar radiation. No account is
taken of radiative heat loss. The inner surface of the wall
exchanges heat with the air in the room which is bounded by
the wall. Once again, the heat transfer coefficient is
constant. The surface of the wall may also be heated by a
part of the solar radiation which has passed through the
window of the room in question, although, in all the
calculations discussed in
this paper it has been
assumed that all the
radiation passing through
the window is absorbed by
the floor of the room.

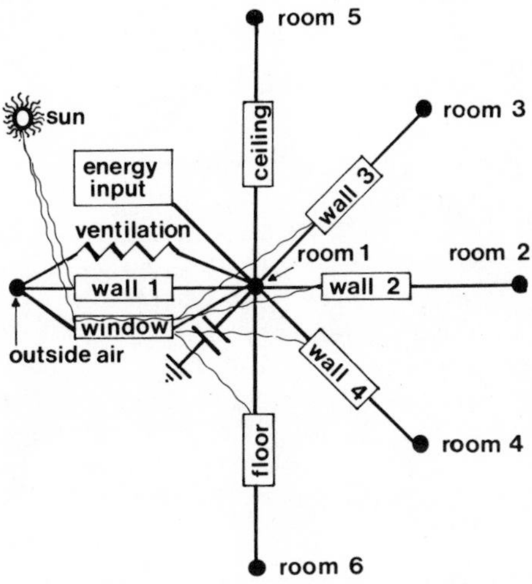

No account is taken of
radiation absorbed within
the glass of a window.
The radiation is assumed to
be either transmitted or
reflected. The proportion
of the radiation that is
transmitted depends on the
angle of incidence and is
calculated by a formula
provided by Pilkington
Bros Ltd.

FIGURE 2 - Model of a Room

Rooms

A room is represented by a
thermal capacity corresponding to that of the air contained in
the room. This gains or loses heat by convection (with a
constant heat transfer coefficient for any one surface) to the
walls, windows, floor and ceiling, by ventilation, at a constant
flow rate, to the outside air and by heat inputs which may be
either direct, modelling heat gains due to occupancy, light,
electrical appliances (e.g. television sets etc) or direct
acting heaters, or which may pass through models of heating
systems of various sorts. The network of walls and other
elements making up the model of a room is shown in Figure 2.

A necessary consequence of this model is that the air within
any one room is assumed to be at a uniform temperature. The
validity of this assumption depends to a large extent on the
way in which the building is heated. If it is heated by
natural convection or by radiation, eg by hot water radiators

or standard storage heaters considerable vertical temperature
gradients may be set up. In extreme cases, when warming up
from cold, temperature differences of up to 6K have been found
between the air near the ceiling and that near the floor.
Such differences clearly affect the distribution of heat loss
from the building, but they do not appear to affect the total
heat loss significantly. In buildings with forced air
circulation the vertical gradients may be rather less severe.

Radiative heat exchange within the room is ignored. In normal
circumstances one would not expect large temperature
differences to exist between the different surfaces of the room
and therefore the contribution of radiation to the flow of
heat to any one surface would be small. In particular cases
for which this assumption might not be justified, for instance
floor or ceiling heating, it would be quite a simple job to
include the effects of radiation in the program.

Heating Systems
Several types of heating system are already incorporated in
the program. Others can be easily added as and when they are
needed.

Storage heaters Two types of storage heater have been
modelled by networks similar to those used for walls, but
with nineteen nodes, and the parameters adjusted to give close
agreement with measured output curves. The power input to the
storage heater can be controlled in a number of different ways.

Direct acting heaters These are represented by heat inputs to

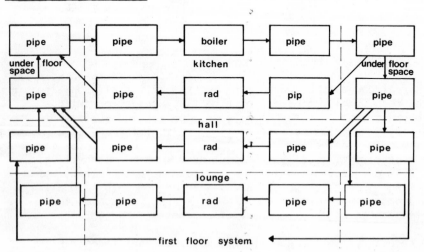

FIGURE 3 - Simplified model of part of a wet central
heating system

the air in a room. The power input can be varied as a function
of the time of day or can be controlled by a combination of a
time clock and a thermostat switching on when a temperature
falls below a given value and off when the same temperature
rises above a second, higher value.

Hot water system Each length of pipe, or radiator, in the
system is modelled by a tank (see Figure 3) in which the water
is well mixed. Water flows into it at the mixed temperature
of the next tank or tanks upstream, and out at its own mixed
temperature. The tank loses heat to its surroundings at a
rate which takes account of both convection and radiation,
but all the heat loss is assumed to go to the air rather than
being radiated to the walls. Heat input to the boiler is
controlled by a room thermostat, a water thermostat and a
time clock.

Occupancy
All the heat gains due to occupancy, whether from the
metabolism of the occupants, cooking, lighting or the use of
electrical appliances, are pooled for any one room. They are
represented as heat inputs to the air in the room, varying
with the time of day, in just the same way as for direct acting
heaters.

Air movement
No account is taken of air movement from one room in the house
to another, or of the opening and closing of windows and doors.
All the ventilation for any one room is assumed to take place
as an interchange of air with the external environment, and at
a constant rate. If the appropriate air flow rates for
internal air movement were known it would be relatively easy
to incorporate such movement. The volumetric specific heat of
the air is assumed to remain constant rather than depending on
such factors as temperature and humidity.

House
The house is modelled by a number of rooms, linked together by
common walls and possibly containing occupants and a heating
system.

External Conditions
The external temperature can be specified to vary with the
time of day, either sinusoidally with the peak occurring at an
arbitrary time, or according to any other curve specified by
values at hourly intervals and interpolated linearly between
them.

As has already been mentioned, no account is taken of the wind
speed and direction since the heat transfer coefficients are
assumed to be constant. Rainfall, atmospheric pressure and
humidity are also ignored.

Sunshine The solar radiation on a horizontal plane is
specified by a sequence of hourly values. It is split into
direct and diffuse components by a method developed from a
formula due to Berlage (1928) which will be discussed in a
forthcoming paper and recombined to give values incident on
vertical surfaces as required.

INTEGRATION OF THE DIFFERENTIAL EQUATIONS

The model as discussed above gives rise to a large number of
differential equations each of which expresses the rate of
change of one of the node temperatures as a function of the
other temperatures and of the energy inputs. Because we are
often concerned with the switching of thermostats it was felt
that the use of a time step longer than two to three minutes
would be unrealistic. At the same time, the very short steps
which would be necessitated by stability considerations if
using Euler's method or a Runge-Kutta method to integrate the
differential equations would be prohibitively expensive. For
this reason the equations are integrated by the Hopscotch
method of Gourlay (1969, 1970). This technique has the
advantage that, for the equations resulting from the house
model, it can be formulated in such a way that the calculations
are entirely explicit, and yet it is unconditionally stable.
The accuracy of the calculations is not outstanding, but it is
adequate for our purposes.

ESTIMATION OF PARAMETERS

Thermal Properties
When the results of calculations for a model of a single wall,
based on the thermal properties given in the IHVE Guide were
compared with actual temperature measurements made in the wall
large discrepancies were found. These discrepancies could be
reduced to within the measurement error by altering the relative
thermal conductivities and the thermal diffusivities of the
materials involved. For some materials the conductivity needed
to be altered by a factor of more than 2. Measurements of the
thermal conductivities carried out in situ by Ashton (1974) do,
however, agree quite well with the relative values found by
adjusting the parameters in the model. Table I shows how
these values compare, it also includes estimates of the
volumetric thermal capacity of the materials derived from the
fitted thermal diffusivities. Previous assumptions have
usually been that the specific heat of inorganic materials was
0.2, giving a thermal capacity of about 840 J kg^{-1} K^{-1} and that
of timber 0.6 giving a thermal capacity of about 2500 J kg^{-1}
K^{-1}. The corresponding volumetric thermal capacitances then
vary only according to the density of the material.

Table 1 - Thermal Properties of Building Materials

Material	Thermal Conductivity k/Wm^{-1}K^{-1}			Volumetric Thermal Capacity $10^{-6}\rho c$/Jm^{-3}K^{-1}
	Quoted	Measured	Fitted	
Plasterboard	0.16	0.19	0.190	1.007
Plastered finish	0.19	0.17-0.19	0.164	0.543
Cellular concrete blockwork	0.18	0.35	0.376	0.917
Brickwork	-	1.0-1.47	1.093	1.357
Rockwool insulation	0.051	0.036	0.059	0.326
Softwood	-	-	0.140	2.000
Plywood	0.14	0.148	0.152	2.173
Wall hanging tiles	-	-	0.287	0.060
Floor coverings	-	0.078	0.087	0.180

The explanation for the discrepancies between the quoted figures (from the manufacturers' data sheets or from the IHVE Guide) and the fitted or measured in-situ ones are largely that the quoted figures have been measured on an oven-dry sample of the material in question and with one face of the sample at about 70°C. When used in a building the materials have a water content of around 5-10% and heat is transferred through the material by the evaporation and recondensation of this water as well as by conduction through the solid material. Gypsum as used in wet plaster and plasterboard loses its water of hydration at temperatures above about 45C so that in some cases the material whose conductivity is being measured is physically different from that used in buildings. Another factor is that up to 20% of the heat transfer area of a brick or block wall consists of mortar, which has quite different properties to those of the bricks or blocks.

Heat Transfer Coefficients
The heat transfer coefficients between the internal surfaces of the walls etc and the neighbouring air were estimated by a similar technique to that used for the thermal properties, but here the estimation was facilitated by the use of a parameter estimation program which was made available to us by Scicon Computing Services. The fitted values and their estimated errrors are shown in Table 2.

It will be observed that the heat transfer coefficients to the floor are much less reliable than those to the walls and ceiling. This is because the temperature differences involved

Table 2 - Fitted Heat Transfer Coefficients ($Jm^{-2}K^{-1}$)

Condition	Heat Transfer Coefficient	Estimated Standard Deviation
Heated by Natural Convection:		
Floor	1.31	± 4.56
Wall	5.90	± 0.74
Ceiling	7.83	± 0.71
Fan Heater: fan on continuously		
Floor	2.13	± 0.71
Wall	6.73	± 0.38
Ceiling	14.43	± 1.82

are quite small and the measurement errors play a
correspondingly large part in the determination. Each
coefficient is calculated as an average of two tests in each
of two houses. Each test lasted 48 hours and the temperatures
required were measured at 30 minute intervals, the room air
temperature varying between about 13 and 23C with the heaters
on a 12 hour on, 12 hour off cycle. Allowing for missing
measurements the number of temperature comparisons involved
for each group of three coefficients is about 1500.

The values given for the floor apply to all horizontal surfaces
with heat flow downwards and those for the ceiling to all
horizontal surfaces with heat flow upwards. The heat transfer
coefficients for the external surfaces of the walls will vary
with the wind speed and direction, but would be expected to be
at least as high as on the internal surface with the fan on
continuously.

COMPARISON BETWEEN BUILDING AND MODEL

Figure 4 shows a comparison of air temperatures in a room
predicted by the model with measured ones. The calculated
temperature follows the measured values remarkably closely if
one takes into account the approximations which have been made
in building up the model. The root-mean-square difference
between the calculated and observed temperatures at hourly
intervals in six rooms in an unoccupied house, over a period
of three days was 0.7K with a maximum difference of 3K. Daily
energy requirements predicted by the model are within 5% of
the metered daily energy supplies. These figures are
comparable with the accuracy expected from the measurements.

PREDICTIONS USING THE MODEL

The model was used to predict the behaviour of well insulated detached houses. The overall U-value of the walls was 0.3Wm^{-2} K^{-1}. Two types of construction were modelled:

thermally heavy

external walls	105mm brickwork internally plastered and with 100mm glass fibre insulation and metal cladding on the outside
partitions	105mm brickwork, plastered both sides

thermally light

external walls	105mm brickwork with 100mm glass fibre insulation and a plasterboard lining internally
partitions	timber framed with plasterboard on both sides

In both cases the other components were: Single glazing, plasterboard ceiling and suspended wooden floor with carpet and underlay. The internal heat gains were those estimated for a family of two adults and two children.

Figure 5 shows the heat gains due to occupancy and the predicted equivalent (0.5 x air + 0.5 x mean radiant) temperature variation in the (north facing) kitchen of this

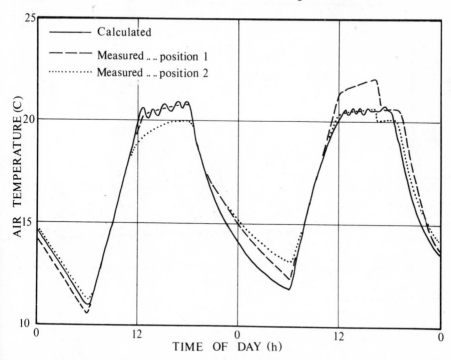

Figure 4 - Comparison between measured and calculated temperatures

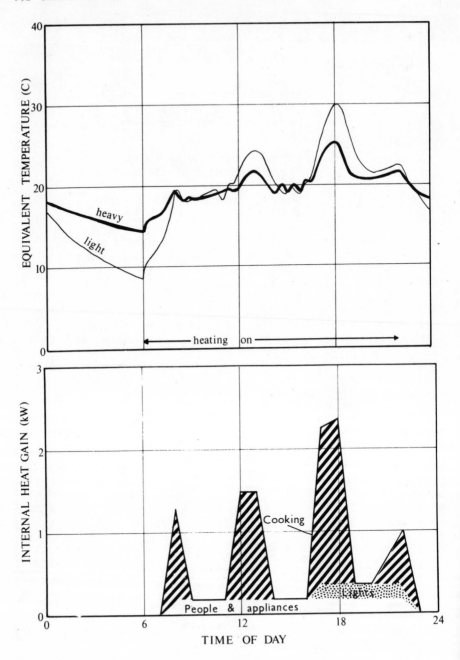

FIGURE 5 – Well insulated houses
Equivalent temperature and internal heat
gain in the (north facing) kitchen for a
dull day in January

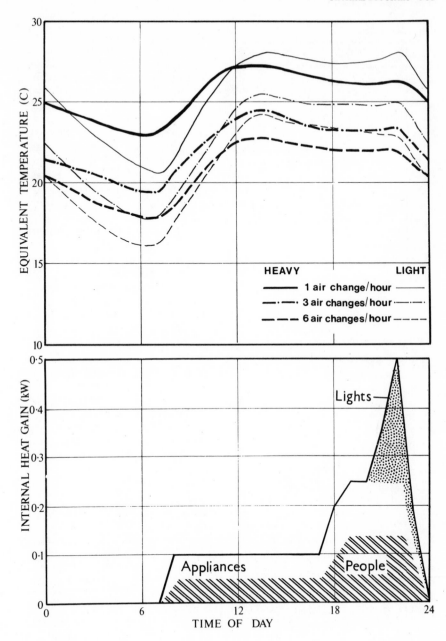

FIGURE 6   Well insulated houses
Equivalent temperature and internal heat
gain in the (south facing) lounge for a
sunny day in July, variation in ventilation
rate

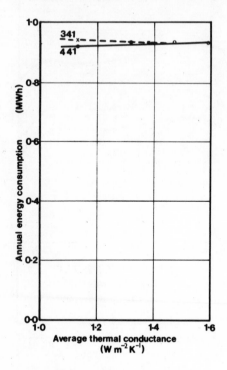

Figure 7 - Variation of annual
energy consumption with thermal
conductance of shell for a
particular office building.
Parameter is average thermal
capacitance of building shell
    $(kJm^{-2} K^{-1})$

building on a dull winter day
with I air change per hour.
It will be seen that the large
fluctuating heat gains due to
cooking cause an excessively
high temperature during the
early evening in the light
building, while the
temperatures in the heavy
building are just acceptable.

Figure 6 shows the interal
gains and temperature
profiles in the (south facing)
lounge for a sunny summer day
with I, 3 and 6 air changes
per hour. It can be seen
that very high rates of
ventilation are needed to
keep this room acceptably
cool during the summer.
Mechanical ventilation could
be needed to provide this
amount of ventilation and
this would tend to reduce
the energy savings made
during the winter by
insulating the building to
this extent. Clearly, if
the building were even better
insulated the problems would
be worse.

FUTURE WORK

We are hoping to extend the
modelling approach to air-conditioned office buildings.
However, a preliminary study using an American program has
shown that in one particular building some 70% of the annual
energy consumption is taken by the lighting and that the bulk
of the remainder is used to remove the heat generated by the
lights. Changing the thermal conductivity of the external
shell of this building by 50% only alters the annual energy
consumption by about 2%, as is shown in Figure 7. The problem
is thus very different from that of an individual house and we
must pay much more attention to thermal storage in the internal
structure and fittings of the building and within the ductwork
associated with the air conditioning system, than to the
external shell.

ACKNOWLEDGEMENTS

We are indebted to P. G. Owen of Pilkington Bros Ltd for data
regarding the angular dependence of the transmission properties
of glass, and to Scicon for the parameter estimation program.
The experimental measurements in the test houses were made by
a team under the direction of J. B. Siviour.

The work reported here was undertaken as part of the Electricity
Council's research programme. Thanks are due to
Dr. A. T. Churchman the Director of the Electricity Council
Research Centre, for permission to publish it.

REFERENCES

Ashton, D.F.   Tests to Measure the Thermal Properties of
                   the External Fabric of the Six Test Houses
                   ECRC/N724, 1974

Berlage, H.P.   Zur Theorie der Beleuchtung einer horizontalen
                   Fläche durch Tageslicht
                   Meteorlogische Zeitschrift, 1928, 45 (5),
                   174-180

Gourlay, A.R.   The Numerical Solution of Evolutionary
                   Partial Differential Equations
                   Conference on the Numerical Solution of
                   Differential Equations, Dundee, June 23-37,
                   1969, pp 168-171

Gourlay, A.R.   Hopscotch: a fast Second-order Partial
                   Differential Equation Solver
                   J. Inst. Maths Applics, 1970, 6 (4), 375-390

Institution of Heating & Ventilating Engineers Guide
                   London, 1970

Waters, J.R.   The calculation of the Thermal Response of
                   Buildings, M. Phil Thesis, Council for
                   National Academic Awards, 1970

MATHEMATICAL MODELLING OF THERMAL POLLUTION IN RIVERS

J J McGuirk & D B Spalding

Professor of Heat Transfer, Imperial College, London.

1. INTRODUCTION

1.1 The problem considered

Recent years have seen an increased awareness of the
detrimental effects of thermal pollution of seas,
lakes and rivers, and brought a need for a reliable
method of predicting the influence of large heat
inputs into natural water bodies; for the laboratory
modelling of these flows is both difficult and
costly. The complexity of the governing partial
differential equations is such that it is necessary
to resort to numerical methods and large digital
computers to obtain useful solutions. The necessary
mathematical methods have recently been developed.
The present paper presents an application of these
methods to the problem of thermal pollution in the
steady state of a river which is free from regions
of flow reversal. The discharge of warm water is
assumed horizontal and parallel to the river flow.

1.2 Previous work

Hot water discharged into a river forms a three-
dimensional turbulent buoyant jet. The literature
contains several studies of such jets in stagnant
surroundings (see for example Abraham (1), Anwar(2)),
but these are more relevant to thermal pollution in
lakes and bays. The present problem of horizontal
buoyant jets in co-flowing streams has received
much less attention.

Experimental studies have been carried out by Ayoub
(3), Winiarski and Chasse (4), (5), McQuivey et al
(6), (7) and by one of the present authors (8). The

first investigated the dispersion of a dense jet in
a co-flowing stream. The results were presented in
terms of plume trajectory and centre-line dilution
rate. Following usual practice, measurements were
analysed in terms of two dimensionless parameters
namely jet Froude number and the jet-to-ambient
velocity ratio, these parameters are also utilised
in the present paper and are defined as:-

$$FR = \frac{u_J}{\sqrt{\frac{\Delta_e}{\rho_a} g \, d_J}} \quad , \quad K = \frac{u_J}{u_a}$$

(all symbols are defined in the nomenclature.) The
first describes the ratio of inertia to buoyancy
forces in the jet. The second represents the effect
of the surrounding stream on the jet flow development.

The three remaining experimental studies are all
concerned with the injection of hot water into a
colder stream. Only in the last two however (6),(8)
were measurements presented of temperature profiles.
All three studies report plume widths and trajec-
tories for ranges of the two parameters mentioned
above.

In real river-discharge situations, the plume often
interacts with the boundaries of the flow. Only
references (4) and (8) have investigated this
situation, the former with the jet injected at the
bottom of the channel, the latter with the jet discharging close to the water surface.

Analytical treatments of the turbulent buoyant jet
in a co-flowing stream have been presented by Ayoub
(3) and Hirst (9). The former used an integral-
profile method and an extension of the entrainment
coefficient concept of Morton, Taylor and Turner
(10) to derive ordinary differential equations.
These were then solved numerically for the values
of centreline velocity and concentration. It was
found necessary to make the entrainment coefficient
a function of both Froude number and velocity ratio
in order to procure good results. Hirst (9) used a
generalised integral method, allowing discharge at
arbitrary angles to the ambient flow. Again the
entrainment function used depended on local mean-
flow conditions within the jet. One disadvantage of
both these methods lies in the profile assumptions

used. These involve rotational symmetry about the
plume centreline, which is erroneous in the
practically interesting situation where the jet
interferes with the flow boundaries.

All the above are concerned with laboratory flows,
usually with jets discharged into rectangular open
channels. A recent paper by Zelazny and Baker (11)
presented a sample calculation of a full-scale
river pollution problem but used a very simple
turbulence model. Spalding (2) has also recently
demonstrated that a general method of computation
exists which is capable of providing realistic
predictions for river flow problems. It is this
method which forms the basis of the present paper.

1.3 Outline of present contribution

Section 2 contains the details of the mathematical
model used in the present work. This includes information on the general solution algorithm
employed and the method of modelling the turbulence.
This is followed by comparison with a range of
laboratory data. Finally some illustrative
calculations of a typical buoyant jet in river
situation are presented. Section 5 summarises the
contribution of the paper and draws conclusions.

2. MATHEMATICAL MODEL

2.1 Governing differential equations

In terms of a cartesian co-ordinate system, the
governing equations have the typical form shown
below:

$$\frac{\partial}{\partial x}(\rho u \phi) + \frac{\partial}{\partial y}(\rho v \phi) + \frac{\partial}{\partial z}(\rho w \phi) = \frac{\partial}{\partial y}\left(\Gamma_{eff,\phi} \frac{\partial \phi}{\partial y}\right) +$$

$$\frac{\partial}{\partial z}\left(\Gamma_{eff,\phi} \frac{\partial \phi}{\partial z}\right) + S_{\phi} \qquad (2.1)$$

u, v and w are the velocity components in x, y and
z directions. The first direction is oriented
along the river main-flow direction and is treated
differently from the other two. Since flow
reversal is excluded, convective influences from
downstream cannot extend upstream. Because the
Reynolds number is high, the diffusional transport
in the x direction can also be neglected. The
equations are therefore parabolic.

ϕ may stand for any one of:- the constant 1 (continuity equation), u, v or w (3 momentum equations), T (temperature), or other dependent variables. S_ϕ is the source term appropriate to each equation (e.g. pressure gradient in the momentum equations), and $\Gamma_{eff,\phi}$ is the relevant transport property (effective viscosity, effective thermal conductivity).

In turbulent flow, it is necessary to prescribe the variation of the effective transport properties over the flow domain. This topic is discussed in the next section, but it may be mentioned here that the turbulence model involves the solution of differential equations for two extra ϕ's namely k, the turbulence kinetic energy and ε, the dissipation rate of k. The mathematical problem of thermal-pollution prediction is thus that of solving seven partial differential equations such as (2.1) (1 continuity, 3 momentum, 2 turbulence, 1 temperature), together with initial and boundary conditions.

2.2 Turbulence Modelling

Reviews of the various levels of turbulence closure proposed by research workers have been given by Harlow (13) and Launder and Spalding (14). The turbulence model which is used in the present work has had considerable success in engineering calculations. Closure is effected at a level which involves solution of two differential equations, one for k, the turbulence energy, and one for the energy dissipation rate ε. The viscosity is then prescribed via an extension of the Prandtl-Kolmogorov formula:-

$$\mu_{eff} = C_\mu \, \rho \, k^2/\varepsilon \qquad\qquad (2.2)$$

The effective thermal conductivity is calculated using a turbulent Prandtl number, and the transport properties in the equations for k and ε are prescribed in a similar manner:-

$$\Gamma_{eff,T} = \frac{\mu_{eff}}{\sigma_T} \, , \quad \Gamma_{eff,k} = \frac{\mu_{eff}}{\sigma_k} \, , \quad \Gamma_{eff,\varepsilon} = \frac{\mu_{eff}}{\sigma_\varepsilon}$$

$$(2.3)$$

where the σ's are taken as constants.

For completeness, the equations for k and ε are

written out below:-

$$\frac{\partial}{\partial x}(\rho uk) + \frac{\partial}{\partial y}(\rho vk) + \frac{\partial}{\partial z}(\rho wk) = \frac{\partial}{\partial y}\left(\Gamma_{eff,k}\frac{\partial k}{\partial y}\right) +$$

$$\frac{\partial}{\partial z}\left(\Gamma_{eff,k}\frac{\partial k}{\partial z}\right) + S_k \qquad (2.4)$$

$$\frac{\partial}{\partial x}(\rho u\varepsilon) + \frac{\partial}{\partial y}(\rho v\varepsilon) + \frac{\partial}{\partial z}(\rho w\varepsilon) = \frac{\partial}{\partial y}\left(\Gamma_{eff,\varepsilon}\frac{\partial \varepsilon}{\partial y}\right) +$$

$$\frac{\partial}{\partial z}\left(\Gamma_{eff,\varepsilon}\frac{\partial \varepsilon}{\partial z}\right) + S_\varepsilon \qquad (2.5)$$

$$S_k = \mu_{turb}\overbrace{\frac{\partial v_i}{\partial x_j}\left(\frac{\partial v_i}{\partial x_j} + \frac{\partial v_j}{\partial x_i}\right)}^{G} - \rho\varepsilon \qquad (2.6)$$

$$S_\varepsilon = C_1.\frac{\varepsilon}{k}.G - C_2\,\rho\,\frac{\varepsilon^2}{k} \qquad (2.7)$$

In the above source terms,G represents the generation of turbulence energy due to shear and has been
expressed in tensor notation. It can be seen that,
to complete the model, values must be supplied for
the constants involved (C_μ, C_1, σ_k, etc.). It should
be noted that the values of these constants (shown
below) are those which have been found valid in two-
and three-dimensional engineering calculations.
They have not been modified to improve agreement.
Further details of the modelling are contained in
references (14) and (15).

C_μ	C_1	C_2	σ_k	σ_ε	σ_T
.09	1.44	1.92	1.0	1.3	0.7

TABLE 2.1   VALUES OF CONSTANTS IN THE
            TURBULENCE MODEL

2.3 Buoyancy modelling

In thermal-pollution problems, it is the buoyancy
forces which cause the hot water to rise to and
subsequently spread over the surface of the river.
In this paper the Boussinesq approach has been
adopted: the variations in density resulting from
temperature changes are assumed to be appreciable
only in the body-force term, which in equation
(2.1) is contained in the source term S_ϕ. The

buoyancy force is non-zero in the vertical (y)
direction only. Hence the v velocity source includes the following term:

$$S_{v,buoyancy} = -g \ (\rho_{local} - \rho_{ref}) \qquad (2.8)$$

If the reference density is taken as the ambient
one and the volumetric expansion coefficient β is
introduced, equation (2.8) becomes:

$$S_{v,buoyancy} = \rho\beta g \ (T_{local} - T_{amb}) \qquad (2.9)$$

2.4   Solution algorithm

The governing equations, typified by (2.1), are of
the three-dimensional parabolic variety. A method
has recently been developed (16) for the solution
of equations of this kind and has met great success
in the calculation of, for example, rectangular
duct flows (see (17)). This algorithm, utilised
in this paper, is called SIMPLE, standing for semi-
implicit method for pressure-linked equations. Its
main features are:-

● The pressure and longitudinal velocity (u) are
  calculated at the nodes of a rectangular grid
  covering the duct or river cross-section.
● The lateral velocities (v and w) are calculated
  for nodes staggered between the pressure nodes
  (see Fig. 2.1).
● The calculation procedure begins from a set of
  known values of u, v, w, p and other φ's at the
  inlet cross-section. A forward step is then
  taken to establish values of these variables on
  a downstream plane. Such steps are executed in
  a marching integration manner down the river from
  upstream to downstream.
● The execution of each step involves the guessing
  of pressure values over the downstream station.
  These are then used in solving the momentum
  equations to give the velocity field (the
  parabolic nature of the equations is enforced by
  de-coupling the pressures in the y and z
  directions (p) from those in the x-direction ($\bar{p}$)).
● Subsequently, corrections to these pressure
  values are found (p' and $\bar{p}$') which lead to
  corrections to the calculated velocity field
  ensuring mass-continuity both for each sub-domain
  of the finite-difference grid (for p'), and for
  the river as a whole (for $\bar{p}$').

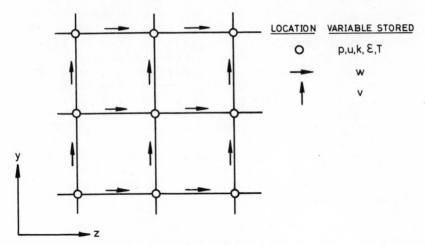

FIG.2.1 The staggered grid system

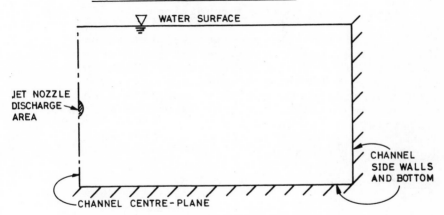

FIG 2.2 Laboratory data flow geometry

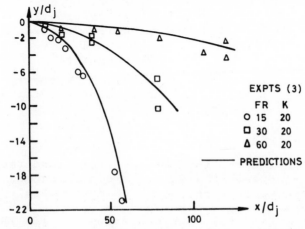

FIG 3.1 Effect of Froude number on Plume trajectory

- The solution of the finite-difference form of equation (2.1) is achieved by line-by-line application of the tri-diagonal matrix algorithm, in multiple sweeps. The finite-difference equations themselves are linearised by using up-stream values in the calculation of the co-efficients. The errors associated with this linearisation are rendered negligible by the employment of rather short step lengths in the x direction.
- Once the new velocity field has been established by way of SIMPLE, more conventional methods are employed to obtain the downstream temperature, k, and ε fields.

Further details of the method can be obtained from Reference (16).

2.5   Initial and boundary conditions

In the predictions of laboratory experiments which follow, the flow cross-section is of the form shown in Fig. 2.2. Before the solution algorithm can be employed, it is necessary to supply information about inlet conditions and boundary conditions. In the present work, these are prescribed as follows:-

Boundary Conditions

Walls   u, v, w - all zero.
                           T   - equal to ambient temperature.
                         k,ε   - near-wall values prescribed from simplified forms of the full differential equations applicable near walls (see (14)) for details.

Centre Plane   )   planes of symmetry,
) all   zero gradient for all
Water Surface) variables- ϕ's.

Inlet Conditions

The practice adopted is to use uniform conditions for all variables. The lateral velocities are assumed zero everywhere, but the longitudinal velocity changes from a uniform value applicable to the jet region to a uniform value outside the

jet equal to the velocity in the co-flowing stream.
The same is true for jet and channel temperatures.
The value of turbulence intensity in both jet and
channel has, for lack of further information, been
assumed to be 3% of the longitudinal velocity.
The specification of energy dissipation rate is
more difficult. The method used here is to
estimate the length scale of turbulence in jet and
channel regions and then to specify ε via the
formula given below, derived from dimensional
analysis:-

$$\varepsilon = \rho \ k^{3/2}/\ell \qquad\qquad (2.10)$$

The above inlet conditions are obviously idealised,
they make no allowance for the boundary layers
which exist inside and outside the jet nozzle, or
the small recirculation region which might exist
just downstream of the nozzle lips. These factors
can dominate the rate of mixing close to the
nozzle exit and, to allow for them, the formula
(2.10) for ε has been modified in the jet region at
the inlet to give a value for the effective
viscosity which results in the correct level of
mixing just downstream of the discharge point.
It must be emphasised that for any set of data,
this modification has been made for just one
experiment and is <u>not</u> then repeated for different
Froude numbers or velocity ratios. The modification
is also only necessary to the <u>inlet</u> value of ε
itself. Subsequently the full differential equations
are solved for the downstream values.

3.   APPLICATION TO TURBULENT BOUYANT   JETS IN CO-
     FLOWING STREAMS

3.1 <u>Dense jets</u>

A comparison is first made with the data of Ayoub
(3) for "downward-buoyant" jets. These have been
simulated by calculating the discharge of cold
water into a warmer ambient stream.

Figs. 3.1 and 3.2 show calculations of the plume
centre-line trajectory. This has been defined as
the location on the vertical centre plane of the
maximum concentration (experiments) or minimum
temperature (predictions). The first graph shows
the effect of varying Froude number, whilst the
velocity ratio remains the same. Agreement is very
good showing that, as FR increases, buoyancy forces
have decreasing influence on the flow. The second

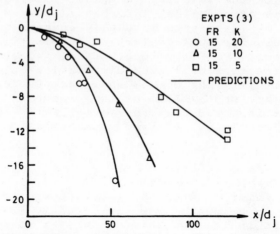

FIG 3.2 Effect of Velocity Ratio on Plume trajectory

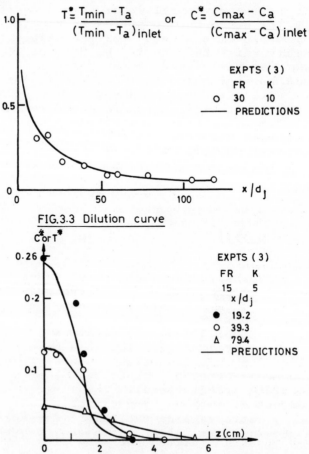

FIG.3.3 Dilution curve

FIG 3.4 Non-dimensional temperature / concentration profiles

graph demonstrates the effect of different velocity
ratios at constant Froude number. Increasing K
values indicate decreasing ambient velocity, the
stream is thus less able to withstand the vertical
buoyancy forces in the jet, so that the trajectory
deflects more quickly. Again the predictions reproduce this behaviour very well. Measurements
were also made of the downstream dilution,
represented by the maximum concentration at each
downstream station. Fig. 3.3 shows a typical
comparison with experimental data. The dilution
is very rapid in the inlet region (it is this
which is fixed by the discharge configuration and
reproduced by modifying the inlet ε values). As
can be seen, the agreement is good and typical of
the comparisons made at other Froude numbers and
velocity ratios.

Fig. 3.4 shows that the spread of the jet is also
well predicted. Only a few measurements were
made of horizontal concentration profiles. However,
suitably non-dimensionalised, they may be compared
with the non-dimensional temperature predictions.
Agreement is satisfactory.

3.2 Hot buoyant jets

One of the present authors (8) has made measurements
in which a hot water jet is discharged close to a
water surface, this provides a stringent test of
the mathematical model. Measurements were made of
the development of the temperature profile along
the centre-plane. Figs. 3.5 - 3.7 show comparisons
of predictions with data for three Froude numbers
and two velocity ratios for an injection depth of
6 cms. Both the spreading and the dilution of the
jet are very well predicted, and the location of
the maximum temperature (plume centre-line) is in
good agreement with the data except when the plume
is very close to the surface.

Measurements were also made at an injection depth
of 3 cms. Fig. 3.8 presents temperature contours
over the channel half-section for three downstream
stations. The predictions exhibit very similar
behaviour in terms of spreading rates and dilutions
but discrepancies appear in two areas. Firstly,
the outermost contour differs from the data, but
this is probably due to the difficulty of making
accurate measurements in the outer regions of a
jet. Secondly, the lateral spreading which occurs
when the plume hits the surface is underestimated

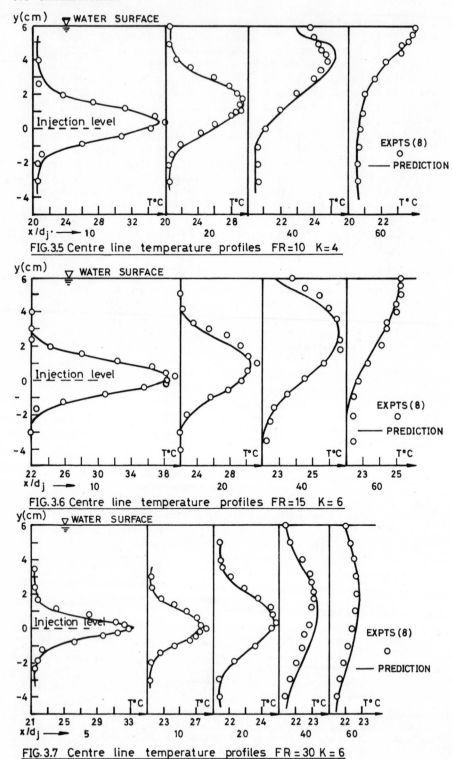

FIG.3.5 Centre line temperature profiles FR=10 K=4

FIG.3.6 Centre line temperature profiles FR=15 K=6

FIG.3.7 Centre line temperature profiles FR=30 K=6

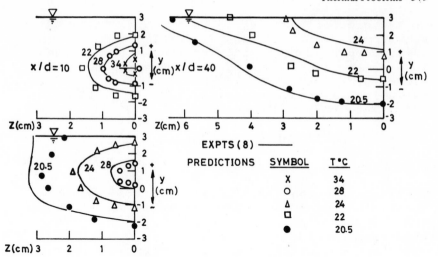

FIG 3.8 Cross sectional temperature contours FR=15 K=6

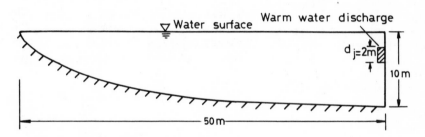

FIG 4.1 Thermal discharge into a river

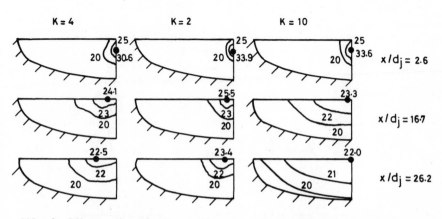

FIG 4.2 Effect of velocity ratio on temperature contours

in the predictions. Again this is partially due to
measurement difficulties in locating a finite-size
thermocouple probe exactly at the water surface.
However it is believed that the treatment of the
water surface as a zero-flux plane for all
variables is an over-simplification and will
contribute to the discrepancy.

4. A RIVER-DISCHARGE PROBLEM

4.1 The situation considered

To illustrate the capability of the mathematical
model, this section presents predictions of an
imaginary thermal discharge into a river. The
situation considered is shown in Fig. 4.1. The
river is 100 metres wide and 10 metres deep at the
centre (symmetry of the river about a vertical
centre-plane is assumed). The river bed is
assumed to be elliptical in cross-section*. The
area of discharge of hot water is shown shaded in
Fig. 4.1 with the hot water at 40^0C. This is 20^0C
above the ambient river temperature. Finally the
jet velocity has been fixed at a uniform value of
1.2 m/s. The river velocity, also uniform, has been
varied from 0.12 m/s to 0.6 m/s (velocity ratio
from 10 to 2).

4.2 Results

The above conditions correspond to a jet Froude
number of 3.87. Fig. 4.2 demonstrates how altering
the velocity ratio at the same Froude number affects
the predictions (for clarity, the vertical scale is
twice the horizontal in Fig. 4.2).

With increasing downstream distance, the plume
spreads and rises. The rate of rise may be
estimated from the location of the maximum-
temperature point also shown in Fig. 4.2. It may
be noticed that eventually, this point hits the
surface and is then carried along it by the lateral
spreading action of the plume. As may be expected,
for a lower velocity ratio, the buoyancy forces
have less prominence and the plume rises more
slowly. The contours show that the rate of spread
is also less, and the maximum temperature is
consequently higher. For a higher velocity ratio,

---

* A method has been developed for treating irregular boundaries with a cartesian finite-difference
grid system, see (8) for details.

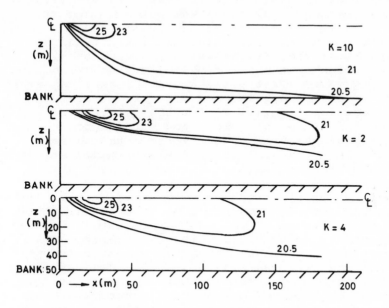

FIG 4.3 River discharge-surface temperature
contours effect of K at FR = 4

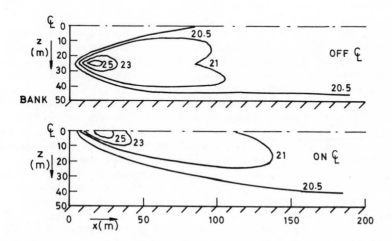

FIG 4.4 River discharge - surface temperature contours —
two discharge locations FR = 4 K = 4

the reverse is true: the plume spreads very quickly
reaching the river bank only 26 jet heights downstream, the dilution is of course greater in this
case as evidenced by the lower maximum temperatures.

An often-used indication for the severity of
thermal pollution is the surface temperature
distribution of the river. Fig. 4.3 shows how the
velocity ratio affects the amount of surface water
which is polluted. The behaviour is similar to
that described above. In the low-velocity-ratio
case, there is a thin elongated surface zone,
whereas for the high velocity ratio the whole
surface is above ambient by 200 metres downstream
of the discharge.

As a final example we have considered splitting the
discharge into two zones offset towards the river
bank by 25 metres. Fig. 4.4 portrays the surface
temperature contours for this case compared with the
same Froude number and velocity ratio for centre-
line discharge. The off-centre-line case exhibits
quicker spreading and dilution. This may be
expected because splitting the discharge in two
has enabled entrainment of cold ambient fluid to
take place over a larger area.

5.   CONCLUSIONS

The paper has demonstrated that a method of
computing realistic river thermal-pollution
problems now exists. The method is based on the
finite-difference, marching-integration procedure
of Patankar and Spalding (16) and uses a two-
equation turbulence model. Predictions have been
presented both of laboratory data and of representative river-flow thermal-pollution situations.
Where comparisons with experiment could be made,
the predictions have been shown to be satisfactory.
The method is more general than previous treatments
and enables hitherto uncalculated phenomena such
as discharge near a flow boundary to be predicted.

6.   ACKNOWLEDGEMENTS

One of the authors (J.J. McGuirk) gratefully
acknowledges financial support received from the
Metropolitan Vickers Fund during the performance
of part of this work. Thanks are also due to
Christine MacKenzie for preparing the typescript,
and to Combustion Heat & Mass Transfer Ltd. for the
loan of its STABLE computer program.

7.   REFERENCES

1. G ABRAHAM   "Horizontal jets in stagnant fluid
                  of other density".
                  ASCE Jnl. Hydraulics   July 1965.
2. H O ANWAR   "Behaviour of buoyant jet in calm
                  fluid".
                  ASCE Jnl. Hydraulics   July 1969.
3. G M AYOUB   "Dispersion of buoyant jets in a
                  co-flowing ambient flow".
                  Ph.D. thesis   Univ. of London.
                  March 1971.
4. L WINIARSKI   "Plume temperature measurements of
    J CHASSE   shallow submerged model discharges
                  with current".
                  Report published by National
                  Environemntal Research Centre,
                  Corvallis, Oregon, U.S.A. Jan.1973.
5. L WINIARSKI   "Laboratory experiments of sub-
    J CHASSE   merged discharges with current".
                  Pacific Northwest Environmental
                  Research Laboratory Working Paper
                  12.   June 1974.
6. R S McQUIVEY
    et al   "Basic data report on turbulent
                  spread of heat and matter".
                  National Thermal Pollution Research
                  Program Open-File Report, Fort
                  Collins, Colorado, U.S.A. Aug.1971.
7. M.A. SHIRAZI
    et al   "Heated water jets in a co-flowing
                  stream".
                  ASCE Jnl. Hydraulics, July 1974.
8. J J McGUIRK   "Prediction of turbulent buoyant
                  jets in a co-flowing stream".
                  Ph.D. thesis.   Univ. of London.
                  July 1975.
9. E HIRST   "Buoyant jets with three-dimension-
                  al trajectories".
                  ASCE Jnl. Hydraulics, Nov. 1972.
10. B R MORTON   "Turbulent gravitational convection
    G I TAYLOR   from maintained and instantaneous
    J S TURNER   sources".
                  Jnl. of Royal Soc. of London. A234.
                  1956.
11. S W ZELAZNY   "Predictions in environmental
    A J BAKER   hydraulics using finite-element
                  method-II-applications".
                  AIAA Jnl. 13.   Jan. 1975.
12. D B SPALDING
                  "The mathematical modelling of
                  rivers".

12. CONTD.   Imperial College, Mech. Eng. Dept.,
                    Report HTS/74/4, Jan. 1974.

13. F H HARLOW   "Turbulence transport modelling".
    (editor)   AIAA Selected Reprint Series, Vol.
                    XIV, 1973.

14. B E LAUNDER   "Mahtematical models of turbulence"
    D B SPALDING   Academic Press, London and New
                    York, 1972.

15. B E LAUNDER   "The numerical calculation of
    D B SPALDING   turbulent flows".
                    Computer Methods in Science &
                    Engineering, 1974.

16. S V PATANKAR   "A calculation procedure for heat,
    D B SPALDING   mass and momentum transfer in
                    three-dimensional parabolic flows".
                    Int. Jnl. Heat and Mass Transfer,
                    15, 1972.

17. D SHARMA   "Turbulent convective phenomena in
                    straight, rectangular-sectioned
                    diffusers".
                    Ph.D. thesis, Univ. of London,
                    Sept. 1974.

8.   NOMENCLATURE

β	Volumetric expansion coefficient = $-\dfrac{1}{\rho}\dfrac{\partial \rho}{\partial T}$
C	Concentration in dense jet experiments
C_1, C_2, C_μ	Constants in turbulence equations
d_J	Jet nozzle dimension (diameter or height.
FR	Densimetric Froude number.
g	Gravitational acceleration.
G	Source term in transport equation for k.
k	Turbulence kinetic energy.
K	Velocity ratio parameter.
ℓ	Turbulence length scale.
p	Pressure.
S_ϕ	Source term in transport equation for ϕ.
T	Temperature.
u, v, w	Velocities.
ρ	Density.
$\Delta\rho$	Differential density between ambient and jet fluids.
x, y, z	Cartesian co-ordinates.
$\Gamma_{eff,\phi}$	Effective transport property for ϕ.
μ_{eff}	Effective viscosity.

ϕ General fluid property, subject of equation (2.1)

$\sigma_k, \sigma_\epsilon, \sigma_T$ Turbulent Prandtl/Schmidt numbers for k, ϵ, T.

Subscripts

a, amb, ref   Ambient conditions.
local   Local conditions.
J   Jet conditions.

Superscripts

— Indicates pressure used in u momentum equation.

' Indicates pressure correction.

COMPUTATION OF ARTIFICIAL TEMPERATURE STRESSES DUE TO
DISCHARGES FROM NUCLEAR POWER PLANTS
T. Audunson, H. Rye, A. Thendrup.

River and Harbour Laboratory (VHL) at the Technical University
of Norway (NTH), Trondheim, Norway.

INTRODUCTION

The planning of thermal power plants in Norway has motivated
the study of thermal effects induced by the cooling water
discharges into fjords and open sea.

During the past decade, a considerable effort has been
concentrated upon the computation of "average" excess
temperatures in the receiving waters (cooling ponds, lakes,
rivers, estuaries) by means of numerical techniques.

However, the temperature conditions of most natural bodies of
waters are observed to fluctuate. Therefore, temperature
changes of importance for the marine biota may not only be a
change in the mean temperatur level. A qualitative and/or
quantitative change in the variational characteristics of the
temperature field may be of equal importance. For instance,
the probability of occurrence of certain extreme temperature
levels may increase significantly or the amplitude of the
temperature variations at certain frequencies may become
significantly larger. One may also envision a shift in the
temperature spectrum in such a way as to induce temperature
fluctuations at frequencies not previously important. In
this paper we shall present, therefore, some simple methods to
evaluate temperature stresses induced by thermal discharges.
The method requires a knowledge of existing temperature or
current variations in the water in addition to an evaluation
of the mean power plant induced temperature increase.

The paper consists of two parts. In the first part, the
temporal distribution of excess temperatures within a certain
time span are computed for the "near-field" zone. The
numerical computations are carried out for a buoyant surface
discharge modified by ambient current variations measured at
the site. In the second part, the increased occurrence of

temperatures above specific temperature levels was computed
for the "far-field" zone. A one dimensional numerical model
was developed to compute "average" excess temperatures from
cooling water discharges within an area restricted by topography (like fjords). Using this model, together with
observed temperature variations, enabled an estimation of the
increased occurrence of temperatures above specific
temperature levels.

It is worth noting that in order to establish design criteria
for cooling water discharges, it may be inconvenient to apply
average excess temperatures, because these may be difficult
to separate from the natural fluctuations in the ambient
waters (Hawes et.al., 1974). However, the effect on the
statistical characteristics of the temperature field may be
easier to establish and thus be a more convenient property to
apply for design criteria.

For the purpose of illustration, consider a planned location
of cooling water discharge shown in fig. 1. Horizontal current

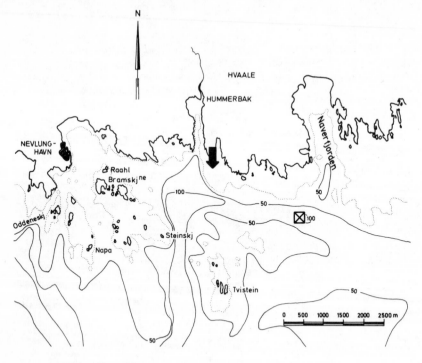

LOCATION OF DISCHARGE

LOCATION OF RECORDING INSTRUMENT

DEPTH IN METERS

Figure 1

speed and direction and water temperatures were sampled every
10 minutes during one month at 15 meters depth. The position
of the recording current meter is indicated in the figure.
Fig. 2 shows the spectrum of the temperature recording.

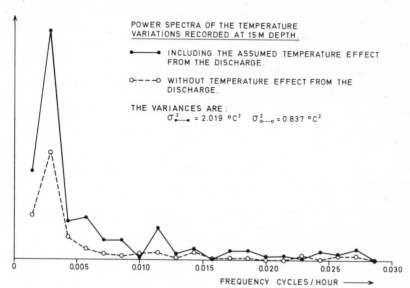

Figure 2

Suppose that the cooling water discharge causes a temperature
rise of 2°C at the location of the current meter every time
the currents flow from west to east, and thus sweeps the
cooling water discharge past the current meter. The change
in the observed temperature field may then by computed by
simply adding 2°C to the temperature recorded every time the
current direction falls within a sector which contains the
current meter, say the sector 0 - 180°. The spectrum of this
modified temperature field is also shown in Fig. 2. Note that
the variance of the spectrum has increased significantly due
to the artificial changes in the temperature field. One may
also note that the change in the spectrum is quantitative only,
i.e., the major contribution to the variance occurs at the
same frequency as for the undisturbed case. If, however, the
observed velocity variations had fluctuated quite differently
from the temperature field, there might also have been a
qualitative change in the temperature spectrum.

THE NEAR FIELD

A buoyant surface jet is often analyzed as a steady-state-
phenomenon, discharging into a uniform flow of ambient waters.
It is quite clear, however, that ambient currents are time and

space dependent. With a tidal flow, for example, a surface
jet will fluctuate back and forth in the discharge area.

No theory for the transient behaviour of a buoyant surface jet
has been brought to the attention of the authors. Prototype
measurements have shown that steady-state-solutions give
erroneous results when the ambient current and water level
change rapidly, while a series of superposed steady-state-
solutions agreed well with mean-value prototype measurements
(Doret et.al. 1973). Therefore, superpositions of several
steady-state-solutions corresponding to various conditions of
the ambient current field seem to be one way of evaluating
some transient characteristics of the buoyant surface jet.

In the present work the steady state spreading and dilution of
a buoyant surface jet has been analyzed by a numerical
model originally developed by Prych (1972). The model is
based on an integral analysis of a turbulent, buoyant,
horizontal surface jet discharging into a large, deep,
homogeneous, turbulent and flowing body of water. In the
analysis similar lateral distributions are assumed for the
temperature and velocity fields along the jet axis. The
analysis yields explicit values along the jet axis of
parameters in these similarity functions.

The steady state numerical solution is then stored in the
computer in a matrix as shown in fig. 3. The example in the
figure corresponds to a discharge of 200 m^3/s with an initial
velocity of 1 m/s and an initial density difference between
the jet and the ambient waters of 2 kg/m^3, corresponding to a
temperature increase of $10^\circ C$. Of course, other initial
parametres will give other results. In the figure the outer
contour of e.g. the 2-region represents a temperature-isoline
corresponding to an excess temperature of $2^\circ C$. The inner
contour corresponds to the temperature-isoline, of $2.5^\circ C$
excess temperature. The matrix of the discharge area is
divided into 9000 rectangles. For each computed jet each
rectangle is given a temperature. The only ambient parameter
which is varied in these computations is the ambient current.
Calculations have been made corresponding to values of the
ambient current ranging from +37.5 cm/s to ÷ 37.5 cm/s at a
right angle to the outlet channel. Since each rectangle
represents a physical location in the prototype, the
variations of the excess temperature at a particular location
can be followed as the ambient conditions change. This
implies that the characteristic time of the rate of change of
the ambient conditions is significantly greater than the
characteristic time of the jet discharge. This requirement
is very often met.

In fig. 4 the result of one such computation is shown. The
figure shows how often during one week the excess temperature

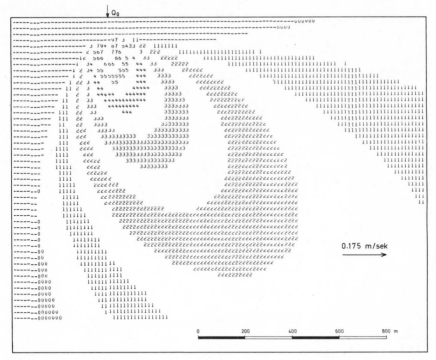

Figure 3   A contour plot of the surface temperature for a buoyant surface jet.

exceeds 2°C in the discharge area. The variations in the jet are as mentioned above due only to ambient velocity variations. The ambient current was measured with a recording current meter in the discharge area. The other parametres are as described for fig. 3.

The ambient velocities in this particular area are mostly governed by a coastal current caused by the fresh water outflow from the Baltic, and the velocities can therefore be nearly constant over a period of one week or more. These computations show that the excess temperature exceeds 2°C more than 90% of the time in a relatively large area, whereas the same excess temperature may be expected in only 10% or more of the time in just a slightly larger area.

Fig. 5 shows how often in a 25 hour period the excess temperature exceeds 2°C at another location. The current measurements here showed that the velocity varied greatly due to tides and topography. These computations indicate that temperature may be expected to exceed 2°C more than 90% of the time in a smaller area than for the other example. On the other hand, the area that attains 2°C excess temperature 10% or more of the time is much larger in this case.

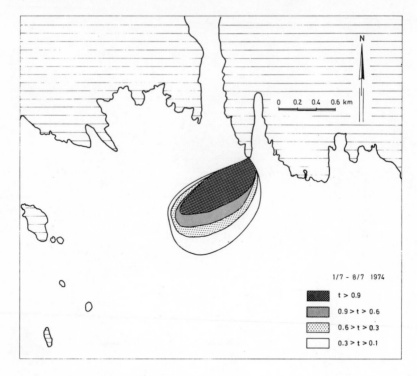

Figure 4   The relative occurrence (t) of surface excess
temperatures larger or equal to 2°C.

The computations thus illustrate the importance of taking
proper account of the variations in the ambient currents
when evaluating excess temperatures at different locations
for thermal power plants.

LONGTERM TEMPERATURE EFFECT

In this part of the paper we shall present some numerical
calculations of thermal effects of power plant thermal
discharges on seasonal temperatur cycles in a stratified sill
fjord; the Vestfjord, near Oslo. The analysis is based on
an one-dimensional transient approach which takes into account
vertical and temporal variations in the vertical eddy
diffusion coefficient and the horizontal in- and out-flows to
the fjord. Temperature effects, salinity effect and wind
shear effect on the vertical diffusion coefficient are
considered through an assumed functional relationship between
the vertical eddy diffusion coefficient and the stability of
the water column. Corroboration of the calculations by actual
observations was used as a criterion for the physical realism
of the model and its boundary conditions.

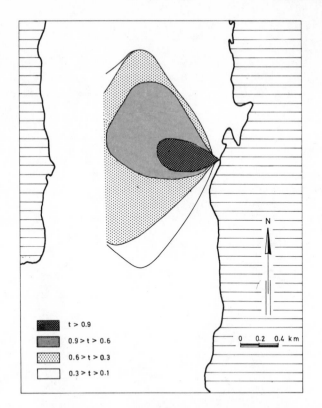

Figure 5   The relative occurrence (t) of
surface excess temperatures larger or
equal to 2°C.

The mathematical analysis is an extension of the methods
presented by Sundaram et.al. (1971) and Huber et.al. (1972).

The mathematical statement of the problem may be expressed as

$$\frac{\partial T}{\partial t} + \omega \frac{\partial T}{\partial z} = \frac{1}{A} \frac{\partial}{\partial z} \left(Af \frac{\partial T}{\partial z} \right) - \frac{q_i}{A} \left(T - T_i \right) \qquad (1)$$

where T is temperature, t is time, ω is vertical velocity, A
is the horizontal cross-section at any depth, f is the eddy
diffusion coefficient, q_i represents horizontal influx
across the sill per unit of vertical length, T_i is the
temperature of the incoming water and z is the vertical
coordinate.

The boundary conditions are:

$$-\rho cf \left(\frac{\partial T}{\partial z} \right) = H \left(T_e - T(0) \right) \qquad z=0 \qquad (2)$$

$$-\rho c f \left(\frac{\partial T}{\partial z}\right) = 0 \qquad z=z_{max} \qquad\qquad (3)$$

where H is the surface heat-exchange coefficient with the atmosphere, T_e is the socalled equilibrium temperature (Edinger et.al., 1968), c is the spesific heat of water, ρ is the density of the sea water and z_{max} (= 100 m) is the maximum depth used in the calculation. Further details about the analysis and numerical solution technique is given by Audunson et. al. (1974).

As already mentioned the applicability of the model was tested by comparing the numerical calculations to actual observations. Averaged monthly temperature observations from four years of observations (1962 - 1965) were used to form a yearly temperature cycle of the Vestfjord. Fig. 6 display the resulting temperature conditions. By and large the agreement is within 1.0°C.

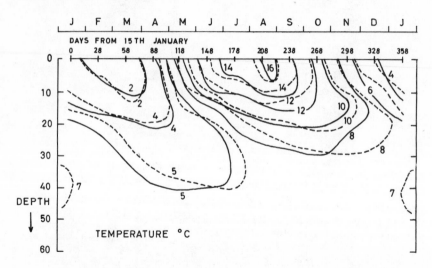

Figure 6   Isopleth diagram of computed (———)
and observed(----) temperature conditions in
the Vestfjord.

Measurements and calculations indicate (Audunson et.al., 1972) that a significant part of the cooling water discharge from a proposed 4000 MWe nuclear power plant located outside the sill, (i.e. at the mouth of a long (10 km) and narrow (2 km) sound connecting the Vestfjord and the outer waters) will be carried across the sill and into the Vestfjord. From March to October it is assumed that this enthalpy transport will mainly affect the surface layers of the Vestfjord. During the rest of the year, however, measurements show that the cooling water discharge can be expected to have the densities required for replacing the deeper waters of the Vestfjord.

As a consequence, waste heat from the proposed cooling-water
discharge may then also directly affect the temperature
conditions in the deeper layers of the fjord.

Proceeding then to the case at hand it is assumed that the
thermal discharges may be accounted for by proper modification
of the boundary conditions and of the source term of equation
1.   (Audunson et. al., 1974).   Calculations have been
carried out for an assumed cooling water discharge equivalent
of 8400 MW.   It is assumed that 50% of the waste heat is
actually transported across the sill.   The results of the
calculations are shown in fig. 7. which display the calculated
temperature variation at six depths in the Vestfjord with and
without any effect from the cooling-water discharge.   The
excess temperature varies with time and depth between $0.5^{\circ}C$
and $1.2^{\circ}C$ beeing on the average around $1^{\circ}C$.

It should, however, be kept in mind that these numerical
results give a deterministic description of the temperature
conditions in the area.   The "monthly" temperature, at any
depth, however, is observed to fluctuate, and may, therefore,
more correctly be regarded as a stochastic variable which
varies more or less randomly from year to year.

The temperature of the deeper water masses in a sill fjord as
the Vestfjord depends upon many factors such as the residence
time of the water, stratification, vertical mixing and the
temperature of incoming water.   It is important that the
amplitude of the temperature variations do not exceed the
tolerance levels of the marine population.   In the deeper
layers such tolerance limits may be narrow.

Temperature observations from as far back as the turn of the
century has been employed in order to estimate the standard
deviation of the monthly mean temperatures at various depths
from 40 m down to 120 m.   Fig. 8 shows the mean temperatures
corresponding to four months.   The amplitude of the standard
deviation is indicated by the dotted line.

Inspection of the data, furthermore, indicated that the
temperature fluctuations may be closely approximated by a
Gaussian distribution function (Audunson et.al., 1972).   In
the following we shall assume that the statistical
characteristics of the temperature fluctuations are unaffected
by the heated effluent.   The discharge-induced temperature
increase may, however, affect the rate of occurrence of
certain extreme temperatures at various depths.   Subject to
the above assumption it is then possible to estimate the
probability of certain temperature levels to be exceeded (for
example $9^{\circ}C$ og $8.5^{\circ}C$) when the mean temperature increases as

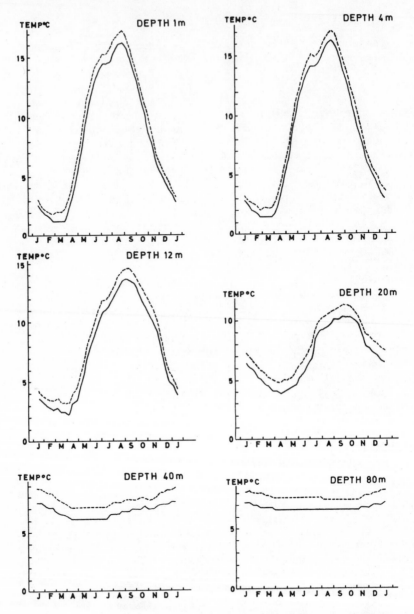

Figure 7   Calculated yearly temperatur cycles with
(---) and without (——) the thermal impact of a
cooling-water discharge.

shown in fig. 7.   The "period" of occurrence of such
temperature levels may be defined as the inverse of the above
probability.   The calculated periode of occurrence is shown
in fig. 9.

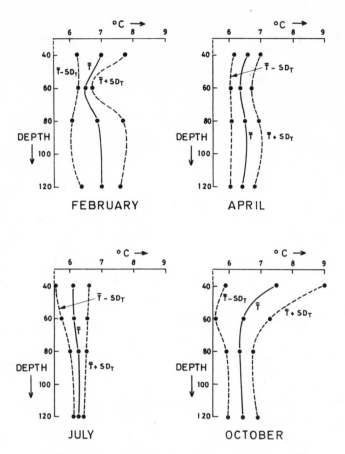

Figure 8   Monthly mean temperature ($\overline{T}$)
and standard deviation (SD_T).

Defining TSC as the relative increase in the probability of
certain temperature levels and G_m and G_u as the period of
occurrence of the same temperature levels with and without
the effect of thermal discharges respectively, we have that
TSC = (G_u/G_m). Examples of the calculations of G_m and TSC
values for two different temperatures at various times and
depths are given in Table 1 below.

The results thus underline the important fact that although
the mean temperature increase itself is only of the same
magnitude as the "natural" temperature fluctuations it induces
a rather pronounced effect on the periode of occurrence
(TSC-values) of certain perhaps biologically critical
temperature levels. It would seem, therefore, that this
indicates a meaningful and perhaps more correct way to
establish the longterm temperature impact of thermal

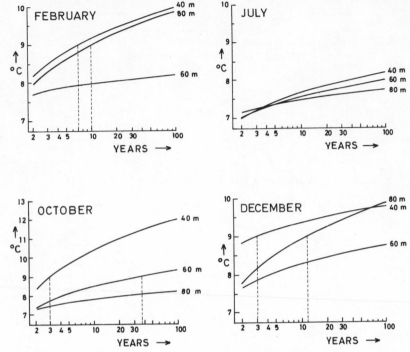

Figure 9   Period of occurrence for various temperatures
in the deeper waters of the Vestfjord, when subjected
to the thermal impact of a cooling meter discharge.

discharges into bodies of water with fluctuating temperature
conditions.

TABLE 1.   PERIOD OF OCCURRENCE AND TSC VALUES FOR TWO
TEMPERATURE LEVELS IN THE VESTFJORD

| Temp. | Month | DEPTH | | | | | |
| | | 40 m | | 60 m | | 80 m | |
		G_m	TSC	G_m	TSC	G_m	TSC
	February	7	>14	>100		>10	10
	July	>100		>100		>100	
	October	3	2	37	3	>100	
	December	3	>33	>100		12	>9
	February	3	12	>100		4	8
	July	>100		>100		>100	
	October	2	2	11	>9	>100	
	December	2	15	25	>4	5	9

REFERENCES

Audunson, T., Dahl, F.E., Jacobson, P. & Land, J. (1972)
Sammendrag av hydrofysiske resipientvurderinger ved byggesteds-
alternativene Brenntangen, Hurum og Vardeåsen (in Norwegian).
River and Harbour Laboratory at the Technical University of
Norway, Trondheim.

Audunson, T., Land, J. & Rye, H. (1974) Computations of the
Temperature Response of Stratified Sill Fjords to Cooling-
Water Discharges. IAIA, Oslo, 113-140.

Doret, S.C., Harleman, D.R.F., Ippen, A.T. & Pearce, B.R.
(1973) Characteristics of Condenser Water Discharge on the
Sea Surface (Correlation of Field Observations with Theory).
R.M. Parsqns Lab. for Water Resources & Hydrodynamics, Dep.
Civil Eng., MIT.

Edinger, J.E., Duttweiler, D.W. & Geyer, Y.C. (1968) The
Response of Water Temperatures to Meteorological Conditions.
Water Resources Research, Vol. 4, No.5: 1137.

Hawes, F.B., Coughlan, J. & Spencer, J.F. (1974)
Environmental Effects of the Heated Discharges from Bradwell
Nuclear Power Station, and of the Cooling Systems of other
Stations, IAEA, Oslo, 423-448.

Huber, W.C., Harleman, D.R.F. & Ryan, P.J. (1972) Temperature
Prediction in Stratified Reservoirs. J. Hydr. Div. ASCE,
Vol. 98, No. HY4:645.

Prych, E.A. (1972) A Warm Water Effluent analyzed as a
Buoyant Surface Jet. SMHI, serie Hydrologi, Stockholm.

Sundaram, T.R. & Rehm, R.G. (1971) The Effect of Thermal
Discharges on the Stratification Cycle of Lakes. AIAA Paper
No. 71-16.

THE ANATOMY OF THE MODELLING PROCESS

R. H. McCuen

Associate Professor Civil Engineering, University of Maryland
        College Park, Maryland   20742

INTRODUCTION

In the past, single-purpose projects have been used in solving
engineering and environmental problems, often because the
actual complexity of a problem was not recognized. Such solutions did not require sophisticated models and thus modelling
techniques were not developed. Because of this modelling remains more of an art than a science.

Solutions to most current environmental problems, however, are
usually not simple. Most "multi-purpose" solutions require a
rational and creative approach to problem-solving. A creative
approach is necessary because of the multiplicity and complexity of the interdependent processes affecting environmental
systems. Thus, the methodology of obtaining an optimal solution has been labeled the systems approach to problem-solving.
And modelling should be recognized as just one phase of the
systems approach to problem-solving.

But why the emphasis on modelling? Can't solutions to complex
problems be found using less formal procedures? To build a
case for modelling, one must consider the value of having a
model of a system. First, most systems and problems are
dynamic in nature; that is, systems and problems vary with
time. And one important consideration in comparing project
alternatives is the effect of changes in the system that
occur over a period of time. A second important consideration
is risk. To assess risk it is necessary to evaluate the effect of change in system components on the output. When
making a decision these evaluations of sensitivity and thus of
risk may be just as important as the specification of the
optimum solution itself. Third, in addition to predicting the
response of the system a model can be used to evaluate the
relative importance of subsystems and external factors that
influence the output. Fourth, verification of a model can

identify deficiencies in both model structure and the information (i.e., data base or resources) required to calibrate and
use the model. In summary, models provide a means of improving
decision-making capabilities and the basis for improved operations.

Because modelling is such an important aspect of problem-solving
and because models are being developed and used extensively in
analyzing almost all environmental problems, it is certainly
worthwhile to examine the role of modelling in the systems
approach to problem-solving. Means of classifying models are
also needed in order to compare models. Thus, before examining
some important aspects of the modelling process, these two
factors (i.e., classification of models and modelling as an
element of the systems approach) need to be discussed.

Modelling and the Systems Process

In recent years, there has been an extensive volume of research
concerning what has been termed systems analysis, systems
engineering, systems theory, etc. Because of the popularity
of this topic, a multitude of definitions have been proposed
for the concept of a system. In considering all of the proposed definitions, there appear to be six phases of the systems approach to problem-solving: 1) goals and objectives,
2) performance criteria, 3) alternatives, 4) resources and
constraints, 5) the modelling process, and 6) modes of decision.
The six components of the systems approach to problem-solving
are shown schematically in Figure 1.

It must naturally be assumed that a problem or potential problem has been identified. To alleviate the problem it is
necessary to formulate one or more goals, which characterize
the state of the system. Additionally, the problem and goals
lead to the specification of operational objectives. While
goals are broad statements of the problem, objectives are more
specific operational conditions that are to be achieved. After
formulating goals and objectives it is necessary to specify
criteria that can be used to measure the level of attainment
of the proposed goals and objectives. The criteria are used
in evaluating the feasibility of alternatives. In developing
a model the resources and constraints must be specified. Resources may include factors such as data and computer facilities while constraints, or negative resources, may be the lack
of data or monetary limitations. The model is the structure
by which resources and knowledge of the system are transformed
into a set of simulated system responses. The response of the
system to different states are then placed in a form used in
making decisions. These modes of decision may consist of
graphs, quantitative indices such as benefit-cost ratios or a
set of design standards. When the solution methodology is inadequate for achieving the desired goals, the systems approach

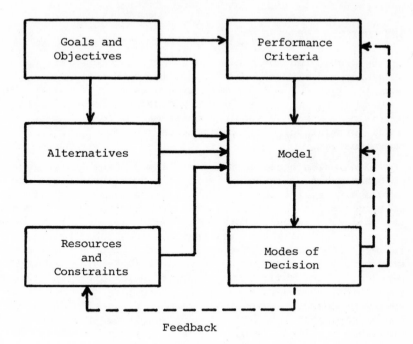

Figure 1.   The Systems Process

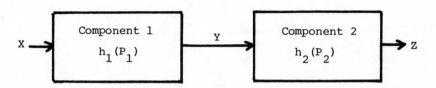

Figure 2.   Two-Component Model

may be iterative in that feedback may be required to improve
the model, acquire additional resources, or propose new alternatives.

THE MODELLING PROCESS

Having considered the goals and objectives, resources and constraints, and alternatives, a model must be developed to represent the system. A model usually proves most effective when
a systematic strategy is used to formulate the model. An
operational strategy should consist of the following phases:
model formulation, model calibration, and model verification
or validation.

The formulation phase of the modelling process is the most
important phase because an improperly formulated model can not
accurately predict the response of the system for a wide range
of values of state variables. To properly formulate a model,
the following three factors must be identified: 1) the most
important variables and processes, 2) the proper structure for
representing the system processes, and 3) the degree and
structure of interaction between variables and/or model components. These three factors may often be identified through
theoretical considerations of the principles governing the
system processes. However, it is more frequently necessary to
use an empirical approach. Several empirical techniques are
available for identifying the most important variables, including correlation analyses followed by principal component
and factor analyses, graphical comparisons of the relationships
between variables and curve fitting techniques. Those variables that do not have a direct cause-and-effect relationship
with the system output and are highly correlated with other
system variables should not be included in the model. Determining the degree and structure of the interaction between
variables and model components is the most difficult of the
above three factors to quantify. A comparison of sensitivity
estimates may provide some indication of the degree of interaction; determining the structure of interaction must often
be based on theoretical considerations.

A number of techniques exist for calibrating a model. If
possible, values for the model parameters should be based on
attributes of the system being modelled. When it is not
possible to synthesize model parameters using attributes of the
system, input-output observations of the system can be analyzed
to determine values for the parameters. However, because it
is difficult to systematically separate the variance in the
input-output data, it is very unlikely that the analysis of
input-output data will provide reliable estimates for more
than a few parameters of a system. Both analytical and numerical techniques exist for the analysis of input-output data.

In order to use a model for either planning or design, the
model should be properly verified. Model verification consists

of a rational analysis of both the computed output and any
empirically derived parameters. If the output vector and/or
parameter values are not rational in either sign or magnitude
then the structure of the model and/or the optimization strategy should be reevaluated. Additionally, to provide a proper
verification, the computed model output should be compared with
output observations of the system. Data used in this phase of
model verification should preferably be data other than that
used in calibrating the model; one would naturally expect the
calibrated model to provide a good fit of the data used in the
calibration phase.

CLASSIFICATION OF MODELS

A means of classifying models may be of value in comparing
models designed for similar purposes. However, because of the
large number of cross-classifications currently used and the
lack of well-defined limits to each classification, categories
for classifying models may be of little value. And individual
components of a single model may be classified differently.
Some commonly used dichotomous categories include: 1) deter-
ministic-stochastic, 2) linear-nonlinear, 3) static-dynamic,
4) iconic-symbolic, and 5) time invariant-time varying.

A deterministic model is one whose output vector is the same
for any given input vector while the output vector from a
stochastic model may vary from one execution to the next even
for the same input vector. A linear model is one which satisfies the principle of superpositioning. A static, or zero-
memory system is one in which the output vector depends only
on the input vector at the time of occurrence of the response;
systems which provide for storage of information are said to
by dynamic. Iconic or material models are scaled transformations of the system while symbolic models use mathematical and/
or logical symbols to represent the processes and interrela-
tionships of the system. The output vector from a time-invari-
ant linear system will not vary in time for a given input vector while the output vector for a time-varying linear system
will depend on both the input and the time at which the input
is applied to the system.

These methods of classification provide an understanding of
the structure of the model. Models can also be classified
according to their purpose and their method of calibration.
Probably the most important means of classification is the purpose of a model. Models developed for planning usually have
characteristics different from those of models formulated for
design or analysis of a specific system. However, since these
two classifications of purpose are not always distinct, it
should be recognized that any one model does not have to be
classified as either a planning model or a design model.

Planning models are usually not very sophisticated in structure

because their primary use is for developing a solution strategy and selecting a group of feasible alternatives that need to
be studied in more detail. Since planning models are usually
designed for use in the initial stage of project development
and are thus used to examine the feasibility of a large number
of project alternatives, the models must be capable of examining any one alternative in a short period of time; otherwise,
the model would not be economically feasible. Because of
their lack of detail, planning models may be of limited use in
the design stage of a project or in identifying the relative
importance of an individual subsystem or an input vector.

Design models, however, are characterized by complex structures
because they are formulated to analyze the feasibility of a
limited number of design alternatives and to identify the relative importance of individual subsystems and input vectors.
Because they are usually formulated specifically for use on a
single project, design models are not as transferable as
planning models. Furthermore, because of their level of sophistication, design models require more input data and specifications of the system than the less sophisticated planning
models. Such information (i.e., input data and system specifications) is usually required for both model calibration and
model verification. If the parameters of a design model can
be determined from theoretical considerations and knowledge of
the system then input and output data would not be required to
calibrate the model. However, only rarely can parameters of a
design model be calibrated without analyzing input and output
data.

The mode of calibration can also be used in classifying models.
Both analytical and numerical techniques exist for calibrating
models. Analytical calibration is based on mathematical techniques and provide explicit values for the model parameters.
However, analytical calibration techniques are usually available only for models of simple structure. Numerical calibration usually involves iterative procedures to test a vector of
state variable conditions. Because an explicit solution is
not obtained, the global optimum vector of parameters requires
the use of a comprehensive calibration strategy. Because of
their generality, numerical techniques are usually capable of
calibrating models with structures more complex than those
calibrated using analytical optimization methods.

MATHEMATICAL FOUNDATIONS OF SENSITIVITY

Why is the concept of sensitivity so important for understanding the modelling process? It should be recognized
that variability is fundamental to all phases of the
modelling process; and, sensitivity is one measure of
variability. For a model to respond in a manner similar
to that of the system, the model must be formulated to reflect
variability in the system response. In model calibration
the determination of the vector of optimal coefficients

is based on the change in the objective function for changes
in the unknown coefficients. And when using a verified model
to identify the relative importance of various characteristics
of a system, the relative importance is usually based on some
measure of the variability of the system response to changes
in characteristics of the system. Thus, since sensitivity is
a means of measuring variability it is one of the most important concepts in modelling.

Definition: Sensitivity is the rate of change in one factor
with respect to change in another factor. Although such a
definition is vague in terms of the factors involved, it
nevertheless implies a quotient of two differentials. Stres-
sing the nebulosity of the definition is important because,
in practice, the sensitivity of model parameters is rarely
recognized as a special case of the concept of sensitivity.
The failure to recognize the generality of sensitivity has
been partially responsible for the limited use of sensitivity
as a tool for the formulation and verification of models. The
intent of this section is to develop a general mathematical
framework of sensitivity that is applicable in all phases of
the modelling process.

The Sensitivity Equation: The general definition of sensitivity can be expressed in mathematical form by considering
a Taylor series expansion of the explicit function:

$$F_o = x(F_1, F_2, \ldots, F_n) \tag{1}$$

The change in factor F_o resulting from change in factor F_i is
given by:

$$x(F_i + \Delta F_i, F_j \big|_{j \neq i}) = F_o + \frac{\partial F_o}{\partial F_i} \Delta F_i + \frac{1}{2!} \frac{\partial^2 F_o}{\partial F_i^2} \Delta F_i^2 + \ldots \tag{2}$$

If the nonlinear terms are small incomparison with the linear
terms, equation 2 reduces to:

$$x(F_i + \Delta F_i, F_j \big|_{j \neq i}) = F_o + \frac{\partial F_o}{\partial F_i} \Delta F_i \tag{3}$$

Thus:

$$\Delta F_o = x(F_i + \Delta F_i, F_j \big|_{j \neq i}) - F_o = (\partial F_o / \partial F_i) \Delta F_i \tag{4}$$

Equation 4 is referred to herein as the linearized sensitivity
equation. It approximates the change in factor F_o that results
from change in factor F_i. The linearized sensitivity equation
can be extended to the case where more than one parameter is
changed simultaneously. The general definition of sensitivity

is derived from equations 1 and 4:

$$S = \partial F_o / \partial F_i = [x(F_i + \Delta F_i, F_j|_{j \neq i}) - x(F_1, F_2, \ldots, F_n)] / \Delta F_i \qquad (5)$$

Computational Methods: The general definition of sensitivity, which is expressed in mathematical form by equation 5, suggests two methods of computation. The left-hand side of equation 5 suggests that the sensitivity of factor F_o to changes in factor F_i can be estimated by differentiating the explicit relationship of equation 1 with respect to factor F_i:

$$S = \partial F_o / \partial F_i \qquad (6)$$

The direct method of differentiation has not been used extensively for analyzing environmental models because the mathematical framework of sensitivity has not been sufficiently developed.

The method of factor perturbation, which is the second computational method suggested by equation 5, is the more commonly used method in engineering analyses. The right-hand side of equation 5 indicates that the sensitivity of F_o to change in F_i can be derived by incrementing F_i and computing the resulting change in the solution F_o. The sensitivity is the ratio of the two differentials and can be expressed in finite difference form:

$$S = \Delta F_o / \Delta F_i = [x(F_i + \Delta F_i, F_j|_{j \neq i}) - x(F_1, F_2, \ldots, F_n)] / \Delta F_i \qquad (7)$$

Parametric and Component Sensitivity: A simplified system or a component of a more complex system is described by three functions: the input vector, the output vector and the system response function. The response function is the function that transforms the input vector into the output vector and is often defined by a distribution that depends on one or more parameters. In the past, sensitivity analyses of models have been limited to measuring the effect of parametric variations on the output vector. Such analyses focus on the output vector and response function. Using the form of equation 5 parametric sensitivity can be mathematically expressed as:

$$S_{P_i} = \frac{\partial \emptyset}{\partial P_i} = \frac{x(P_i + \Delta P_i, P_j|_{j \neq i}) - x(P_1, P_2, \ldots, P_n)}{\Delta P_i}$$

where $\emptyset$ represents the output vector and P_i is the parameter under considertion.

Unfortunately, the general concept of sensitivity has been overshadowed by parametric sensitivity. As models have become

more complex the derivation of parametric sensitivity estimates have become increasingly more difficult, and most often
impossible, to compute. However, by considering the input and
output vectors the general definition of sensitivity, equation
5, can be used to derive a new form of sensitivity. Component
sensitivity measures the effect of variation in the input
vector I on the output vector $\emptyset$:

$$S_c \equiv \frac{\partial \emptyset}{\partial I} = \frac{\Delta \emptyset}{\Delta I} \tag{9}$$

Combining component and parametric sensitivity functions
makes it feasible to estimate the sensitivity of parameters
of complex models. For example, in the two component model
of Figure 2 the sensitivity of Y to variation in P_1 and the
sensitivity of Z to variation in P_2 are readily computed
using sensitivity as defined by equation 7:

$$S_1 = \partial Y / \partial P_1 \quad \text{and} \quad S_2 = \partial Z / \partial P_2 \tag{10}$$

However, the sensitivity of the output from component 2 to
change in the parameter of component 1 can not always be
estimated directly from the differential $\partial Z / \partial P_1$. In such
cases, the component sensitivity function of component 2
can be used with the parametric sensitivity function S_1 to
estimate the sensitivity of Z to change in P_1. Specifically,
the sensitivity $\partial Z / \partial P_1$ equals the product of the component
sensitivity function $\partial Z / \partial Y$ and the parametric sensitivity
function $\partial Y / \partial P_1$:

$$\partial Z / \partial P_1 = (\partial Z / \partial Y) \cdot (\partial Y / \partial P_1) \tag{11}$$

Whereas the differentials $\partial Z / \partial Y$ and $\partial Y / \partial P_1$ are often easily
derived, an explicit sensitivity function $\partial Z / \partial P_1$ can be
computed only for very simple models.

Absolute and Relative Sensitivity: Sensitivity can be expressed in two forms: absolute and relative. The form in
which sensitivity values are presented depends on the intended
use. Sensitivity values computed with the definition of
equation 5 are in absolute form. Such a definition is inappropriate for the comparison of sensitivity values because
values computed using equation 5 are not invariant to the
magnitude of either factor F_o or F_i. Dividing the numerator
of equation 5 by F_o and the denominator by F_i provides an
estimate of the relative change in F_o with respect to a relative change in F_i:

$$R_S = \frac{\partial F_o / F_o}{\partial F_i / F_I} = \frac{\partial F_o}{\partial F_i} \cdot \frac{F_i}{F_o} \tag{12}$$

Relative sensitivity values are invariant to the magnitude of F_o and F_i and thus, provide a valid means for comparing factor sensitivity.

A Correspondence Between Sensitivity and Correlation: The Pearson product-moment correlation coefficient R is used as a measure of the linear association between two random variables:

$$R = (\Sigma xy)/ \sqrt{\Sigma x^2 \Sigma y^2} \qquad (13)$$

where x is the difference between the random variable X and the mean value $\overline{X}$, and y is the difference between Y and $\overline{Y}$. The square of the correlation coefficient represents the pro-portion of the variance in Y that can be attributed to its linear regression on X.

Least squares regression analysis is commonly used to derive a linear relationship between two random variables. There is a strong structural similarity between correlation analysis and regression analysis. The linear regression coefficient b can be determined from the correlation coefficient and the standard deviations of X and Y:

$$b = \Sigma xy/\Sigma x^2 = RS_y/S_x \qquad (14)$$

Equation 14 suggests that for values of R near one changes in X will produce comparatively large changes in Y.

For a linear regression equation relating two random variables the sensitivity of the dependent variate Y to variation in the independent variate X can be determined by differentiating the regression equation with respect to X:

$$\partial Y/\partial X = b \qquad (15)$$

Equation 15 indicates that the regression coefficient repre-sents the rate of change in Y with respect to change in X. Furthermore, equations 14 and 15 suggest that there is a direct correspondence between correlation and sensitivity.

Multiple-effect Sensitivity: In many cases it is desirable to examine the effect of simultaneous changes of two or more parameters or elements of the system input vector. For example, urban development often results in simultaneous changes in land uses; increases in impervious land uses must be accompa-nied by decreases in pervious land uses. Such multiple-effect changes can be measured using a Taylor series expansion in-volving change in more than one variable; a Taylor's expansion of a function F(x, y, Z) is given by:

$$f(x+\Delta x, y+\Delta y, Z) = f(x,y,Z) + (\Delta x \frac{\partial f}{\partial x} + \Delta y \frac{\partial f}{\partial y})$$

$$+ \frac{1}{2!} (\Delta x \frac{\partial f}{\partial x} + \Delta y \frac{\partial f}{\partial y})^2 + \ldots +$$

$$\frac{1}{(n-1)!} (\Delta x \frac{\partial f}{\partial x} + \Delta y \frac{\partial f}{\partial y})^{n-1} + R_n \qquad (16)$$

where x and y are variables whose values are changed simultaneously, Z is a vector of variables whose values are not changed, Δx and Δy are the changes in x and y, respectively, and R_n is the remainder term, which is usually assumed to be negligible. If the nonlinear terms of third order and higher are considered negligible then equation 16 reduces to:

$$f(x+\Delta x, y+\Delta y, Z) = f(x,y,Z) + (\Delta x \frac{\partial f}{\partial x} + \Delta y \frac{\partial f}{\partial y}) +$$

$$[\frac{\Delta x^2}{2!} (\frac{2f}{2x})^2 + \frac{\Delta x \Delta y}{2!} \frac{\partial^2 f}{\partial x \partial y} + \frac{\Delta y^2}{2!} (\frac{\partial f}{\partial y})^2] \qquad (17)$$

If the differentials are determined numerically the term $2^2f/2x2y$ can be approximated by:

$$\frac{\partial^2 f}{\partial x \partial y} = \frac{f(x+\Delta x, y+\Delta y, Z) - f(x-\Delta x, y+\Delta y, Z) - f(x+\Delta x, y-\Delta y, Z) + f(x-\Delta x, y-\Delta y, Z)}{4\Delta x \Delta y} \qquad (18)$$

Equation 18 can be used to determine the effect of simultaneous changes in two parameters. It is also useful for estimating the degree of interaction between variables.

SENSITIVITY AS A TOOL IN MODELLING

The use of sensitivity analysis in model calibration is well documented. It forms the basis for most numerical optimization techniques, such as steepest ascent and pattern search. But the potential value of sensitivity analyses in the formulation and verification of models is often not recognized.

Sensitivity in Model Formulation

As indicated previously, three factors are important in formulating a model: 1) identifying the processes and variables to include in the model, 2) determining the proper structure for representing the system processes, and 3) specifying the degree and structure of interaction between variables and processes within the model. If observations of the system response are available, it is often possible to use the mathematical concepts previously discussed to identify those processes and variables that have the most significant effect on the response of the system. The component sensitivity concept expressed in the relative form of equation 12 can be used to rank the individual processes in order of importance.

The structure of a model component will determine the change
in the response of the component to change in state variables,
and thus, an improperly formulated structure may lead to
improper decisions. Specifically, the use of a linear structure to represent a process implies that the response of that
process, say Y, is proportional to the state variable X:

$$Y = bX$$

where b is a proportionality constant. Therefore, regardless
of the level of X, a unit change in X causes a change of b
units in Y. If the response Y depends on the state of the
process X then a structure that is nonlinear in the state
variable will be more realistic. For example, the structure

$$Y = cX^d$$

indicates that for a unit change in X, Y will be changed by
cdX^{d-1}. Thus, the change in Y depends on the state of the
system X as well as the structural coefficients c and d.

Sensitivity in Model Verification   To properly verify a model,
the response of the model should be compared to observed data
and all calibrated coefficients should by checked for ration-
ality in both sign and magnitude. However, when observed
input data is inadequate or not available it is often necessary
to use input data that was generated synthetically. Using
either the observed or synthetic input data the response of
the model should be compared to the observed response of the
system. And synthetic input data can be used to examine the
response of the system during critical states of the system.
The change in the model response to either input traces or
model parameters is useful for verifying the model structure.
These sensitivity estimates are often used to assess the
relative importance of the processes and variables under a
variety of states of the system.

CONCLUSIONS

Modelling should be recognized as a valuable decision-making
tool that is both an art and a science. Science has provided
information indicating the theoretical relationship between
variables and processes. But modelling requires the investi-
gator to select the important processes and formulate
relationships to represent these processes. When scientific
evidence does not provide knowledge of the true relationships,
the artistic aspect of modelling surfaces. The techniques
discussed herein provide a means of obtaining the maximum
possible information from observed data and thus provide a
basis for formulating a rational representation of the system.

RANDOM SEARCH OPTIMIZATION : STOPPING RULES

P. Thoft-Christensen

Professor, Aalborg University Center, Aalborg, Denmark

INTRODUCTION

During the last twenty years or so the theory of non-linear optimization has undergone a development making it more usable for engineers, scientists etc.. The interest in application of modern optimization techniques is considerable, primarily as a result of the development of modern computers. Only very simple optimization problems can be solved by classical methods without rather extensive numerical calculations.

Most optimization techniques to day are of the so-called iterative type, that is the optimum point is approached by a step by step method. As usual when using a numerical method the intention is to get an approximate solution and if possible to evaluate the degree of approximation. In almost all methods used it is necessary to specify a way to terminate the iterative process. It turns out that the stopping rule or termination criterion is of great importance for the effectiveness of an iterative method, so it is strange that stopping rules seems to be a neglected research area. In particular for multimodal functions where more than one optimum point exists a good choise of termination criterion is essential.

With the non-linear optimization techniques available now unimodal problems can be handled with a satisfactory result in most cases although it can be difficult for a user to choose between the great number of methods. Only in some very special cases problems arises.

But in the case of multimodal functions serious problems are obvious and only some of these problems are partly solved. Further it is often impossible for a user of optimization theory to make out whether his objective function is unimodal or multimodal.

In this paper stopping rules will be discussed with reference to a recently presented very simple optimization strategy based on random search.

OPTIMIZATION TECHNIQUES

In this paper the discussions will for the sake of simplicity be restricted to unconstrained parameter optimization problems, that is the problem of finding minimum
(or maximum) for the so-called CRITERION FUNCTION

$$F : R^n \rightarrow R. \tag{1}$$

The ordered set of n parameters $\bar{x}_o \in R^n$ is called a
GLOBAL MINIMUM for the function F, if

$$F(\bar{x}) \geq F(\bar{x}_o) \text{ for all } \bar{x} \in R^n. \tag{2}$$

If there exists a neighbourhood $\omega(\bar{x}_o)$ of the point $\bar{x}_o$ so
that

$$F(\bar{x}) \geq F(\bar{x}_o) \text{ for all } \bar{x} \in \omega(\bar{x}_o) \tag{3}$$

then $\bar{x}_o$ is called a LOCAL MINIMUM for the function F.

It is outside the intention with this paper to give a review
of methods of optimization. Excellent presentations and
discussions of widely used methods are given in the
books by A. LAVI and T. P. VOGL (1966), F. A. LOOTSMA
(1972), S. L. S. JACOBY, J. S. KOWALIK and J. T. PIZZO
(1972) and many others. As mentioned earlier most methods have one very serious drawback, namely that they
only work satisfactory if the criterion function F is unimodal. If the starting point for an iterative method is
outside of the field of influence of the global optimum for
a multimodal function there exists a risk that methods
based on gradient techniques only will disclose a local
optimum. As the main objective by most methods is to
arrive in the nearest minimum as fast as possible the iteration has to be initiated from a number of different starting points if the criterion function is multimodal. This
local-global problem has only been attacked by few research workers. It is usually believed that random search
methods in this connexion have some potentials not yet
fully investigated. The strategy by P. THOFT-CHRISTEN-
SEN and U. HARTMANN (1974) is a creeping random
search method based on a combination of local and global
search technique. The method is compared with other

random search methods in a paper by P. THOFT-CHRI-STENSEN (1975).

The basic principle in creeping random search is very simple. A starting point $\bar{x}_0$ is chosen and a new point $\bar{x}_1 = \bar{x}_0 + \overline{\Delta x}_0$ is determined in a way depending of the strategy used. If $F(\bar{x}_1) < F(\bar{x}_0)$ the step $\overline{\Delta x}_0$ is called a success and the point $\bar{x}_1$ is used as starting point for the next step, etc.. If $F(\bar{x}_1) \geq F(\bar{x}_0)$ the step $\overline{\Delta x}_0$ is called a failure and it is replaced by a new step until a success takes place. In the strategy by P. THOFT-CHRISTENSEN and U. HARTMANN two types of steps is used namely LO-CAL and GLOBAL steps. The intention with the local steps is to obtain a high degree of convergence to the nearest minimum not depending on whether it is a global or a local minimum. So the stepsize for a local step is "rather" small. On the contrary the global steps are not limited in size as their purpose only is to escape from a local minimum by making sufficiently large steps. The global steps must be arranged so that any point in the feasible region can be reached.

The local part of the algorithm is arranged in the following way. First a starting point is chosen random. Then some trial steps are taken with different step-sizes and with a directional adaptation so that the direction of the last successful step is given a preference. When a pre-scribed number of successful steps are carried out a global trial step follows. Here a stochastic local search has been employed but almost any of the non-random me-thods mentioned above can be used. The choise of term-ination criterion for this local part will be discussed later.

As the intention with the global steps is to be able to reach any point in the feasible region no information con-cerning a "good" direction can be given in general. There-fore the stepsize and the direction for a global step is chosen random. In this way a prescribed number of global steps are made until an improvement may happen. In such a case the new point is used as starting point for a new set of local steps. Otherwise further local steps are made from the same point but now with new directions and step-sizes. The procedure described above continues until a predescribed number of successful steps has occured or until no further improvements by local steps can be found within the stopping rule used.

The algorithm sketched above has with some success been used on several testfunctions with a considerable number of parameters. One of the conclusions based on these experiments is that the choise of stopping rules for both the local and the global part is a crucial one. It was

therefore decided to look closer at the problems connected
with stopping rules. In the next sections a discussion of
stopping rules will be given in relation to the algorithm
above. The results are only preliminary as the investigation is not closed. It is therefore not possible to make final conclusive statements concerning these important
questions.

STOPPING RULES

It is emphasized by several authors that slight changes in
the termination criteria makes a big difference in the
performance of an algorithm (see e.g. D.M.HIMMELBLAU
(1972)). In the same paper by D.M.HIMMELBLAU it is
also emphasized that more than one stopping rule usually
must be used to take care of specific characteristics by
some functions. Below some very often used stopping rules
are presented and some of their advantages and disadvantages are discussed.

Stopping rules based on functionvalues $F(\bar{x})$
In the litterature one will often find that the fractional
change in the functionvalue $F(\bar{x})$ is used as a stopping rule.
In an iterative process the functionvalues $F(\bar{x})$ are
evaluated at a sequence of points $\bar{x}_1, \bar{x}_2, \ldots, \bar{x}_i, \bar{x}_{i+1}, \ldots$

It will therefore be natural to use stopping rules of the
following types:

$$\left| F(\bar{x}_{i+1}) - F(\bar{x}_i) \right| < \varepsilon \qquad (4)$$

$$\left| \frac{F(\bar{x}_{i+1}) - F(\bar{x}_i)}{F(\bar{x}_i)} \right| < \varepsilon \qquad (5)$$

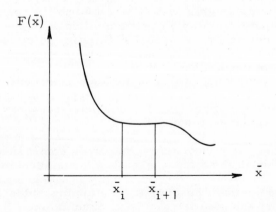

Unfortunately such stopping rules will terminate prematurely on a flat plateau. The same situation will arise by any stopping rule based on differences between functionvalues $F(\bar{x}_{i+1}) - F(\bar{x}_i)$. Further in case of a flat minimum the algorithm may terminate too far-away from the exact minimumpoint $\bar{x}^*$.

Stopping rules based on the parameters $\bar{x}$

A simple way to remove the disadvantages by using the stopping rules defined in equations (4) and (5) is to use stopping rules of the following types

$$| \bar{x}_{i+1} - \bar{x}_i | < \varepsilon \tag{6}$$

$$\left| \frac{\bar{x}_{i+1} - \bar{x}_i}{\bar{x}_i} \right| < \varepsilon \tag{7}$$

But such stopping rules based on $| \bar{x}_{i+1} - \bar{x}_i |$ will

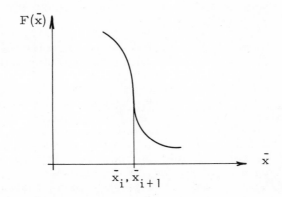

terminate prematurely on a very steep slope. A combination of stopping rules based on functionvalues and the parameters x may be a usable solution.

Stopping rules based on the gradient vector $\nabla F(\bar{x})$

If the gradient vector

$$\nabla F(\bar{x}) = \left(\frac{\partial F(\bar{x})}{\partial x_1} , \cdots , \frac{\partial F(\bar{x})}{\partial x_n} \right) \tag{8}$$

exists, it is likely that it can be used as a stopping rule because a necessary condition for $\bar{x}$ to be local minimum point for the differentiable function F is, that $\nabla F(\bar{x}) = \bar{o}$. The stopping rule

$$| \nabla F(\bar{x}) | \; < \; \varepsilon \qquad\qquad (9)$$

is often used in connexion with the stopping rules (6) or (7)
(see e.g. R.W.H.SARGENT and D.J.SEBASTIAN (1972)).
If the stopping rule (9) is used solely it has the same de-
fiencies as the stopping rules (4) and (5).

Stopping rules based on the number of functionvalue calculations

The number of functionvalue calculations can be of decisive
importance in some optimization problems when the objective function is very complicated. To keep the computertime down it is in such cases necessary to stop the iterative process when a prescribed number of functionvalue
calculations have taken place. It is important to have in
mind that such a stopping rule can be effective far-away
from the minimum point, so it must be used together with
a stopping rule, which can secure the minimum.

It may be a good idea when attacking a new optimization
problem to use stopping rules based on the number of
functionvalue calculations to encircle a good starting point
for the iterative process.

For an optimization strategy based on random search it is
in most cases necessary to use a stopping rules of this
type.

Stopping rules based on the number of successful steps

When using an optimization strategy based on random
search a great number of trial steps will be failures. The
number of successful steps will therefore of course be less
than the number of functionvalue calculations. So a particular stopping rule based on the number of successful
steps is not relevant as a protection against using too
much computertime if a stopping rule based on the number of functionvalue calculations already is used.

However, when both local and global search are used, as in
the algorithm presented above, it may be appropriate to
aim at a certain number of successful local steps before
a global step is taken. The interaction between the local
and global steps will be treated more detailed in the next
chapter.

RANDOM SEARCH

In the last chapter a number of stopping rules was presented and some of their advantages and disadvantages was
discussed. When the objective function is unimodal and a
non-random optimization method is used the main problem
in relation to stopping rules is to choose the values for

the numbers ε in the termination criteria. At least two stopping rules must be used to prevent the algorithm to terminate prematurely. It is in general possible to get a good solution of the optimization problem by choosing small numbers for ε but the numerical calculations may then be rather expensive. So the ε-values must be choosen as a compromise between the desire to get a good solution and the limitations in computer time.

However in the case of a multimodal function it is clear that the use of small ε-values will not guarantee that the algorithm will end up with a good solution. It will only secure that a good local minimum is determined. In this chapter stopping rules for random search methods will be discussed in relation to the specific strategy sketched above. The special idea behind this strategy is the use of local and global steps. But some of the considerations here will also be of interest for other random methods and for non-random methods when used on multimodal functions.

The main problem concerning the local steps is the following. The local steps should be choosen in such a way that the convergency to the local minimum is fast. But it is a waste of computer time to get very close to the minimum point if it is only a local minimum. If the local search is very close to the minimum point it may be difficult to escape from it. On the other hand it is inexpedient to leave a local minimum if it is the global minimum as it may be difficult to come back to it again. So the local search should be so arranged that it ends up relative close to the local minimum point with respect to the functionvalue. That is the stopping rules based on functionvalues should be used with not too small ε-values. Later when the global minimum is encircled one can always use a smaller ε-value and combine the stopping rule with one based on the parameters $\bar{x}$.

As mentioned earlier the intention with the global steps is to be able to escape from a local minimum. The global part of the algorithm should be arranged in such a way that any point of the feasible region can be inspected. The number of trial global steps will therefore depend of the type of the feasible region to secure a reasonable covering of the region. So it is reasonable to let the search by global steps terminates by a stopping rule based on the number of trial steps that is the number of functionvalue calculations. It is important to remember that in general it is impossible to be sure that the global minimum point is disclosed.

A number of tests with the strategy by P. Thoft-Christensen and U. Hartmann has been carried out with combi-

nations of stopping rules based on the number of functionvalue calculations and stopping rules based on the number
of successful steps. In a typical experiment with the
function

$$F(x, y, z) = 2 - e^{-\frac{1}{4\pi} \sqrt{x^2 + y^2 + z^2}} \cdot \cos x \cdot \cos y \cdot \cos z \quad (10)$$

the starting point was $(-1, 10, 10)$. After 18 successful
steps the search was catched by a local minimum
$(F = 1.458)$. A successful global step was then taken and
a better local minimum $(F = 1.296)$ was disclosed in 11
successful steps. Finaly a global step made it possible to
reach the global minimum $(F = 1.000)$ in 30 steps. The
experience from several experiments with this strategy
shows clearly that the number of global trial steps compared with the number of successful local steps is of very
great importance. As the examination of this problem is
not finished yet it is not possible to go into further details
here. But it seems to be advantageous to use a combination of stopping rules based on the number of functionvalue calculations and stopping rules based on the number
of successful steps and perhaps finish the search with
stopping rules based on functionvalues and parameters $\bar{x}$.

CONCLUSIONS

As the problem of choosing relevant and effective stopping rules not is solved yet there is a great need for
more research in this area. First of all it is important
when random optimization methods is used to get more
experimental experience. The strategy by which the random steps are choosen is important in this connextion.
Therefore the combination of probability distributions and
stopping rules must be theoretical and experimental investigated.

REFERENCES

Himmelblau, D.M. (1972) A uniform evaluation of unconstrained optimization techniques, pp. 69-97 in F.A. Lootsma (1972).

Jacoby, S.L.S., J.S. Kowalik and J.T. Pizzo (1972) Iterative
methods for nonlinear optimization problems, Prentice-
Hall, Englewood Cliffs.

Lavi, A. and T.P. Vogl (1966) Recent advances in optimization techniques, John Wiley and Sons, N.Y.

Lootsma, F.A. (1972) Numerical methods for non-linear
optimization, Academic Press, London.

Sargent, R. W. H. and D. J. Sebastian (1972) Numerical experience with algorithms for unconstrained minimization, pp. 45-68 in F. A. Lootsma (1972).

Thoft-Christensen, P. and U. Hartmann (1974) A strategy of optimization based on random search, Stochastic Control Symposium, Budapest, Hungary, september 1974, pp. 297-303.

Thoft-Christensen, P. (1975) Application of stochastic methods in optimization, VII International Congress on the Application of Mathematics in Engineering, Weimar, DDR, june 1975.

ON THE ACCURACY OF SOLUTIONS OF THE NAVIER-STOKES EQUATIONS
FOR UNSTEADY VISCOUS FLOW AT HIGH REYNOLDS NUMBERS

T. Bratanow, H. Aksu, T.J. Spehert, G.A. Exner

University of Wisconsin - Milwaukee, U.S.A.

INTRODUCTION

As the governing differential equations of fluid dynamics, the
Navier-Stokes equations are suitable for the solution of a remarkable variety of problems; from the complicated time-dependent motions in winds within the atmosphere to the problem of
motion of an aircraft. The Navier-Stokes equations are the most
frequently applied approximation of the nonlinear Boltzmann
equation for molecular transport. From the point of view of
physics, they are very complicated and to present time there is
no general method developed for their integration (Chapman et.
al., 1975).

There has been a need for efficient routine analysis of
pressure and velocity distributions about complex configurations in unsteady flows at high Reynolds numbers. From a research point of view, it has also become increasingly important
to deduce accurate results of unsteady flow characteristics
from the Navier-Stokes equations for the overall flow field. A
popular approach for computer flow simulation has been the modelling of the flow field by grid points or finite elements. In
the finite difference method the governing differential equations are approximated by corresponding finite difference equations for the gridwork. In general, for accuracy in finite difference computation, a very large number of closely spaced grid
points is required.

Some of the factors and parameters contributing to the accuracy of finite element solutions of the Navier-Stokes equations are examined and discussed.

MATHEMATICAL BACKGROUND

The governing differential equations of motion for the analysis of two-dimensional incompressible viscous flow are

$$\frac{\partial \underline{u}}{\partial t} + (\underline{u} \cdot \nabla)\underline{u} = \frac{1}{\rho} \underline{F} - \frac{1}{\rho} \nabla p + \nu \nabla^2 \underline{u} \tag{1}$$

$$\nabla \cdot \underline{u} = 0 \tag{2}$$

Equations (1) are the Navier-Stokes equations and Eq. (2) is the continuity condition. A direct solution of Eqs. (1) and (2) can be obtained for the primitive variables $(\underline{u}, p)$. The stream function-vorticity interpretation of the Navier-Stokes equations is given as

$$\nabla^2 \psi = -\omega \tag{3}$$

and

$$\frac{\partial \omega}{\partial t} + (\underline{u} \cdot \nabla)\omega = \nu \nabla^2 \omega \tag{4}$$

where the stream function and the vorticity are defined as

$$[\psi_y \quad -\psi_x] = \underline{u} \qquad\qquad \omega = \nabla \times \underline{u} \tag{5}$$

Equations (3) and (4) can be combined into another form in terms of the stream function as

$$\frac{\partial \nabla^2 \psi}{\partial t} + \psi_y \frac{\partial \nabla^2 \psi}{\partial x} - \psi_x \frac{\partial \nabla^2 \psi}{\partial y} = \nu \nabla^4 \psi \tag{6}$$

The left hand sides of Eqs. (1),(4), and (6) contain inertia terms and the right hand sides describe the viscous dissipation. At high Reynolds numbers the inertia forces are much larger in comparison with the viscous forces. However, the viscous forces cannot be neglected because they preserve the essential characteristics of the Navier-Stokes equations. Euler's equation for ideal fluids can be obtained from Eq. (6) by neglecting the viscous terms.

The instantaneous pressure distribution for a given velocity distribution can be determined from

$$\nabla^2 p = 2\rho(u_x v_y - u_y v_x) \tag{7}$$

The presented analysis of unsteady flow consists of the simultaneous solution of Eqs. (3) and (4).

FINITE ELEMENT FORMULATION

The general boundary conditions for an arbitrarily shaped obstacle subjected to an arbitrary motion in a flow field with a free stream velocity are given in Table I. The solution domain used in the finite element discretization and the coordinate systems are shown in Figure 1.

Table I. Applied Boundary Conditions for the Governing Equations.

Obstacle Boundary Conditions			Outer Boundary Conditions		
Stream Function	Vorticity	Pressure	Stream Function	Vorticity	Pressure
ψ = constant $\left.\begin{array}{l}\psi_x =\\ \psi_y =\end{array}\right\}$ Instantaneous Velocity of Obstacle $\dfrac{\partial u}{\partial \xi} = \dfrac{\partial u_i}{\partial \xi}$ $\dfrac{\partial v}{\partial \xi} = \dfrac{\partial v_i}{\partial \xi}$ $\psi_\eta = 0$	$\omega = (v_x - u_y)$	$\dfrac{\partial p}{\partial n} = 0$	$\psi = U_\infty y$ $\psi_x = 0$ $\psi_y = U_\infty$ $\psi_{xx} = 0$ $\psi_{xy} = 0$ $\psi_{yy} = 0$ $\psi_\eta = 0$ (on 1 and 3) $\psi_\eta = -U_\infty$ (on 2) $\psi_\eta = U_\infty$ (on 4)	$\omega = 0$	$p = 0$

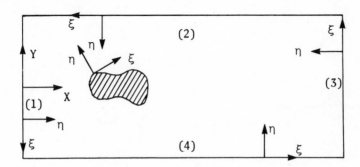

Figure 1. Solution Domain, Local and Global Coordinate Systems.

Variational Formulation

The stream function and pressure equations, Eqs. (3) and (7), may be formulated in a variational form as

$$\Phi_s = -\int_A (\psi_x^2 + \psi_y^2)\, dA + 2\int_A \psi\omega\, dA \qquad (8)$$

and

$$\Phi_p = -\int_A (p_x^2 + p_y^2)\, dA - 4\rho\int_A p(u_x v_y - u_y v_x)\, dA \qquad (9)$$

A linearized form of the variational functional for the vorticity-transport equation, Eq. (4), is obtained as (Bratanow et. al., 1975)

$$\Phi_\omega = -\nu\int_A (\omega_x^2 + \omega_y^2)\, dA - \int_A \omega(u\omega_x + v\omega_y)\, dA - 2\int_A \left(\omega\, \frac{\partial\omega}{\partial t}\right) dA \qquad (10)$$

Finite Element Discretization

The variational functionals for the governing equations, Eqs. (8), (9), and (10) are discretized using first a nonconformable third order triangular finite element, then, a conformable fifth order finite element is applied. The improvements in the solution are discussed.

Nonconformable Finite Element (Bratanow et. al., 1973). The variation of the stream function over a triangular finite element was approximated by a complete cubic polynomial in two dimensions in terms of the natural coordinates

$$\psi \, (\zeta_1, \zeta_2, \zeta_3) = \underline{C}^* \, \underline{A}^* \, \underline{\psi}^* \tag{11}$$

where $\underline{A}^*$ is a rectangular matrix describing the approximation function and

$$\underline{C}^* = [\zeta_1^3 \;\; \zeta_2^3 \;\; \zeta_3^3 \;\; \zeta_1^2\zeta_2 \;\; \zeta_1^2\zeta_3 \;\; \zeta_2^2\zeta_3 \;\; \zeta_3^2\zeta_1 \;\; \zeta_3^2\zeta_2 \;\; \zeta_1\zeta_2\zeta_3] \tag{12}$$

$$\underline{\psi}^{*t} = [\psi_1 \;\; \psi_{x1} \;\; \psi_{y1} \;\; \psi_2 \;\; \psi_{x2} \;\; \psi_{y2} \;\; \psi_3 \;\; \psi_{x3} \;\; \psi_{y3}]$$

The vorticity was considered to vary linearly over a triangular finite element as

$$\omega = [\zeta_1 \;\; \zeta_2 \;\; \zeta_3] \begin{bmatrix} \omega_1 \\ \omega_2 \\ \omega_3 \end{bmatrix} = \underline{B}^* \, \underline{\omega}^* \tag{13}$$

Conformable Finite Element (Bratanow et. al., 1975). The stream function variation over a finite element, Figure 2, was approximated by a complete quintic polynomial; the stream function at any point in the domain of an element is thus given as

$$\psi \, (\zeta_1, \zeta_2, \zeta_3) = \underline{C} \, \underline{A} \, \underline{\psi} \tag{14}$$

where

$$\underline{C} = \{\zeta_1^5 \;\; \zeta_2^5 \;\; \zeta_3^5 \;\; \zeta_1^4\zeta_2 \;\; \zeta_1^4\zeta_3 \;\; \zeta_2^4\zeta_3 \;\; \zeta_1\zeta_2^4 \;\; \zeta_1\zeta_3^4 \;\; \zeta_2\zeta_3^4 \;\; \zeta_1^3\zeta_2^2 \;\; \zeta_1^3\zeta_3^2 \;\; \zeta_2^3\zeta_3^2 \;\; \zeta_1^2\zeta_2^3$$

$$\zeta_1^2\zeta_3^3 \;\; \zeta_2^2\zeta_3^3 \;\; \zeta_1^3\zeta_2\zeta_3 \;\; \zeta_1\zeta_2^3\zeta_3 \;\; \zeta_1\zeta_2\zeta_3^3 \;\; \zeta_1^2\zeta_2^2\zeta_3 \;\; \zeta_1\zeta_2^2\zeta_3^2 \;\; \zeta_1^2\zeta_2\zeta_3^2\} \tag{15}$$

and

$$\underline{\psi}^t = \{\psi_1 \;\; \psi_{1x} \;\; \psi_{1y} \;\; \psi_{1xx} \;\; \psi_{1xy} \;\; \psi_{1yy} \;\; \psi_2 \;\; \psi_{2x} \;\; \psi_{2y} \;\; \psi_{2xx} \;\; \psi_{2xy} \;\; \psi_{2yy}$$

$$\psi_3 \;\; \psi_{3x} \;\; \psi_{3y} \;\; \psi_{3xx} \;\; \psi_{3xy} \;\; \psi_{3yy} \;\; \psi_{4\eta} \;\; \psi_{5\eta} \;\; \psi_{6\eta}\} \tag{16}$$

The variation of the vorticity over a finite element was approximated by a quadratic polynomial as

$$\omega \, (\zeta_1, \zeta_2, \zeta_3) = \underline{B} \, \underline{\omega} \tag{17}$$

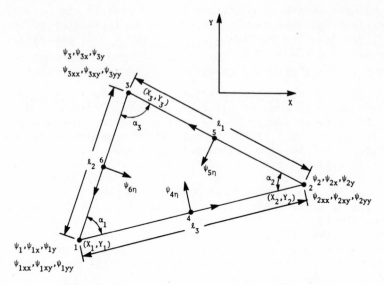

Figure 2.   Stream Function Finite Element with Quintic
            Polynomial Approximation.

where

$$\underline{B} = \left\{ \zeta_1 (2\zeta_1 - 1) \quad \zeta_2 (2\zeta_2 - 1) \quad \zeta_3 (2\zeta_3 - 1) \quad 4\zeta_1 \zeta_2 \quad 4\zeta_2 \zeta_3 \quad 4\zeta_1 \zeta_3 \right\} \quad (18)$$

and

$$\underline{\omega}^t = \left\{ \omega_1 \quad \omega_2 \quad \omega_3 \quad \omega_4 \quad \omega_5 \quad \omega_6 \right\} \quad (19)$$

Using the discrete forms of the stream function and vorticity
Eqs. (14) and (17), the variational functionals, Eqs. (8) and
(10), are minimized to obtain the following element stiffness
equations:

$$[S_s^e] \{\underline{\psi}\} = \{R_s^e\} \qquad [S_\omega^e] \left\{\frac{\partial \omega}{\partial t}\right\} = \{R_\omega^e\} \qquad (20)$$

where

$$[S_s^e] = \int_A [\underline{A}^t (\underline{C}_x^t \, \underline{C}_x + \underline{C}_y^t \, \underline{C}_y) \, \underline{A}] \; dA$$

$$\{R_s^e\} = \int_A (\underline{A}^t \underline{C}^t B) \; dA \; \underline{\omega}$$

$$[S_\omega^e] = \int_A [\underline{B}^t B] \; dA \qquad\qquad\qquad (21)$$

$$\{R_\omega^e\} = -\int_A \{\nu [\underline{B}_x^t B_x + \underline{B}_y^t B_y] + [\underline{B}^t \underline{C}_y A \, \underline{\psi} \, \underline{B}_x - \underline{B}^t \underline{C}_x A \, \underline{\psi} \, \underline{B}_y]\} \; dA$$

The element stiffness equations for the case of the nonconformable finite element may be obtained by replacing the vectors $\underline{A}$, $\underline{B}$, $\underline{C}$, and ψ by the vectors $\underline{A}^*$, $\underline{B}^*$, $\underline{C}^*$, and ψ^*, respectively, in Eqs. (20) and (21).

ON THE ACCURACY OF THE BOUNDARY CONDITIONS

Improvement of the Velocity Solution in the Boundary Layer

At high Reynolds numbers the characteristics of the flow change and the boundary layer thickness on an obstacle becomes very small, causing much higher normal velocity gradients around the boundary. As the Reynolds number increases, the occurrence of physical instabilities around the obstacle becomes more likely. An accurate determination of the velocity field in the boundary layer represents an essential part of the analysis. A requirement for accurate representation of the velocity distribution around the boundary is that the velocity solution must be compatible between element interfaces. An incompatible finite element with respect to first derivatives of the stream function produces a discontinuity of the velocity solution at element interfaces, thus causing a violation of the no-slip condition between nodal points on the boundary. Figure 3 illustrates the velocity solution obtained by the cubic polynomial approximation of the stream function over a finite element, where the inter-element compatibility was not satisfied. The discontinuities in the representation of the velocity field in the boundary layer along the element interfaces are shown in Figure 4. Figures 5 and 6 show the improvement in the velocity field when using the conformable quintic polynomial approximation. The sample problem for Figures 3 to 6 is a NACA 0012 airfoil in a free-stream at $Re=10^4$.

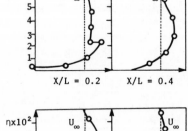

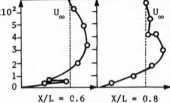

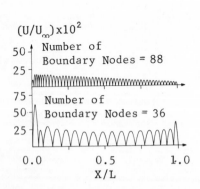

Figure 3. Distribution of the Tangential Velocity Component on the Boundary Using Cubic Polynomial Approximation (L = chord length).

Figure 4. Distribution of the Tangential Velocity Component in the Normal Direction to the Boundary Using Cubic Polynomial Approximation.

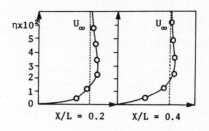

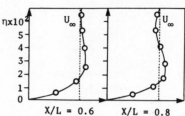

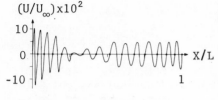

Figure 5. Distribution of the
Tangential Velocity Compo-
nent on the Boundary Using
Quintic Polynomial Approxi-
mation (Number of Boundary
Nodes = 30).

Figure 6. Distribution of the
Tangential Velocity Component in the Normal Direction
to the Boundary Using Quintic Polynomial Approximation.

A numerical experimentation indicated that the conventional
practice of excluding the imposition of the velocity boundary
condition in the normal direction to the boundary $(\psi_\xi = v_{(\eta)} = 0)$,
and applying only the condition $\psi_\eta = 0$ may cause significant inaccuracy in the solution field for boundaries of complex configurations, Figure 7.

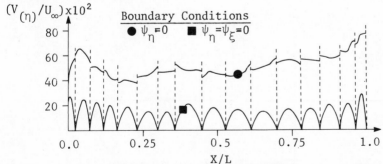

Figure 7. Distribution of the Normal Velocity Component on the
Obstacle Boundary (NACA 0012 Airfoil at Re=10^4, Using Cubic Polynomial Approximation).

In the above two cases of different finite elements, contrary
to the appreciable changes in the solution of the velocity
field in the boundary layer, the overall streamline patterns
show basically the same characteristics, Figure 8. Moreover, it

seems that it is possible to obtain qualitative solutions in terms of streamlines using approximate analyses such as the potential flow analysis (Martin 1969, Usuki 1974, Davis and Hardin 1973, Bratanow and Ecer 1973). The above discussion emphasizes the fact that appearance of the overall flow pat- terns produced from numerical calculations may not be indi- cative of the order of accuracy of the solution. A detailed analysis of flow characteristics in critical flow regions are more appropriate.

a	b	c

Figure 8.   Streamlines Around a NACA 0012 Airfoil at $Re=10^4$
            Obtained by: a) Potential Flow Analysis, b) Solution
            of the Navier-Stokes Equations Using Cubic Polynomi-
            al Approximation, c) Solution of the Navier-Stokes
            Equations Using Quintic Polynomial Approximation.

Treatment of Singular Points for Sharp Corners

For boundary conditions given as derivatives of flow parameters in the normal and/or tangential directions to a curved boundary which is represented by a series of nodal lines, the local nor- mal-tangential coordinate system is not uniquely defined. As shown in Figure 9, at nodes on the obstacle boundary the normal direction can be located at any direction between η_1 and η_2, in the range of the angle γ. On airfoils, cylinders, or other types of curved boundaries which are defined by analytical ex- pressions, numerical experimentation indicated an advantage in defining the tangential direction from the first derivative of the expression describing the boundary (Bratanow et. al.,1975).

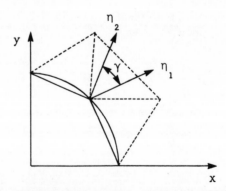

Figure 9.   Definition of Tangential and Normal Directions
            on the Obstacle Boundary.

The difficulty of defining a unique coordinate system cannot be overcome unless a finite element with curved boundaries is used in the analysis. The choice of a selected η-direction causes a slight violation of the compatibility property of conformable finite elements. The order of inaccuracy introduced by this choice can be observed in Figure 5. The velocity distribution, in Figure 5, which must theoretically be zero continuously throughout the obstacle boundary shows slight deviations; approximately 5% of the free stream velocity. This effect is magnified at boundary regions with larger curvatures.

The problem of defining unique local coordinates at the boundary nodes becomes more complex for boundaries that involve rigid walls containing sharp corners; for instance, flow over a cavity, obstacles in a flow field containing sharp corners, etc. For airfoils, application of the Kutta-Jukowski condition may resolve this complication (Vooren and Labrujere, 1973). For problems involving flow near singular points of a wall boundary the singularities may be treated by specially constructed singular finite elements (Hutton, 1974). The significance of such treatment of singular points and their effect on the accuracy of the solution are worth investigating. In most finite element applications involving problems of sharp corners the treatment of singular points has not been reported. The results presented for such applications do not indicate inaccuracies in the overall flow characteristics that might have been caused by this problem (Baker 1974, Oden 1973, Olson 1972, Skiba 1971).

Vorticity Boundary Conditions

The vorticity boundary condition on the obstacle or wall boundary (Table I) is specified in terms of the instantaneous numerical solution of the second derivatives of the stream function at nodal points. To obtain a stream function solution field from which vorticity boundary conditions can be uniquely generated, specification of stream function second derivatives as nodal freedoms of the finite element is necessary. Using the finite element described previously, where the stream function is approximated by a cubic polynomial, this condition is not satisfied. Table II presents numerical results for the stream function second derivatives at different nodal points, obtained from the interpolation over different neighboring finite elements using Eq. (11). A portion of the finite element gridwork used in this analysis is shown in Figure 10.

THE SYSTEMS OF EQUATIONS AT HIGH REYNOLDS NUMBERS

At high Reynolds numbers, the convective terms dominate the damping effect of the viscous terms, Figure 11, and influence the stability of the flow condition. A frequently encountered observation in reports on finite element solutions of flow problems has been that of the tendency of the resulting system of algebraic equations to become ill-conditioned with increasing Reynolds number (Lee 1973, Tong 1974, Kawahara 1974, Olson 1972). Such a behavior of the algebraic system may be interpreted as indication of physical changes in the flow.

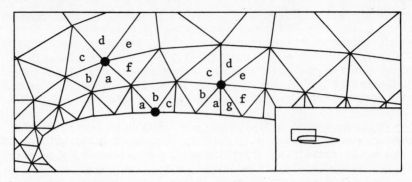

Figure 10. Finite Element Gridwork (Used for Obtaining the Results Shown in Table II).

Table II. Stream Function Second Derivatives at Nodal Points Obtained Using Cubic Polynomial Approximation Over Neighboring Finite Elements (F.E.).

NODE I (THE BOUNDARY)			NODE II (LAYER 1)			NODE III (LAYER 2)		
F.E.	ψ_{xx}	ψ_{yy}	F.E.	ψ_{xx}	ψ_{yy}	F.E.	ψ_{xx}	ψ_{yy}
a	-5.48	48.55	a	-0.58	4.71	a	-0.193	0.622
b	45.15	55.96	b	13.30	11.40	b	0.757	0.893
c	16.70	34.21	c	8.30	14.03	c	0.512	1.100
			d	-0.08	4.55	d	-0.159	0.760
			e	-0.44	-0.91	e	-0.180	-0.001
			f	-0.27	-1.12	f	-0.198	-0.047
			g	-0.47	5.13			

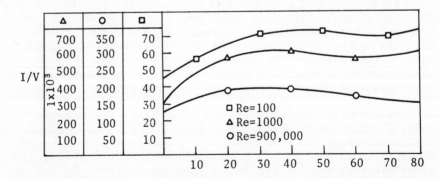

Figure 11. Ratio of Convective Terms to Viscous Terms (I/V) vs. Reynolds Numbers (for NACA 0012 Airfoil Boundary at 25% Chord Length).

Kawahara et. al. (1974) applied the finite element method
in conjunction with a Galerkin approach for the solution of
the Navier-Stokes equations in terms of the primitive variables, Eqs. (1) and (2), and analyzed the convergence characteristics of different methods for the solution of the resulting nonlinear algebraic systems. The algebraic systems for
physically stable problems such as parallel flow between walls
or a sudden expansion in a duct, exhibit ill-conditioning at
moderately high Reynolds numbers (Re~400). Among the several
methods of solution discussed, evidently, a combined procedure
of the Newton-Raphson and perturbation methods were found to
be suitable for solving the nonlinear system of equations for
steady incompressible viscous flow. Olson (1972), using finer
subdivisions for steady flows of Re~400, reported rapid convergence in the solution of the nonlinear algebraic system using
also the standard Newton-Raphson method. Such improvement in
the convergence properties of the algebraic system, when compared with results of Kawahara (1974), may be due to the use
of higher order compatible finite elements as well as to the
difference in the formulation of the problem.

The analysis of unsteady viscous flow at relatively high
Reynolds numbers outlined in this paper involved linearization
of the variational form of the vorticity transport equation,
Eq. (10), and since the stream function equation, Eq. (3), was
linear at the outset, both resulting systems of algebraic equations are in linear form. Condition numbers of the coefficient
matrices of the two algebraic systems were calculated at different time instances. It was observed that these systems preserve their well-conditioning throughout the time domain of integration even at higher Reynolds numbers (Bratanow et. al.,
1975). The inverse of the coefficient matrices for the linear
systems of algebraic equations may be stored for use at each
time step, thus leading to a substantial reduction in the computational effort for the solution.

CONVERGENCE REQUIREMENTS FOR THE FINITE ELEMENTS

For cases of conformable finite elements, several convergence
criteria have been established related to solutions of partial
differential equations in continuum mechanics (Zienkiewicz,
1972). Proofs of convergence for nonconformable finite elements
have been mostly based on a physical criterion of the so called
"patch tests" or on an empirical study of the solution of the
specific problem (Bazeley et. al., 1965). In addition to such
general convergence requirements on the solution of partial
differential equations, using conformable and nonconformable
finite elements, the considerations described below were found
to have significant influence on finite element solutions of
fluid flow problems.

For an accurate representation of velocity boundary conditions at the wall boundary, the finite element has to be

conformable with respect to velocities. This requires compatible approximation of the velocity vector at element interfaces
in formulations using primitive variables and compatibility of
both stream function and its first derivatives for other formulations.

The second order derivatives of the main flow variable
($\underline{u}$, for formulation in primitive variables and ψ, for other
formulations) must be specified as nodal freedoms whenever any
of the boundary conditions is given in terms of these derivatives.

Special considerations must be given for a proper geometric representation of curved boundaries when using higher
order conformable finite elements with straight edges. A significant violation of compatibility properties of the finite
element approximation may occur if the boundary is not discretized using sufficiently fine subdivisions. Although use of
isoparametric finite elements have been mentioned for such applications, their usage would introduce another factor for investigation; convergence of numerically integrated elements
(Zienkiewicz, 1972).

For nonconformable triangular finite elements, the convergence is directly related to the geometric properties of
the finite element, the element Reynolds number, the aspect
ratio, the internal angles, etc. For this class of finite elements, the effect of uniformity in size and shape of finite
elements has been discussed by Bratanow and Ecer (1974).

ACKNOWLEDGEMENT

This research was supported by the U.S. National Aeronautics
and Space Administration under grant no. NGR-50-007-001.

REFERENCES

[1]Baker, A. (1974) A Finite Element Solution Algorithm for
the Navier-Stokes Equations, NASA CR-2391.
[2]Bazeley, G., Cheung, Y., Irons, B., and Zienkiewicz, O.C.
(1965) Triangular Elements in Bending - Conforming the Non-
Conforming Solutions. Proc. Conf. Matrix Methods in Struct.
Mech., Airforce Inst. of Tech., Wright-Patterson AFB, Ohio.
[3]Bratanow, T., Ecer, A., and Kobiske, M. (1973) Finite Element Analysis of Unsteady Incompressible Flow Around an Oscillating Obstacle of Arbitrary Shape. AIAA J., Vol. 11, 11:1471-
1477.
[4]Bratanow, T., and Ecer, A. (1973) Finite Element Analysis and Computer Graphics Visualization of Flow Around Pitching
and Plunging Airfoils. NASA CR-2249.

[5]Bratanow, T., and Ecer, A. (1974) On the Application of the Finite Element Method in Unsteady Aerodynamics. AIAA J., Vol. 12, 4:503-510.

[6]Bratanow, T., Aksu, H., and Spehert, T. (1975) A Rigorous Solution of the Navier-Stokes Equations for Unsteady Viscous Flow at High Reynolds Numbers Around Oscillating Airfoils. Paper No. 75-863, AIAA 8th Fluid and Plasmadynamics Conf., Hartford, Conn., 16-18 June.

[7]Chapman, D.R., Mark, H., and Pirtle, M.W. (1975) Computers vs. Wind-Tunnels for Aerodynamic Flow Simulations. Aeronautics and Astronautics, 4:22-73.

[8]Davis, P.O.A.L., and Hardin, J.C. (1973) Potential Flow Modelling of Unsteady Flow. Numerical Methods in Fluid Dynamics, Proc. of the Int. Conf. held at the University of Southampton, England, 26-28 Sept.: 42-64.

[9]Hutton, A.G. (1974) On Flow Near Singular Points of a Wall Boundary. Finite Element Methods in Flow Problems, Int. Symp. on Finite Element Methods in Flow Problems, Swansea, England, 8-12 Jan.: 67-83.

[10]Kawahara, M., Yoshimura, N., and Nakagawa, K. (1974) Analysis of Steady Incompressible Viscous Flow. Finite Element Methods in Flow Problems, Int. Symp. on Finite Element Methods in Flow Problems, Swansea, England, 8-12 Jan.: 107-120.

[11]Lee, C. H. (1973) Finite Element Method for Transient Linear Viscous Flow Problems. Numerical Methods in Fluid Dynamics, Proc. of the Int. Conf. held at the University of Southampton, England, 26-28 Sept.: 140-152.

[12]Martin, H. (1969) Finite Element Analysis of Fluid Flows Proc. of the Sec. Conf. on Matrix Methods in Struc. Mechanics, AFFDL - TR - 68-150: 517-535.

[13]Oden, J.T. (1973) The Finite Element Method in Fluid Mechanics. Lectures on Finite Element Methods in Continuum Mechanics at the NATO Adv. Study Inst., Lisbon, Portugal, Univ. of Alabama in Huntsville Press: 151-186.

[14]Olson, M.D. (1972) A Variational Finite Element Method for Two-Dimensional Steady Viscous Flows. The Univ. of British Columbia, Dept. of Civil Engineering, Struct. Res. Series Rep. No. 5, Vancouver, British Columbia.

[15]Skiba, E., Unny, T.E., and Weaver, D.S. (1971) A Finite Element Solution for a Class of Two-Dimensional Viscous Fluid Dynamics Problems. Proc. Symp. on Computer-Aided Engineering, Univ. of Waterloo, Waterloo, Ontario: 493-508.

[16]Tong, P. (1974) On the Solution of the Navier-Stokes Equations in Two-Dimensional and Axial-Symmetric Problems. Finite Elements in Flow Problems, Int. Symp. on Finite Element Methods in Flow Problems, Swansea, England, 8-12 Jan.: 57-66.

[17]Usuki, S. (1974) Finite Element Methods via Local Potential. Finite Element Methods in Flow Problems, Int. Symp. on Finite Element Methods in Flow Problems, Swansea, England, 8-12 Jan.: 333-335.

[18]Vooren, J. V., and Labrujere, Th. E. (1973) Finite Element Solution of the Incompressible Flow Over an Airfoil in a Non-Uniform Stream. Numerical Methods in Fluid Dynamics, Proc. of the Int. Conf. held at the University of Southampton, England, 26-28 Sept.: 23-41.

[19]Zienkiewicz, O.C. (1972) Finite Element - The Background Story. The Mathematics of Finite Element and Applications, Proc. of the Brunel Univ. Conf. of the Inst. of Math. and Its Applications: 1-35.

LIST OF SYMBOLS

A = area of triangular finite element, in^2.

$\underline{B}, \underline{B}^*$ = modal vectors for the vorticity finite elements

$\underline{C}, \underline{C}^*$ = modal vectors for the stream function finite elements

$\underline{F}$ = body forces vector, (lbf)

p = pressure, lbf/in^2.

$\underline{R}$ = right hand side vector for stiffness equations

$\underline{S}$ = stiffness matrix

t = time, sec.

$\underline{u}$ = velocity vector (u,v), in./sec.

ξ_1, ξ_2, ξ_3 = area coordinates

η = normal direction to the boundary

ν = kinematic viscosity, in^2./sec.

ξ = tangential direction to the boundary

ρ = mass density, lbm/in^3.

Φ = general quadratic functional for variational formulations

ψ = stream function, in^2./sec.

$\underline{\psi}, \underline{\psi}^*$ = vectors of nodal stream function values, in^2./sec.

ω = vorticity, 1/sec.

$\underline{\omega}, \underline{\omega}^*$ = vectors of nodal vorticity values, 1/sec.

$\underline{\nabla}$ = del operator, $\underline{\nabla} = \dfrac{\partial}{\partial x}\, \underline{i} + \dfrac{\partial}{\partial y}\, \underline{j} + \dfrac{\partial}{\partial z}\, \underline{k}$

∇^2 = Laplace operator, $\nabla^2 = \dfrac{\partial^2}{\partial x^2} + \dfrac{\partial^2}{\partial y^2} + \dfrac{\partial^2}{\partial z^2}$

Subscripts

p = pressure

s = stream function

x,y = partial derivative with respect to x and y directions respectively

ω = vorticity

∞ = free stream conditions

η,ξ = partial derivative with respect to η and ξ directions respectively

(η) = velocity component in the direction of η

Superscripts

e = belonging to a single finite element

t = transpose

PART 2. DISCUSSION

1.   DISCUSSION: REGIONAL MODELS

1.1   Strategic Models of Energy Usage

P.B. Morice   Could I perhaps start off by asking how do you deal with today costs of money?

D.J. Fisk   Essentially we were working in what we term in real costs.

I. Bogardi   Before I give my three questions, I would like to add two general comments. One is that I think that this Conference has two languages. One language is English, and the second language is modelling. We do understand - I think all of us - these two languages. Second comment is that we all have so many and so different disciplines, and though I agree that modelling needs interdisciplinary way of looking, I do think that we should concentrate to speak our two common languages. In that respect I have my three questions.

One is concerning the structure of the model which is unclear for me. It is common to models, I guess, that they have different variables. Let us see more details if possible in this respect.

The second question refers to the uncertainties in the variables. I understand that it is a forecasting model with different independent variables, which are uncertain. Can the model incorporate or take care of these uncertainties, and if it can how?

The last question concerns the validation of the model. Can it be compared to actual observation data, and if yes, how was the result?

D. J. Fisk   I think actually there are probably three languages. There is English, modelling, and cockney, which is what I speak. What I am going to attempt to do is to reiterate a little of the philosophy of this particular model. I think the first thing that I ought to establish is that there are certainly two types of forecasting model and I think that the motive for adopting a particular type of forecasting model is essentially to answer what is the application of the forecast? I think I opened by saying that you could certainly make a very best guessed estimate of what future requirements would be thirty years from now, but you would not necessarily

need that forecast now, rather you would probably need immediately the forecast for the energy consumption of the next
five years, and probably with a certain amount of laxity for
the next ten. If you like, we are approaching the forecasting process with the options in mind that we are having to
close. This is I think traditional energy management policy,
particularly in the United Kingdom, of really trying to keep
the options open simply because the longer they are kept open
the more information is bought. Dr. Bogardi emphasized quite
rightly the problem of uncertainty in forecasting, and there
is very real problem in saying that if we rely very heavily
on a model and optimise our options now on that basis then in
fact we may not necessarily be taking the optimal decision.
We could have stalled or waited for a period and, by the cost
of doing that, in a sense we would have bought more information and brought our forecasting model nearer to realism.
The particular model that we are building here is not the
model that we would have used for that purpose. Indeed it is
not the model that we use for making estimates of, for example,
the impact of raising the regulations for thermal insulation
in the United Kingdom. That model carries our own internal
prejudices in terms of how we set up the econometric model.
But it was not the type of model that we had in mind here.
Here we were really talking to an audience much less erudite
than those present today who simply needed to be convinced of
the consequences of running a particular type of housing
stock. We can try to validate the model. In fact, because
it has so many parameters it is trivially easy to get it to
fit very well over the last ten years. This is in a sense
what I was trying to get across, that if you were going for
an econometric model you're really saying something about why
you need those results. You are really saying, "I want to
know, how much fuel oil is going to be imported next year",
because this is a balance of payments problem. We weren't
really concerned with that particular type of problem. We
have done that out of amusement, but as I said there wasn't
very much modelling satisfaction because we were aware of the
number of variable parameters we had at hand. In a sense
validation does not fit for this type of model. We are really
trying to get across a feeling for what it is like to manage
this energy economy to people who normally are not aware of
that sort of problem. One of the reasons why the programme
is in its modula structure is that very often one has uncertainties in the structure of the model itself. This is particularly true in econometric models where, if you are not
careful, you very often find a simultaneous equation being
solved somewhere in the middle of a procedure which within
itself is implicitly assumed that the whole market is totally
competitive and all that that implies about non-reality. So
in a sense we were very nervous about making the structure
too implicit. People who design individual buildings are not
at the moment, quite understandably, used to thinking of the

effects of their design in its aggregated consequences.

The model could always fit the data and we are not really concerned with that sort of forecasting. We are concerned with trying to get the quality of the data fairly robust in respect to its structure. We are in some sense more interested in looking at changes in structural content than we are in the action of the price mechanisms. We make no claim for a particular scenario be it likely or not. We are really more concerned with the structure that it is reflecting. On the econometric basis, as I think I said, I would normally view the econometric models as dealing with relatively short term problems. Here we are talking about areas of speculation so that the econometric model is a different market for the consumer. The paper discussed building a model so that the people who received its results could take in exactly what the model was trying to say.

1.2 The Interdependency between Environment and Transportation Planning

D. Weihs   I would like to ask about the effects of response time between housing, employment and transportation on your model. If, for example, a new factory or new jobs are produced in a certain place, the housing would take a few years to catch up. How would such a time delay influence your model?

R. Hamerslag   It isn't very important to know the delay. Of course in the model it may be possible to include it but it is more important to get a description of the real situation in long rather than in a very short term.

Y.F. Ballintyn   Employment and let us say houses are exogenous variables in your model so I can't see in fact what is the problem with the time. If you are able to have a good guess at what is coming available in the years, then you can still prepare your exogenous variables in this model so I can't see in fact the problem for instance with the time delay.

R. Hamerslag   I think there are two kinds of problem. The first one is the length of planning, and secondly, the fact that things do not come out just as planned. People react on what people are planning so that your plans are not always used as people planned them. The Netherlands plans to keep the heart of Holland clean, but in reality this is the part of the Netherlands which has had the greatest growth over the past years. What I was trying to do was to understand what is happening in reality.

D. Weihs   That means in fact that you cannot neglect interaction between your transportation model and the environment

as you did by treating them as more or less exogenous variables.   If there is such a strong connection between transportation facilities and what is actually going on in the
economic and housing market, then you could neglect interaction between them.   Is that what you are saying in fact?

R. Hamerslag   I think that these are different types of
exogenous variables.

1.4   Human Activity, Pollution and Resources

I. Bogardi   I think that this approach really has merit to
help solving environmental problems as a whole.   However, I
wonder whether you succeeded in formulating more specifically
systems aspects of the problem, e.g. what are the states of
the system and the state transition functions, could you
formulate for such a case the input of the system, and what
do you regard as the output of the systems.   Can you tell us
specifically?

J.W. Bryant   In my presentation I've explained that we've
been looking at interactions involved in particular systems
in a number of areas, and I can give you information about
these.   It is fairly easy to build up a rough picture of
the physical flows, including the energy flows, involved in
systems such as the ones I have described, and to establish
the states of the various materials involved.   One can in
principle build up a picture of all the related human activity systems.   However, there are other systems involved.   As
far as the abstract systems (that is, the decision making
systems) are concerned, we are again trying to build up fairly
structured models of the way in which decisions are made in
different sorts of organisations.   In fact within one of the
other areas that we are looking at, we have got a number of
different models in use at the moment which attempt to represent the decision-making mechanism in the various decision-
making systems involved in that study.   To summarise,we have
built models of both physical systems and abstract systems
in a fairly specific form and we hope to use these two in
conjunction to describe the way in which the total system will
behave in various scenarios.   I hope that this answers your
question.

I. Bogardi   Well I have now only one question left because
we are also facing similar problems.   Do you believe that in
the near future you will be able to use such broad systems
approach for solving practical questions.

J.W. Bryant   I think that it is now possible within the areas
that we are now looking at and with the information that we
have, to build up a fairly clear balance sheet of the physical
resources involved.   However, decision-making within these

systems has proved more difficult to analyse. At this stage
we have constructed a crude environmental balance sheet for a
number of physical systems and this alone provides policy-
makers with information on which to base their decisions.

1.5 A Model Criterion for Site-Selection of Large Scale Technical Facilities in the 'Upper Rhine Region'

Y.F. Ballintyn   I was wondering how many points in your linear programme you have to generate to be able to construct
the solution of your final game theoretical approach. If I
understood you well, you have to generate all the feasible
solutions of both problem one and problem two.

G. Halbritter   I must not generate all feasible solutions of
the problems. I can formulate a new optimisation problem.
With a linear programme I can solve this problem.

Y.F. Ballintyn   You say here in your discussion that you need
to generate all the feasible points of your problem one and
problem two.

G. Halbritter   Yes, theoretically, but practically I can
formulate a new linear programme.

Y.F. Ballintyn   What are the generating points in this final
region which you are using for your game theory? What is the
criterion?

G. Halbritter   In the linear case every two-person-zero-sum-
game can be formulated as a linear programme. In game-theory
it is the same, to search all possible solutions or to formulate the linear programme.

Question   I am wondering what criteria do you use to generate the best solutions for problems 1 and 2.

G. Halbritter   In practice I search for the best linear
combination of the extreme values of the convex polyhedron,
that means of the corner values of the polyhedron. The convex polyhedron encloses the number of possible solutions to
the problem. These solutions are fixed by the constraints.
To find this best linear combination, a linear programme can
be formulated.

I. Bogardi   I would like to congratulate this paper for
three reasons. First it is a real worked problem and then it
is a really up-to-date model you used, and third the model is
applied and solved.
    Well, I have some comments. The first concerns multi-
objective programming. I think that multiobjective programming is really not only fashionable today but really useful,

realistic and desirable tool in environmental planning because
we have to acknowledge that goals in environmental protection
are really multiobjectives in character. At least, as in
your paper, there are two different goals; one is economic
efficiency and the other is environmental pollution protection. There are other goals, social or political goals in
many cases which are just as important or even more important
as the previous ones. Well, as far as multiobjective programming is concerned you used really one of the possible
methods and I would like to add only that we have to acknowledge again in that case that multiobjective programming
cannot assure any optimum solution, only, as you mentioned,
best compromise solution. But this best compromise solution
depends on the preferences the decision maker feels, and the
goodness of a multiobjective programming is reflected by the
way these preferences are taken into consideration by the
analyser. That means for instance that you regard such
preferences that the losses due to non reaching optimum
solution for objective function 1 and 2 are equal so the
losses in environmental protection are in a mathematical
sense just as important in economic aspects.   Well, I think
that it is quite good, but I could perhaps suggest you just
try to use another method of multiobjective programming, e.g.
the weighting method, and regard for instance if water pollution problem has greater weight than economics, and so on.
I think it is very important but difficult to take into
consideration the stochastic nature of the problem as you
also mentioned. It is really a stochastic problem because
pollution is changing in a random way. You used expected
values. It is quite understandable because nobody could use
in parallel with multiobjective programming stochastic analysis, but I think that would be later necessary. Another
thing: you plan for a definite time horizon for the future,
and received best compromise solution for a definite time
horizon, but what about the timing of the plan. Probably
in a next step you should give an answer how to reach this
level in the near future, so how to plan the development
e.g. in a five year basis. What is the best compromise step
in a multiobjective programming way? It is not easy to
answer but it's worth trying to.

<u>G. Halbritter</u>   Thank you very much for your comments. You
are right, that vector valued optimization is the problem
of regarding different interests to find the best compromise.
This is a problem for politicians, how to find the economic
way and how to make minimal pollution. It is very difficult
to solve such problems with a mathematical theory, because it
is a problem of valuation by the population and of politics.
But I would say that these models can help to find better
decisions, especially when we have more data about the costs
and more data about technical possibilities. You are also
right, that it is very unsatisfactory to regard only the

expectation values of pollution but we can improve the model,
and I am working on this. One can extend the list of constraints and can regard not only the long time value but also
the short time values of pollution. It is a problem of the
correct input-data and of computer time. It's the first step
I have presented here and one must go step by step.

1.6 Parameter Estimation of a Distributed System Related to the Biomass Dynamics in Aquatic Ecosystems

Question   You have found out that differences were found
when introducing vertical movements in your model. I just
wonder how important it is to introduce this and other
physical processes in your model.

F. Argentesi   The model takes into account the relevant
physical processes responsible for the vertical movement, see
e.g. the eddy diffusivity and mixing terms. Therefore the
sensitivity analysis is related both to the physical and
biological processes. The degree of sophistication of the
sensitivity analysis performed was not so light to permit
comparative judgements on the relative influence of the
physical and biological processes on the model's sensitivity.

D. Weihs   Many of these population models have a periodic
solution and not a steady state solution. In your model you
must, so to speak, get a steady state solution. This is
really because you have assumed or will assume all kinds of
constants, you will get a steady state solution. Is it clear
that this is the real situation?

F. Argentesi   Yes! I will try to explain properly the
results of the situation. It was not our intention to produce
a model of this kind. We did not try to produce a model in
order to reach equilibrium, i.e. to describe some process
with a long period of assumptions . Our model is only a
tool, a tool for solving an optimum control problem. We are
not interested in the kind of models that you mentioned, our
parameter is not constant or functional; but tables that we
can compute from experimental data. It is not our intention
to produce a model for the forecasting of the behaviour of
the ecological system in a long time scale. We only take a
piece of the past experimentally observed. We use a model
as a form of structure. We formulate the optimum control
problem. We solve the optimum control problem and we extract
the solution of the optimum control problem. It is the performance of the system in the past that we have studied. We
are not interested in this study in what could be the future.

D. Weihs   No, I do not mean that. You may be taking as part
of your experiment just one point on this periodic cycle
solution, which may be basing the optimum solution on just a

chance point.

F. Argentesi   Not random point on the curve. We take this
experiment, for example there are times when we take a proper
sampling of this biomass. We don't make an assumption about
what could be the low of changing of solar radiation during
the year. We compute only the optimum of control. Our
function is something that describes this piece of the past
studied that is meaningful for us from a biological point of
view. When you make an experiment and you achieve your data,
some times you used a proper transformation and analysis of
your results before proposing a fairly general model of your
process. Our problem is that of producing these transformed
data and not the theory of the process.

Correction   The first reference in the paper (page 77)
should be replaced by the following:-

1.   Argentesi, F., Di Cola, G. and Verheyden, M. (1974)
     The Modelling of Biomass Dynamics in Aquatic Ecosystems.
     In: R. Trappe and F.R. Pichler (Eds)
     Progress in Cybernetics and System Research
     Vol. 1: General Systems, Engineering Systems and
     Biocybernetics and Heuzel Systems.

2.   Parker, R.A. (1973)
     Some problems associated with computer simulation of an
     ecological system.
     The mathematical theory of the dynamics of biological
     populations.
     Edited by M.S. Bartlett and R.W. Hiozus.
     Academic Press

2. DISCUSSION: HYDRAULIC SYSTEMS

2.1 Design of Large Urban Sewer Systems with a Waterflow
     Simulation Program

R. Sutherland   I have a question regarding the two calibration parameters needed for your model – the runoff coefficient
and the time delay function. How do you go about estimating
these parameters?

C. De Rham   Yes, they are. First the runoff coefficient.
This is perhaps the easier coefficient to determine. We can
do it by planning out a whole area and we know quite accurately values about the different types of area, if it's a
street, or grass, or bushes, or things like this and there
we had not much difficulty to get accurate values. Second
the time delay. This is more a rule of thumb than anything
else. First you must look not to have too big areas, then
you overgo this problem because then the time delays are in
the pipes and not outside. But if you want to determine
accurate time delays you must look at the slope of the area,
at its repartition of street and other soil types, and as we
saw we have values between three and five minutes normally but
of course if you have a very steep rain storm it goes only
one minute. In conclusion it must be said that the runoff
coefficient is much more important because it influences
directly the volume of water, whereas the time delay only
influences the time axis.

R. Sutherland   Are you assuming any type of runoff from
pervious areas? It appears to me that you are using your
runoff coefficient in a modified rational method to predict
the quantity of water entering the pipe network.

C. De Rham   Yes. It is only this. We just take exactly the
same method as the rational method but we do it perhaps somewhat more exactly.

R. Sutherland   In the estimation of the runoff coefficient
are you only concerned with directly connected impervious
area?

<u>C. De Rham</u> Well, I didn't go into details so far. We take
the weighted mean of the different surfaces. And do not for-
get that other coefficients like the roughness coefficient of
the pipe plays also a great role. I mean you must level the
different uncertainty so as to have about the same for everything.

<u>R. Sutherland</u> Although your model works in Switzerland, it
may not work that well in various parts of the United States.
Storms that are not extremely significant in terms of rainfall duration and return frequency such as summer thunder-
storms have been known to produce significant amounts of
runoff from both pervious and impervious areas. Antecedent
soil moisture conditions and the physics of overland flow
become extremely important in the prediction of runoff from
these short duration high intensity rainfalls. Your paper
was quite interesting and I enjoyed it.

<u>R. Butterfield</u> I think that what you are saying is really
that the job interpretation of the problem is the input to
this model. But he is talking about the model. In fact if
I interpolate, all your slides were showing input. You didn't
show anything which showed what actually happens in your sewer
system. Have you any measurement of what happened within the
system which is what your program is mainly predicting, isn't
it?

<u>C. De Rham</u> Yes. The last slide showed the measured output
at the end of the network.

<u>R. Butterfield</u> Your measurements in manholes were fitting
your predicted figures?

<u>C. De Rham</u> Oh, yes. It must because if it does not fit, the
lower end will not fit.

<u>G.K. Verboom</u> In determining the time step, you say you
start with the smallest one and then increase the time step.
To me this seems to be the wrong way. I think you ought to
start with the large one and then decrease the time step,
because otherwise you start with the most expensive program.

<u>C. De Rham</u> Well yes, of course. Now say we have experience
values about the time step which are working for one or the
other problem, and then if we see that the rain is not too
steep, then we try to increase the time step.

<u>Question</u> Before you start calculating, or not?

<u>C. De Rham</u> No. First we anyway have to do a run with one
time step and this we do with a small one so as to be sure
that it works well.

Question   Then you have the answers, or do you stop before
you have completed the calculations? If you start with the
small one and do the whole calculation, you have the answers.
Of course, you can check with the larger time step I think.

C. De Rham Yes thank you, but you never calculate a sewage
network only one time because you do different things. You
try with different pipes, with the storm water tank and other
things and this is normal for a sewage network you have to
correct. You do ten or twenty calculations and therefore
it's important to have the right time step but at the beginning of course we have to have the right solution, and therefore we take a small one.

C.M. De Turville   There is a close analogy between the artificial network you describe for stormwater evacuation, and
the corresponding natural system of rivers and their tributaries. In spite of the limited catchment area served by a
particular network, there may still be large fluctuations at
times between the rainfall in different parts of the area.
With complex interconnections between all your pipework, that
could render the model rather less predictable in the actual
course of events.

P. Kaufmann   First in Switzerland, you know that there are
many mountains and not much area which is flat. This of
course helps to solve the problem in that you don't have much
interrelation between different parts of the network. Then
if you have rain passing over the whole network you can steer
this by the runoff delay. This is a simple and efficient
means. You just take the effective time delay it takes from
the rain to the runoff, plus the delay the rain needs to get
at that part of the network.

2.2 A Mathematical Model for the Analysis of Multi-Reservoir Flood Control Systems

E.F. Joeres   Is it possible in your model to include other
objectives besides this control?

J.S. Windsor   Yes. At this stage I have looked only at the
flood control aspect. However, the procedure in a multi-
purpose situation would be to treat flood runoff as a separate sub-problem within the overall system. The optimal
allocation of flood storage and spillway capacities may then
be obtained using a mixed integer programming model before
optimizing the complete system. At the next level of optimization flood storage would be regarded as a constraint in
determining the optimal allocation of conservation storage
within the system.

E.F. Joeres Would you still be getting an optimal solution?

J.S. Windsor   You would in effect. Flood control should be
analyzed independently of the other benefits, such as power
and irrigation, since we are working on a different time
scale. Another reason is that by breaking the overall problem
down into separate sub-problems for analysis we reduce the
amount of data which has to be handled at any one time in the
solution procedure.

E.F. Joeres   I was just sitting here thinking about how you
might go about it. I have played with this problem and used
chance constraint programming to specify allowable flood discharges with their probabilities of occurrence, without,
however, associating damage costs, and in some sense you do
this too in that you limit discharge capacities. So if you
look at it as a threshold problem, then perhaps you can go at
it from that point of view and drop the flood damage cost out
of the objective function by simply limiting flood discharge
to certain levels and then pulling the other objectives into
the model in terms of discharges for irrigation or what have
you.

J. S. Windsor   I should imagine there are a number of ways
of tackling the problem including chance constrained programming. This would depend to some extent on the system
under consideration. In the case of major flood control
systems the accepted practice is to provide sufficient flood
storage and outlet capacity to control the probable maximum
flood. In other situations such a high level of protection
may be impracticable and the optimal level of development
would be one which minimized total system costs including
risk of failure cost.

E.F. Joeres   Well your algorithm has very much the characteristics of an operational tool that one would apply with a
simulation model after the design is completed to operate the
system which is, I think, very useful.

I. Bogardi   You mentioned that it is assumed that the uncontrolled inflows to the reservoirs are known. Well I am sure
that in reality they are not known and so how you manage to
consider the stochastic effects in the optimization?

J.S. Windsor   I have based my study on the assumption that a
fairly good set of flood records are available for the river
basin development. Given this information we can then select
or derive equally likely sets of flood hydrographs to define
flood variability in space and time. These are then used as
input data to the model along with the synthetically derived
probable maximum flood for the individual sub-basins within
the system. For a more sophisticated study we might relate
flood peak and flood volume to probability of occurrence to
obtain a better estimate of the average annual flood damage
costs.

I. Bogardi   So if I understand well, you say that if you can assume some probability density function for the controlled inflows then the flood control system can be optimized.

J.S. Windsor   As far as the design stage is concerned, it uses the same input data as in the conventional approach. Under actual operating conditions, on the other hand, the regulation plan is continually modified to match the changing runoff conditions. This involves a two-step procedure. The first step is to generate a set of flood hydrographs at all significant points within the basin using updated hydro-meteorological data. This information is then used as input data to the programming model to determine the optimal release schedule for the system.   Repeating these steps at suitable intervals during the floor period ensures that the system is operated on foresight basis. I feel this is a more realistic operating policy than one which is based on a fixed set of releases irrespective of the flood runoff.

I. Bogardi   Concerning the short term policy, we have quite positive experiences with updating by Bayes' approach.   That is there is a model already existing which can control the system given some short term flood forecast in a probabilistic sense. In this case the Bayesian rule can be used in order to update and improve the normal operation policy.

G.K. Verboom   First of all, I am not very familiar with linear programming techniques so perhaps my question is irrelevant, but how are you sure that you will find one solution in your optimization problem? I could imagine that you will find degenerate solutions whereas the programme, at least to my knowledge, often still gives you an answer.

J.S. Windsor   So far I have not had the opportunity to use the model in a practical design problem so I can't say what difficulties are likely to arise. I have however used a similar model for the analysis of a multi-purpose river basin development and I had no problem as regards degeneration.

G.K. Verboom   Can you still be sure that you have only one optimum, because I know of very similar examples in which you have for instance a line of solutions, whereas the programme gives you only one of them, and if you start at another point you will find another solution?

J.S. Windsor   I agree that you cannot be sure that you have only one optimum. Although, in the case of a single reservoir, you do have a good idea what the optimum discharge should be for a given flood runoff.

G.K. Verboom   So you use physics and common sense to judge whether you have one solution.

R. Butterfield   This seems to be an interesting question.
How do you intend to validate your programme and how do you
intend to substantiate that you have in fact found an optimum?

J.S. Windsor   One possible method would be to find the value
of the objective function for small variations from the
optimal solution. There is no guarantee, however, that the
solution will be the global minimum unless the problem is
convex.

C.M. De Turville   You have to rely on past records in order
to make prognostics about the future and presumably in many
places these records will only extend back 50 or 100 years.
However, there are such things as astronomically freakish
events which may occur say once in a thousand years. That
may seem pretty rare, but a pipe network which is to last
for 50 years will have a 5% probability of encountering these
conditions. How do you assess the upper bounds to the sort
of situation you should contemplate and plan for?

J.S. Windsor   As I mention in the write up, the model is
designed for the analysis of major reservoir systems. This
implies that the input flow data includes a range of potential
floods up to and including the probable maximum flood for the
catchment. The frequency of occurrence of this extreme flood
cannot be estimated at this stage but it is believed to be
somewhere in the order of once in 10,000 years. Any design
which provides assured control of the probable maximum flood
should therefore have a high level of security against failure
by overtopping.

C.M. De Turville   That seems most uneconomic then, ten
thousand years is an extreme.

J.S. Windsor   This is the design policy in North America in
the case of major structures since these should have only a
negligible risk of failure. Due to a number of intangibles
such as loss of life from failure it is difficult to design
these structures on an economic basis. In other situations
such as high level of protection may be impracticable and
prohibitively expensive. The alternative approach, therefore,
is to structure the model to include risk cost of failure in
the objective function and then to determine the design which
minimizes total system costs. This may result in an optimum
design which is less extreme than the probable maximum flood.

C.M. De Turville   Presumably you have to assign present values to these various costs.

J.S. Windsor   There is generally a choice. You can either
convert all costs to present day values, or to annual values
for comparison, knowing the discount rate, and design life

for the structures. In my study I have considered total
annual costs.

C.M. De Turville   My second query relates to ground water,
and the structure and permeability of soils. Presumably a
good deal has to be ascertained about this before one can
carry out realistically the kind of exercise you described.
For instance the same rainfall will have a very different
outcome depending upon whether it was preceded by a long dry
spell (so that many pores in the ground are vacant) or by a
rainstorm, leaving few pores unfilled. How would you take
this into account?

J.S. Windsor   This would be part of the forecasting procedure. Variables such as antecedent rainfall and its effect
on the initial wetness of the catchment are normally taken
into account in the estimation of flood runoff. One of the
simplest techniques is to estimate the effective rainfall
after allowing for losses and then use a unit hydrograph to
give the predicted storm runoff.

C.M. De Turville   Do you actually monitor what is going on?

J.S. Windsor   Yes. The hydrometerological records are continuously updated and this information is used to obtain a
revised estimate of the flood runoff and hence the operational policy.

R. Sutherland   The firm that I work for has done a considerable amount of reservoir systems modelling. They have
computer programs that will solve for optimal dam heights and
reservoir volumes once the appropriate criterion function has
been chosen. The criterion could be flood control, agricultural irrigation, power generation, or recreation. All of
their dams are designed to pass a probable maximum flood.
The probable maximum flood is estimated from developing a
rainfall-runoff function in which the rainfall used is a
critical arrangement of the maximum probable precipitation.
In designing a large dam the designer must be concerned with
the excepted damage if the dam were to fail. If a dam failure
would result in the loss of human lives, then the design must
be extremely conservative.

2.3 Optimization Methods for Planning Waste Water Management
Systems

E.F. Joeres   I am sorry I had to bore you with reading this
paper, but I couldn't give it to you off the cuff, and this
is the only way to fairly represent the achievements of Drs.
Orth and Ahrens.

C.M. De Turville Several contributors have set out to

minimize the cost function, but I wonder whether they have
sufficiently debated that particular objective with economists,
as there are other criteria which are coming into fashion,
such as cost benefit analysis. Perhaps in some situations one
ought to question more closely the initial economic criteria.

E.F. Joeres   You are quite correct and I think there is a
good deal of work going on in this regard where there is a
whole hierarchy of objectives, one of them for example being
income distribution in terms of benefits received. I think
there is a very serious attempt being made in terms of
multiple social objectives in defining some of the trade-offs
between these. If you look at the literature, there is some
work by Profs. Cohon and Marks on a project in Argentina in
comparing the trade-off between maximum return versus distribution of regional income, where a trade-off curve analogous
to a product substitution function is derived, which requires,
in order to find out where you want to be on the trade-off
curve, a knowledge of the social indifference curve among
these objectives which you don't know, but the trade-off curve
turned out to be so peculiar in shape that it was quite obvious that only a particular portion of the curve gave a
rational mix of these two objectives. In other words, this
was a regional water resources development project where the
interactions of the elements in the model applied to an entire
region. Yet there are distinct political sub regions and a
great deal of political tension would result if one sub region
was preferred over another beyond a certain degree. The
difference between maximizing regional benefits as. opposed to
maximizing the overall benefit is that they are two different
objectives. In water resources, there are other problems in
defining objectives. I think we talked about the flood control problem earlier. One can state different objectives
that are of the form of minimizing the fluctuation of the
water pool if you are interested in recreational objectives.
That's possible too. I agree with you that the economic
efficiency objective is one that we lean on too much, although
by and large I guess it is still the most important.

C.M. De Turville   Thank you for drawing our attention to the
need to give due weight to social and political considerations when planning to meet apparently purely technical
objectives.

E.F. Joeres   I might say on this specific issue that in the
model Orth and Ahrens have dealt with, i.e. the regional waste
water treatment problem, some political realities can be
incorporated. The whole problem is initially set up by
defining a feasible network with all possible elements, and
of course in the choice of these elements - where one could
build an interceptor between communities,. which communities
allow regional cooperation, which nodes allow waste water

treatment plants and what maximum capacities these could have
according to their environmental impact – a political
accommodation is included for all decisions in terms of setting up the problem as a function of the local area. There
are certain node connections which are disallowed not because
of political jurisdictions, but because of physical or technical problems. You would not, for example, want to cross a
river or a mountain range if you could avoid it, even though
the model allows for the inclusion of this possibility.

I. Bogardi   In regard to the problem of designing in an
optimum way regional waste water plants, we used game theoretical approach. In the following way we regard the well-
known problem of a stream and different polluters along this
stream say industrial plants, and now we consider the problem
from the point of view of each pollutant. Well, naturally
each polluter would like to have the greatest benefit in a
sense, regardless of the others. If you would like to solve
the waste water problem an oligopol type of game can be
considered as a game where each polluter plays against all
the others. Well, I am not going to tell you the results of
the formulation only some interesting results. It can be
demonstrated that if all the other polluters join a trust for
instance, they build a treatment plant except one polluter,
this is the best for this single one. However naturally
each polluter can realize this fact therefore either each of
them separately tries to solve the waste water problem by
constructing several treatment plants, or the polluters join
and construct a regional treatment plant. So once more, by
the result of the oligopol game, it can be demonstrated that
a regional waste water plant in a given situation is the most
economic under the used criteria of optimality. I can give
you further details because we have prepared a paper on this
use of an oligopol game.

E.F. Joeres   That is a very interesting discussion which I
think describes the general problem that is very much under
study in terms of relating multiple discharges to the assimilative capacity of a stream or whatever. I would like,
however, to remind you that we should stick in this discussion
to the problem that Orth and Ahrens have solved, and what you
describe is not the problem they have solved. What they are
talking about is basically the much more specific situation
of the trade-off of having a community construct its own
waste water treatment plant (and we know that these waste
water treatment plants exhibit economies of scale and consequently have concave cost function, or of joining into a
regional system, and if so, which plants are built, and who
ships to where. It is better to make treatment plants larger
for many reasons, and Orth and Ahrens state many of these
reasons initially. As a simple illustration, if you then
take two communities required by law to treat, the question is,

should they treat together and have a single regional plant?
Without further restrictions to the example it doesn't matter
whether you build the plant at one community or the other, or
in the middle, in each case you must then build interceptor
pipes to bring the waste together and the decision to be
determined is that even for this very simple example there is
a direct cost comparison or trade-off showing that at some
point the separation of the communities causes enough additional cost due to transport of waste that the cost savings
due to scale are overcome. What Orth and Ahrens have done is
to extend this to a whole region. Each community may or may
not necessarily be along the same stream, so the assimilative
capacity is not an issue beyond *a priori* fixing treatment
efficiencies. It is simply a legal requirement to treat at
a given level and this is specified. As a matter of fact,
you can include the assimilative capacity problem by fixing
the upper capacity limits of individual plants in terms of
allowable hydraulic discharge for specified treatment and
maximum allowable effluent concentrations. The optimization
problem then is if you consider all reasonably possible
interceptors,(some may for example be excluded as being
politically and technically unfeasible, as discussed before)
which configuration of plants and interceptors is least
costly. It becomes an incredibly complex problem which essentially if you set it up as a binary problem is a combina-
torial problem of such dimension that it couldn't be solved
until you had a computer and efficient algorithm to do it.

2.4 Modelling of Aquifer Behaviour for Long Time Periods using Interactive Analogue-digital Computers

R. Butterfield   The solution which you have described has
been concerned with linear problems whereas the other authors
of this Session have been discussing non-linear problems.
Can the analogue-digital system cope with non-linearities?

K.R. Rushton   There are two forms of non-linearity in aquifer
problems, non-linearities due to variations in the parameters
and non-linearities due to the change in an internal or
external boundary. Both of these can be included in the
analogue digital system. For example the second of these
typified by an intermittent river can be represented directly
by an electronic switch. For the variations in the parameter
values, it is often more convenient to use the digital computer to control the changes in a similar manner to the IF
statement in FORTRAN.

R. Butterfield   It appears that most of the tasks are being
carried out by the digital computer leaving very little for
the network?

K.R. Rushton   It is true that few tasks are left to the

network, but these account for over 95 per cent of the time
in a normal digital computer programme. Therefore if 95% of
the calculation can be carried out easily and cheaply on the
network, there is much to commend this approach.

C.Y. Liu   I would like to ask why, in the example of groundwater flow, did the digital computer fail but the analogue
computer succeed. Is that because the analogue computer
with the capacitor-resistor network automatically provides
its own smoothing, spatially and timewise , so the singularity is effectively removed or smoothed out.

K.R. Rushton   It was only certain of the finite difference
approximations which failed in the digital computer solutions.
The backward difference formulation always gave stable results. In fact the analogue and backward difference digital
results are identical provided that the backward difference
time step is sufficiently small. The great advantage of the
analogue is that each run is inexpensive, so that the technique can be used economically for a sensitivity analysis.

C.Y. Liu   Perhaps the reason why both the backward difference
and the analogue give satisfactory results is that they each
provide their own smoothing. Could I also ask whether you
have tried using a variable time step.

K.R. Rushton   Variable time steps are usually adopted for
digital computer solutions with small steps required each time
the pumping rate varies.

G.K. Verboom   May I ask you how much money it costs to make
this network. To me it seems a very complex and very costly
thing. Is this network for one situation only, or is it
large enough and, above all, flexible enough so that it can
be used for several different situations?

K.R. Rushton   The cost of the digital and analogue system
is approximately £10000. The operating costs are virtually
nil.

G.K. Verboom   Can the system be used for only one problem?

K.R..Rushton   The digital computer and peripherals cost about
£7000, analogue to digital and digital to analogue convertors
£2000 and networks representing three aquifers roughly £300
each. This approach could be used for other physical problems for the small additional cost of suitable networks.

G.K. Verboom   You mentioned that you need to go down to a
time step of one-tenth of a day using the ADI methods. Is
that right?

<u>K.R. Rushton</u> Changes in pumpage are usually sudden, not
gradual. This corresponds to a singularity in time. Very
small time steps are needed with the ADI method in such a
situation.

<u>H. Zehlein</u> I have three more questions on your time inte-
gration. The unconditional stability of implicit schemes can
only be bought at the sacrifice of accuracy and an increase
of computer time so my first question is, "How do you keep
track of the accuracy and was your time step dictated by
stability of the accuracy?" and the second question is, "Do
you use a one-step backward difference or a multi-step
backward difference, and whichever you choose how do you get
it started?", and the third question is, "How do you match
the different time scales in digital and analogue computing.
Do you do it by software or by hardware?"

<u>K.R. Rushton</u> In a detailed study of different numerical
approximations we have found that the one step backward
difference approach gives accuracies which are better than
the problems require. Any of the other numerical schemes
which have been tested are liable to instability. The standard stability and convergence analyses are not applicable in
this situation since they assume that the function changes
smoothly. However in groundwater flow problems, sudden
changes occur in the head whenever pumps are switched on or
off. As far as initial conditions are concerned, it is convenient to start with a steady state solution, and use these
heads as initial conditions. It is then necessary to run
the calculation for a number of cycles to obtain a dynamic
balance.
    Both the digital and analogue parts are real time calcu-
lations. The time scale of the analogue calculation is made
as long as is possible but is limited by the need to keep the
effect of leakage currents sufficiently small. It is usually
possible to arrange that the digital part of the calculation
can be carried out faster than the analogue part. The actual
timing is controlled by a clock in the digital computer.

<u>R. Butterfield</u> Our experience with networks is that they
don't cost a lot of money but they take a lot of time. How
long has it taken to assemble one of these networks?

<u>K.R. Rushton</u> Usually, when solving groundwater flow problems,
we make both a digital and an analogue model, therefore we can
make valid comparisons of the effort required. Much of the
data is similar and is read either into the large computer
or, in the case of the analogue-digital system, directly into
the minicomputer. However when arranging data concerning the
field parameters, a data card in the digital model is equivalent to a resistor or capacitor in the analogue model. The
time taken to punch a card or to insert a component are

roughly the same. When it comes to proving the model, the immediate solutions obtained on the analogue model are of great advantage when attempting to trace errors.

R. Adey   I want to put two questions. One is very similar to the last question of how problem dependent is the analogue model. Do you have to set up a complete network for each particular problem? And the second question is, when you talk about non-linear effects are you talking about non-linear terms in differential equations because they cause considerable problems with digital computer simulations. They tend to cause large computer times. Can you see any likelihood of analogue computers providing a more efficient solution than digital computers for non-linear problems?

K.R. Rushton   For each aquifer we have a different network of resistors and capacitors which can be interconnected with the minicomputer. Instead of having a deck of cards for each problem, we have a network.

   With regard to non-linearities there are two kinds, the first is a non-linearity in the differential equation, the second is a non-linearity in the boundary or internal conditions. It is the second which tends to be more significant in groundwater flow problems.

   For mathematical non-linearities, an electronic device can sometimes be found which directly represents a change of coefficient with unknown functions (change of resistance with head). Alternatively, the minicomputer can sample the potentials at relevant nodes and adjust input currents accordingly.

   Of far more significance in aquifer problems are situations such as the fall of water levels from above to below the top of the aquifer. The conditions then change from artesian to water table and the storage coefficient (by which the term $\partial h/\partial t$ is multiplied) increases by at least 1000. These changes can be controlled automatically by a voltage controlled switch and have a significant influence on the aquifer response.

W.K. Tayler   One thing that interests me is that you are using at the moment a two-dimensional scheme. It seems to me that the analogue would have great advantages for a time dependent three-dimensional problem where again you have got very large storage problems in the digital computer. Could you say something about that please?

K.R. Rushton   Three-dimensional networks are quite straightforward, and we do have one such network at the University of Birmingham. However, in our experience it is usually not necessary to represent the whole field in three-dimensional form. Taking the example of the paper, vertical components of flow are only significant in the vicinity of the wells.

Rather than covering the whole field with a three-dimensional grid it is preferable to obtain a two dimensional solution, and then examine the behaviour in the vicinity of the well using a separate radial flow solution in which vertical flow components are represented.

R. Butterfield   There is an allied problem where you have more than one aquifer; for instance in Venice where there are at least three aquifers which are affected by pumping in the upper two. Presumably this kind of problem you could tackle.

K.R. Rushton   Yes, this is just the sort of problem for which these techniques of groundwater flow analysis are well suited.

2.5   A Stochastic Model of Levee Failure

R. Butterfield   Could I just ask if a PF 0.06, is that thought to be acceptable?

I. Bogardi   Well that is another question. Based on the reliability estimation an economic analysis is in order which strives to determine in a sense an optimum probability of failure PF. There can be cases when a PF of 0.06 can be acceptable,   but   naturally   it   is   not   enough in a densely populated urban area. Anyway, that's the first step of a systems analysis. The second is an economic analysis or other kind of political or social analysis seeking a design PF which should be applied.

R. Butterfield   I was interested. Not knowing I wondered what value PF was thought to be.

I. Bogardi   Well it depends, in different places different PFs. I can say that six per cent is rather high, that is, the probability of failure is high and in most cases PF should be about one or even less.

F. Argentesi   You say that your probability of failure is also a random variable because your H, your W and your X are also random variables. Could you explain how you can compute or estimate the moments of these random variables and if you have tested these in some way.

I. Bogardi   The question refers to the handling of soil-mechanical uncertainties. It is not easy, and therefore it was a good point. Generally there are engineering methods by which you can estimate one single resistance value. Then in many cases based on practical experiences on past floods you can characterize the uncertainty of the one estimated value by a variance. Nothing can be done in most cases then to assume that the "true" resistance follows normal distribu-

tion and with an estimated mean and a subjective variance.
The variance can be as high as 40 per cent. Now the distribution is given and you can simulate different values H
according to this given distribution. I would like to add
that we have used subjective   probabilities extensively
and have had quite good experiences. Also, we could up-date
these subjective probabilities by regional data on sand boil
forming, and again as I mentioned in the morning we used the
Bayes theory to combine subjective probabilities with regional
data. Therefore in our mind we used the best possible
information on the uncertain resistances.

2.6 Finite Element Models for Circulation Studies

R. Butterfield   The full line in figure is measured result
and the circles one predicted? Does that apply to the North
Sea diagram as well?

P. Partridge   No, I don't have exact information on the wav
heights in the North Sea, only the cotidal and corange lines
diagram may be drawn from the computed results.

R. Butterfield   This is what I was indirectly asking. You
have no evidence of validity of what you produced for the
North Sea?

P. Partridge   The results may be compared in two ways. The
velocities may be compared against the tidal streams atlases
of which there are two for the North Sea, the waveheight results may be compared against the chart of   cotidal and corange lines. This chart indicates what the range should be
approximately and also approximately when high and low water
should occur. Reasonable agreement is obtained, the comparison however is general and application to specific node
points is difficult.
     The same information is available for the Solent, but in
addition we have the variation of waveheights in the system.
It must be remembered that the Solent is a much smaller
system. The North Sea has many different tidal streams,
the Solent only one main one.

G.K. Verboom   I have a large number of questions to ask.
The first is concerning the Chezy coefficient. You used 10,
20 and 30, but to my knowledge a better value would be between
50 and 60. Can you tell me how does the model behave with
such a value of the Chezy's coefficient?

P. Partridge   One starts the model with Chezy 10, then many
different variations of Chezy are possible. We changed Chezy
in finite increments at the end of evens couple of cycles,
10, 15, 20, 30, 40, 50, 60. First,then we tried seeing what
else could be done i.e. proceeding with C = 10, 20, 40, 60.

We have also tried variation from C = 10 through to 40 over a couple of cycles logarithmically since one is dealing with C^2. We have also used different Chezy coefficients related to topography, and used a variable Chezy coefficient to relate the Chezy coefficient to depth as the total depth H changes round the cycle.

At low Chezy values the velocity ellipses are small in amplitude. They spiral outwards and settle at new values aft after 3-4 cycles with the new Chezy coefficient. As the Chezy coefficient is reduced small drifts become apparent in different parts of the North Sea.

Velocity ellipses for a Chezy coefficient related to total depth (Chezy changes round the cycle) were also obtained. A total water depth $(\eta + h) = 50$ m yields $C = 75m^{\frac{1}{2}}/$ sec.

G.K. Verboom   You prescribe the water level at the boundaries, then, to my knowledge, the water level will be accurate in the whole area; so especially the velocities are influenced by the Chezy coefficients. Now, as you have measurements for the Solent I am very anxious to hear about the influence of the Chezy coefficients on the comparison between measured and calculated velocities. Specially for the Solent where there are measurements.

P. Partridge   Computer results for Solent velocities are presented in reference [1], where they are compared against experimental results. The agreement is reasonable.

For the Solent it is necessary to use a larger Chezy coefficient than for the North Sea, as the system is less stable because of large variations of depth with distance. The North Sea is more uniform, and Chezy coefficients of greater than 60 may be used. General trends were seen to be represented. The model should not be interpreted at a local level because a fairly coarse mesh was used.

[1]   Partridge, P. "The Use of Higher Order Finite Element Models for the Study of Shallow Waters". Ph.D. Thesis, Dept. of Civil Eng., University of Southampton, Southampton, 1976.

G.K. Verboom   The civil engineer wants to use these types of models, among others, to predict the influence of new structures on the water movement. He wants to use a fine grid in order to get accurate answers and not to have trends only. In my opinion it still must be shown that accurate results can be obtained with finite element methods as with finite-difference methods at comparable costs.

P. Partridge   If one wanted to predict the effects of a structure one would do two things. You would start by building a large scale coarse mesh around the whole outside and then one would build a much finer mesh around the actual structure you were representing. I have been presenting res- ults of the North Sea without any particular end in view other than seeing what the results are like. These may be consid- ered as the preliminary coarse mesh. I am not saying that here we are interested in any specific development. The model is as yet at an early experimental stage.

G.K. Verboom   Concerning measurements, I am sure there must be a large number of measurements of water height and veloci- ties, even from the North Sea and even in England because of Tonswap 1973. As you know, this was a large international measuring campaign in the North Sea; I think these measure- ments must be available to you.

My next question concerns boundary conditions. The shallow water equations are a system of hyperbolic equations (with characteristics) if you drop the dissipative terms. According to my knowledge there are two characteristics going into the area where the water is moving in and one moving in where the water is moving out of the area. So, one has to prescribe two boundary conditions at the inlet and one at the outlet of the area. Now you said you prescribed only the water level at the entrance. Is there somewhere a hidden boundary condition; this is often the case for instance in finite difference methods, or do you not agree with the state- ment that you need two boundary conditions.

C.A. Brebbia   In order to fully understand how boundary conditions are introduced into finite elements, let us con- sider the case of shallow water equations without convective terms, Coriolis or friction, i.e.

$$\frac{\partial q_1}{\partial t} = gh \frac{\partial \eta}{\partial x_1} \quad , \quad \frac{\partial q_2}{\partial t} = gh \frac{\partial \eta}{\partial x_2} \tag{1}$$

plus the continuity equation,

$$\frac{\partial q_1}{\partial x_1} + \frac{\partial q_2}{\partial x_2} + \frac{\partial \eta}{\partial t} = 0 \tag{2}$$

where $q_i = \int_{-h}^{\eta} v_i \, dx_3$, $i = 1,2.$

We can take derivatives of the first momentum equation with respect to x_1 and the second with respect to x_2 and substitute $\partial^2 q_i / \partial x_i \partial t$ terms in the continuity equation derivated with respect to t. This gives the wave equation,

$$g\{\frac{\partial}{\partial x_1}(h \frac{\partial \eta}{\partial x_1}) + \frac{\partial}{\partial x_2} (h \frac{\partial \eta}{\partial x_2}) \}- \frac{\partial^2 \eta}{\partial t^2} = 0 \tag{3}$$

The boundary conditions corresponding to (3) are,
a) On S_2 part of the boundary the normal velocity is prescribed according to the specialized momentum equation,

$$gh \frac{\partial \eta}{\partial n} = -(\frac{\partial q_n}{\partial t}) = f \tag{4}$$

or in particular $\frac{\partial \eta}{\partial x} = 0$ (no flux, or land type boundary).

b) On S_1 part of the boundary one specifies the elevation (i.e. ocean type boundary).

$$\eta = \bar{\eta}(x_1 \; x_2 \; t). \tag{5}$$

The initial conditions are η and the derivatives $\partial \eta / \partial t$. The finite element statement corresponding to this equation and boundary conditions can be written,

$$\int_0^{\Delta t} \left\{ \int \int \left[\left(g \frac{\partial}{\partial x_1} (h \frac{\partial \eta}{\partial x_1}) + \frac{\partial}{\partial x_2} (h \frac{\partial \eta}{\partial x_2}) \right) \delta \eta - \frac{\partial^2 \eta}{\partial t^2} \delta \eta \right] dx_1 dx_2 \right\} dt =$$

$$= \int_0^{\Delta t} \left[\int \int_{S_2} (gh \frac{\partial \eta}{\partial n} - f) \delta \eta dS \right] dt \tag{6}$$

with $\eta = \bar{\eta}$ on S_1. $(S = S_1 + S_2)$.

Integrating by parts equation (6) we have that,

$$\int_0^{\Delta t} \left\{ \int \int \left[g \{ h \frac{\partial \eta}{\partial x_1} \frac{\partial \delta \eta}{\partial x_1} + h \frac{\partial \eta}{\partial x_2} \frac{\partial \delta \eta}{\partial x_2} + \frac{\partial^2 \eta}{\partial t^2} \delta \eta \right] dx_1 dx_2 \right\} dt =$$

$$= \int_0^{\Delta t} \{ \int \int_{S_2} f \; \delta \eta \; dS \} \; dt. \tag{7}$$

plus $\eta = \bar{\eta}$ on S_1.

Hence we have to know the value of η in the S_1 part of the boundary or the value of f in S_2. In a channel for instance, one will prescribe η at the entrance and the outlet and the $f = 0$ condition on the walls of the channel.

Question   My question is not really all that related. It's just a theoretical question on boundary conditions. If you have got periodic boundary condition tidal heights, are the steady state velocities periodic necessarily? You seemed to be implying that they were. You expected them to be?

P. Partridge   The North Sea itself never reaches any sort of
steady state.   There is a drift of water through the system.
The water is never at exactly the same level at the end of
the tidal cycle as what it is at the beginning at a given
point.   It is only because for the purposes of the computer
programme, the computer simulation, we are slightly simplifying things and are making the tidal heights to be exactly the
same at the beginning and end of the tidal cycle that the
velocity ellipse comes round and nearly catches up with its
own tail.   Even so this does not imply any sort of real steady
state.   The drift implied the lack of origin centredness of
some of the velocity ellipses would imply water movement
through the system, see ref. A.4. We only used steady state in
a loose sense.   We were not really trying to imply that the
North Sea reaches this condition. It's a means of testing
whether the computer program has steadied or if there are
still effects of previous simulations appearing in the
results.

G.K. Verboom   You said that it takes 1600 seconds for one of
the problems on an ICL 1906A machine.   I really don't know
what kind of machine this is.   Can you compare this for
instance with the IBM360/65 or the CDC 6600   or something
like that.

C.A. Brebbia   It is difficult to compare these results with
those obtained in an IBM 360/65 because we never had access
to one.   We found in running certain programs in a 360/95
that it was 5 times faster than the ICL. The CDC 6600 seems
to be still faster than the IBM 360/95.

Written Contribution. Topological Study of Finite Differential Element Nets   by H. Zehlein

Finite element methods are a numerical tool well suited for
a unified approach to environmental problems where different
physical effects acting simultaneously have to be described
over the same topological partition of the considered domain.
The necessity to handle very large territory-specific networks [1] often makes direct solution schemes extremely
awkward. It is one aim of this note to remind of the "Finite
Differential Element Method" (FDEM) invented by Visarion
and Iovănescu [2] as an extension of the well-known transfer
matrix concept to 2D- and 3D-models. It requires only solutions of equation systems having the size of the local transfer matrices. Another purpose of this note is to mention
a new concept for network description which comprehends a
generalized definition of node valency, auxiliary nets and a
generalized adjacency matrix [3,4] .

    The FDEM requires a choice of an initial edge, where a

sequential ramification process begins, which successively
covers the whole net (see edge A in Fig. 1) with arrows –

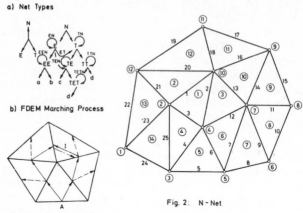

a) Net Types

b) FDEM Marching Process

Fig. 1: Net Types and FDEM

Fig. 2: N - Net

each indicating a local transfer matrix operation. The
topological concept proposed here helps to find a best choice
of this start. It also allows the automatic finding of all
boundary nodes or edges, if the net is defined in the usual
way by an adjacency or an incidence matrix.

The FDEM [2] requires a triangle net, where it defines
linear transformations (local transfer matrices) between
pairs of state vectors containing the unknown parameters of
shape functions attributed to each edge of a triangular
domain. These matrices are set up consecutively following a
ramification process indicated in Fig. 1b. There, whenever
a new matrix is created (symbolized by an arrow), a new set
of unknowns becomes involved. Modifications come into play
when an arrow hits a boundary edge (dotted arrows) thereby
entering an additional boundary condition. The number of
sets of unknowns involved is reduced whenever two arrows meet
(see I in Fig. 1b). This situation (called intersection in
[2]) ends the circumnavigation of an inner node and gives an
initial situation for embracing the next internal node during
this transfer matrix front advancement. The last operation
touches the last boundary edge, now "knowing" all boundary
conditions. Therefore the last set of unknowns is then
determined definitely. Entering these values back into the
scheme, all other sets of unknowns may then successively be
computed, because all transfer matrices are now established.
The entire process may be formally represented by a binary
tree. Such an "expansion tree" is shown in Fig. 5 for edge
24 as the starting edge of the triangle net (Fig. 2). For
economizing purpose like grid layout and/or repeated runs
with local modifications, it is useful to know for a particular initial edge after how many transfer matrix operations
and at which location in the net the sequence of intersections
occurs.

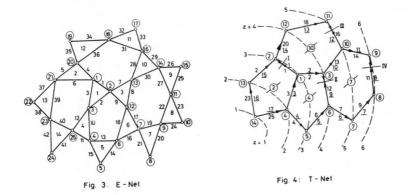

Fig. 3. E - Net

Fig. 4: T - Net

Before an algorithm delivering this insight is given, we explain the derivation of the E-net (Fig. 3) and the T-net (Fig. 4) from the original triangle net (N-net; Fig. 2).

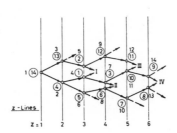

Fig. 5: Expansion Tree **(N-edge 24)**
(i.e. T - Node 14)

The E-net is created by connecting the midpoints of the edges within the N-net for every triangle contained there. The T-net is constructed by drawing all the edge-bisectors pertaining to an inner edge of the N-net. Thus, the triangles of the N-net become nodes of the T-net (reciprocal cell partition), and a one-to-one mapping exists between the edge-sets of both nets, too.

The expansion tree (Fig. 5) may be obtained from the T-net by cutting all edges coincident with an intersection referring to the same initial T-node (N-triangle). The z-lines in Fig. 4 are lines of constant Euler distance referring to T-node 14 there. They correspond to the successive front advancement steps indicated by the expansion tree (Fig. 5).

There are typical row sum properties concerning the adjacency and incidence matrices describing the various nets

1. GZ (14 × 14)   2. GZS (14 × 6)

0	1	2	3	4	5	6	7	8	9	10	11	12	13	14		1	2	3	4	5	6
1	0	1	1	1	2	2	3	4	3	2	3	2	2	2		3	6	3	1	0	0
2	1	0	2	2	3	3	4	5	4	3	2	1	1	2		3	4	3	2	1	0
3	1	2	0	2	2	1	2	3	2	1	2	3	3	3		3	6	4	0	0	0
4	1	2	2	0	1	2	3	4	4	3	4	3	2	1		3	4	3	3	0	0
5	2	3	2	1	0	1	2	3	4	3	4	4	3	2		2	4	4	3	0	0
6	2	3	1	2	1	0	1	2	3	2	3	4	4	3		3	4	4	2	0	0
7	3	4	2	3	2	1	0	1	2	3	4	5	5	4		2	3	3	3	2	0
8	4	5	3	4	3	2	1	0	1	2	3	4	6	5		2	2	3	3	2	1
9	3	4	2	4	4	3	2	1	0	1	2	3	6	5		2	3	3	3	1	1
10	2	3	1	3	3	2	3	2	1	0	1	2	4	4		3	4	4	2	0	0
11	3	2	2	4	4	3	4	3	2	1	0	1	3	4		2	3	4	4	0	0
12	2	1	3	3	4	4	5	4	3	2	1	0	2	3		2	3	4	3	1	0
13	2	1	3	2	3	4	5	6	6	4	3	2	0	1		2	3	3	2	1	2
14	2	2	3	1	2	3	4	5	5	4	4	3	1	0		2	3	3	3	2	0

```
*ANT
3.
          *              *
    1  X
    2 XX             XX
    3 XX    X    X
    4 X    X              X
    5   X X
    6  X X X
    7        X X
    8        X X
    9         X X
   10  X      X X
   11            X X
   12 X            X
   13 X                  X
   14    X               X
```

```
*ANN
4.
            *            *
    1  XX          X
    2 X XX        X X
    3 XX XX
    4  XX X X   X
    5    XX XX
    6     X XX
    7    XXX XXX
    8     XX X
    9        XX XX
   10  X X  X X XX
   11            XX X
   12 XX        .XX.
```

```
ANNT
5.
          *          *              *
    1                 XX
    2 XX X            XX
    3     XX             X
    4 X XXXX
    5     XXX
    6      XX
    7  X  XXXXX
    8      XX
    9      XXX
   10 XXX            XXX
   11               XX
   12  X             XX
```

FIG. 6: TYPICAL ADJACENCY AND INCIDENCE MATRICES

1. GZ(14x14):	GENERALIZED ADJACENCY MATRIX
2. GZS(14x6):	GENERALIZED NODE VALENCY MATRIX
3. ANT(14x14)	(=ATN=AET) : ADJACENCY MATRIX OF THE T-NET
4. ANN(12x12):	ADJACENCY MATRIX OF THE N-NET (SEE FIG.2)
5. ANNT(12x14):	NODE-TRIANGLE INCIDENCE MATRIX OF THE N-NET (SEE FIG.2)

[3,4]. An entire progeny of auxiliary nets may be constructed by repeated application of the rules for E- or T-derivation (Fig. 1a). Some adjacency as well as incidence matrices representing those nets are collected in Fig. 6. Several of the above mentioned row sum criteria can be utilized to identify the boundary-forming nodes, edges or triangles of these nets [4]. Here we are particularly interested in the generalized adjacency matrix (GZ in Fig. 6). There an integer at position (i,j) gives the smallest number of edges to be passed within the T-net (Fig. 4) when travelling from node i to node j (= Euler distance). Of course, the pattern of the 1's yields the "classic" adjacency matrix of the net (here: T-net). All other entries z > 1 may be interpreted as a generalized node degree (valency) of the neighbourhood class z [3]. The following algorithm finds out, when and where for a given initial node the intersections occur during the FDEM's ramification process: Build the T-net of the given net; then

1. Establish a rectangular "cycle matrix" C housing as rows the T-nodes forming a "cycle" there.
2. Perform sweeps through that row of the generalized adjacency matrix of the T-net which represents the starting T-node (k). The first sweep enters the column indices of all 0's consecutively in a "location vector" L, the 2nd sweep continues the procedure for all 1's and so on.
3. **Build the "inverse location vector" J:** it contains the position of the 1, 2 etc. within the location vector L at the 1st, 2nd, etc. position.
4. Replace every integer contained in the cycle matrix C by that integer contained in the inverse location vector the position of which is equal to the considered C-integer; thus a "sequence matrix" S is received such that

$$S_{ij} = J_k (C_{ij})$$

For an example illustrating this algorithm consult [4]. The sequence of the highest numbers within each row of S indicates after how many transfers the pertaining intersection occurs. In our example (k = 14): I (II, III, IV) passing T-node 2 (6, 11, 9) after 5 (8, 12, 14) operations Fig. 4 confirms this result.

Applying the above algorithm to all boundary N-edges (T-nodes 5, 7, 8, 9, 11, 12, 13) one obtains the following table of intersection occurrences:

	5	7	8	9	11	12	13	14
I	5	8	6	8	7	7	5	5
II	11	9	10	10	11	10	10	8
III	12	13	12	11	13	12	11	12
IV	14	14	14	14	14	14	14	14

T-nodes 9, 13 (= N-edges 15, 22) are optimal starters when the
first 3 intersections have to be found as fast as possible.
If only the first two intersections are to be identified after
a minimum number of transfers, then the answer is unique; only
T-node 14 (i.e. N-edge 24) is optimal under this condition.

[The author gratefully acknowledges the help contributed by
Miss R. Vierling who wrote a little pilot code nicknamed
TOPFUN (= Topological Fundamentals) to create and operate the
required Boolean matrices.]

1. S. Kaden, et al, (1974). Application of Finite Element
   Methods ..., pp 721-735 of Oden et al. (edts.): Finite
   Elements in Flow Problems (Proc. Int. Symp. on FEMs in
   Flow Problems, Swansea, Jan. 1974), UAH Press.

2. V. Visarion, R. Iovănescu (1973). Modelul Elementului
   Diferential finit, Matrice de Transfer in Probleme
   Bidimensionale ale Teoriei Elasticitatii. St. Cerc. Mec.
   Apl. 32, 3, 1227-1241 (In Rumanian)

3. H. Zehlein (1974). Topologische Aspekte hexagonaler
   Netze für Ersatzfachwerke zur Simulation der Verformung
   von Stabbündeln unter Querkraft; Atomkernenergie (ATKE)
   23, 1, 44-49.

4. H. Zehlein (1975). Topologische Grundlagen der Methode
   der finiten Differential-Elemente. Unpublished internal
   research report. To be published as KFK-report, 1976;
   Abbreviated draft in English available from the author.

3. DISCUSSION: AIR POLLUTION

3.1 On the Calculation of Optimal Long Term Air Pollution
Abatement Strategies for Multiple-Source Areas

Question   I would like to ask two questions if I may. The
first one concerning the cost function F, if I understand
your notation correctly. How sensitive is the result to the
linearity you assume, but how severe an assumption is that?

S.A. Gustafson   It is very difficult to get cost functions in
practice and we have tried test examples because one has to
get authorities to believe in those models. It turns out that
there is a natural hesitation to apply optimization. But I
think still that even if you must use a bad cost function you
are not worse off than if you don't optimize.

Question   Can I perhaps rephrase that question and incorporate the second one then. Where in fact does the greatest
uncertainty arise with the models? It is well known that the
diffusion processes which are implicit in what you are doing
have got uncertainties. Where do you think the greater uncertainty lies? In the optimization of the economic aspects
you are looking at or in the more physical aspects of it? I'll
be blunt, I mean just what reliance can one put on the outcome
from the models themselves.

S.A. Gustafson   The concentration field is generated by a
diffusion model and of course I can choose any model. We have
tried to get the best one on the market. A diffusion model is
an input in an optimization scheme.

Question   Yes, but there are certain uncertainties in what you
get from the diffusion model which is one stage of the process.
There are then other uncertainties in the second part of the
model you are looking at and taking the two combined, what sort
of answer do you get out of it. I mean, you come up with a
certain optimum strategy but may there not be three or four
strategies which in fact would fit within an acceptable error.

S.A. Gustafson   I don't know which uncertainties are the
worst. One could say that if you had a bad cost function you
still would get a policy which meets the standard. That means

one takes the risk of having a too expensive policy and I
think that is not so dangerous. As I said, one has to chase
for the best diffusion model and we have made some test calculations. In Stockholm we used an adaptation of the Fortak
model. This adaptation is done by Bringfelt and this model
behaves very well. I think it estimates the monthly average
with an error of 10% which I think is good for this type of
model.

E.F. Joeres   I was interested in the various policy options
that you described, particularly how the taxation one would
fail if the tax can be passed on and nothing would be done. I
would think that a partial answer to the uncertainty question
that was just asked would be the policy that you enumerated on
zoning the pollutors into groups, which in a sense avoids
interfering with the perfect or imperfect competition, as the
case may be, by forcing groups of pollutors to be at the same
level. It would seem to me that the zoning problem, if you
can handle it that way, would allow you to use industry-wide
cost curves for removal, which is really one of the uncertainties that was asked about. It has been our experience in the
water pollution field that it is sometimes very difficult in
approaching industries, for example, a paper mill, to find out
what their removal costs really are. If, however, you approach
a community and try to find out in terms of the operation of a
municipal waste water treatment plant what the cost relationships are, then that is much more readily available, but
industries have a great deal of hesitancy to allow people into
their plant to look, much less to say what they are doing.
Thus grouping pollutors and using industry wide cost curves
published by industrial organizations that they belong to in
a sense avoids this information requirement and forces those
firms with higher costs simply to adhere to the industry average. Could you comment on using the zoned model which you
indicated as one of your policies, on the formulation that you
have just presented.

S.A. Gustafson   Yes. First one thing which I think some
people have missed when I mentioned this topic earlier, namely
that the sources which comprise a group can be widely separated geographically. The transfer functions u_r could have many
local maxima. So it's quite natural if you take one u_r for
each industry. I think that would a very good idea.

E.F. Joeres   Grouping waste sources by industry has been done
for pollutors along a river, where members of a group category
may or may not be geographically adjacent so that you can have
such groupings as paper mills and refineries, where individual
firms may be completely interspersed, yet you come up with a
removal requirement that uniformly applies to an entire group,
and a different removal requirement that applies to a different
group which minimises the cost according to industry average

cost curves to meet a standard. This policy still allows the competition within industries to proceed as it will, and you have at least avoided that political problem.

S.A. Gustafson   Yes. I think it's very good. May be that is the solution of the problem. I have also studied a lot of literature about it and I think your suggestion opens a way of really applying these results. Are those cost functions accurate for various industries?

E.F. Joeres   It doesn't really matter because usually the cost functions come from the trade groups themselves and they won't admit that the costs are not accurate if they gave them to you.

G. Halbritter   I have just a question about the diffusion model, especially about the coefficient which expresses the influence from one country to the other. We use a model which describes the influence within a region of about 50 miles and there is the problem to have good numbers for the concentrations. I think it is not possible to get the influence from one country to the other with the Fortak model.

S.Å. Gustafson   One should not use a Fortak model for that purpose. I don't think that we as yet can compute these constants but later on, hopefully. I mentioned the paper by Bolin and Persson how they consider transportation models for long ranges, but I don't think that the results are accurate enough for use in my optimization model.

3.2 The Use of Mixed Integer Programming for the Evaluation of Some Alternate Air Pollution Abatement Policies

G.B. Brundit   I wanted to contrast this gentleman's talk with the talk that we heard yesterday, from Karlsruhe. It seems to me, not working in this field, that two different aspects contrast with each other. The one is the emphasis that you have made on maximum standards rather than average standards, and the other is the input to the diffusion models. I think you used many weather stations whereas I understood the Karlsruhe study to be based on one weather station. Could you comment on this?

L.F. Escudero   Concerning the first question we have introduced average concentrations because in our case the diffusion model was rather poor due to our many special conditions, hence the standard variation of the real concentration is very high. Regarding the second question, the input to the algorithm comes from the diffusion models.

3.3 The Application of Numerical Modelling to Air Pollution in the Forth Valley

G. Halbritter I have just a question. What set of dispersion parameters do you use, and have you made calculations with different sets, Pasquill, Klug and St Louis?

A.W.C. Keddie At the present time we use Pasquill grouping. We are in fact going on to use other ones, not because we believe that any one set is better than another because they have all been developed for different areas and strictly speaking one should not use diffusion coefficients which have been developed let us say for an open plane area (i.e. such as Pasquill ones). We use Pasquill modifying them for a surface roughness and so forth. We put in our own modifications but we try and use a range of dispersion coefficients to get some idea of the uncertainty introduced into the results if in fact they are wrong for a particular area in question, and this is one of the limitations of using this type of solution. On the other hand, because of the type of data requirements there are, we just do not have the data which is required for very much more sophisticated models which to some extent generate the diffusivities internally. I don't know if that answers your question, but in fact we use a range of them to allow for the uncertainty. In a sense it is a form of sensitivity analysis. One looks at the model and sees how sensitive it is to the diffusion coefficients.

G. Halbritter Have you found that the dispersion parameters are the most sensitive part of the model and what is the result of the sensitivity analysis?

A.W.C. Keddie At the present time, I will give you a preliminary answer to that. The further you are away from the source and the lower the source is the less critical it is, but if you are looking at what we term high-level sources or if you like power stations or oil refineries which have got high stacks and are emitting effectively between 250 metres and 500 metres above the ground, then in fact the answers one gets within a distance of 10-15 km of that source are highly dependent on the vertical diffusivity and one gets very extreme answers. That is if one looks at the variability of the concentration to be taken with the distance from the source. In fact if one looks at the diffusion equation it is quite obvious that one does not really expect this. But one has got to be careful that one does not read too much into that because we are primarily concerned with the accumulated frequency distribution throughout the year. We are not particularly worried whether a concentration of a certain value occurs at a particular point at a particular time. From the planning point of view that doesn't really matter. The important thing is whether in fact you can represent for that location what statistically will happen throughout the year. When it comes to that part of it, then the solutions aren't quite so dependent on the dispersion parameters.

G. Halbritter   I would like to ask a question about the mixing
height. What values do you take for the mixing height, in the
box model you had values L, L means the mixing height I think,
you have taken very small values about 37 metres.

A.W.C. Keddie   Now we have got to be very careful here. There
are two things here. There is the mixing height which is
determined by let us say an inversion in the atmosphere. That
is one, and generally speaking it will not in fact affect a
small area like the ones we are looking at. We are not looking at something on the scale of London in this particular
case and the mixing height is of the order 100 metres.
What governs the height of the box if you like is the rate of
vertical dispersion. If one was looking at the regional area,
let's say the South of the U.K. as a whole, then in fact it
probably would be determined by the inversion height rather
than the vertical dispersion.

G. Halbritter   And what values do you take for the exact
mixing height in the model for long-range dispersion. It's
very difficult to get values I think.

A.W.C. Keddie   At the present time we in fact have been relying on quite variable observations of upper air gauges from
the radius on the stations near to there. However we are
concerned with this and in fact we are just extending the work.
We are buying an acoustic radar to send up acoustic sound up
into the atmsophere and from the return signal one can get a
relative measure of the temperature variance. This is done
on a continuous load and one can then get an idea of where the
inversion heights are, whether they are multiple or not.

G. Halbritter   What typical values do you get about inversion
heights?

A.W.C. Keddie   During the night somewhere between 100 and 250
metres, during the day they go up to about 2,500 metres. It
depends on conditions.

G. Romberg   I have a question concerning your formula 11.
I think it is only applicable in the far field. Do you have
any idea about a realistic near field approximation? Consider
the plume rise above the top of a chimney. The plume is,
itself, a three dimensional turbulent shear flow embedded in
a turbulent atmospheric boundary layer. The model underlying
your formula 11 approximates the mixing region about the core
of unmixed effluent as a point source. This modelling can
provide reasonable results only at positions, of which the
distance from the top of the chimney is very large compared
with the average characteristic dimension of the mixing region
mentioned.

A.W.C. Keddie   The approximation you are referring here to in fact is in the inclusion of the inversion height L because the solution itself is an approximation and essentially one solves that equation with the boundary conditions which were introduced there.

G. Romberg   Your solution might be reasonable in the far field but not in the near field.

A.W.C. Keddie   For what reason? I don't quite follow.

G. Romberg   As I pointed out before, the model underlying your formula 11 approximates the mixing region about the core of unmixed effluent as a point source. Formula 11 cannot be applied in the near field.

A.W.C. Keddie   How did you find far and near field. I mean what sort of scales are you talking about?

G. Romberg   The modelling underlying your formula 11 can furnish reasonable results only at positions, for which the distance from the top of the stack, is very large compared with the average characteristic dimension of the mixing region mentioned. I think you didn't consider this point.

A.W.C. Keddie   Yes, I did consider it. I mean we are as interested in what happens 100 metres from the source as we are from 15 km from it.

G. Romberg   Not say several hundred metres away from the stack. I think at such a distance the application of formula 11 is subject to doubt.

A.W.C. Keddie   If one is talking about let us say several hundred metres from a power station stack, well all right, this formula doesn't fit that situation. If one is looking statistically over a year then the contribution from a large stack to a ground level of concentrations within several hundred metres, or even a few kilometres of it, is virtually negligible.

G. Romberg   Formula 11 is reasonable say at a distance of several kilometres away.

A.W.C. Keddie   I agree. Yes, the actual physics of the situation aren't well represented.

G. Romberg   The model underlying formula 11 is too gross in the near field. Have you an idea about improvement of the model for these areas close to the air pollutant sources?

A.W.C. Keddie   The important thing of course is what you are
asking from the model. I mean we are essentially looking for
representation which fits the facts as we observe them within
certain constraints and we don't use this type of model under
all conditions anyway. It depends on the local structure of
the turbulence round the source. If in fact building structures as such that it alters the turbulence field, then in fact
that formula won't apply and you won't use it.

C.M. De Turville   It is reckoned as a rule of thumb that
under normal conditions of atmospheric stability, the distance
at which the maximum ground level pollution from a power
station chimney occurs is about 15H, where H is the height of
emission plus the thermal rise of the plume. However, under
the unstable conditions which rapidly break up the polluted
layers due to low lying sources, fumigation episodes may occur
quite near the chimney, due to large scale vertical looping.
These brief episodes do not really constitute a health hazard,
but they can be a transient nuisance which is not often repeated at any given point, since fumigation is rare anyway and
fumigation at a selected point is rarer still. However, this
is the sort of situation which might contribute to the upper
2% of the observed cumulative frequency distribution of concentration.

A.W.C. Keddie   The point is well taken. In fact it has been
allowed for in our recent modelling work, which is by no means
fully described in this paper. One finds from the modelling
techniques themselves that under stable conditions such as
Pasquill G type situations, power stations do not contribute
at all to local pollution, and it is only the small but low
level sources that do. On the other hand, under Pasquill AB
or more particularly A conditions, power stations do contribute quite significantly. This is taken into account, but the
A type conditions are very infrequent anyway and may only occur
two or three times a year at a particular point.

C.M. De Turville   Bearing in mind that air pollution forecasts
based on a formula model are limited by the extent of the
available data, what are your views on improved means of data
acquisition? Do you visualise for instance a much more auto-
mated collection of pollution and meteorological data which
would be relayed to a central operations room where it might
be taped or computerised and analysed?

A.W.C. Keddie   The setting up of the automatic system you
mentioned would depend on its purpose. If the objective is to
control the pollution from large or low level emitters in real
time, then a fast response system is required to deal with
adverse meteorological conditions. On the other hand, modelling of say the Forth Valley for long range planning purposes
over the next 10 or 20 years does not call for this immediate
response. In any case the requirement is for better meteoro-

logical and emission data, and not for better observed or
planned concentrations. In fact we have the equipment for
doing that either on line or off line, but we do require improved techniques to obtain the relevant meteorological data
and more accurate emission factors from individual sources.
These are where the two major uncertainties lie. In the more
sophisticated air pollution models which are currently under
study, such as finite difference and finite element models,
one of the greatest uncertainties from a meteorological point
of view lies in determining the diffusivities Q_x, Q_y and Q_z.
One can try and express these analytically in a form involving
some physics, but we have little information which will tell
us that we are using the correct values, especially in the
vertical dimension. Remote sensing is in fact one of the
methods we are actively pursuing.

3.4 Shallow-Water Approximation for the Transport of Pollutants in an Urban Basin

G.K. Verboom   You said one of the advantages of integrating of
the vertical direction was that you do not need to prescribe
the absorption at the bottom but this is not true. You will
need a condition either that there is no flux through the
bottom or that there is an absorption so in my opinion you
cannot get round that problem.

C.Y. Liu   I know what your comment is. In integrating
vertically, you impose them once and for all, for example
boundary conditions at the bottom i.e. the non-penetrating
conditions. From that point on you don't have to concern about
it further.

G.K. Verboom   You have assumed there is no absorption.

C.Y. Liu   What I am trying to say is you don't have to model
the absorption from point to point, but you do introduce from
the Leibnitz rule that a boundary condition at the bottom and
a boundary condition at the top. Non-penetrating was the
boundary condition.

G.K. Verboom   May I ask another question. You have integrated
the equations vertically; what I missed is the contribution due
to the non zero gradients of the velocities and the concentration in the vertical direction. Are these quantities not a
function of the vertical direction?

C.Y. Liu   You have to make the assumption that U is represented as in most of shallow water theory, by a $\bar{U}$ in the integration of Udz from zero to H.

G.K. Verboom   In the aquatic environment the dispersion coefficients due to these contributions are usually much larger than

the diffusion coefficients.

C.Y. Liu   What you are saying is then that the gradient in U and V in the vertical direction is much larger.

C.M. De Turville   You mentioned about 12 ppm carbon monoxide in the air of Los Angeles, which seems a very high figure. Could you give us some indication on how this compares with toxicity levels?

C.Y. Liu   No, carbon monoxide at 12 parts per million is not bad at all. Probably the background on carbon monoxide is very close to 10 parts per million. It depends on which pollutants. For example, take SO_2, the subject presented by the author before me, if we have 10 parts per million of SO_2, then most of us would get killed over a 24 hour period.   But the Californian standard on SO_2 for example is 0.1 parts per million. On the other hand, for carbon monoxide, 10 parts per million is not toxic at all. I think the toxicity varies from pollutant to pollutant.

C.M. De Turville   That I understood well, but I am surprised that carbon monoxide is so relatively innocuous.

C.Y. Liu   Yes. We may not accept in Southampton, but I think in London the carbon monoxide level is quite high.   30 parts per million is about the level where significant damage takes place.

C.M. De Turville   That is on the basis of continuous daily exposure to 30 parts per million?

C.Y. Liu I can't remember what the exact values are, but I think the American standard, for 8 hour exposure, it is 20 or 30 parts, between 20 and 25.

B.M. Mollowney   To test the relative importance of diffusion in your model you compared the solution for a turbulent diffusivity of zero and of $800m^2/s$. However in using upstream differencing you have included an implicit (numerical) diffusion which may be so large that the change in the total diffusion is quite small. Please comment?

C.Y. Liu   The numerical turbulence is about 9 times the actual turbulence. I just want to say that in any numerical scheme errors are inevitable, the error there gives you effectively a viscous coefficient, or diffusion coefficient. It depends on where the question is coming from, and in this particular case, you could estimate it. Since the numerical diffusion is about 9 times the actual turbulence diffusion so you have the large damping factor in the numerical scheme that you used.   It is correct that this large factor dominates the integration.

B.M. Mollowney   Yes, I was just wondering how you can say then that it is not important, I mean it could mean that you have not tested that in particular.

C.Y. Liu   Because I had no way to eliminate the numerical diffusion completely. The very fact that I go to higher-order finite difference scheme does not help me in this particular problem because the input function itself has very strong discontinuity in the first derivative.

B.M. Mollowney   Yes, I agree that if you have point sources, you tend to get oscillations. I have found this myself.

C.Y. Liu   This is the reason why I would like to make a point that the numerical scheme here is very important and further investigation in this is warranted.

Question   Following on the point about the importance of turbulence diffusion. You said it wasn't important relative to the advection term. I presume that this is because you are essentially dealing with a ground level source, motor vehicles. I think if you had sources distributed in the vertical as one has for instance with sulphur dioxide, then this wouldn't be the case. I know this is a particular class of model or type of model you are looking at, but I don't know whether you would agree with that comment or not.

C.Y. Liu   When I say that the turbulent diffusion is not important, I really mean that turbulent diffusion in the horizontal direction is not important in comparison with advection. Vertical diffusion is very important because that is the major mechanism in vertical mixing.
   If I put in your model, and in the Gustafson solution that Sigma Z (σ_z) equals zero, I have no solution.

Question   One other quick question. Have you made any comparisons of the predictions from this model with other models, for instance the 'Afrack'. I don't know if you are familiar with Afrack model for carbon monoxide. I think it has been applied to Los Angeles anyhow. It's a semi empirical semi diffusion model. I just wondered if you had made any comparisons with other types of models.

C.Y. Liu   In the United States there is another finite-difference model. There are only two models of this nature available, one is done by a commercial organisation and we have not been able to get it. We have not compared the performance of this model with other types of models.

3.5   Changes in Atmospheric Pollution Concentrations

C.L. Roach   In your paper, the classical time series for the
pollutant concentrations contained a stochastic component.
This component was broken down into autoregressive and moving
average processes. How did you establish the order of both of
these processes?

R.J. Bennett   In this particular paper, we determined the
order of the model (the so-called identification stage in the
analysis) merely by inspection of the structure of the autocorrelation function, the partial correlation function, which
is not given in the paper, and the spectrum. Now, in fact,
this is open to a number of criticisms. There are various
other methods of identification in an iterative form by
sequentially estimating successively higher order models. This
is the approach proposed by K.J. Astrom at Lund and can be
combined with the various other diagnostics which Whittle has
given. This form of classical time series analysis gives tests
of the significance of each order as an increment explanation
based on chi squared. The approach we adopt is fairly simple.
Looking at the spectrum of smoke and SO_2 in the paper, and
also the autocorrelations, it is evident that the periodic
component has not been removed prior to the analysis. One
should, perhaps, remove this either using estimates of the
dominant fourier elements or moving averages. The periodic
component was not removed since, as you will see from the
inspection of the logged spectrum, the relative contribution
to the overall variance is fairly small.

C.L. Roach   The stochastic component has been written as
though no correlation exists between the SO_2 and smoke contributions. Did you establish this to be true? If it were
correlative, do you not think that the stochastic component
should have been written as a joint series containing contributions from both SO_2 and smoke concentrations?

R.J. Bennett   No, we have not done this yet but it would be
very interesting to try. Obviously one is looking here in a
very partial way at a very complex system in which there are
a whole set of pollutants, say m. Thus a complete system
representation would require an mxm matrix transfer function.
The model of the system is still a black box, but since there
are a set of inputs some of which are measurable and some of
which are not measurable, or have not been measured, one ought
to look at the whole structure of the box and derive the
matrix of transfer functions between all of the outputs and
inputs.

Question   Two comments primarily on the method as such, if
I may: first, on the point referred to by the previous
questioner (the cross-correlation between smoke and sulphur

dioxide) it is obvious from the paper that you consider the possibility of photo-chemical reactions as being one of the controlling factors as regards sulphur dioxide. I think it should also be borne in mind that the presence of smoke particles in the atmosphere can have an influence on sulphur dioxide and this emphasizes the importance of looking at the cross-correlations in that respect. Second, looking at the technique as a whole, it probably has even greater value if shorter sampling periods between observations are used, i.e. less than 24 hours. I am thinking in particular here of look-ing at what we would term secondary pollutants or those which are the consequence of photo-chemical reactions. Not just sulphur dioxide but things like ozone, oxides, nitrogens and so on, where on physical and chemical grounds one would expect a phase difference between the primary pollutant as emitted and the secondary pollutant as observed. There are various structures in the observed time series of these various pollutants to which this type of technique could be applied quite easily.

R.J. Bennett   The analysis in this paper has obviously been constrained by the sampling interval of the data that is avail-able. I think that analysis of hourly variations, for example, will exhibit different processes than the present analysis. This is something that we have not yet attempted but could be done in the future. Much more might be expected from such an analysis than the use of the daily values adopted here.

WRITTEN CONTRIBUTION : COMPUTATION OF ATMOSPHERIC CONTAMINATION PRODUCED BY A SOURCE OF GASEOUS EMISSIONS by A.C. Mendez

This work is based on the theoretical study done by experts of the Meteorology Institute (WBA) and sponsored by the Physical Planification Institute (IPF) of Cuba.
    It shows,among other aspects, a method for the study and practical evaluation of atmospheric contamination produced by a point source of gaseous emissions.
    The **goal** was to supply the specialists with a tool for determining the consequences that may derive from the micro-localization of an industry. A programme was written which can determine the environmental contamination for any source.

Proposed Method
The solution is based on statistical methods, through which algebraic mathematical expressions are obtained. These ex-pressions evaluate,

    - the average concentration at a given point
    - the instantaneous concentration at a given moment
    - the maximal range (maximal distance) of the gases and of
      the solid particles (if these are present in the
      emission)
    - maximal gas concentration

<u>Description of the method</u> In order to perform the calculations
tions we suppose that the source of the emission coincides with
axis Z of a rectangular coordinated system, and axis X coincid-
ing with the direction of the wind (Fig. 1). Different
planes parallel to the ground are considered (Fig. 2).

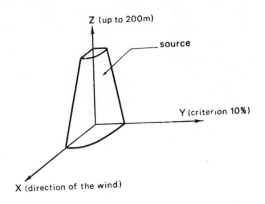

Z (up to 200m)

source

Y (criterion 10%)

X (direction of the wind)

Fig.1

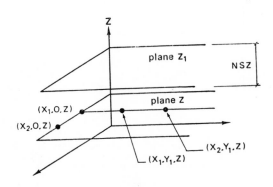

Z

plane Z_1

NSZ

$(X_1,0,Z)$

plane Z

$(X_2,0,Z)$

(X_2,Y_1,Z)

(X_1,Y_1,Z)

Fig.2

Consider a plane Z. We begin by obtaining the average
concentration in point $(X_1,0,Z)$ or which is the same, a point
on the axis corresponding to X on the plane which is being
analyzed and thus we obtain 10% of that concentration. Next
we compute the concentration at the point (X_1,Y_1,Z) separated
from the previous one by a NSY interval, and compare the concentration result with the 10% already obtained. If this is

greater than the 10% previously found, we increase Y_1 in NSY again and the computation and comparison are repeated until we find an average value concentration smaller than the initial 10% (Fig. 2). It may occur that for any of the points we are interested in the average concentration is smaller than the initial 10%. For any of the previous two cases we next increase the NSX interval chosen for X variable.

Repeating the previous process, we will begin by evaluating the concentration in point (X_2, O, Z) for which $X_2 = X_1 + NSX$ and thus obtain the 10% of that value, and doing this sequentially we reach the maximal distance in X.

We must then consider a new plane for the computations and thus successively, until we reach to the maximal height to be investigated (200m). The computations are being centred at the intersection point of the mesh shown in Fig. 3. The process was done using a computer program.

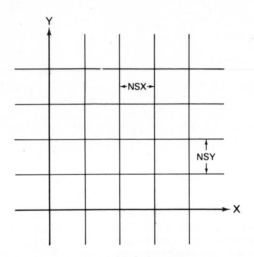

Fig. 3

Mathematical expressions The expressions used for the computation of the different parameters are the following:

$$\bar{C}_s(X,Y,Z) = \frac{Q_s \exp(-Y^2/C^2 X^{2-n})}{\pi C_y C_z \bar{u} X^{2-n}} \left\{ e^{-\left[\frac{(Z-h)^2}{C_z^2 X^{2-n}}\right]} + e^{-\left[\frac{(Z+h)^2}{C_z^2 X^{2-n}}\right]} \right\}$$

where:

$\bar{C}_s$: average concentration for a point

Q_s : average intensity of source emission

C_y, C_z : coefficients of generalized diffusion

n : parameter that depends on atmospheric stability

$\bar{u}_s$: average velocity of the wind

h : height of the source

$$\bar{C} = \bar{C}_s \left(\frac{Q_s}{Q}\right) \frac{\bar{u}_s}{u} \qquad (2)$$

where

C : instantaneous concentration in a given point

C_s : average calculated concentration

Q_s : average intensity of source emission

u : instantaneous velocity

In order to obtain the expression for the maximal range of the solid particles, the equations corresponding to the movement of a project thrown from a height Z with components of initial velocity in axis X and Z, were applied. At present the work is being extended to include the topographic characteristics of the area under investigation.

Programme Synthesis
Objective The fundamental objective of the programme is to investigate the environmental contamination which can be produced by a source of gaseous emission, that may be considered as a point of emission, with or without solid particles; determining, if needed the instantaneous values of concentration at a given point (adjusted values).

Data In order to find the average concentration (with or without adjusted values) we need to know,

- maximal distances to be investigated in the same direction and perpendicularly to the wind.
- intervals in X, Y and Z.
- height of the source.
- diffusion coefficient generalized in X and Z.
- average and instantaneous velocities of the wind
- average and instantaneous intensities of the source emission.

In order to find adjusted values one has to input,

- number of values to be adjusted.
- average concentration of each point whose adjusted value is needed.

In order to obtain the maximal distance travelled by the solid particles one has to give,

- density of the particle (supposedly spheric).
- air density.
- air viscosity coefficient.
- gravity value.
- radius of the particle.

Results   Four types of results may be obtained from the program,

- a list of average values of concentration specifying the corresponding point, plane and source.
- a list similar to the previous one but with a column of adjusted values.
- a list with adjusted values for the given average concentration.
- a tracing, by planes, of the contamination curves.

Bibliography

1. Roberts, O.F.T., Proc. Royal Soc. (London) Vol. 104.

2. Sutton, O.G. Proc. Royal Soc. (London) Vol. 135, 1935.

3. Sutton, O.G. Quart J. Royal Met. Soc. Vol. 73, 1947.

Acknowledgements
We wish to acknowledge that the program was written with the collaboration of Licentiados Rosendo Alvarez and Luis Lecha (Academy of Sciences) in the theoretical studies and the system programmers Lic. Ana Boquet (IPF) and Arch. Alexis C. Mendez (CEMACC).

DISCUSSION

G. Halbritter   I have just one question. How specific is your meteorological statistic to compute the average values for the pollutant concentrations, how many combinations of possible weather situations do you have, indicating categories of the atmosphere, wind speeds and wind directions.

A.C. Mendez   All the parameters that we used in this work are taken from the literature. We may be able to buy equipment to measure the necessary parameters for our weather conditions in the near future.

WRITTEN CONTRIBUTION.   COMPUTATION OF SO_2 - LONG TERM
CONCENTRATION IN THE VENETIAN AREA   by E. Runca, P. Melli
and P. Zannetti

Many attempts have been made in the last two decades to simulate SO_2 concentration fields in areas affected both by
industrial and urban emissions (Pooler [6], Turner [10], Shieh
[8], Calder [1], Martin [4], etc.) The models developed for
such a purpose have proved to work well in situations in which
the parameters affecting the dispersion were rather uniform
over the whole area. In more complicated areas, on the contrary, further implementations of diffusion models up to now
realized are needed in order to formulate a satisfactorily
precise idea of their reliability as well as of their limits.
        Venice and its surroundings are a typical example of an
area in which the dispersion of the atmospheric pollutants is
greatly affected by the non-uniformity of its geographic
characteristics. In this area the presence of different types
of adjacent surfaces (land, lagoon and Adriatic Sea, see Fig.
1) induces a local circulation which interacts with the
synoptic wind making it very difficult to identify the dispersion patterns of a pollutant.
        On the other side the study of Air Pollution problem in
Venice is made urgent by the damages that pollution causes to
its priceless artistic patrimony.
        In order to give a practical contribution to this problem
an application of diffusion models is being carried out.
        The problem was tackled by applying, as a preliminary
attempt, a Gaussian type model, by which three-monthly average
concentrations as well as the annual ones were simulated for t
the years 1973 and 1974. The obtained results are discussed
in the present article.

Application of the model

Since the region under investigation shows the presence of a
large industrial area (situated in the mainland) as well as
three densely populated urban areas (Marghera and Mestre on
the mainland, Venice on the islands at the center of the
Lagoon, see Fig. 1) both industrial and urban pollution must
be taken into account in the model.
        Data concerning industrial sources were taken from an
inventory carried out by the Local Government in 1972 according to the National Law about Pollution promulgated in April
15th, 1971.   Such an inventory showed the presence of 74
stacks with a total emission rate of 160000 tons/year and a
range of heights from 10 to 120 m.
        The knowledge of the average strength of sources intro-
duces in the model computations a certain inaccuracy, which
otherwise is somewhat reduced by the fact that long term
averages are calculated. The evaluation of the spatial
distribution of domestic heating emissions was made on the
basis of the last national general census, taken in 1972,

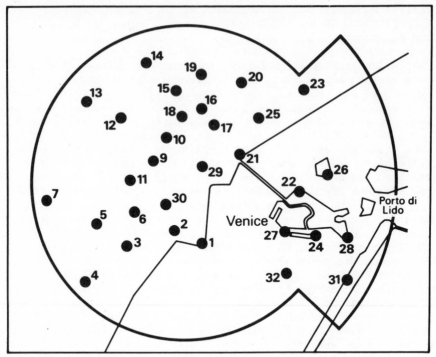

Fig. 1 Venetian Area — Dots indicate the location of the SO$_2$ monitoring
stations (2, 6, 9, 10, 16, 17, 22, 24, 29, 30 were operating since Feb.'73)

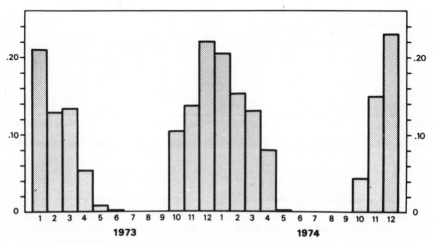

Fig. 2 Histogram of domestic heating emissions distribution throughout
the years 1973 and 1974

which furnished a great mass of information not only about the
distribution of the population but also about the state of
buildings and their facilities (e.g. domestic heating plants).

For the 272 sections, in which the urban districts of the
Venetian Area were subdivided, the consumptions of polluting
fuels and therefore the yearly emissions of SO_2 were computed.

As for the definition of the emission rates (variable
throughout the different periods of the year), it was achieved
by using the concept of day/degree, defined as:

$$dd = T_b - \frac{\sum\limits_i^{24} T_{h,i}}{24}$$

where T_b is the temperature at which heating starts and $T_{h,i}$
is the average hourly temperature at i-th hour of the day.

In Venice T_b is equal to 15,5 C. The total yearly
emission was distributed over the whole "cold period", pro-
portionally to the days/degree, as shown in Fig. 2.

The above calculated fractions of the total yearly emission were then used to calculate the emission rates for each
of the 272 above mentioned sections. Every area emission
was finally introduced in the model as an equivalent constant
strength point source, located in the barycenter of the corresponding section.

The height of the urban emissions, including plume rise,
was estimated to be about 30 m in the historical center of
Venice (whose buildings are generally old and low) and around
45 m in the urban areas of the mainland, which have developed
in the last three decades and show taller buildings. Meteorological data as well as SO_2-concentration data were supplied
by the network that Tecneco installed in Venice by appointment
of the Istituto Superiore di Sanità (Superior Institut for
Health). It consists of one meteorological station situated
in the historical center of Venice and of 24 monitoring sensors
(Fig. 1).

The meteorological station records on an hourly basis
wind speed, wind direction according to the eight sectors of
the wind rose, temperature, pressure, rainfall, humidity,
cloudiness and fog. Concentration data recorded by the 24
monitoring sensors are transmitted to a small computer which
elaborates the data and prints the hourly average values as
well as daily statistics. Besides that, every time the 30
minutes average SO_2-concentration "standard" (0.30 ppm) imposed
by the Italian law is exceeded in a station the computer gives
an alert. Since only 10 stations were regularly operating
from February 1973, the model has been tested on the data
recorded by them in the period February 1973 – January 1975.
Anyway some results will also be given for the other operating
sensors in the year 1974.

Diffusion equation

The equation used for the computation is the classical
Gaussian plume formula (Pasquill [5]), written according to
the modifications introduced by Martin [4] and Calder [1]).
For a single point source the concentration at a receptor
point P is given by:

$$C_P = \frac{n}{\pi^{3/2}} \cdot \frac{Q}{\sqrt{2}} \cdot \sum_{\substack{iw=1 \\ is=1 \\ it=1}}^{6,6,4} \frac{F(id,iw,is,it)}{U_{iw} D_P S_z(D_P,is)} \exp\left[\frac{-h^2(iw,is,it)}{2S_z^2(D_P,is)}\right]$$

where:

n	number of wind rose sectors (n=8, in our computation)
Q	source emission rate (Kg/s)
$F(id,iw,is,it)$	denotes the relative frequency of winds blowing into the given 45 - wind direction sector (id), for a given wind speed class (iw), atmospheric stability class (is) and temperature class (it).
U_{iw}	average wind speed for the iw-class at source height (m/s)
D_P	projection along the wind direction of the distance between the receptor point P and the point source
S_z	vertical standard deviation obtained from Gifford's plots (Slade, 1968) (m)
h	source effective height (m)

The above mentioned hourly meteorological data were used
to determine the joint frequency distribution of meteorological conditions. As to wind speed the following six classes
were used:

0 ———⊣ 1.57,   1.57 ——⊣ 3.14, 3.14 ——⊣ 5.24, 5.24 ——⊣ 8.38,

8.38 ——⊣ 11

and greater than 11 m/s; the representative speed U_{iw} was
computed as the arithmetic mean of the measured values belonging to the iw class. In order to take into account the variation of the wind speed with the height an exponential law was
used, whose exponent was assumed equal to 0.25 for unstable
and neutral classes and 0.5 for stable ones.

Frequencies of calms were so low that it was decided to
disregard them. Wind directions were grouped into 8 classes
corresponding to the standard 8 compass directions (N, NE,...
NW).

Atmospheric stabilities were grouped into 6 classes,
according to Pasquill's criteria. Finally, in order to take
into account the influence of temperature on the plume rise,

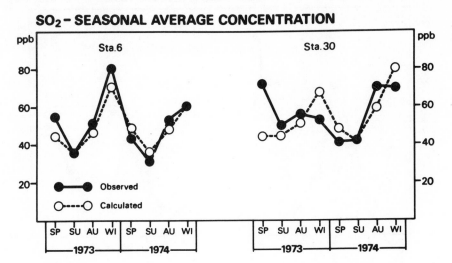

Fig. 3

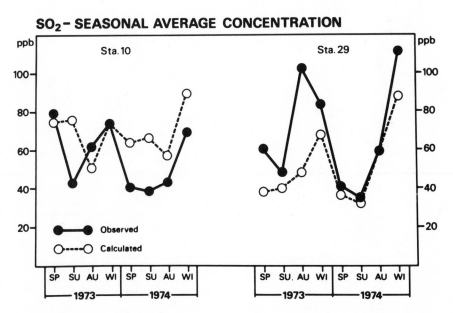

Fig. 4

SO₂ - SEASONAL AVERAGE CONCENTRATION

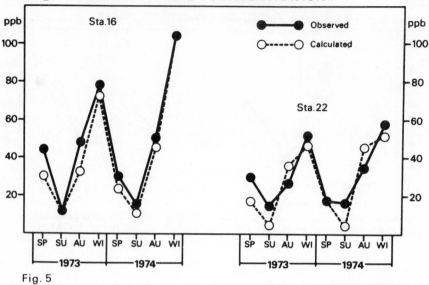

Fig. 5

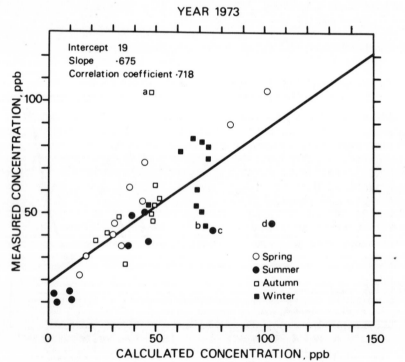

Fig. 6 Regression line of observed versus calculated average SO₂ concentration (ppb) for three-monthly periods from Feb.'73 to Jan.'74

the following classes were introduced: less than 0, 0 ⟶ 10, 10 ⟶ 20, and greater than 20 C; the representative temperature has been evaluated as the arithmetic mean of the measured values belonging to the it class.

The plume rise has been evaluated according to the Concawe formula (Dètrie, 1969). Since no suitable information was available neither the height of the inversion layer nor the decay of SO_2 were introduced in the model.

Results

The monitoring stations were divided into three groups according to their geographical location. Figs. 3,4,5 show measured three-monthly average concentration as well as the calculated one for two stations chosen out of each group. Fig. 3 refers to sensors 6 - 30, located at the southern edge of the Industrial Area, while stations 10 - 29 (fig. 4) are situated between the Industrial Area and the urban centers of Mestre and Marghera and finally Fig. 5 shows the results for sensors 16 - 22 located in Mestre and in Venice respectively. The model simulates fairly well the observed values for all the stations but 10 and 29. This is an expected result since the areas in which they are located show discontinuities (i.e. variations in surface roughness, and land-lagoon transition) greater than elsewhere. To this it must be added that they are very close to the strongest point sources and therefore much more affected by possible inaccuracies in the evaluation of their mutual locations. All the results have been summarized in Figs. 6-7, which also show the regression lines for 1973 and 1974 respectively. The correlation coefficients are 0.72 for the year 1973 and 0.8 for the year 1974.

The model was also used to calculate SO_2-annual average concentration for the years 1973 and 1974; the relative results are plotted with the experimental ones in Figs. 8-9. As it was expected, the model proved to give better results if the period of calculation was extended. The encouraging results obtained by applying the model led to extend the calculations over the whole area of interest in order to get a visible description of the spatial distribution of the pollutant. This made it possible to draw the isolines of concentration, shown in Figs. 10-11, for the periods June-August 1973 and December 1973-February 1974 respectively. By comparing the two maps a conclusion can easily be drawn that because of the local meteorological conditions (Runca and Zannetti, [7]), in summer SO_2 "keeps away" from the historical center, and concentrates itself near the industrial sources. In the winter the different meteorology prevailing over the area as well as the presence of urban emissions causes a wider spread of the SO_2 and consequently raises the pollution level in the urban center of Venice.

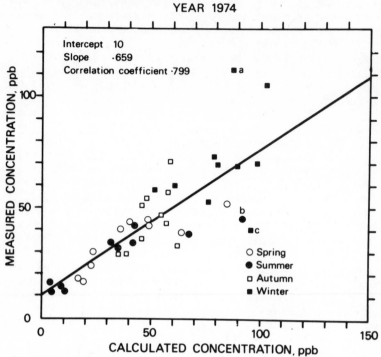

Fig. 7 Regression line of observed versus calculated average SO₂ concentration (ppb) for three-monthly periods from Feb.'74 to Jan.'75

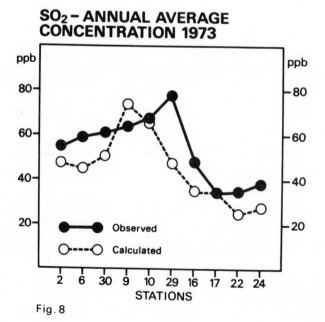

Fig. 8

SO₂ - ANNUAL AVERAGE CONCENTRATION 1974

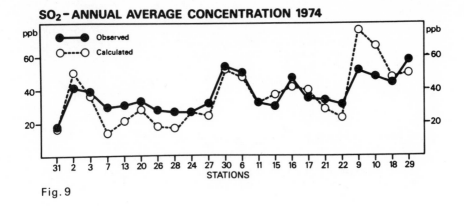

Fig. 9

SULPHUR DIOXIDE CONCENTRATION ISOLINES
AT GROUND LEVEL IN THE VENETIAN AREA
Industrial and Urban emissions
Period from 1/6/73 to 31/8/73

Data minimum 0·001   Maximum 0·101   Plotting Interval 0·004

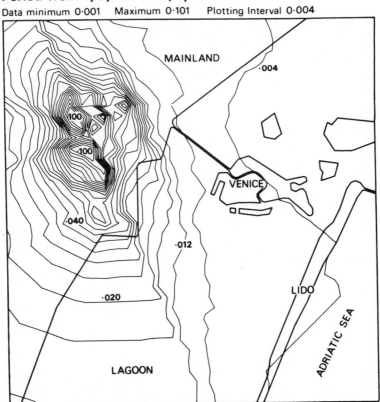

Fig. 10 Concentration values are in ppm.

SULPHUR DIOXIDE CONCENTRATION ISOLINES AT GROUND LEVEL IN THE VENETIAN AREA
Industrial and Urban emissions
Period from 1/12/73 to 28/2/74

Data minimum 0·018   Maximum 0·115   Plotting Interval 0·004

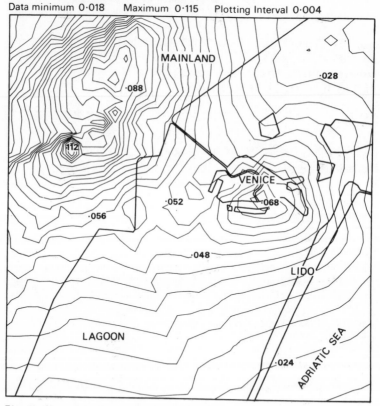

Fig. 11 Concentration values are in ppm.

Conclusions

The application of a gaussian-type model to compute long term SO_2 average concentration in Venice and its surroundings has been presented. Although it is difficult to describe the local meteorology, the choice of characterizing the atmospheric stabilities according to Pasquill's categories as well as the assumptions concerning height variation of the wind and the plume rise proved to be satisfactory. Since the obtained results showed that the seasonal patterns of SO_2-concentration can be described by the model, it has been used to illustrate the influence of seasonal climate on the SO_2 dispersion over the area and the contributions of urban and industrial emissions to the pollution level in the historical center of Venice. Improvements can be brought to the model by introducing in it a proper definition of the atmospheric stabilities on the basis of a more detailed knowledge of the local meteorology as well as by better defining the industrial emissions rates and locations.

In such a way the model could become a valid tool for land planning purposes and for optimizing the monitoring network.

References

1. Calder, K.L. A climatological model for multiple source urban air pollution - Nato Committee on the Challenges of Modern Society, Air pollution n.5 1971.

2. Detrie, J.P. La Pollution Atmosphérique - Dunod, 1969.

3. Gifford, F.A. Atmospheric diffusion in an urban area - II IRPA Conference, Brighton, England, 1970.

4. Martin, D.O. An urban diffusion model for estimating long term average values of air quality - Journal of Air Pollution Control Association, January, 1971.

5. Pasquill, F. Atmospheric diffusion - D. Van Nostrand, 1962.

6. Pooler, F. A prediction model of mean urban pollution for use with standard wind roses - Intern. J. Air and Water Pollution, 4, 199-211, 1961.

7. Runca, E. and Zannetti, P. A Preliminary Investigation of the Air Pollution Problem in the Venetian Area - IBM Technical Report CRV007/513-3524, December 1973, Venice Scientific Center, Italy.

8. Shieh, L.J. et al. The IBM air quality diffusion model with an application to New York City - Palo Alto Scientific Center IBM, 1971.

9.   Slade, D.H.   Air Pollution – Academic Press vol. 1, 1968.

10.   Turner, D.B.   A diffusion model for an urban area – Journ. of Applied Meteorology, 3, 1964.

4.   DISCUSSION: WATER POLLUTION

4.1   Computer Modelling of Pollutant Transports in Lake Erie

G.K. Verboom   In this paper you calculate the concentration
of some quantity.   You have mentioned that one can use the
same programme for the temperature; have you actually done
that, and if so, have you actually calculated the thermo-
clime?

D.C.L. Lam   We have done that in Lake Ontario.   Because we
measured the temperature in Lake Erie and we believe that an
observed temperature is more reliable than a computer temperature.   But in Lake Ontario we computed the temperature too.

G.K. Verboom   And you observed the formation of the thermo-
clime?

D.C.L. Lam   Yes, stratification occurred in the computed and
observed temperatures in Lake Ontario.   I can show you some
papers on this.

G.K. Verboom   May I ask you a second question again concerning the upwind-differencing.   If one calculates the artificial
viscosity again, it is very much larger than the physical one
you put in; if the numerical one is much larger than the real
one, why put a real one in?

D.C.L. Lam   I am not quite sure whether the forced diffusion
in this case is large.   We tried different numerical values
and obtained different results.

G.K. Verboom   That's why it is so large.

D.C.L. Lam   No, the analysis of Professor Raithby shows that
for very large wind scale the upwind differencing tends to be
optimum for advection predominant problems.   The forced
diffusion is diminishing for steady state problems.   For time
dependent problems, we are not yet certain and he is working
on it.

B.M. Mollowney   You mention in your paper that it has been
shown that the false diffusion effects of upstream differenc-

ing may be quite small when advection is dominant. Can you
expand on this please?

D.C.L. Lam   I hesitate to make further comment on this false-
diffusion because people usually calculate from the Taylor's
series truncation terms and say the false-diffusion is 9 times
as much as the actual diffusion, or 7 times, or what not.
You expand the advection derivative and say, OK the next one,
the second derivative, is the diffusion term which you are
missing, and so you call that false-diffusion. But how can
you do the Taylor's expansion for a very large delta x?
Taylor's expansion holds only for a small delta x. I think
that there is a considerable number of recent papers on the
investigation of this. This is why I use instead, the eigenfunction analysis.

     For central differencing, if $|uh/2|$ is greater than 1,
then the solution becomes oscillatory, while upstream differencing gives no oscillatory solution. If your grid is small
enough ($|uh/2|$ < 1) the central difference works, and up-
stream differencing is really bad. But beyond that, the space
part in the eigenfunction becomes complex and numerical
dispersion has no clear meaning at all. You have oscillations
in central differencing no matter how small a time step you
use, because this is a pure spatial discretization problem,
see e.g. Price et al. (1966).

4.2 A Water Quality Optimization Model for Non-Serial River Systems

Question   Your very first equation looks extremely odd, that
is you have a positive range of discontinuity with whatever
happened on the right hand side. Is your equation wrong?

M.B. Bayer   Equation (1) is the rate of change of BOD concentration. The ultimate BOD of an effluent is the maximum
amount of oxygen uptake that the effluent or sewage can exert.
As oxygen is used up the BOD remaining becomes less. Because
B_0 is ultimate BOD and BOD exerted in time t is some smaller
value, you will always have a positive right hand side.
     Presumably it is the way you look at it. Consider BOD
uptake and dissolved oxygen deficit. The dissolved oxygen
deficit decreases with time in the reaeration reaction.
Therefore, the sign of coefficient k_2 in equation (3) is negative. BOD uptake increases in time so therefore the sign of
coefficient k_1 in equation (1) is positive, indicating that
the dissolved oxygen deficit concentration increases although
oxygen level decreases. The differential equation given by
equation (12) shows the change in dissolved oxygen deficit as
equal to the change in BOD less the change in dissolved oxygen
deficit due to reaeration. Thus the differential equations
deal with the oxygen deficit which is the difference between
the actual dissolved oxygen concentration and the saturation
oxygen concentration at a particular temperature.

E.F. Joeres   You seem to have to find the constraint sets in each reach only at the beginning and at the end of the reach. Is that correct?

M.B. Bayer   Yes!

E.F. Joeres   What happens to the characteristic oxygen sag, which of course does not necessarily fall in the middle but might fall between the beginning and the end of the reach? Aren't you really only interested in constraining the critical point?

M.B. Bayer   Your question reminds me of a discussion I had at a conference in the United States not so long ago about whether you have to consider the oxygen sag curve at its minimum point. Well, I made a comment earlier about the shortness of the reaches because if you have very long reaches you have all sorts of problems with regard to changes in channel configuration, changes in flow, changes in the mixing that goes on in the river system itself. But if you have a very unusual situation where there is no change in channel configuration and all the other things are constant down the reach, then you can have a very long reach, and it is possible that the oxygen sag curve in fact will reach its minimum before the end of the reach. In view of the other problems I make sure that the reaches are very short and therefore the oxygen sag curve hardly ever reaches its minimum before the end of the reach. Also, if you are dealing with very, very low values of BOD, in the majority of cases where we limit BOD as I have in my paper to 4 parts per million or less, the probability of the oxygen sag curve reaching its minimum between the reaches is very, very small. I have checked this out by having done hundreds of these calculations, and then when in fact the sag curve does reach its minimum between reaches that sag curve is very flat. The likelihood of violating the constraint is so small that I find it unnecessary to complicate the model to the point where I need to determine where the sag curve reaches its minimum. Now if you are dealing with untreated waste going into a river system, then you may want to determine this minimum point but in the models that I have dealt with I haven't had to do it. When I first started my modelling of river systems back in 1965, I was very much concerned with determining where that minimum was. It was then that I found it quite adequate to use only end points and assume that the major changes in DO and BOD occur at those points. As you know, you model such that the ends of your reaches are where there are major changes in DO, BOD or temperature as the case may be.

Question   I would like to know more about the hydrodynamic side of your model. Could you please expand on this?

M.B. Bayer   Hydrodynamics is not my area and in order to

collect data from river systems for application in this model,
I would have to get a colleague in that area to work with me.
As I have been concerned mostly with developing techniques,
I have not taken specific river systems and worked on them. I
have had a number of requests for the work I have done and presumably there are people who are trying to apply it. I know
of a number of papers where this type of model has been applied. In testing against actual situations, using mean values
for flows, temperature, concentrations, etc., the errors were
within 10% and seem to be acceptable.

A certain flow regime has to be assumed. The generally
accepted one which I use is the 7 day minimum flow during the
low flow period of the year. The measurements are taken at
the worst part of the diurnal cycle which happens in the early
hours of the morning. Therefore, I am dealing with worst cases,
and of course, during the rest of the year the situation is
better, and the constraints are not likely to be violated.

4.3 Simulation of Nonlinear Stochastic Equations with Applications in Modelling Water Pollution

Question The problem of dealing with stream parameters on
the model I presented, was clearly deterministic except for
some concern about mean levels; rather the variation about
mean values through observations. It was mentioned in my
paper; I'm curious to know , if on examining your results –
the assumed mean flow rates and other parameters, how different a solution do you get?

C.J. Harris The model parameters can be very different from
those obtained from purely physico-chemical modelling.

Question To me that is a justification for using a more
complicated model.

C.J. Harris Yes, if it is a deterministic model. That is
one of the reasons for using a simpler but stochastic model.
The other reasons for using a stochastic model, is when using
a lumped parameter model as against distributed parameter
model (based on the physics), the stochastic model accounts
for any inadequacy in modelling, by including a noise term to
account for this error; apart from the fact that the processes
involved may also be random, such as flow rates or concentrations. So we have to estimate the parameters of the noise
term, and so whilst modelling the process we. have to re-
estimate at each data point the noise term.   In other words
this is our lack of knowledge of the process and its dynamics.

Question Presumably if you have a continuous modelling
device, you can estimate the parameters?

C.J. Harris   Yes, by standard recursive identification schemes, such as least squares or extended Kalman filters, which both will estimate the modelling noise terms.

Question continued: My question really concerned how much results you have from what you might check against a certain field. In the system of course in any case it is not worth the extra effort.

C.J. Harris   If your modelling is good, via a good under-standing of the physics of the processes involved then the noise terms become very small and insignificant. However, for poor modelling, they can become significant. It was found that because of the very large perturbations in the inflow rates around the mean level, then a deterministic physical modelling is impossible.

Question   I can see this for the reactor situation, but then the reactor becomes a leveller and the output from your sewage treatment plant will have considerably smaller varia-tions in BOD and of course very low values of DO unless of course you reaerate at that point.

C.J. Harris   A major aspect of my paper is to high-light the advantages that stochastic simulators have for those research-ers who wish to investigate various control strategies upon complex physical processes. We are in the process of con-sidering more sophisticated models. It is clear from the simple models we have considered that realistic control schemes are not viable.

G.B. Brundrit   I didn't understand whether your stochastic noise on the input function is superimposed on a periodic function or a constant function.

C.J. Harris   The mean values were assumed for simplicity to be sinusoidal with period 24 hrs. Although it doesn't really matter, since in the paper, the stochastic perturbations are in fact both parametric as well as additive, and that the poor modelling is reflected in some of the parameters being stochastic (they probably are)! Hence the model is nonlinear and also, as I have previously mentioned, the lack of know-ledge of modelling includes an additional noise term to produce a combined stochastic nonlinear model.

G.B. Brundrit   The reason I ask is that it seems that the input is very much periodic. It may not be sinusoidal, but certainly periodic and the output function retains this periodicity, while the amplitude is of course decreased relatively, takes on the same shape as the input function, and yet you don't seem to have taken advantage of this.

C.J. Harris   I do mention briefly at the end of the paper about the use of optimum control; a future publication uses a more sophisticated modelling than included here, which takes advantage of this periodicity. The simulation results presented at this Conference, for the mean value of flow rates, concentrations, assumed that they were sinusoidal. The mean values were modelled according to observational data, and we found that they were almost sinusoidal, and the variations around the sinusoids were taken as stochastic perturbations with a gamma distribution.

Question   Presumably you can add in your stochastic contribution given any basic physical system. Is this what you are saying?

C.J. Harris   Exactly! Either as a stochastic parametric variation or as an additive term to make up for inadequacy of modelling. For example, to represent a 4th order differential equation by a 2nd order equation requires an additional error term to account for approximation.

Question   Your approach could become complicated if there are a large number of random variables. Is there an upper limit on this?

C.J. Harris   Purely a computational aspect, for example an 8th order differential system with four correlated noise terms, requires at least 5000 realisations or simulation runs; taking approximately five hours on a medium scale digital computer, to evaluate the mean, variance and probability density functions of the solutions.

Question   It is important to keep in contact with the physics of the process.

C.J. Harris   Yes, I might add that Beck and Young first made their model of the river Cam, most of the data was obtained during warm sunny weather, and they ignored photo-synthesis effects upon DO, and found their model estimations poor. Some knowledge of the physical modelling is very important, and had they made their observations during a mixed weather period with large temperature variations, then this would also have to be taken into account in the model.

4.4 A Mathematical Model for Estimating Pollution Loadings in Runoff from Urban Streets

P. Kaufmann   With regards to your last remark concerning the storage and treatment of storm water runoff. It seems rather impractical to provide storage for all the water draining from a watershed after a rainfall. Do you know anything about the time function of the pollutants observed in storm

water runoff? The first wave of runoff is the most polluted
water, so how much of the runoff should one store and treat?

R. Sutherland   Many researchers investigating the quality of
storm water runoff have observed a phenomena which has been
named the "first flush" effect. Essentially, the "first flush"
phenomena is the observation that during a storm event, the
runoff that reaches the outflow point first is of the worst
quality and the quality of the water draining from the watershed improves as the storm progresses. The Basic Inlet
Hydrograph Model modified to include the Yalin equation, which
was the research tool used to develop the rainfall portion of
my model, did predict a first flush phenomena.
    The City of Chicago has funded the design of a deep tunnel
and reservoir system that will store and eventually treat combined sewer overflows and urban storm water runoff. Harza
Engineering Company is the designer of the main stream section
which upon completion will store a maximum volume of 90,000
acre-ft. (i.e. 4.5 inch total volume storm over 375 square mile
watershed) at an estimated cost of over four billion dollars.
    Certainly the cost of a storm water storage project is an
important factor and the cost will increase with an increase in
the volume being stored. But, my research found that the
ability for a city to store and eventually treat all the rainfall from a 1/2 inch total volume storm would remove approximately 78.5% of the pollutants accumulating on the street.
For a mountainous country such as Switzerland, the removal
percentage will increase for a decreased storage volume because
of the overall increase in street slopes.

4.5 The Advection-Dispersion Equation for an Isotropic Medium Solved by Fractional-Step Methods

C.Y. Liu   I would like to ask two short questions. The first
one is this. The two step analysis is based on one time step
in advection amd then another time step in diffusion. Could
you enlarge your domain in the ΔT, ΔX and ΔY quite a bit by
allowing yourself to take one step in advection and then, let's
say, ten steps in diffusion.

G.K. Verboom   It is possible if the scheme is only of first
order in Δt, not if the scheme is of higher order in Δt. I
have never tried this, but I should prefer to use an implicit
scheme for the diffusive step if this is allowed by accuracy
criteria.

C.Y. Liu   Yes, because the diffusion time step normally is
smaller than the advection time step by some magnitudes. Right?

G.K. Verboom   In the aquatic environment advection is often
dominant, i.e. the time step is usually determined by the
advective step. Perhaps this may be different for studies in

the atmosphere, but this presents no real problems. One can
use an explicit scheme for one step and an implicit for
another.

C.Y. Liu   I think this surely can be determined by the combination of the velocity and the diffusion coefficient both
very locally, so I think that there is something to be gained
by giving them another degree of freedom.

G.K. Verboom   I don't want to make general comment because
it depends so much on the kind of problem you have. I think
you have to investigate it again and again for every kind of
problem. For instance, I have not shown the influence of the
velocity, of course it's rather strong. If the velocity is
smaller, the line due to the phase error may move to the
right or to the left so you have to study its influence.

C.Y. Liu   You have already said that Δt is determined by three
factors, accuracy, stability, and the amount of money you've
got. You have probably got another one, that is the good
behaviour of the concentration function.
     That gives rise to another question I have. In your
analysis you did not take into consideration the function P
which you give in the first slide. Now, could one visualise
how P would affect the stability as well as the accuracy, if
P is taken into consideration.

G.K. Verboom   If P is not a function of the concentration
itself it will affect the accuracy only and not stability.
Stability is affected if P is a function of the concentration.
If P is proportional to the concentration it is a simple
matter, as according to the von Neumann stability analysis
exponential growth is allowed.

C.Y. Liu   I am not certain about it.

D. Lam   I am also concerned about the function P. For
example, P is a linear combination, may be a linear coefficient
times the concentration.   Can you do a fractional time step
in that case? You have one step for advection and one step
for diffusion, and then another step for say alpha times C.
Besides the fractional operators do not necessarily commutate
so in that case you have to do one, two, three, three, two,
one and so on.

G.K. Verboom   That's right. The sequence of the operators
must be reversed in the next time step, but only if the scheme
is to be of second order in time.

D. Lam   Does this time step have to be the same. Because,
considering a system of equations, where one of the coefficients is much larger than the others, so that you have a stiff

system, i.e. one of the constituents has a much smaller time
scale than the others. Do you think it is worth while to try
to allow the time step to be different for some processes, say
much smaller than for the others.

G.K. Verboom   Your first question was about the function P.
How it is treated in the fractional step method. I think
there are a lot of examples in the book of Yanenko. For
instance, fractions of P can be included in each step, or P
can be included in one step in this case usually in the last
one: it doesn't seem to matter very much. Concerning your
second question: if the scheme is to be of more than first
order in time, say second order, and if the fractional-opera-
tors do not commute then the sequence of the fractional-
operators must be reversed every time-step.
     The scheme is only of second order after each pair of
steps. For these two steps the time step must be the same,
but it may be different for the next pair of steps. I don't
know whether it is possible to use different time steps for
different constituents in case of a system of equations.

Question   You use a one dimensional equation in this
case. In a two dimensional case how would you make the
advection steps? Diffusion in one direction first and,
advection in the other, or the other way round I don't really
know, so which do you prefer as a way of doing that?

G.K. Verboom   If the time step used is set by the accuracy
criterion it doesn't matter at all. In fact, the last two
examples were two dimensional. In these cases the advection
in both directions was treated first and after that the
diffusion. But again, if the accuracy analysis is done for
the combined scheme, and the resulting time step is used then
it doesn't matter which step was done first.

N.S. Heaps   I would like to ask whether you have done any
three dimensional calculations using the approach you have
described.

G.K. Verboom   Not yet because first of all the computations
become quite expensive. This drawback can partly be overcome
if one limits itself to that area in which one really needs
three dimensional knowledge of the concentration profile.
Apart from that, the main areas of interest at least in the
Netherlands are so shallow that at a distance of about 50 times
the depth from the injection point it's well mixed across the
vertical. It is only in the near zone where one is really
interested in the 3-D profile and there the phenomenon is much
more complicated than the one described by this simple
equation. Basically it is no problem at all to extend these
kind of computations to the three dimensional domain.

B.M. Mollowney   You made a point that you thought that the Crank-Nicolson method was less accurate than the explicit method. Could you say a bit more about this. Under what circumstances does this happen?

G.K. Verboom   We performed a Fourier-series analysis of the one-dimensional diffusion equation

$$\frac{\partial c}{\partial t} = D \frac{\partial^2 c}{\partial x^2}$$

with the first-order Euler-scheme and the second-order Crank-Nicolson scheme. We want to know which solution deviates more from the theoretical solution depending on the parameter

$$\beta = D \frac{\Delta t}{\Delta x^2}$$ and $L/\Delta x$, where L is some wave length.

It turns out that Crank-Nicolson is more accurate than Euler if $\beta > 0.35$. My conclusion is, taking computation costs into account, that Euler is to be preferred (except in some exceptional cases when β is of order 1 or larger) because:
- when Euler is used $\beta < 0.5$ because of stability and $\beta < 0.25$ to prevent oscillations
- when Crank-Nicolson is used $\beta < 1.0$ to prevent oscillations
- an implicit-scheme takes at least three times as many operations as an explicit-scheme.

B.M. Mollowney   Yes, that is very interesting. I found it rather difficult with this lower region.

J.J. Morris   How do you deal with source terms?

G.K. Verboom   Up till now I have simply put the source terms in. In case of a very local source, say a delta function, one gets $2\Delta x$ waves disturbing the solution. One can solve this problem either by refining the grid near the source, by using another kind of scheme, perhaps upstream differencing and accepting the large amount of diffusion, or by using an analytical solution near the source.

J.J. Morris   In which fractional step is the source term included?

G.K. Verboom   It was done in the diffusive-step i.e. in the last step.

4.6 Solution of the Advection-Diffusion Equation by the Method of Moving Coordinate Systems with Particular Reference to the Modelling of Estuarine Pollution

Errata

Page Number	Line or Equation	As Printed	Change
313	line 1	ADVECTIVE	ADVECTION
315	line 27		delete second 'D^{ij}'
	Equation 24	g_k	g_{kl}
	Equation 30	$\dfrac{a^i}{x^j}$	$\dfrac{\partial a^i}{\partial x^j}$
320	Equation 35	a^i_i	a^i
321	Equation 44		delete '8'
322	Equation 52	$\dfrac{c'}{\partial a^i}$	$\dfrac{\partial c'}{\partial a^i}$
325	Equation 67	Replace vertical lines by square brackets	
	line 6	$a^i,(\alpha^j,t)$	$a^i(\alpha^j,t)$
	line 16	R	R'

<u>C.K. Verboom</u>   In a real situation, in a tidal river with very complicated boundaries, is it then rather difficult to do this kind of transformation?

<u>B.M. Mollowney</u>   In my paper I referred to one dimensional applications of the method to both time dependent and steady-state problems and these have been quite successful. At present I am applying the transformed steady-state equations to two two-dimensional estuaries. The first which is fairly well vertically mixed, has large areas of sand flats which dry out at low water. The figure below illustrates the positions of the moving element mesh at high and low water. The second system to which the method is being applied is to a narrow vertically stratified estuary with a well identified gravitational circulation in the vertical and here the approach is to move the element mesh with the mean tidal velocity over the cross-section and have the circulation flowing as a residual through the moving grid.

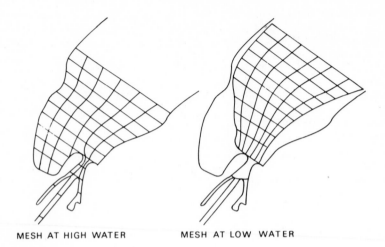

MESH AT HIGH WATER   MESH AT LOW WATER

N.S. Heaps   Do you not think that many problems would become too difficult if a solution was sought to it using a moving system?

B.M. Mollowney   Well, the equations themselves will not be more difficult of course. Where the difficulty arises is in actually tracking this moving system and there could be problems there. The geometry may get quite complicated but this remains to be seen. In one dimension this method works beautifully. In fact it is the answer to one dimensional problems, but in two dimensions, and three dimensions may or may not be the answer.

4.7 Stochastic Modelling of Bi-hourly River Dissolved Oxygen Records Monitored at a Fixed Cross-Section

M.B. Bayer   If I understand you correctly, the system you have described is a sample data system which can respond to small changes in the inputs. What you appear to be looking for is a system that will respond to large step changes. For example, if you suddenly got a very heavy increase in BOD then the dissolved oxygen is going to change by a large amount, and this Box-Jenkins approach, as far as I can understand it, would not respond to such very large step increases or decreases in the sampled data. Is that correct?

E.F. Joeres   If I understand you correctly, the answer is "No!" It is not correct. Any single event that does happen

in the watershed in terms of pollution problems that is
within the range of the memory system that was used to generate the forecast. In terms of all inputs considered, such as
pollution loadings, etc., the short term forecast can only be
accommodated in a statistical sense as part of a time series
used for predicting what quality conditions will be. It is
not a deterministic prediction. It is still an estimation
with a confidence associated with it. However, if you have
any sudden major event, such as a break in a sewer line or a
sewer overflowing due to a fifty year recurrence interval rain
storm, or something like this, the model would obviously not
be able to make an accurate prediction of the major change in
the time series for which it might no longer be representative.
I must point out, however, that the "failure" of the model in
cases like these has important advantages from the operational
point of view, because large discrepancies alert the operator
to problems in the system. In other words, the model gives a
stochastic prediction for stationary conditions; any major
departure from these serves as an alarm signal for the operator.

M.B. Bayer   That was my question exactly; and a second
question: What is the response time to adjust the physical
inputs, like plant flows or releases from a reservoir, and the
other kinds of control options available to improve the water
quality because of a rather major catastrophy of that kind?

E.F. Joeres   We are only supposing that the kind of prediction horizon that we have chosen is quite reasonable to
accommodate the response time of the water quality manager.
It's a management problem which depends to a large extent on
local conditions.   I have no specific experience to draw on,
but I think it would be reasonable that if the decision-
making authorities for making the water release decisions out
of Lake Winnebago, for example, rested with the same Department of Natural Resources in Wisconsin that is monitoring the
quality readings, the adjustments could easily be accomplished
in a short period of time.

M.B. Bayer   In what period of time, three days or one hour?

E.F. Joeres   No, a number of hours. But other management
alternatives could be applied as well, such as mechanical
reaeration that could take more time than that.

M.B. Bayer   O.K., because the problem is, if you do have some
sort of catastrophy upstream, then what happens downstream;
the damage is done in a very few hours and this is what I am
concerned about - the response time from your management
system.

E.F. Joeres   I should say that the flow time of the river in question is a matter of 3 to 8 days, depending on the time of the year.

M.B. Bayer   O.K.

R. Sutherland   My firm has also worked with the QUAL II model. Have you ever gotten the dynamic portion of the program to work?

E.F. Joeres   Well, we got it to work as well as possible, but in comparing the output to what the monitors were reading (and we had done some previous analyses within the present studies to make sure the monitors were accurate). QUAL-II wasn't getting anywhere near what the real condition was in terms of the variability of the system as it was being recorded by the monitors.

R. Sutherland   Is the real system that you are simulating a series of reservoirs created by man-made dams? How did you account for the reaeration that occurs when the water passes over the dam?

E.F. Joeres   Yes. In setting up the QUAL-II model we divided the river into reaches at every major discontinuity, just the way one always does this, and took care of the appropriate mass balances etc. at the divides for inputs to the next reach; we had over 40 reach divisions - not just 12 due to elevation changes, but also because of the major effluent inflow points. All that works quite well in QUAL II in terms of a predictive, causal model for expected value conditions, but it is really the short-term dynamic behaviour that got us interested in trying a statistical approach.

R. Sutherland   I was wondering if you knew of the existence of a new water quality model called RECEIVE II developed by the Raytheon Company located in Portsmouth, Rhode Island. The model is supposed to be dynamic in both quality and quantity. It is supposed to be able to simulate reaeration occurring when water passes over a dam. It would be interesting to find out if the RECEIVE II model did a better job on Fox River.

E.F. Joeres   No, I don't know about the Raytheon model. We simply wanted to have a comparison to our statistical model and decided to take QUAL-II, which is widely used by the United States Environmental Protection Agency, and tried to make it dynamic in behaviour,but there are so many assumptions such as the linear growth rates of algae as a function of temperature, that it just doesn't work.

R. Sutherland   Well, I agree with you. I've used QUAL II and it is not an extremely sophisticated model. Thank you.

<u>N.S. Heaps</u>   If you get your system to work, is anybody going to use it? Who wants to use it and who is going to pay for that use? In other words, is there an end user?

<u>E.F. Joeres</u>   I can only interpret the question as I see it. First of all in terms of investment there is relatively little to be done, because the money has already been spent for the hardware of this monitoring system. Consequently carrying out this kind of analysis would have been pointless before the physical system existed that made it possible to think about real-time management.

Can we get somebody to use it? Who is the User? Well, the user is the public in the sense that the public agencies are charged with fulfilling a certain social goal which after a while does become an institutional bias which the agency takes rather seriously. This social objective in Wisconsin is preserving the environment, which in that state has strong economic implications, since Wisconsin is sometimes facetiously referred to as the playground of Chicago - the economic base of the state is approximately one-third agriculture, one-third recreation, and one-third industry. There is thus a great deal of consciousness about the environment and the state officials, that I have been in contact with about this project are quite receptive to improving the system. What they have done now in an effort to monitor a critical river is spent a lot of money on hardware, but they don't do much with this incredible data file except to publish a summary of their statistics on a monthly basis. What we can do right now, for example, is derive frequency curves and histograms that give (just in terms of evaluating one policy against another) the percent of time that given quality conditions were violated in any one year, which, although the fish wouldn't care either way as long as they were dead, does allow some comparison of whether one particular quality management policy worked better than another. So all this information is there and is not being extracted.

<u>N.S. Heaps</u>   I thought your objective was the setting up of a real time system which means that you would have to have people to run it on a continuous basis.

<u>E.F. Joeres</u>   I see what you mean. No, we are trying to convince the State that there is a point to setting up a real-time system. The study is to investigate the feasibility of such a system. It is an initial effort in this direction and I would therefore assume that further investigations will be needed before it could become fully operational. One of the issues for example, is how to integrate a mini-computer into the monitoring system hardware and then use it for real-time control without reliance on large, external computers, as we did in our study (the UNIVAC 1110 at the University of Wisconsin).

W. Schmid   I have another question. How far do you have to
go back in collecting data for, let us say, good forecasting
of three days. That seems to me a real problem because the fit
of your data is directly dependent upon this collective data.

E.F. Joeres   We found it sufficient to take two weeks to
generate an equation. It is very easy once the programme is
going to execute the programme and generate a new forecasting
equation. There are some indices you can use to tell you that
the model is not doing very well, but in fact you can always
compare your forecast to information coming in. It will cost
about one dollar to one dollar-fifty to generate another
equation if you feel that things have changed somewhat. If we
incorporate this model generation program as on-line software,
you can automate it to the push of a button.

W. Schmid   But your confidence in the work does not look so
nice.

E.F. Joeres   Well, it is a 90% confidence, and three days
into the future is pretty far. It's no problem if the response
time is sufficiently short, as discussed with a previous
question of what can one expect. The system could be organ-
ised to have a response time of a matter of hours. Perhaps
you don't need to make a forecast of more than one day into
the future.

N.S. Heaps   Yours is a statistical model and again the
question must be asked as to whether a dynamical model might
not be more appropriate. Which is going to prove the best in
the end?

E.F. Joeres   It is our contention that both statistical and
causal models have their place and in being so explicit about
the kind of criticism raised with statistical models, we want
to make clear that in no way do we wish to negate the use of
causal models. I have used them a lot and have played a lot
with optimization management models based on constraint sets
completely structured around causal response, but so far they
are still largely able to handle only the steady state situation. They are nevertheless the best analytical tools we have
for comparing alternative management plans and for predicting
river response to various hypothetical inputs and changes in
the system. In principle they could also be used for on-line
real-time forecasting as we attempted to do with the QUAL II
model. Aside from the computer size and costs involved in
such an operation, the main problem is that it would require
setting up a much larger telemetric network capable of providing continuous records of all the input data required (i.e.
hydrologic and meteorologic information, and measurements of
all effluent discharges). From this perspective the statistical approach appears as a more practical tool to utilize most

effectively the telemetric networks presently being installed on many river systems.

M.B. Bayer   Just one more comment. This has got to be the way ultimately for the regional management of water resources. You must have a real time response system that feeds data to the water pollution plants, to the supplies of stored water which you might use for dilution, and to other facilities in the system.   I fully support the speaker in what he is trying to do, and you can automate this system, just like most of your treatment plants are almost completely automatic. You won't need hundreds of people collecting data; you have continuous monitoring devices. If somebody comes up with a continuous monitoring device for BOD we'll be very happy.

G.J. Farquhar   I too support your enthusiasm over ARIMA models and I too think that they are the way to go in the future. However, I would like to ask just one very short question about your work with the QUAL-II model, particularly with reference to the first projection which you gain. It is linear.   I wonder if you would comment on how you got such a linear projection when you had included in the QUAL-II model a sinusoidal term to describe the diurnal production of oxygen by photosynthesis. You said you tried very hard to make it dynamic and I am sure you did. I wonder if you could explain why that projection was linear.

E.F. Joeres   I am trying to remember just how we made those modifications. I don't think we put in a sinusoidal term for the photosynthetic production. We simply tried to include a time-variation of inputs to the model by getting as much information as possible from sampling programmes of local communities on variation of effluents through the day, as well as putting in a variation of radiation input to the algae portion through the day, which may or may not have been sinusoidal. I don't recall exactly. I do remember that we had great difficulty in estimating parameters. That is as far as we could go with the structure of the program to make it dynamic, and that is perhaps just the reason why we couldn't get the computed response to move more.

G.J. Farquhar   There have been some more successful projections with the sinusoidal term in. It is not a very difficult thing to do as you're aware compared to obtaining parameters for the production coefficients.

E.F. Joeres   Our major effort in this overall investigation was not in making the deterministic quality model dynamic, but demonstrating the viability of statistical predictions.

We did feel we had to make the comparison between the two
types of models to see what sorts of differences would be
observed.

W. Schmid   Did you try to superimpose your QUAL- II model
and your stochastic model?   It would be quite interesting to
have a superposition of both models, because you have in the
QUAL-II model a deterministic model. We are working with
this model in Hamburg and have quite good results and I
think it would be worth trying to superimpose the QUAL-II
model and the stochastic model.

E.F. Joeres   That is exactly what we are doing. That is
what the slide shows. If you compare the results of QUAL-II
to measured daily average values it predicts very well. But
the values shown are hourly values and that is exactly what
we couldn't simulate in terms of computed response of the
system. What we are saying is that the predictive quality
models that compute steady state expected daily average
values, whichever way you set up the boundary conditions in
terms of critical values, are absolutely necessary for planning purposes, but for anything that gets into very short time
periods of hours and days, the only thing that we see as a
viable approach right now is simply to look at the behaviour
of observed signals. I'm back to the time series. We were
sure that from the control point of view that this seemed the
best approach to take.

Question   As a professional statistician and also a
controller, I will make two comments and ask a question.
One of the problems about using autoregressive moving average
processes is that they are only applicable to systems which
do not have feedback in them.   As soon as you develop a
controlled procedure in which you try to minimise the level
of BOD you are no longer allowed to use the autoregressive
moving average process method for estimating parameters,
so whilst everybody seems very keen on that I'll warn them,
because you will lead yourself right 'up the garden path'.
There are other methods and one would suggest something like
a maximum likelihood estimator, and this brings me actually
to a question.   In the model that you produced, do you
mention anything of how you estimate the number of parameters
because it is often a very crucial part of the estimation
procedure in terms of the amount of information that you
need to produce a viable estimate of say 3 days' prediction?

E.F. Joeres   Yes, I agree with you that data collected under feedback operation are not of much value in initial identification of the system. In natural systems such as rivers , information is usually available about the system prior to setting any control, and such data can be considered as having been collected under an open loop condition. Once the initial model is identified, it is correct to use the closed loop data collected when the feedback control was present to refit or to update the model.

As to your question regarding the estimation of the number of parameters in the model, I must emphasize that ARIMA model building is an iterative procedure. You start with an intelligent guess based on the form of your autoregressive and partial autoregressive function. You then make various analyses (such as chi-square tests) on the resulting residuals and adjust the choice and number of parameters accordingly. For each choice of parameter sets the estimation of their values is carried out using some sort of nonlinear optimization technique. Using maximum likelihood estimators is possible but was found by G.E.P. Box to be inferior.

Question   But this would be the total number of parameters rather than your individual selective orders because there are three sets of parameters that you need. Isn't that it? (Yes!) Or you combine with that the sum of orders? It's rather complicated.

E.F. Joeres   You are right. That combines the total number of parameters and their specific selection. You can check it with the original publications on ARIMA modelling in the statistical literature.

Question   But I would just make that point about autoregressive processes. They are extremely valuable. As soon as you implement a control in this particular example where in fact the dynamics will be affected by your control procedure, the procedure will just break down. Just as a trivial example this was applied in an econometric sense by people trying to find models of advertising, the relationship between sales and advertising. They wanted to find out what the optimal policy was. They applied this technique and after applying the optimum control procedure they found the optimal advertising rate was a negative one. If you think about this it meant you were paying for your competitors advertising, so I give you fair warning.

E.F. Joeres   Well, we haven't really gotten into an extensive analysis of the feedback control in this study. We have only outlined such a possibility by developing an example of a hypothetical control model. At this point we focused primarily on trying to find out if predictive forecasting had a point and that is why we analyzed so many series. I am not sure if your

comment is directly applicable to our study because optimal
control procedures can be used in many different ways. But
it is certainly something to look at for the future. Thank
you for your comment.

M.B. Bayer   I think that the two types of models we have
been talking about here have been confused a little bit. Some
are long term planning models of which the deterministic models work reasonably well. The others are operating models
of which the deterministic models don't work very well at all.
So you need two kinds of predictive models, and the one which
our speaker has been talking about is a short time span predictive model.   QUAL-II, although I do not know very much
about it, seems to me to be a long time span model, and may
work much better in those kinds of conditions.

5. DISCUSSION: THERMAL PROBLEMS

5.1 Modelling the Effects of Weather, Heating and Occupancy on the Thermal Environment inside Houses

G.K. Verboom   May I ask you about Figure 4. There is a peculiar sinusoidal disturbance in your calculated results with a period of approximately one-and-a-half-hours, where does this come from?

P. Basnett   That represents the control mechanism on the thermostat, it not being important. It happens because I was taking values from the predictions at times which didn't fit in very well with the periods at which the thermostat was switching.

U. Navon   What is the typical size of a cavity inside the wall? If the cavity is too big, natural convection may start and the overall insulating effect may be worse than with no cavity at all.

P. Basnett   The typical cavity size is, I think, 50 mm in Britain. It's a normal cavity wall construction. I quite agree with you that it is not always the best way to build a house but the Building Regulations require it. There is a current trend towards filling the cavities in existing houses with thermal insulating material, but one has to be very careful not to introduce moisture bridging.

Question   Wouldn't you get a better thermal insulation also by having the insulation outside because you avoid heat bridges. Did you take that into your calculation?

P. Basnett   That wasn't taken into account. The walls are assumed to be uniform over their area.

Question   Even at the corners? Where an internal joins up with an external wall. If you then have the insulation outside, no heat can pass through without passing through the insulation. If you have it inside, in that T shaped corner, something serious is going to happen.

P. Basnett   That wasn't taken into account. It certainly is

a possibility. There are other much more important arguments
for putting the insulation outside to do with condensation in
the wall and so on which I haven't mentioned here.

5.2 Mathematical Modelling of Thermal Pollution in Rivers

R.C. Sutherland   You mentioned that it was an economic method
to go about solving that problem. I was wondering if you can
expound on that because I think my company would be very
interested in the technique in terms that we get a lot of
pollution problems.

J.J. McGuirk   For the kind of calculations that Professor
Spalding has been talking about, the execution time was
between 5 and 10 minutes on a CDC 6600 machine.

R.C. Sutherland   Is that the total time?

J.J. McGuirk   Yes! That's CPU time.

R.C. Sutherland   Now what type of grid system were you using
in terms of distances and depths? I know you were talking
about an experiment there.

J.J. McGuirk   The grid in the cross stream plane. We made
grid refinement tests and we found that the finest grid we
needed was one in which there were 20 grid nodes in each
direction. As far as the downstream distance goes, the step
length, it was necessary to take small steps near the inlet
where the more rapid changes were taking place; then the
step length downstream could be increased for a more economic
solution. Again speaking from memory, the number of steps
required was about 600.
    Well, I will probably talk to you about it later!

J.E. Cordle   It appears from your slides that you have taken
the density as constant in the momentum equations. Would you
explain how you can then model the buoyancy?

J.J. McGuirk   We made the assumption that we could use a
Boussinesq approximation so that the density was considered
constant in all the inertia terms but the variations in
density were cnnsidered as causing the buoyancy forces in
the vertical momentum equation.

J.E. Cordle   Thank you. My other question is, how crucial is
the river velocity? Can your model be used for low river
speeds and for stagnant conditions?

J.J. McGuirk   No!   In stagnant ponds the boundary layer

assumptions   tend to break down towards the edge. In fact
I haven't used this programme for injection into stagnant
surroundings because we were mainly interested in river flow
problems. So I couldn't really say about stagnant ponds, but
certainly in low river velocities.

J.E. Cordle   What is the lowest relative river speed for which
you have used the method successfully?

J.J. McGuirk   We tried velocity ratios of the order of
20 so the river velocity will be 1/20th of the jet velocity.

B.D. Spalding   I would just like to add to that. I think we
can go down to zero but there mustn't be a negative velocity.
Now if you do inject into a stagnant pond you are likely to
induce some re-circulation. Just as soon as that happens you
have to stop the marching integration and solve by some other
means.

Question   When you get to the state where you have a hot
film on top of the river then you are surely going to get
some effect of air cooling. Can you take this into account?
This is fairly important as you get downstream of a river.

J.J. McGuirk   Yes. It can be taken into account by merely
altering the boundary condition at the water surface so that
heat transfer through the surface is permissible. We didn't
take it into account because in the flows that we were concerned with the hot water had not spread over a sufficient
region on the surface to cause surface heat transfer to be
appreciable, but it is possible to take it into account.
     This is quite important in a big river system where you
are putting a lot of heat input, say from power stations.
This is absolutely critical. You know, your fish can live
underneath. It's how quickly you can get the heat off the top.

W.K. Tayler   I am not quite sure how far downstream of the
actual outfall do you take your model. I would have thought
that once the thing gets fairly well mixed you could switch
to an ordinary diffusion-convection model with stratification
and possibly use less computing time.

J.J. McGuirk Yes, that's true. We went up to 100 jet diameters to discharge jet diameters downstream. We considered
that to be the end of the nearfield zone and we just didn't
make any further calculations.

G.K. Verboom   May I ask you why you use the steady state
equations and solve them iteratively, as this is almost equal
to solving the time dependent equations.

J.J. McGuirk   Sometimes what you said is true but it happened

not to be true in this case. If you were to solve that problem in a time dependent way you would require three dimensional storage from all variables because at every point you
would need to know what existed there before. Now we don't do
that because we solve iteratively only when making one step
forward, we now iterate over this plane. So we have only two
dimensional storage. It is of enormous value.

G.K. Verboom   Yes. May I ask you another question about the
free surface. Is it necessary to adjust the free surface
during each iteration or is the distance so small that it is
almost flat and remains at the same place? Don't you get any
trouble with the pressure for instance?

J.J. McGuirk   The velocities and pressures which fit the
equations come out of the solutions of the equations themselves.

G.K. Verboom   But you are iterating them and so they don't
fit it exactly.

J.J. McGuirk   They are made to fit it exactly by not only
solving the momentum equation. It is also making sure that
the continuity equation is solved exactly.

G.K. Verboom   And you do something special about the
pressure?

J.J. McGuirk   Yes.

5.3 Computation of Artificial Temperature Stresses due to
Discharges from Nuclear Power Plants

U. Navon   It can be seen from Figure 7 that the temperature
difference between the curves with and without the thermal
impact of a cooling-water discharge is constant during the
whole year and is about 1°C. I think that this result is
obvious and can be estimated by a short paper and pencil calculation. Would it, indeed, be necessary to use such complicated
modelling to calculate the effect of the thermal impact?

A. Thendrup   I don't think the problem is that easy. As
stated in the paper, measurements and calculations have indicated that a significant part of cooling water discharge from a
nuclear power plant located outside the sill will be carried
across the sill and into the fjord. From November to February
measurements show that the cooling water discharge can be

expected to have densities required for replacing the deeper
waters of the Vestfjord. This is the main reason for the
relatively high excess temperatures in the deeper layers of
the fjord. Before the calculations we knew there would be
some excess temperatures, but we did not know the values. At
least to us it was surprising that the excess temperatures in
the deeper layers would remain high throughout the year.

U. Navon   The temperature variation during the year is, of
course, complicated, but my comment referred to the temperature difference due to the thermal impact. Because this
difference is more or less constant (about 1°C) and consistent
in all 6 charts, I wonder if it cannot be used as a rule of
thumb for similar situations. Moreover, as I stated before,
such results can be probably predicted by a simple heat
balance based on the thermal energy injected to the water.

A. Thendrup   It is perhaps always easy to predict by rule of
thumb after a more complicated computation. Calculations
from other fjords have shown different result from these,
both in the absolute values of the excess temperatures and in
the vertical distribution of the excess temperatures. Another
point is that very important economical decisions are to some
extent depending on these calculations. Confidence in the
results was therefore considered important. We therefore
found it necessary to incorporate some dynamical properties
of the fjord in the model so as to meet objections that very
easily arise from simple "rule of thumb" calculations, in
particular for our complicated situation.

Question   Can I just ask for a point of information. What
value did you use for the heat exchange coefficient?

A. Thendrup   The heat exchange coefficient was calculated
by methods proposed by Edinger et al. (1968) and Harleman and
Ryan (MIT, Report No 161, 1973). The values varied between
8 W/m^2 °C in winter and 20 W/m^2°C in the summer.

G.K. Verboom   I suppose that Figure 9 is the follow up of
Figure 8. There is a little temperature inversion in
February in Figure 8 of less than 1°, but in Figure 9 there
is a temperature difference of 2 - 2$\frac{1}{2}$ degrees. Isn't this an
unstable situation, so that this situation will not happen
actually?

A. Thendrup   We think your comment is correct if you mean
that instabilities can occur when we draw the curves in
Figure 9 beyond the observation period. But we will stress
that the temperature difference would then have to be large

enough to exceed the stability resulting from vertical
salinity gradients. The fjords in Norway are mostly stratified
due to differences in salinity, and the warmest water is typically during cooling periods found in an intermediate layer
(see Figure 6).

WRITTEN CONTRIBUTION. EXPERIMENTAL AND ANALYTICAL EVALUATION
OF THERMAL ALTERATIONS IN THE MEDITERRANEAN by L. Castellano
and G. Dinelli.

As a consequence of the ever increasing capacity of fossil and
nuclear power stations, in many Mediterranean countries it is
becoming necessary to improve the modelling of the intake and
discharge structures in order to achieve a more efficacious
dispersion of the heated cooling waters into the receiving
water bodies.
        In this respect experimental and analytical work is in
progress at ENEL (Italian Electricity Board) for an assessment
of dilution and circulation patterns of surface discharges
under predictable environmental conditions.
        The experimental surveys, based on infra-red remote
sensing techniques combined with in-situ measurements of the
temperature at different depths, provide data to convalidate
the mathematical models to be used in the planning phase of
new thermal power stations [1].
        Instead of a general prediction method, it is believed
that a rather semiempirical approach should be pursued in
order to establish a few local predictive models for the
prevailing environmental conditions met in Italian coastal
waters.
        The experimental surveys conducted till now have con-
cerned several coastal sites some of which were chosen for
sake of comparison out of the influence of industrial or
urban effluents. Incidentally it seems worth noting that in
the delta of the Po river, which has so far developed almost
free of industrial stress, thermal alterations higher than
3°C may occur during a diurnal period due to solar heating
[2] [3].

EXPERIMENTAL RESULTS

Selected results of a wide experimental campaign conducted at
Vado Ligure thermal power station, in the western side of the
Liguarian sea, will be briefly described. The main character-
istics of the power station are given in Table I.

Table I - Operating conditions at Vado Ligure thermal power
          plant

Electric power output MW	1000
Coaling water flow m^3/s	40
Outfall densimetric Froude number	5
Discharge channel aspect ratio	0.1
Sea bottom gradient (%)	1.7

The near field, jet type, phase of the plume was found to be almost independent of ambient conditions as far as the centreline thermal alteration exceeds 30% – 40% of the initial discharge temperature rise – inside this phase the temperature decrease is due to the dilution with ambient cooler waters while in the next far field passive diffusion phase surface cooling to the atmosphere becomes the predominant factor. The surface heat transfer coefficient was evaluated from thermal infra-red mapping equal to 60 $W/m^2 {}^oC$ while its value computed from meteorological conditions was found to be 50 $W/m^2 \ {}^oC$. This confirms the good accuracy of the collected experimental data.

In the far field region of the plume the thermal altera-tion is confined in a very thin surface layer; as a reference the surface areas per unit power output corresponding to a residual alteration of 3^oC and 2^oC were found to be 0.5 km^2/GWe and 1.5 km^2/GWe respectively [3] [4].

Finally the time of exposure to specified temperature rises for biota in the thermal plume derived for Vado Ligure indicates that the time during which an organism in the plume will be subject to excess temperatures equal or greater than 50% of the initial discharge temperature rise is less than 5 minutes while the time of exposure to temperature rises equal or greater than 40% of the initial thermal alteration is of the order of 15 minutes.

MATHEMATICAL MODELLING

The mathematical modelling effort is being developed following two directions: a jet type modelling approach and a quasi-three-dimensional approach.

Concerning the first approach the relative simplicity of such models makes them very useful for a fast evaluation of the several situations that may develop in different environ-ments [5]. However the comparison of the numerical results with the experimental data collected at Vado Ligure indicates that further improvements are required mainly in order to better simulate the bottom interaction and the vertical entra-inment of ambient waters.

In the quasi-three-dimensional model the governing equations contain empirical functions by which it is possible to simulate depths effects such as bottom irregularities.

The velocity and temperature fields are given by the product of two functions one of which is the function des-cribing the variation with depth

$$u(x,y,z,t) = \tilde{u}(x,y,t) f(z)$$

$$v(x,y,z,t) = \tilde{v}(x,y,t) f(z)$$

$$T(x,y,z,t) = \tilde{T}(x,y,t) g(z)$$

Thus the starting three-dimensional equations may be interpreted according to the Leibnitz rule between the bottom and the surface to give a two-dimensional equations system which is solved numerically employing a MAC-like method [6] [7].

The magnitude of the turbulent shear stress is given as a function of the time average velocity according to the turbulence model proposed by Prandtl. In this context the mixing length depends on the bottom and free surface patterns characterized by two smooth functions $a(x,y)$ and $b(x,y)$.

$$\ell = \chi \left[z - a(x,y) \right] \left[1 - \frac{z - a(x,y)}{b(x,y) - a(x,y)} \right]$$

χ : Von Karman constant

The eddy thermal diffusivity is evaluated in accordance to a Prandtl number equal to one and the heat exchange to the atmosphere is taken into account by a source term of the form:

$$Q_s = - \frac{\beta(T - T_n)}{\rho c h}$$

where ρ is the water density, c the water heat capacity, h the depth, T_n the natural undisturbed temperature and β the water-atmosphere heat transfer coefficient.

Finally the pressure is assumed to be independent of the depth in analogy to the usual boundary layer assumption.

With the above assumptions the governing equations become:

Continuity:

$$-\frac{\partial I_1 \tilde{u}}{\partial x} + -\frac{\partial I_1 \tilde{v}}{\partial y} = 0$$

X - Momentum:

$$I_1 \frac{\partial \tilde{u}}{\partial t} + \frac{\partial}{\partial x}(I_2 \tilde{u}^2) + \frac{\partial}{\partial y}(I_2 \tilde{u}\tilde{v}) = -\frac{1}{\rho} I_3 \frac{\partial P}{\partial x} + \frac{\partial}{\partial x}(2 I_4 \sqrt{\tilde{u}^2 + \tilde{v}^2}\frac{\partial \tilde{u}}{\partial x}) +$$

$$+ \frac{\partial}{\partial y}(I_4 \sqrt{\tilde{u}^2 + \tilde{v}^2}(\frac{\partial \tilde{u}}{\partial y} + \frac{\partial \tilde{v}}{\partial x})) + \xi_{\tilde{u}}$$

$$I_1 \frac{\partial \tilde{v}}{\partial t} + \frac{\partial}{\partial x}(I_2 \tilde{u}\tilde{v}) + \frac{\partial}{\partial y}(I_2 \tilde{v}^2) = -\frac{1}{\rho} I_3 \frac{\partial P}{\partial y} + \frac{\partial}{\partial x}(I_4 \sqrt{\tilde{u}^2 + \tilde{v}^2}(\frac{\partial \tilde{u}}{\partial x} + \frac{\partial \tilde{v}}{\partial y})) +$$

$$+ \frac{\partial}{\partial y}(2I_4 \sqrt{\tilde{u}^2 + \tilde{v}^2} \frac{\partial \tilde{v}}{\partial y}) + \xi_{\tilde{v}}$$

Temperature:

$$I_5 \frac{\partial \tilde{T}}{\partial t} + \frac{\partial}{\partial x}(I_6 \tilde{u}\tilde{T}) + \frac{\partial}{\partial y}(I_6 \tilde{v}\tilde{T}) = \frac{1}{Pr_t} \frac{\partial}{\partial x}(I_7 \sqrt{\tilde{u}^2 + \tilde{v}^2} \frac{\partial \tilde{T}}{\partial x}) +$$

$$+ \frac{1}{Pr_t} \frac{\partial}{\partial y}(I_7 \sqrt{\tilde{u}^2 + \tilde{v}^2} \frac{\partial T}{\partial y}) + \frac{\tilde{Q}}{\rho C_p (b-a)}$$

where:

$$\xi_{\tilde{u}} = \left\{ \ell^2 (\frac{\partial f}{\partial z})^2 \sqrt{\tilde{u}^2 + \tilde{v}^2} \Big|_{z=b} - \ell^2 (\frac{\partial f}{\partial z})^2 \sqrt{\tilde{u}^2 + \tilde{v}^2} \Big|_{z=a} \right\} \tilde{u}$$

$$\xi_{\tilde{v}} = \left\{ \ell^2 (\frac{\partial f}{\partial z})^2 \sqrt{\tilde{u}^2 + \tilde{v}^2} \Big|_{z=b} - \ell^2 (\frac{\partial f}{\partial z})^2 \sqrt{\tilde{u}^2 + \tilde{v}^2} \Big|_{z=a} \right\} \tilde{v}$$

$$I_1 = \int_a^b f \, dz \qquad\qquad I_5 = \int_a^b g \, dz$$

$$I_2 = \int_a^b f^2 dz \qquad\qquad I_6 = \int_a^b fg \, dz$$

$$I_3 = \int_a^b dz \qquad\qquad I_7 = \int_a^b \ell^2 \frac{\partial f}{\partial z} g \, dz$$

$$I_4 \int_a^b \ell^2 f \frac{\partial f}{\partial z} \, dz$$

$$\tilde{Q} = -\frac{1}{b-a} \int_a^b \beta(T-T_n) \, dz$$

Numerical tests performed on a stretch of the Po river
downstream a surface discharge have proved the adequacy of
the model so far as simple geometries are concerned [3].

For the specific case the river's width (250 m) was subdivided in 15 cells and the stretch's length (4000 m) in 28
cells; the grid was taken not uniform with the mesh size varying in both directions by a factor of 1.2/1.3. With a time
step of 0.5 sec the memory requirement was 32 K and the CPU
of about 20 minutes using a H 6000 system.

CONCLUSIONS

Presently available mathematical models are inadequate for a
comprehensive analysis of the dispersion of a heated plume
when in presence of strong bottom and coastline interaction,
ambient turbulence, sea currents and wind induced effects.

In this context both jet-type models and three-dimensional models will require additional analytical work and experimental data to convalidate the computed results under a wide
range of environmental conditions.

References

1. Dinelli, G. et al. "Airborne Infra-red Scanning Surveys of
    Thermal Alterations of Water Bodies"(in Italian) AEI - 75
    Annual Meeting, Rome, 1974

2. Borgese, D. et al. "A Site Study of the Multiple Effects
    of Thermal Releases on the Aquatic Life in an Estuarine
    Area" IAEA - SM 197/27, Stockholm,1975

3. Dinelli, G. "Evaluation of Thermal Impact of Cooling Water
    Discharges into Mediterranean Coastal Waters" ICHMT -
    Dubrovnik, 1975

4. Dinelli, G. and Parrini, F. "An Experimental Evaluation of
    Heat Transfer to the Environment by Cooling Water Dis-
    charges from Vado Ligure Power Plant using an Infra-red
    Technique". XVIth Int. IAHR Congress, Sao Paulo, 1975

5. Harleman, D.R.F., Stolzenbach, K.D., Adams, E.E. "A Users'
    Manual for Three-Dimensional Heated Surface Discharge
    Computations" EPA Report-Rc-73, 1973

6. Harlow, F.M. and Amsen, A.A. "A Numerical Fluid Dynamics
    Calculation for All Flow Speeds" J. Comp. Physics, 8.2 1971

7. Castellani, L. and Tozzi, A. "A Mathematical Model for the
    Prediction of the Velocity and Temperature Distributions
    in Shallow Open Channels" (in Italian) Applicazioni
    Ricerche Scientifiche, Report 74-40 Milan, 1974

6. DISCUSSION: MODELLING TECHNIQUES

6.3 On the Accuracy of Solutions of the Navier Stokes Equations for Unsteady Viscous Flow at High Reynolds Numbers

<u>D. Weihs</u> In the calculation of oscillating wings, how many cycles of oscillation did you have to get till the initial Wagner effect type lift disappeared?

<u>T. Bratanow</u> At this stage we have not been thinking in terms of initial Wagner effect type of lift or 'growth of lift' functions.

<u>D. Weihs</u> That means you start off from steady flow going over oscillating flow which means you had some kind of initial effects of suddenly starting at an angle of attack. I have done similar calculations with potential flow models, where you have to take at least two or three cycles before you obtain a pure oscillating motion. What I was asking is in this type of programme, how many cycles are required.

<u>T. Bratanow</u> We haven't jumped yet from the steady flow condition to a real oscillating angle. You should start from $\frac{1}{2}^o$, 1°, and then continue along the programme. But as you saw in the last finite element scheme, we have not run our program at a higher angle so we do not know this amount.

<u>D. Weihs</u> One other short question is, usually when you do potential flow calculation of oscillating wings you have the problem of finding the stagnation point. I suppose, with your program, you can answer exactly finally the controversy about where the stagnation point is really because it seems that the Kutta condition isn't fulfilled at high reduced frequencies. So perhaps with this type of calculation one can say what takes the place of the Kutta condition in high reduced frequency calculations.

<u>T. Bratanow</u> No. The Kutta condition was used here. Two years ago there was a paper presented by Vooren and Labrujere [1], and they used the Kutta condition. I don't know myself much, unless some of the operators. My partners know more about it. If you would write me a letter you will get a detailed answer on this. May be you should. It would be nice to insert it in

the Proceedings.

[1]   "Numerical Methods in Fluid Dynamics". Edited by
      C.A. Brebbia and J.J. Connor, Pentech Press, London,
      1974.

D. Weihs   We will discuss this later.

S. Smith   You mention steady state. I would have thought
that at the high Reynolds numbers you are talking about, the
steady state as such wouldn't have existed. In other words,
I am proposing that at those Reynolds numbers, the overall
flow is changing all the time due to the unstable nature of
the flow, hence there is no steady state in real problems.

T. Bratanow   We speak of steady state here in reference to
the flow solution around a stationary airfoil, as a preliminary step of the computational analysis of an unsteady flow.
It has to be achieved before proceeding with the unsteady
analysis. I agree with you that there may not be a steady
state as such around the airfoil at high Reynolds numbers and
that the flow is changing continually.

C.M. De Turville   You discussed oscillations in the flow
field around a wing without any reference to the internal
mechanics of the wing itself. Are you assuming that to be
absolutely rigid, and if not, what allowance are you making
for its non-rigidity? It seems to me that the surface of the
airfoil acts as an interface between two very different systems which are coupled together. What is going on inside the
metallic structure?

T. Bratanow   Ultimately we have vibrations in mind, since
this analysis is aimed to produce unsteady pressure distribution around an oscillating wing. It is true that nothing was
said here about the internal mechanics of the airfoil. In
this analysis, it is assumed that the wing is rigid and that
there is no added effect on the unsteady flow characteristics
due to wing deformations. Naturally, such effects can be
introduced in a flutter type of analysis of the wing.

LIST OF PARTICIPANTS

ADEY, Dr. R.A.   University of Southampton, Southampton, ENGLAND, SO9 5NH.

ALLIOT, J.M.   Institut Francais du Petrole, 1 et 4, Avenue de Bois-Preau, Boite Postale 18, 92501 Rueil Malmaison, FRANCE.

ARGENTESI, F.   c/o Cetis, CCR Euratom, 21020 Ispra (VA), ITALY.

ASHTON, N.R.   Ashton and Wilson, 123 Erskine Street, Middle Park, Victoria 3206, AUSTRALIA.

BAILLE, A.   Centre de Recherches Aerodomiques, du Sud-Est, Station Di Bioclimatologie, Domaine Saint-Paul, Cantarel-84, Montfavet, FRANCE.

BALLINTYN, Y.F.   Koninkiijke/Shell-Laboratorium, Badhuisweg 3, Amsterdam-Noord, HOLLAND.

BARRIGA, E.G.   Petroleos Mexicanos, MEXICO DF.

BASNETT, P.   Electricity Council Research Centre, Capenhurst, Chester, CH1 6ES.

BAYER, Prof. M.B.   Faculty of Business, University of Calgary, Calgary, Alberta, CANADA.

BENNETT, R.J.   University College, Gower St., London, ENGLAND, WC1 6BT.

BENSTED, I.H.   Senior Administrative Engineer, c/o The Director of Operations, Thames Water Authority, New River Head, Rosebery Avenue, London, EC1E 4TP.

BOGARDI, Dr. I.   Water Resources Centre, Ovh Vizkeszlet-gasdalkodasi Kozpont, 1054 Budapest, V., Alkotmany u. 29, HUNGARY.

BONOMETTI, G.   Societe Nationale Des Petroles D'Aquitaine, C.I.R.N. - Laboratoire Pollution Lacq,BP No.23, Lacq, 64170 Artix, FRANCE.

BRADDOCK, Dr. R.D.	Mathematics Department, Queensland University, St. Lucia 4067 AUSTRALIA.
BRATANOW, Prof. T.	University of Wisconsin-Milwaukee, Mechanics Department, College of Engineering and Applied Science, Milwaukee, Wisconsin 53201, U.S.A.
BREBBIA, Dr. C.A.	University of Southampton, Southampton, ENGLAND, SO9 5NH.
BRUNDRIT, Prof. G.B.	Department of Applied Mathematics, University of Cape Town, Rondebosch, Cape Town, S. AFRICA.
BRYANT, J.W.	University of Sussex, Falmer, Brighton, ENGLAND, BN1 9RH.
BUTTERFIELD, Dr. R.	University of Southampton, Southampton, ENGLAND, SO9 5NH.
CASTELLANO, Dr. L.	Calisma, Milano, ITALY.
CASENAVE, M.	Department "Laboratoire National d'Hydraulique" Electricite de France, 6 Quai Watier, 78400 Chatou, FRANCE.
CHALLIS, N.	British Gas Engineering Research Station, 59 Forest Avenue, Forest Hall, Newcastle upon Tyne 12, ENGLAND.
CHAPLIN, Miss H.K.	c/o Scott Wilson Kirkpatrick & Partners, Scott House, Basing View, Basingstoke, Hants, ENGLAND, RG21 2JG.
CORDLE, Dr. J.E.	Central Electricity Generating Board, South Eastern Region, Bankside House, Sumner Street, London, ENGLAND, SE1.
CROFTS, Dr. I.P.	Welsh National Water Development Authority, Cambrian Way, Brecon, Powys, LD3 7HP, WALES.
CUENA, Dr. J.	Eyser, Auda Generalisimo 67, Madrid 16, SPAIN.
DEAM, Prof. R.J.	Queen Mary College, 327 Mile End, London, E1 4NS, ENGLAND.

DE CARVALHO, M.J.S.M.   Laboratorio Nacional de Engenharia Civil, Av. Brasil, Lisboa-5, PORTUGAL.

DE RHAM, C.   Systems Consult, Furst & De Rham, Thunstrasse 42, CH-3005 Bern, SWITZERLAND.

DE TURVILLE, C.M.   Central Electricity Generating Board, South Western Region, 15-23 Oakfield Grove, Clifton, Bristol, BSB 2AS.

DINELLI, Dr. Ing. G.   ENEL-CRTN, Bastioni Porta Volta, 10-20121 Milano, ITALY.

DIVER, Miss C.M.   Hydraulics Research Station, Howbery Park, Wallingford, Oxon, OX10 8BA.

ESCUDERO, L.F.   UAM-IBM Scientific Center, Paseo de al Castellana, 4, Madrid-1, SPAIN.

FARQUHAR, G.J.   University of Waterloo, Ontario, CANADA, N2L 3G1.

FISK, Dr. D.J.   Building Research Establishment, Garston, Watford, ENGLAND, WD2 7JR.

FLEMING, C.   Sir William Halcrow & Partners, Newcombe House, 45 Notting Hill Gate, London, W11 3JX.

FROSTLING, H.   Statens Brandnamnd, Box 6029, 102 31 Stockholm, SWEDEN.

GEERTS, J.B.   Rijkswaterstaat - Data Processing Division, THE NETHERLANDS.

GLENNIE, E.B.   British Gas Engineering Research Station, P.O. Box 1Lh, Killingworth, Newcastle upon Tyne, ENGLAND, NE99 1LH.

GRANIER, M.J-P.   Direction des Etudes et Recherches, Electricite De France, 6 Quai Watier, 78400 Chatou, FRANCE.

GUSTAFSON, S.A.   Department of Numerical Analysis, Royal Institute of Technology, S-10044 Stockholm 70, SWEDEN.

HABIB, Prof. I.S.   Chairman, Dept. of Mechanical Engineering, School of Engineering, The University of Michigan-Dearborn, 4901 Evergreen Road, Dearborn, Michigan 48128, U.S.A.

HALBRITTER, G.	Gesellschaft Für Kernforschung M.B.H., 75 Karlsruhe 1, Postfach 3640, GERMANY.
HAMERSLAG, Dr. R.	Dwars, Heederik, Verhey, BV., P.O. Box 85, Amersfoort, THE NETHERLANDS.
HANRAHAN, M.J.	Software Sciences Ltd., Abbey House, 282/292 Farnborough Road, Farnborough, Hants, ENGLAND.
HARA, Dr. F.	Associate Professor, Tokyo University of Science, 1-3 Kagurazaka, Shinjuku-ku, Tokyo, JAPAN.
HARRIS, C.J.	University of Manchester, Institute of Science and Technology, Oxford Road, ENGLAND, M13 9PL.
HEAPS, N.S.	Institute of Oceanographic Sciences, Bidston Observatory, Birkenhead, Cheshire, ENGLAND.
HOLLAND, J.P.	Thames Water Authority, Metropolitan Public Health Division, Broadway Buildings, 60-64 Broadway, London, ENGLAND, SW1H ODB.
HOLMBERG, Mrs C.	Research Institute of National Defence, Box 716, Sundbyberg 4, SWEDEN.
JOERES, E.F.	2260 Engineering Building, University of Wisconsin, Madison, Wis. 53706, U.S.A.
KAUFMANN, Dr. P.	Balzari Blaser Schudel, Consulting Engineers, Kramburgstrasse 14, 3006 Bern, SWITZERLAND.
KEDDIE, Dr. A.W.C.	Department of Industry, Warren Spring Laboratory, Gunnels Wood Road, Stevenage, ENGLAND, SG1 2BX.
KÜHNER, Dr. J.	Harvard University, 111 Pierce Hall, Cambridge, Mass., 02138, U.S.A.
KUZMIC, M.	UNDP Project "Protection of the Human Environment in the Yugoslav Adriatic Region" "Rudjer Boskovic" Institute, Bijenicka 54, 41000 Zagreb, YUGOSLAVIA.

LAM, Dr. D.C.L.   Basin Investigation and Modelling
                       Section, A.R.D., Canada Centre for In-
                       land Waters, 867 Lakeshore Road,
                       Burlington, Ontario, CANADA, LTR 4A6.

LENCIONI, M.   Department "Laboratoire National
                       d'Hydraulique" Electricite de France,
                       6 Quai Watier, 78400 Chatou, FRANCE.

LINDHOLM, O.G.   P. Box 333, Blindern, Oslo 3, NORWAY.

LIU, C.Y.   Department of Mechanics & Structures,
                       University of California, Los Angeles,
                       California 90024, U.S.A.

LOPEZ-GARCIA, L.   INTECSA, Condesa de Venadito 1, Madrid-
                       27, SPAIN.

MALHERBE, M.   Department "Laboratoire National
                       d'Hydraulique", Electricite de France,
                       6 Quai Watier, 78400 Chatou, FRANCE.

MELLI, P.   IBM Italia SPA, Centro di Ricerca,
                       S. Polo 1364, 30125 Venezia, ITALY.

MENDEZ, Mrs. A.C.   Section of Architecture, CEMAC, Center
                       of Appl. Maths. and Computation of
                       Construction, Ave 26 Y 45, Nuevo Vedado,
                       Havana, CUBA.

MOLLOWNEY, B.M.   Water Research Centre, Stevenage Labor-
                       atory, Elder Way, Stevenage, Herts,
                       SG1 1TM.

MORICE, Prof. P.B.   University of Southampton, Southampton,
                       ENGLAND, SO9 5NH.

MORRIS, J.J.   Imperial Chemical Industries, Ltd.,
                       Central Resource Group, Petrochemicals
                       Division, Wilton, Middlesbrough,
                       Cleveland, TS6 8JE.

MULERO, M.   Institutomnacional de Tecnica Aerospac-
                       ial (INTA), Torrejon de Ardos, Madrid,
                       SPAIN.

McGUIRK, J.   Sonderforschungsbereich 80, Universitat
                       Karlsruhe, WEST GERMANY.

NAU, Dr. B.S.   BHRA Fluid Engineering, Cranfield,
                       Bedford, ENGLAND.

NAVON, Dr. U.	Department of Mechanical Engineering,
Technion, Israel Institute of Technology
Haifa, ISRAEL.

NOYE, Dr. B.J.	Applied Mathematics Department, University of Adelaide, Adelaide, SOUTH
AUSTRALIA.

OBRADOVIC, D.	Energoprojekt - Energodata, Zeleni venac 1
18, 2nd Floor, 11000 Beograd,
YUGOSLAVIA.

ONO, Dr. T.	University of Osaka Prefecture, 804
Mozu Umemachi 4, Sakai, Osaka, 591
JAPAN.

PAPWORTH, M.	B.H.R.A. (Fluid Engineering) Ltd.,
Cranfield, Bedford, U.K.

PARTRIDGE, P.W.	University of Southampton, Southampton,
ENGLAND, SO9 5NH.

PERROTT, J.M.A.	Sir M. MacDonald & Partners, 34 High
Street, Inverness, SCOTLAND.

ROACH, C.L.	University of Southampton, Southampton,
ENGLAND, SO9 5NH.

ROMBERG, Dr. G.	DFVLE-AVA, 34 Göttingen, Bunsenstr. 10,
GERMANY.

ROUX, J.	FRANLAB., 4 avenue de Bois Préau, 92504
Rueil Malmaison, FRANCE.

RUSHTON, Dr. K.R.	Department of Civil Engineering,
University of Birmingham, P.O. Box 363,
Birmingham, B15 2TT.

SCHAARSCHMIDT, H.	ERNO, Bremen, GERMANY.

SCHMID, Dr. W.	F.H. Kocks, KG, Consulting Engineers,
Augustrastr. 30, D-4000 Dusseldorf 30,
GERMANY.

SCHULER, Dr. W.	Studiengruppe für Systemforschung,
69 Heidelberg, Werderstrabe 35, GERMANY.

SMEDILE, Dr. E.	ENEL-CRTN, Bastioni Porta Volta, 10 -
20121 Milano, ITALY.

SMITH, S.	University of Southampton, Southampton,
ENGLAND, SO9 5NH.

SORENSSEN, Dr. A.   River and Harbour Laboratory, Norwegian Institute of Technology, Kalebuvn 153, 7034 Trondheim - NTH, NORWAY.

SUTHERLAND, R.C.   Jarza Engineering Company, 2737 N. Mildred Ave. 1, Chicago, Ill. 60614, U.S.A.

SVENSSON, J.   Swedish Coniferous Forest Project, Agricultural College, P. Box 7008, S-75007, Uppsala, SWEDEN.

TAYLER, W.K.   Clyde River Purification Board, Rivers House, The Murray Road, East Kilbride, Strathclyde, SCOTLAND, GL75 OLA.

THENDRUP, A.   River and Harbour Laboratory, Norwegian Institute of Technology, Klaebuvn 153, 7034 Trondheim - NTH, NORWAY.

VAN DER KLOET, P.   Department of Civil Engineering, Delft University of Technology, Stevinweg 1, Delft, HOLLAND.

VAN DER WILT, M.   National Aerospace Laboratory, Anthony Fokkerweg 2, Amsterdam-1017, THE NETHERLANDS.

VERBOOM, Dr. G.K.   Delft Hydraulics Laboratory (Waterloopkundig Laboratorium), P.O. Box 177, Delft, THE NETHERLANDS.

WEIHS, Dr. D.   Department of Aeronautical Engineering, Technion, Research and Development Foundation, Technion City, Haifa, ISRAEL.

WINDSOR, Dr. J.S.   Department of Civil Engineering, The University of Natal, King George V Avenue, Durban, S. AFRICA 4001. (also (CSIR)

YU, M.J.   8 Claremont Terrace, Newcastle upon Tyne, ENGLAND, NE2 4AE.

ZEHLEIN, H.   Institut fur Reaktorentwicklung, Kernforschungszentrum Karlsruhe, 7500 Karlsruhe, Postfach 3640, GERMANY.

ZIKIC, M.   Energoprojekt-Energodata, Beograd, YUGOSLAVIA.